A punch press used in making electrical equipment in the Sharon, Pennsylvania, works of Westinghouse Electric and Manufacturing Company.

THE NEW ENCYCLOPEDIA OF MACHINE SHOP PRACTICE

A GUIDE TO
THE PRINCIPLES AND PRACTICE
OF MACHINE SHOP PROCEDURE
edited by
GEORGE W. BARNWELL
PROFESSOR OF PRODUCTION PRACTICE
STEVENS INSTITUTE OF TECHNOLOGY

New York
Wm. H. WISE & CO., Inc.
1941

CONTENTS

v

CONTENTS

ACKNOWLEDGMENT

T HE preparation of a book of this type would be well-nigh impossible without the assistance of a number of interested persons. Among those who have contributed their time and help, grateful acknowledgment is therefore made to Mr. W. Hughes White of the Faitoute Iron and Steel Company for able assistance in preparing manuscript; to Mr. Frank W. Curtis of the Van Norman Machine Tool Company for the use of material on Jigs and Fixtures; to Mr. Alfred J. Barchi for numerous drawings and other assistance; to Professor Gregory Jamieson Comstock and Professor William Reeder Halliday and other members of the Stevens faculty for valuable suggestions; and to Miss Betty Roth for secretarial assistance.

Appreciation is also due to the following manufacturers for permission to reproduce many of their latest models of machine tools: To Brown and Sharpe for an Automatic Screw Machine, Plain Milling Machine, Universal Milling Machine, Vertical Milling Machine, Grinding Machine, and Lathe; to Jones and Lamson for a Universal Turret Lathe and a Fay Automatic Lathe; to Cincinnati Grinders Incorporated for a Centerless Grinding Machine; to the Bullard Company for a Vertical Turret Lathe; to American Tool Works Company for a Shaper; to the Ohio Machine Tool Company for a Planer; to the E. W. Bliss Company for an Inclinable Power Press and a Toggle Drawing Press; to the Lobdell Car Wheel Company for a Power Hammer; to the Mesta Machine Company for a Hydraulic Forging Machine; to the National Machinery Company for a Forging Machine; and to the Erie Foundry Company for Drop Forging Hammers.

GEORGE W. BARNWELL

CHAPTER 1

BENCH WORK

FILING, KINDS OF FILE, HOLDING THE TOOL, DRILLING, TWIST AND CENTER DRILLS, SHARPENING DRILLS, HAND AND BREAST DRILLS, DRILL SPEED, REAMING, BLIND HOLES, CUTTING METAL, HACK-SAWS AND THEIR TEETH, SHEARS AND SNIPS, CHISELING, RIVETING, THE RIVET SET, CUTTING SCREW-THREADS, TAPS, THREAD GAUGES, VISES, METAL-WORKING BENCH.

DESPITE the immense mechanization of the machine shop, the hand processes, such as filing, drilling, and riveting, remain of first importance. Before anyone can lay claim to the title of machinist he must understand these processes and be able to do them correctly. It is, of course, possible to train a man to operate an automatic machine tool without first teaching him to use ordinary hand tools, but it is unlikely that he will be as efficient as one who had started at the beginning.

There is another important aspect of the skillful use of hand tools: the various processes are essential to the fitter, to whom machines are often of little use. Once the apprentice is able to file accurately, to lay out the metal on which he is to work, and to cut and drill it and form screw-threads, he is well on the way to success.

To many readers who have had a good deal of workshop experience this section may seem elementary, but all other readers should study it with the greatest possible care. Learn to use a vise and a file, and you have made good progress; but do not be satisfied until you can work to a high standard of accuracy. In filing, for example, an accuracy of one-half of one-thousandth of an inch—which is usual in engineering—is impossible, but one-hundredth of an inch should be regarded as a large dimension where accuracy is concerned.

FILING

FILING is without doubt the most important of the hand operations. It is generally the first process to be learned by the metal-worker, and one of the most difficult to master.

The file consists of a blade or body with a tang for fixing into a wooden handle. Teeth of a suitable kind are cut on the blade, which is then hardened and tempered. The wide variety of operations in which filing is involved makes it necessary that there should be a wide variety of files available on the market. There is a type of file to suit every requirement and one which will do a certain job better than any other.

Files are classified and named according to three principal factors involved in their manufacture—length, sectional form, and type or cut of the teeth. The length varies within fairly wide limits, but usually files between 4 in. and 20 in. in length can be obtained. This dimension does not include the tang, which is the pointed end that is forced into the wooden handle (Fig. 1). In contrast to the body or blade, it is tempered so as to be soft and tough, since if it were as hard and brittle as the blade it would be easily broken where the handle meets the blade.

The lengths in general use are from 10 in. to 16 in., and from 4 in. to 6 in. for finer work.

Cut of the Teeth

The number of teeth per inch varies slightly with different manufacturers, but the following list represents a fair average:

Rough, 20 teeth per inch.
Middle, 25 teeth per inch.
Bastard, 30 teeth per inch.
Second Cut, 40 teeth per inch.
Smooth, 50 to 60 teeth per inch.
Dead Smooth, 100 or more teeth per inch.

The teeth may be single cut or double cut, as indicated in Fig. 2. On single-cut files the teeth are cut parallel to each other across the file and at an angle of from 65–85 degrees to the center line. Single-cut files are frequently referred to as "floats," and are chiefly used on very hard metal.

In a double-cut file there are two sets of teeth, the first or over-cut teeth being cut at 40 to 45 deg. to the center line, and the second cut or upcut at 70 to 80 deg. to the center line. The shape of the teeth has been scientifically designed. It may be seen on examination that the front part of the tooth slopes backward, or has a *negative rake*. The width at the base of each tooth is important, for teeth which are too narrow for their height are easily chipped and broken off. The angle of the cut to the axis of the file is designed so that a slicing cut is obtained, causing the metal to curl off much more readily than if each tooth met the metal along its whole length at the same time.

Where special work is being done, the file-makers will cut files that are designed especially for use on one particular kind of material. Thus, for wrought iron the cuts are best at 30 deg. and 60 deg., while for brass filing the upcut is practically 90 deg. Specially cut files may be obtained for working in aluminum and the various non-ferrous alloys.

Shape and Cross Section

While it is possible to order a file made to any given section, there are standard forms which cover most requirements. Fig. 3 shows the more common shapes, along with their names.

Fig. 1. Files are named and classified according to three principal factors involved in their manufacture—length, sectional form, and cut of teeth. The length of a file does not include the tang, or pointed part that fits into the wooden handle.

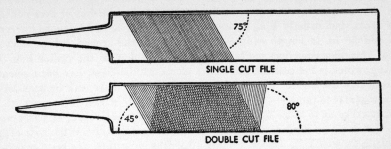

Fig. 2. Single- and double-cut teeth. On single-cut files the teeth are cut parallel to each other across the file at an angle of 65 deg. to 85 deg. to the center line. Double-cut files have two sets of teeth, the over-cut teeth being cut at about 40 deg. to 45 deg. and the upcut at 70 deg. to 80 deg. to the center line.

Flat files are always double cut on the faces and single cut on the edges, and they taper both in width and thickness towards the end. The hand file is parallel in its width, and in thickness it tapers slightly from a point about one-third of its length from the base. One edge is *safe;* that is, it is left uncut, and is therefore helpful when filing angles or sinkings where one surface only must be filed without touching the other.

Pillar files are narrow and of rectangular section; they may be parallel or tapered and are usually double cut, having one or two safe edges. The square file is double cut on each face and is normally tapered for the last third of its length; it may, of course, be ordered *parallel square.* Round files are generally single cut and are usually tapered, when they are termed *rat-tailed.* When parallel they are described as *parallel round.* Half-round files are generally double cut on the flat face and single cut

on the curved surface. The section is not really semicircular, and the files taper for the last third of their length both in width and thickness as shown in Fig. 3.

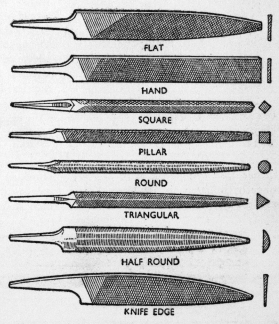

Fig. 3. Standard types of file. The diagram shows the most common types of file together with their sections which are likely to be required for ordinary work.

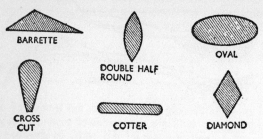

BARRETTE

DOUBLE HALF
ROUND

OVAL

CROSS
CUT

COTTER

DIAMOND

Fig. 4. Less common types of file. Sections of files used for special work. The cotter, for instance, is used chiefly when filing slots with rounded ends, while angular files are used for grooving, saw sharpening, etc.

Triangular files are usually single or double cut and taper to a point from about two-thirds of their length from the tip. The shape is that of an equilateral triangle and if designed for saw-sharpening the edges are slightly rounded and have teeth cut on them. The type which does not taper is known as *three-square parallel.* Knife files are useful for cleaning out acute-angled corners. The two faces are double cut, while the edge is single cut. Other less common sections are shown in Fig. 4.

Other special files are ward or warding files. These are fine-cut files, from 3 to 10 in. in length, designed in the first place for filing a key to fit the wards of a lock. They are widely em-ployed for all kinds of fine work.

Needle files (Fig. 5) are made in sizes from 4 to 8 in., of various shapes and cuts. They are extremely delicate and are used for fine work such as pierced designs in thin metal. They are very easily broken, and care should be taken that undue weight is not applied when using them. *Swiss* is the name given to a class of file which probably originated in Switzerland. These are very finely cut and are used when, for example, trimming a bearing journal. They are made in the usual sections, but are not longer than 8 in. The cuts are graded between 0 and 6. No. 0 has between 40 and 70 teeth to the inch, while No. 6 may have teeth as fine as 200 to the inch.

Rifflers (Fig. 6) are curved upward at the ends into an arc. They are used to reach the bottom of a sinking and for such work as filing the insides of curved castings. For the former purpose it is often convenient to use a straight file and *set* it to one of the shapes shown in Fig. 7. These setting files, as they are termed, are especially useful for filing a key-seat or other sunken faces.

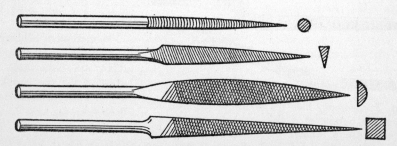

Fig. 5. Needle files. These tools are made in sizes from 4 to 8 in. They are very delicate and are used for fine work such as pierced designs in thin metal.

The file is set by heating it to a dull red and striking with a lead or wooden hammer on a block of lead so that the teeth of the file are not damaged. The file is then heated to redness and dipped in cold water so that it is re-hardened. The tang should not be dipped, but must cool slowly so that it remains comparatively soft.

Block files are used for similar purposes. They are square or rectangular in section and are provided with holes on the sides into which a handle fitted with a pin can be placed.

Files, like all other tools, should be handled carefully, since their useful life may be greatly prolonged by correct use. The handle should be a good fit, otherwise there is a tendency to produce a curved surface due to the handle and the file not being held firmly in line with each other.

Files should not be thrown together in a drawer, because there is then a danger of their teeth being damaged. They are better kept in vertical racks or in drawers with partitions between the files. It need hardly be pointed out that the file should not be allowed to rust, for then the sharp edges of the teeth are seriously blunted. In the

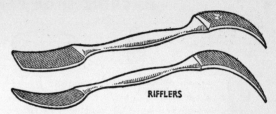

RIFFLERS

Fig. 6. Rifflers are used to reach the bottom of a sinking and for filing the insides of castings. They are curved upwards at the ends, as shown.

course of manufacture the file is quenched in oil, and this is helpful in minimizing rust formation.

The correct order in which a new file should be used is important. Thus, if it is used on, say, copper, aluminium, zinc, brass, wrought iron, and mild steel, in that order, its life will be far longer than if the new teeth were dulled by using it on the harder metals first.

During use the file teeth become choked or *pinned* with small pieces of metal, especially when working on non-ferrous metals. A wire brush (Fig. 8) or file card, and sometimes even the point of a scriber, must be used to remove the *pinning*. If this were not done the file would scratch the surface of the metal being dealt with, and at the same time become less and less effective. Chalk is very often rubbed along the file to prevent pinning, when filing aluminium; paraffin or turpentine is often helpful for the same purpose.

The method of holding the file and the correct working height are important. The height of the vise should be such that with a bent arm the elbow is on the same level as the top of the vise. Very often a small platform or plank is used on the floor so

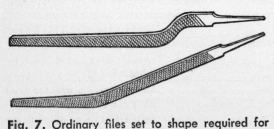

Fig. 7. Ordinary files set to shape required for filing the bottom of a sinking or the inside of a curved casting. Known as setting files, they are especially useful for filing such sunken faces as key-seatings, etc.

Fig. 8. The teeth of files become clogged by frequent use, especially on non-ferrous metals. They may be cleaned by means of the file card shown above.

that a shorter man may reach the correct height conveniently.

The feet are placed well apart, left foot about 24 in. in advance of the right. The file may be held either with the handle in the right hand and the tip of the file on the left hand or vice versa. It is only necessary to consider the former case, since the position of the hands will merely be reversed for the left-handed person. The position of the left hand on the tip of the file should be varied according to the type of work or file in use, but the grip of the right hand on the handle is always the same, as is shown in Figs. 9, 10, and 11. The file handle rests in the palm of the hand, the thumb is along the top of the handle and the index-finger points along the side. This grip enables the file to be kept perfectly level while weight is applied first to the left hand at the beginning of the stroke, then later to both hands equally

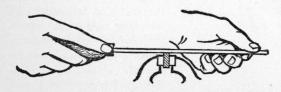

Fig. 10. For very accurate work, or when filing curved surfaces, the file should be held as shown. The tip of the file is held by the thumb and index-finger.

in the middle of the stroke, and finally to the right hand at the end of the stroke.

The tip of the file should be gripped with the left hand as shown in Fig. 9, where the tip of the file is under the palm of the hand and all the fingers are underneath. This is a powerful grip and one which enables the maximum weight to be applied. It is therefore used with a medium or long file on work which requires a large quantity of material to be removed quickly.

Fig. 10 shows a better position for doing more accurate work, when using

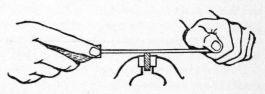

Fig. 9. Correct method of holding a file. The feet are placed well apart; the handle is gripped in the right hand and the tip in the left, as shown above.

the smaller files, and when filing curved surfaces. It will be seen that the tip of the file is held by the thumb and index-finger.

In the third method (Fig. 11) the thumb and fingers are stretched as far as possible and are pressed evenly against the file. This insures that the weight is more evenly distributed over the whole length of the file, so that there is a greater tendency for it to remain horizontal. The *run* of the file can be felt, and any unevenness in the work will be readily detected. Additionally, the hand is not in the way of the work and therefore the full length of the file can be used.

Beginners' Faults

The fault with most beginners is that they allow the file to rock or see-saw, with the result that a convex surface is obtained. This can be avoided if care is taken to keep the body still and to make the arms pivot about the shoulders.

On narrow pieces of metal it is often found easier to keep a flat surface if the file is held diagonally to the work, filing forward and to the left in one continuous movement and then, after a few strokes, going forward and to the right. This is shown in Fig. 12.

Downward pressure should be applied only on the forward stroke, the file being drawn lightly backward without actually being lifted from the face of the work.

This is desirable because the teeth are designed to cut on the forward stroke only, and any pressure applied on the backward stroke serves to dull the teeth more quickly without serving any useful purpose.

Generally, when a particular job has been filed to size and shape it is finished by draw-filing. The file is held as shown in Fig. 13, with the fingers on the edge away from the body and the two thumbs on the edge toward the body. The file is then drawn and pushed along the surface with an even pressure. A smooth file is used, and

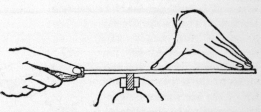

Fig. 11. By holding the file as shown the weight is evenly distributed over the whole length of the file and any unevenness in the work can be readily detected.

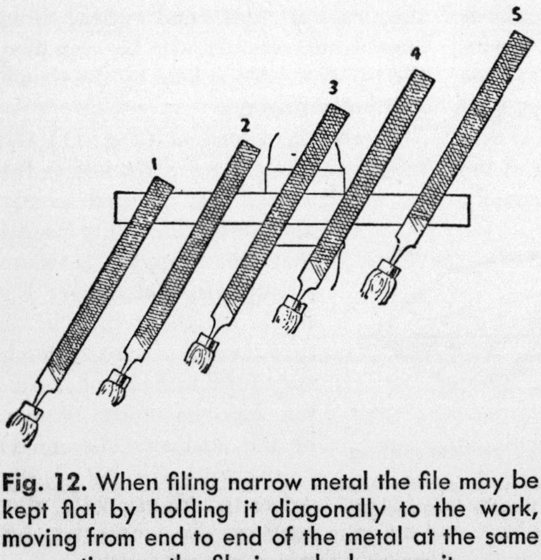

this makes comparatively few very fine cuts or scratches along the work, parallel to the longest edges. This gives a much better appearance than scratches running across the surface. The tendency for the beginner is to apply most of his effort when the file is in the middle of the long edge. In consequence, the surface becomes hollow. This fault must be guarded against by careful testing after draw-filing, and rectified, if necessary, by making a few more strokes at the ends.

Draw-filing produces a sharp *wire edge* on each edge

Fig. 12. When filing narrow metal the file may be kept flat by holding it diagonally to the work, moving from end to end of the metal at the same time as the file is pushed across it.

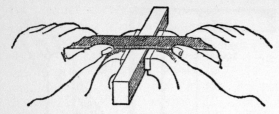

Fig. 13. Method of holding the file for draw-filing. A smooth file should be used, and it should be drawn and pushed along the surface of the job with an even pressure.

of the surface being filed; this is easily removed by holding the file at an angle and running it lightly down each edge. In doing this the tip of the file (safe edge down) should be supported on the vise-jaws.

The work can be further finished by polishing with fine emery-cloth and oil. A surface treated in this way will withstand rust better.

The high finish obtained by much effort may easily be marred by careless fixing of the work in the vise. The jaws of a vise are cut in the same way as a file in order to secure a firm grip on the work. Any polished work or soft metal should therefore be held between soft jaws or clamps, as shown

in Fig. 14. These are generally made from stout-gauge copper, brass, zinc, or tin-plate. For aluminum and lead, wooden jaws are used, and for highly polished work in mild steel, or for fine screw threads, leather is used.

If files have been carelessly used they may be renovated to a certain extent by boiling them in a strong solution of soda and water for a

LEAD, COPPER

Fig. 14. When holding highly polished or delicate work in the vise, loose jaws or clamps should be used.

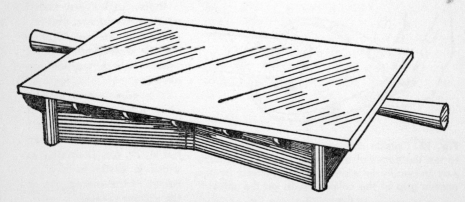

Fig. 15. A surface plate which is covered with red lead to test the accuracy of a job. Any parts not colored are hollow, and the high parts must be filed down. An accurate job will be coated all over with a thin film of red lead.

few minutes; this removes the grease and dust, and after a good scrub with a file card or wire brush the file should be dipped in kerosene to prevent rusting.

If the work is to be filed true it will have to be tested frequently. It is generally best to file one edge true (straight and at right angles to a face) and then to make the layout from that edge. An ordinary steel rule or the blade of a try-square held on the work and against the light will give a fairly accurate test of straightness; any hollows are clearly shown by light shining under the straight edge.

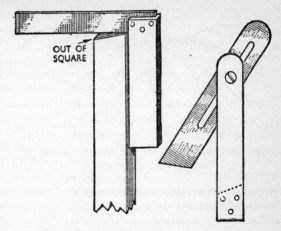

Fig. 16. Right angles may be tested with a try-square (*left*). Other angles may be tested with a bevel square (*right*) set to the required angle.

A more accurate method is to use a surface plate, which is a plane-table of cast iron of heavy section and which is well ribbed underneath (Fig. 15). The surface is machined and scraped to a perfectly plane surface. A thin film of powdered red lead and oil is smeared on the surface plate. The surface of the job to be tested is then held firmly on the surface plate and rubbed once or twice backward and forward. This has the effect of smearing with red lead all the parts of the work that touch the surface. If any part is not colored there is a hollow, and the high spots must be filed down. It is clear that only the thinnest possible film of red lead should be used, for otherwise the value of the test would be completely lost.

Right angles are tested with the try-square, and angles which are not 90 deg. may be tested with a bevel square set to the required angle (Fig. 16).

The edges of a narrow piece of metal may be tested for parallel by using a pair of outside calipers, as shown in Fig. 17. Any inequality in width is easily noticed by reason of the uneven grip of the caliper points.

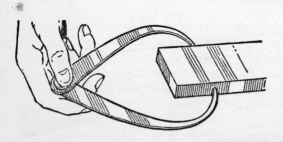

Fig. 17. Outside calipers may be used as shown to test the edges of a piece of metal for parallel. Any inequality in width is easily noticed by the uneven grip of the caliper points on the sides of the metal.

DRILLING

DRILLING is the operation of making a hole in a material. The process is frequently confused with boring, a term which should be used only for the operation of increasing the diameter of a hole previously formed in some way, not necessarily by drilling.

There are several forms of drill which may be held and rotated so as to pierce the work in many types of machine.

Types of Drill

Probably the first type to be designed for metal drilling was the flat drill made by flattening out a round bar of tool steel until the required diameter was obtained; this was then ground to the shape shown in Fig. 18 and hardened and tempered to a dark brown. This drill is easily made and is capable of withstanding rough use, but its action is really that of scraping, and not cutting. In consequence, it is necessary to use a great amount of pressure to force the drill into the work.

As shown in Fig. 18, the angle formed by the cutting edges is 90 deg., but since the point of the drill must be working in the metal when the extremities of the cutting edge begin to drill, it follows that if thin metal is being drilled, the point may burst through before the maximum diameter of the whole is reached, and the result is generally an elliptically-shaped hole. This fault may be overcome to a large extent by having a flatter angle for thin metal.

The cutting edges of the drill are backed off more for the softer metals, being about 3 deg. for cast iron or mild steel, but much sharper for copper, brass, aluminum, etc. This type of drill is never very accurate, and has a tendency to work to the softer parts of the metal. This is especially noticeable when drilling cast iron or cast brass, and this causes *wobbling* of the drill, with consequent lack of truth. Furthermore, every time the drill is sharpened it becomes smaller in diameter, and the hole drilled is therefore not the correct size. This type of drill, in consequence, has practically disappeared from modern workshop practice and has been almost entirely superseded by the twist drill.

The Morse Twist Drill

The Morse twist drill is now most widely used for all purposes, and is made in sizes from .0135 in. upward. For larger drills it is customary to use high-speed steel, with a shank of tough steel butt-welded to it. Small drills (up to ½ in.) are usually made with parallel shanks, while larger drills are more frequently designed with a tapered shank.

The tapered shank wedges itself in the spindle of the drilling machine, which has a corresponding tapered hole, and as more pressure is applied, the drill becomes more firmly gripped.

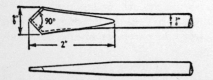

Fig. 18. Typical flat drill, with grinding angle of 90 deg. This type has been largely superseded by the twist drill.

In addition, however, the drill is made with a tongue or tang which fits into a corresponding slot in the spindle of the drill press. This provides a more positive drive.

Twist Drill Terms

The drill body is the main portion that is used for the actual drilling, and is made accurately to the specified size, although it is usually ground slightly less toward the shank end, so that there is a small clearance of not more than $\frac{1}{1000}$ in. The lands are the narrow strips along the cutting edge of the flutes. It is the diameter across these which is made accurately to size, and which represents the size of the drill. The portion of the body marked X in Fig. 19 is ground away slightly to prevent friction.

The flutes are made so as to insure the correct cutting angle and at the same time give sufficient clearance for

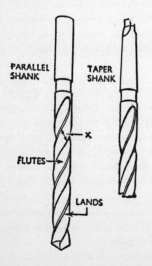

Fig. 19. Two widely used types or twist drill. The part marked X is ground away slightly to prevent friction.

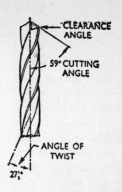

Fig. 20. Standard twist drill, showing the clearance angle, cutting angle, and angle of twist.

the waste material to flow out of the hole. This angle (Fig. 20) is called the angle of twist, and is usually about $27\frac{1}{2}$ deg.

The cutting angle is the degree of sharpness or bluntness of the drill, and varies with the kind of material to be drilled. Standard drills are usually ground to a cutting angle of 59 deg., and this is most suitable for all general work. The surfaces formed by grinding the end of the drill to the cutting angle are then further ground so that the cutting edge slopes back at from 10 to 15 deg.; this angle is known as the clearance angle, and is also indicated in Fig. 20.

Drill Faults

Great care must be taken to insure that the cutting angle and the clearance angle are maintained when a drill is re-ground; the angle of twist cannot, of course, be altered by grinding.

The following are a few of the faults that are likely to occur when drilling, owing to faulty grinding. If the hole is larger than the drill, it is

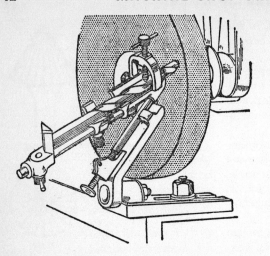

Fig. 21. Drill-grinding appliance shown in use with a power-driven grinding wheel.

pose the drill is fed into the work so as to take a cut $\frac{1}{100}$ in. deep for each revolution; this is an exceptionally good feed, and if by inaccurate grinding one cutting edge is $\frac{1}{100}$ in. longer than the other, it follows that one lip is removing the whole of the cut each time it revolves. This defect can be overcome to a certain extent by reducing the amount of feed, but this means a corresponding reduction in the number of holes drilled in a given time.

In modern shops, twist drills are accurately ground by the use of a special drill grinder (of the type shown in Fig. 21). The drill rests in a V-shaped channel, which may be pivoted and set to make any desired angle with the face of the grinding wheel. The drill is kept in contact with the grinding wheel by means of a screw clamped to the V-shaped channel.

probable that the two cutting angles are not identical. This would throw the drill-point out of center and cause the drill to *wobble*. As a result, the hole would be larger than it should be. In addition, if the angles of both the cutting edges are not the same, one lip does all the work, and dulls quickly. To correct this the drill must be reground. If the drill will not feed into the work, the clearance angle is probably insufficient, and the drill should be backed off more.

Other faults may occur due to the drill running at too high a speed, in which case it becomes worn excessively on the outside and tends to become very hot. If the drill is fed into the work too quickly, the point on the cutting edges will break, even though the drill has been correctly ground.

Extreme accuracy in grinding the drill cannot be overemphasized. For example, sup-

The test for accurate regrinding is to place the drill in the hole it has made and see if it will drop vertically by its own weight through the hole. If it does not, it is clear that the hole is no larger than the drill that made it, and that the drill is therefore accurate. This is a very severe test.

When the drill is used for special work it may be reground to a different cutting angle. Thus, 45 deg. to 50 deg. is a better cutting angle for cast iron than is the more general 59 deg. An angle of 45 deg. is also more suitable for brass, although special drills may be obtained for brass

Fig. 22. Drill sharpened for use on copper or zinc.

which have their flutes straight, in addition to having the smaller cutting angle.

Softer metals, such as copper or aluminum, are best cut with a drill having a cutting angle of 90 deg. and made with a small pip to act as a guide, as shown in Fig. 22.

Very hard steel, such as manganese steel, may be drilled more satisfactorily by using a drill having an angle of twist of less than normal—say 24 deg. The cutting angle should also be flatter—about 75 deg.

Whenever a large hole has to be drilled, it is good practice to drill first a small hole to act as a guide. This provides a center for the larger drill and reduces the risk of drilling a hole that is not exactly true. If a series of holes is to be drilled, it is wise to drill the first two or three at a lower speed, in order to warm up the drill. This enables it to withstand more strain than if it were used immediately at its maximum speed.

Other faults will naturally occur if the drilling-machine spindle or chuck is not running true.

Apart from the drills already mentioned, there are specially designed drills for other kinds of work. The following are the chief types.

The combination center drill shown in Fig. 23 is used for drilling the ends of bars and rods that have to be turned between centers on the lathe. It drills and counter-sinks in one operation, and thus saves considerable time. An-

other type of countersink drill is shown in Fig. 24. It is used in making holes to take screw-heads or rivets, and is sometimes used to remove the burr from a punched hole. This type of countersink drill is intended mainly for use on the soft metals. For normal countersinking a twist drill twice the size of the hole that has been drilled is used.

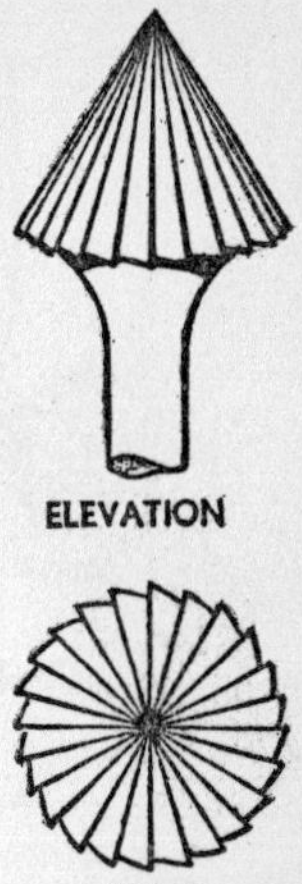

Fig. 25 shows a flat-ended drill by means of which a hole previously drilled to the correct depth with

ELEVATION

PLAN

Fig. 24. Rose or countersink bit for use with wood and soft metals.

a twist drill may be squared out to a flat bottom; the small *pip* is necessary to insure that the drill runs concentrically.

Fig. 26 shows a slotting drill, which is a slight variation of the previous one. It is used to prepare a shallow slot or a keyway. A flat-bottom hole is drilled first, and the slotting drill is then employed. As it revolves, the work is slowly moved along, forming the slot.

Fig. 27 shows another variety of the flat-ended drill that is used for recessing an existing hole to accommodate a bolt-head or cheese-headed screw. The pin on the drill must be the same in diameter as the hole to be recessed. The three flat-ended drills referred to are all similar in their cutting action, and it is the outside edges that do most of the work.

Large holes in thin metal are best cut by using a cutter and bar, the prin-

Fig. 23. Combination center drill used for centering work for the lathe. It drills and countersinks in one operation and thus saves time.

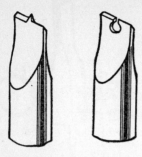

Figs. 25 and 26. *Left,* tip of flat-ended drill. *Right,* slotting drill for shallow slots or keyways. It has a straight edge and is notched in the center.

Laying Out

Prior to laying out the work the surface of the metal is generally chalked, and the positions of required holes are then marked, using a steel rule, square, and a scriber. The centers of the holes are then center-punched to prevent the point of the twist drill from *wandering*. A representative center punch is shown in Fig. 30. It is generally made from ⅜ in. octagonal cast steel about 5 in. long, and the point is ground to an angle of 90 deg. It is tempered to a pale straw color and is used for marking the ends of work to be cen-

ciple of which is shown in Fig. 28. A small hole is drilled first, and the center rod revolves in this; the cutter is then adjusted to the correct radius and the wedge-cotter tightened. The principle is extended in Fig. 29 to a washer-cutter which, as may be seen, can be adjusted to form a washer or to cut a hole of large diameter in thin metal.

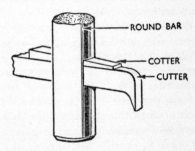

Fig. 28. Special drilling tool used for cutting large holes in thin metal sheet.

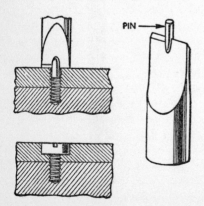

Fig. 27. Countersink drill for cheese-headed screws. Its use is shown in the sketches on the left.

tered for turning in the lathe, as well as all centers of holes for drilling.

A smaller center punch, made from about ¼-in.-diameter cast steel with a sharper point—say 60 deg. (right, Fig. 30)—is often used for marking positions of lines and centers of circles to be drawn with the dividers.

Sometimes when the position of a hole must be set very accurately, the center is marked with a *dot* punch and a circle drawn with a pair of dividers. Four light dots are punched equidistantly on the circumference of the circle, and the drill is just allowed to start the hole. It is then withdrawn and its position checked with the four dots; if it is slightly out, the center is pulled over with a center punch or a round-nosed chisel before recommencing the drilling. If a large-diameter hole is to be drilled, a smaller circle should be drawn, so that the position of the hole can be checked at an earlier stage than by waiting until the full diameter has been reached.

Fig. 31 shows the laying out for a plate that has to be drilled and cut to the shape shown. A slot has to be cut in the work, and the first stage after setting out is to drill a series of holes as shown. It should be noted that in marking the work the dots are fine, evenly spaced, and of equal size, but the centers for drilling are punched much larger.

Where repetitive drilling is being carried out, the location of the holes is often done by the use of a jig or template. This is a hardened-steel plate with holes of the required size and spacing drilled in them. The jig is clamped to the work, and the drill passes through the hole and drills into the work in exactly the correct posi-

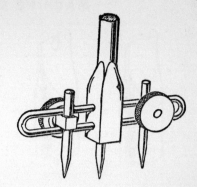

Fig. 29. Type of washer-cutter. The two cutters are adjustable, one being set for the hole in the washer and the other for the outside diameter.

tion each time, without the need for setting out the holes afresh. The same principle is used when drilling holes in plates that have to be riveted, one plate previously drilled being used as a template when drilling the second and subsequent plates.

There is a wide variety of drilling machines, and these may be either power driven or, in the smaller types, hand operated. Drilling may also be

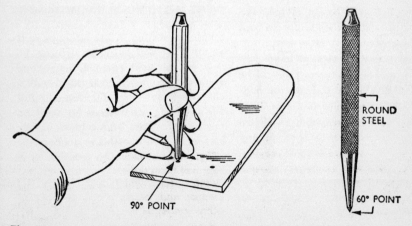

Fig. 30. Representative examples of a center punch (*left*) and a dot punch (*right*). Note that in using a punch the tip of the third finger is held against the bottom of the punch in order to steady the point and prevent it from sliding off the mark.

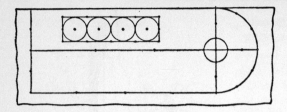

Fig. 31. Typical example of setting out a job for drilling and filing. The plate has to be drilled and cut to the shape shown. A slot has also to be cut in the work.

done in the lathe, but that aspect is dealt with elsewhere in this book.

The small hand drill of the type shown in Fig. 32 is used chiefly for drilling small-diameter holes in thin sheet-metal, and is especially useful for repair work and for drilling in positions where it is impossible to use a more powerful and larger machine. The length is about 12 in., and the three-jaw chuck will take drills up to ¼ in. in diameter. Care must be taken when using a hand drill to keep it quite steady and in line with the twist drill. If this precaution is not observed the resulting hole will be out of true and the drill will almost certainly be bent or broken.

There is another type of hand drill to which passing reference should be made, because of its wide use in modern airplane and other factories. This is of compact construction, as shown in Fig. 33, and can be used in any position, and even in awkward corners. It may be driven by electricity or compressed air, depending on the type selected and the available power supply. Both forms of machine run at high speed, and therefore the choice of drill, in relation to the metal being worked, is of great importance.

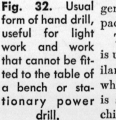

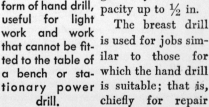

Fig. 32. Usual form of hand drill, useful for light work and work that cannot be fitted to the table of a bench or stationary power drill.

The breast drill of the type shown in Fig. 34 is larger and more strongly made than the hand drill, and has an adjustable breast-plate, by means of which a much greater pressure may be applied to the drill. The machine shown in Fig. 34 has two alternative speed ratios. These are obtained by moving the spindle of the driving wheel into one or another of the positions indicated in Fig. 34. When in the first position the teeth around the outside of the larger bevel wheel drive the small wheel attached to the chuck spindle; this gives a high-speed drive. By moving the spindle the inner set of teeth are engaged so that the chuck is rotated at little more than the speed of the handle. It is only necessary to press a spring-loaded plunger to allow the spindle to be withdrawn from either bushing. The three-jaw chuck on this type of machine generally has a capacity up to ½ in.

The breast drill is used for jobs similar to those for which the hand drill is suitable; that is, chiefly for repair work, where it is necessary to take the drill to the job rather than bring the job to the drill.

Drill Post and Ratchet

With both types of drill just referred to, the operation of drilling even a small hole through a piece of mild steel $\frac{1}{4}$ in. thick is a rather tedious one, and for comparatively thick metal, which it is necessary to drill by hand, quicker results are obtained with a drill post and ratchet shown in Fig. 35.

The drill post consists of a base plate with an upright spindle welded

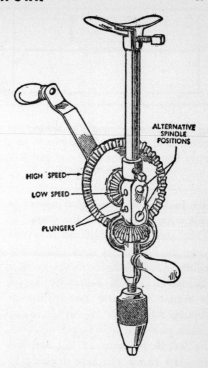

Fig. 34. Breast drill with two speed drive. Different speeds can be obtained by moving the spindle of the driving wheel to which the handle is attached. Provision is sometimes made for mounting a drill of this type on a bench stand.

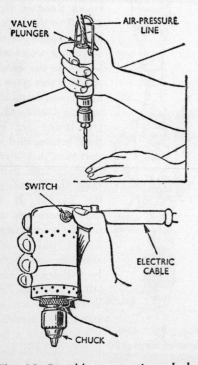

Fig. 33. Portable pneumatic and electric drills are widely used for modern high-speed production. The illustration shows two such drills in use. Stopping and starting is finger-controlled by pressing a button or switch on the drill, as shown above.

to it. The base plate is slotted so that it may be bolted down if convenient; or it may be held by C clamps. The arm may be raised, lowered, or swiveled to a suitable position. As the twist drill is made to revolve by means of the long handle and ratchet arrangement, it is fed slowly into the metal by means of a fine screw thread on the spindle and on the inside of the octagonal sleeve. The drill generally has a square tapered hole for square-shank drills instead of the three-jaw chuck.

Bench drills are stronger and more rigid than the types mentioned pre-

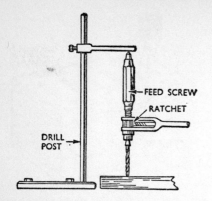

FEED SCREW

RATCHET

DRILL
POST

Fig. 35. Drill post and ratchet: it is generally made for use with a tapered square shank drill.

viously. They are bolted or lag-screwed down to a bench, are provided with a hand or automatic feed, and are frequently adaptable to a power drive. For other than the lightest work, or where general motive power is not available, a bench drill is indispensable.

A common type is shown in Fig. 36. This has a strong slotted base, which is bolted to the bench. The pillar is usually about 30 in. high, and the drill can quickly be converted for use in a horizontal position with the work held against the wall. Although this is not often necessary, it is extremely useful when drilling holes in the ends of long bars or shafting.

The large hand-wheel acts as a flywheel and reduces the amount of effort required, besides helping to keep the speed steady. The small hand-wheel above the drill is used to advance or return the drilling spindle. By means of a cam on the hand-wheel spindle an arm is arranged to engage with the teeth cut on the wheel which is keyed to the feed spindle. This is moved round a certain distance every time

the hand-wheel revolves, and thus the feed is made automatic. This is frequently found to be either too fast or too slow, and many machinists prefer to feed the drill by means of the hand-wheel. A sense of feel is of great value in drilling, and after some experience it will be found that the correct amount of feed (which governs the speed of drilling) is guided largely by the use of feeling both in the right hand on the large hand-wheel, and in the left hand on the feed-spindle wheel.

When the drill is just protruding through the metal that is being drilled.

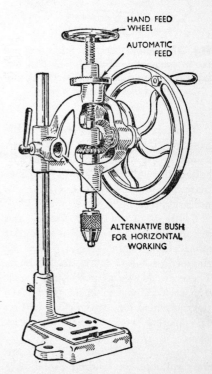

HAND FEED
WHEEL

AUTOMATIC
FEED

ALTERNATIVE BUSH
FOR HORIZONTAL
WORKING

Fig. 36. Bench drill that can be used either vertically, as shown, or horizontally. Provision is made for either automatic or hand feed. In addition, there is often a choice of two or more speeds of operation as in the case of the breast drill shown in Fig. 34.

care is needed to prevent the drill from being pulled quickly into the partly-cut hole and thus being broken.

After some experience the operator can feel when this is about to happen, and he reduces the feed. Even so, considerably more effort is required to keep the work stationary and prevent it from revolving with the drill; this difficulty is especially noticeable when drilling sheet-metal.

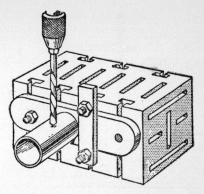

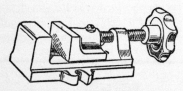

Fig. 37. Simple form of table vise for use in conjunction with a bench drill. The base is clamped or bolted to the bed of the drill for heavy work.

To keep the work stationary on the base plate a small vise of the type shown in Fig. 37 is used. This may be bolted through the slots to the base plate for heavier jobs, but it is not necessary for light work.

Castings of awkward shape, and metal that has to be drilled at angles other than right angles, may be clamped or bolted to box-angle plates. These are blocks of good-quality cast iron accurately machined, which have slots provided for conveniently bolting or clamping work to them (see Fig. 38).

V-blocks and clamps (Fig. 39) are most suitable for holding round bars while they are drilled at right angles to their axis, marked out for keyways, or having their ends centered preparatory to being turned in the lathe. The work is held firmly in the blocks by means of a clamp, as shown.

Fig. 38. Type of box-angle plate used for mounting work at an angle on the bed of a bench drill. Other angle plates simply consist of an angle-shaped casting having holes and slots. They are used for the same purpose as the box pattern illustrated, but are not by any means as universal in their application.

Where holes have to be drilled *blind* —that is, to a certain depth in solid metal—it is customary to use the twist drill, and then, if the hole needs to have a square bottom, it is finished by the flat-ended drill already described. The depth is measured by means of a depth-gauge, as shown in Fig. 40. A

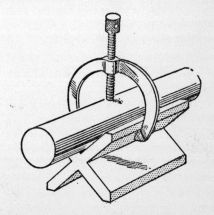

Fig. 39. V-block and clamp. These are used for holding circular bars for centering, drilling, etc.

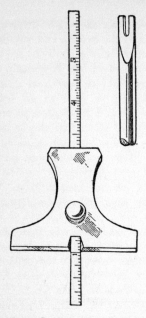

Figs. 40 and 41. *Left,* simple type of depth-gauge used for measuring or checking the depth of blind holes. *Right,* tool used for extracting broken drills; it can be made from an old drill or piece of silver-steel rod. The fingers formed at the end fit into the flutes of the drill.

No definite rule, however, can be laid down as to the rate of speed or feed, because so much depends on the kind of material being drilled, and of course on the accuracy of the drill, especially after being re-ground. Considerable experience in the use of drills has proved that the best speeds of their cutting surfaces for different metals in average circumstances are:

30 ft. per min. for cast iron and mild steel.

150 ft. per min. for brass and copper.

The following table shows the number of revolutions per minute at which each size of drill must be run to comply with the above figures.

The drill must be well lubricated during use, and while for small jobs

direct reading may be obtained, or the gauge can be first fixed to a particular measurement and used for testing the depth.

Working the Drill

The correct speed at which to work a drill is important; the larger the drill, the more slowly it must revolve. If a drill revolves too fast it becomes overheated, the correct temper is lost, and the drill becomes soft and useless. On the other hand, if it is being run more slowly than necessary, the rate of drilling is cut down and production costs are thereby increased proportionately.

SPEED OF DRILLS

DIAMETER OF DRILL.	SPEED FOR BRASS BRONZE.	SPEED FOR CAST IRON MILD STEEL.
INCHES	R.P.M.	R.P.M.
$\frac{1}{16}$	9170	1833
$\frac{1}{8}$	4585	917
$\frac{3}{16}$	3056	611
$\frac{1}{4}$	2287	458
$\frac{5}{16}$	1830	367
$\frac{3}{8}$	1525	306
$\frac{7}{16}$	1307	262
$\frac{1}{2}$	1143	229
$\frac{5}{8}$	915	183
$\frac{3}{4}$	762	153
$\frac{7}{8}$	654	131
1	571	115
$1\frac{1}{4}$	458	92
$1\frac{1}{2}$	381	76
$1\frac{3}{4}$	327	65
2	286	57

using hand, breast, or bench drills it is sufficient to apply the oil-can freely, this method is not satisfactory with the larger drilling machines. For these a mixture of soap and water, or a mixture of soft soap, soda, and water, is used freely, and this allows the drills to be run at increased speeds and feeds, and at the same time prolongs the life of the drill by preventing overheating. The question is similar to that involved in lathe-turning and dealt with more fully in the chapter on the lathe.

It frequently happens that a drill is broken—generally owing to careless use or bad grinding—and the body is left securely wedged into the partially drilled hole. It is then often very difficult to withdraw the broken portion. If any slight portion of drill projects, the ends may be gripped with pliers and the broken end withdrawn; unfortunately the drill is so brittle that these small bits frequently crumble away before any real grip can be obtained. If it is at all feasible, the job should be heated to redness and allowed to cool as slowly as possible—say by burying it in cinders. The drill is then tough and soft, and the projecting portions can be used to pull out the broken part.

Where there is no projecting portion, a small tool (Fig. 41) is made. The two small fingers then fit into the flutes of the broken drill and it is possible to revolve the drill in the hole and so unscrew it out. Failing these methods the drill has to be softened as described and drilled out with a new drill.

REAMING

THE process of reaming has a number of applications, the chief of which are: to enlarge existing drilled holes; to make a parallel hole into a tapered hole; and to bring existing holes accurately to size. It will be clear from this that there must be two main types of reamer, one of which is parallel and the other tapered. These are shown in Fig. 42.

In some respects, hand reamers are similar to screw-cutting taps, for they cut away metal from the inside of a hole. Additionally, they are held in a wrench of similar type to that used for taps. When buying reamers care should be taken that the correct pattern is ordered, since many of them have a tapered, or Morse, shank; this is for fitting in a drilling machine or lathe. Reamers for hand use have a cylindrical shank with square end, as shown in Fig. 42.

It is possible still further to divide these tools, for, while some reamers have straight flutes, others have spiral flutes, rather resembling those of a drill, but often of much greater pitch. In general, the spiral-flute type is to be preferred for accurate work, since there is less tendency for it to *chatter* when in use, and therefore a smoother finish is produced. It is also better when a good deal of metal has to be removed. It should be noted that the spiral flutes are left-handed, although the reamer is turned in a right-hand or clockwise direction.

Still further sub-dividing, there are some reamers which are made to a taper for their full length, and others which are tapered for only about half the length of the flutes, the remainder being parallel. In the tapered types we have that which is made to the standard Morse or B. and S. taper, and used for forming holes to receive a Morse or B. and S. shank or pin, and that which is given the very small taper of about $\frac{1}{4}$ in. per foot. The latter is used for making slightly tapered holes for locking pins used for shaft collars, pulleys, and the like. In this case the nominal diameter, by which the reamers are listed, is the diameter about halfway between the ends of the fluted portion. This means that the diameter at the tip is less than the nominal diameter, the diameter at the shank end being greater. Because of this, it is possible to produce a full range of reamers where each overlaps the next.

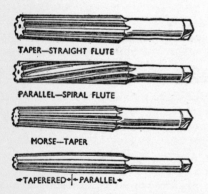

Fig. 43. Expanding reamer with variable cutting edges.

a certain limited range. For example, a smaller reamer of this type may have a range from $1\frac{3}{32}$ in. to $1\frac{5}{32}$ in., while a larger one may cover the range from $3\frac{1}{32}$ in. to $1\frac{1}{8}$ in.; it will be seen that the expansion in the former case is $\frac{1}{16}$ in., and in the latter case $\frac{5}{32}$ in.

Hand reamers are generally made of carbon steel (high-speed steel is also used), and their cutting edges are backed off in the same manner as those of twist drills, to give suitable clearance. A rather special and unusual type has notched cutting edges, so that the metal chip is broken as reaming proceeds. In general, however, this pattern is intended only for machine use, where the tool is turned at comparatively high speed. In hand work the reamer is turned slowly, the speed being only slightly greater than that of a screw tap.

When an existing hole is to be slightly enlarged to accurate size—to receive an axle or pin, for example— it is generally best to use a reamer of the type which is tapered toward the tip and parallel nearer the shank, since this gives easier working. The size should be such that the reamer will enter the hole for a distance at least equal to half the length of the tapered portion, or one-quarter the length of the flutes. The work must be held absolutely rigid, and the reamer turned with a tap wrench, applying a steady pressure and keeping the turning speed as uniform as possible. A few drops of light machine oil may be used as lubricant.

TAPER—STRAIGHT FLUTE

PARALLEL—SPIRAL FLUTE

MORSE—TAPER

◄TAPERERED►|◄PARALLEL►

Fig. 42. The principal types of hand reamer used with wrench or holder.

There is yet another important type of reamer, of the expanding type; an example is shown in Fig. 43. In this case there are five or more cutting blades carried in collars mounted on a central threaded shank. By means of a cone adjuster the diameter over the cutting edges can be varied over

Reaming *Blind* Holes

This type of reamer cannot, of course, be used in a *blind* hole, which does not go completely through the work-piece; the parallel type is then essential if the hole is to be the same diameter right to the bottom. The end of the reamer is very slightly tapered to simplify entry, and the tool is used in the same manner as described above in connection with the tapered reamer. It should, of course, be only very slightly larger than the original hole, for otherwise a start could not be made. If the stock of reamers is limited and the correct size is not available, it is permissible to open out the end of the hole with a large tapered reamer before starting with the parallel one. In that case great care must be taken to keep the tapered reamer exactly in line with the hole.

An alternative method to that just described is to employ an adjustable reamer, gradually increasing the diameter as consecutive cuts are taken. Before making the final cut, however, it is essential that the reamer should be set very precisely, and this may be done by testing it in a drill-

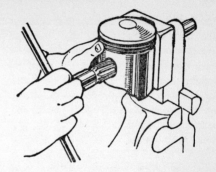

Fig. 45. Pilot-ended reamer used in conjunction with a guide plate.

gauge plate; this is simply a steel plate having a number of holes of accurate diameter, the sizes being stamped or engraved on the plate.

Morse reamers are used in the same manner as taper reamers. When these are being used the precise diameter of the finished hole at any particular point is not always of great importance. It is the angle of taper which is of first importance. The reamer is therefore fed into the hole until the Morse shank will just enter to the desired point.

Reamers are widely used by the fitter for making accurate holes to receive pins, etc. In that case the exact size of the pin will probably be known before commencing work, and the reamer chosen accordingly. In other instances the pin may be of an odd size, when an adjustable reamer would be used and enlarged until a good fit is obtained.

The automobile machinist uses reamers fairly extensively for opening out the bushings which carry steering swivel pins, or king pins; for opening out the bosses of a new piston to receive new wrist pins, or enlarging and truing the holes in an old piston to receive over-size wrist pins; for tru-

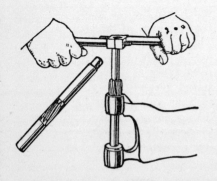

Fig. 44. Reamer used for opening out bushings. The plain cylindrical end, or "pilot," acts as a guide.

ing the main bearings and insuring that they are all exactly in line, so that the crankshaft will run true.

The first two of these uses for reamers are illustrated in Figs. 44 and 45. In Fig. 44 it will be seen that the reamer is of a different type from those previously referred to, since there is a plain cylindrical end. This is to serve as a *pilot*, or guide; it fits into the lower bushing while the upper one is being opened out, and vice versa, so insuring that the two reamed holes will be exactly in line. If the pilot were not provided there might be a danger of the reamer tilting slightly, and so throwing one bush hole slightly out of line with the other. Were that to happen, the steering pin

would not fit through both bushings despite the fact that both had been correctly sized.

There is far less danger of this happening when dealing with the piston-pin bosses, since the holes are long in relation to the gap between them. With an old piston the wrist-pin holes are generally found to be oval, so it is often best to run a taper reamer through them first, to make them more nearly circular, and then to finish to size with a parallel reamer of the ordinary kind. More accurate work results from the use of a pilot-ended reamer, however, and this is shown in Fig. 45, where a guide plate is also placed behind the piston to support both this and the reamer pilot.

CUTTING METAL

METAL bars, rods, and tubes are usually cut to length with some kind of saw. Sheet metal may also be sawed to shape, and a hack-saw is used for all such general work. It consists of a frame, and a handle and a blade, the frame being either of the fixed type taking only one length of blade, or adjustable to take blades of various lengths. Representative examples of the two types are shown in Fig. 46. In both cases the blade is made taut by screwing up the wing or knurled nut, thus pulling on the square-section blade holder shown in Fig. 46.

The blades are usually designed to cut on the forward stroke only, and the blade must therefore be fixed in the frame with the teeth pointing away from the handle. In a few special cases, however, the teeth are designed to cut in both directions. In general,

blades are made in lengths between 8 and 14 in., but longer ones may be obtained for special jobs. Standard sizes for the teeth run from 14 to 32 teeth per in.

The blades are generally $\frac{1}{2}$ in. wide and about $\frac{1}{40}$ in. thick, the teeth being *set* so as to make a cut wider than the saw blade, and so prevent tightness of the blade in the cut. The *set* is obtained by having alternate teeth bent slightly outward. In some types of hack-saw blades, designed for use solely on soft metal such as copper, the blade is made thinner toward the back. This avoids the necessity for having any *set*, in the usual sense, on this type of blade.

Types of Blade

The teeth of hack-saw blades are, of necessity, extremely hard, and, un-

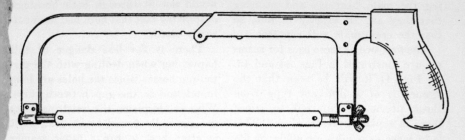

Fig. 46. Adjustable hack saw to be used with blades from 8 to 12 inches.

like a saw for woodworking, they cannot be either sharpened or set when they become worn. Some blades are hardened and tempered all over to the same degree, but the most widely used type are tempered so that the teeth are hard and the rest of the blade comparatively soft. It is especially useful when sawing in awkward corners, when the saw is more likely to be twisted and convenient for such jobs as cutting pipes, angle irons, thin sheets, channels, and other awkward sections.

Blades hardened right through last longer and cut better than the others, and are generally more suited to the skilled worker, while the soft-backed blades are much less easily broken in the hands of the unskilled worker.

The blades should be tightened in the frame so that they do not whip sideways when cutting. At the same time they should not be made too tight, especially when new, since there is then a greater risk of breakage if the frame is slightly twisted when sawing.

The blades, like files, last longer if used on the softer metals first, until the teeth have become slightly dulled. Also, the cut must not be started against the edge, but downward, as shown in Fig. 47.

The rate of cutting should not be too quick, or the teeth become too hot and lose their correct temper; in addition, the teeth do not bite into the metal, but tend to slide over the surface. Between forty and fifty strokes per minute is quite fast enough for good sawing if the saw is held correctly, with the left hand gripping the front of the frame and the right hand

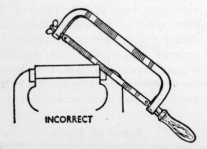

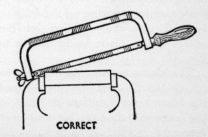

Fig. 47. Starting a hack-saw cut: the right and the wrong way. The cut should be started downward, not against the edge, so as to preserve the life of the blade.

Fig. 48. A backed metal-cutting saw, such as this, is useful to art metal workers for cutting light sections of tubes, bars, rods, etc., in brass or copper.

used in the same manner as on the handle of a file. Downward pressure should be applied with the left hand on the forward stroke only.

Fine and Coarse Blades

The finer-toothed blade should be used on tool steel, brass and copper tubes, and thin sheet-metal where a smooth cut is essential to prevent the blade being broken. The coarser teeth are used for all jobs in wrought iron, although a somewhat finer tooth is better for cutting mild steel or cast iron. Many engineers claim that blades with 18 teeth per in. are most satisfactory for general use on all kinds of metal.

If a blade is broken when partly through a piece of metal it is best to begin the cut from the other side rather than work through the old saw cut. The cut is slightly narrower than that which the new blade will make, and in working down the old cut the *set* is likely to be impaired and the blade damaged. It is a good plan to keep two hack-saws, one with a new blade for brass, copper, etc., and one with a slightly worn blade for steel and iron.

Other Hand-Saws for Metal

Although hack-saws are by far the most generally used for sawing metal, there are at least two other hand-saws for metal; the piercing saw and the small, backed saw. The backed saw shown in Fig. 48 is used for cutting small sections of brass and copper bar or tubes, and is more useful to the art metal-worker and electrician than to the machinist.

The piercing saw, shown in Fig. 49, is used for cutting internal holes, slots, and shapes. It consists of a frame with jaws and a handle; the lower jaw is adjustable so that saw-blades of various lengths may be gripped. Blades are fixed with the teeth pointing toward the handle so that the cut is made on the downward stroke. The method of holding the saw is shown in Fig. 49. Piercing saws are used

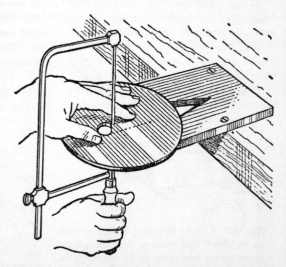

Fig. 49. The handle of the piercing saw is held from below in the right hand, the work being steadied by the left hand.

chiefly for decorative work in thin sheet metal. To cut a slot or any other enclosed shape, it is first necessary to drill a small hole. The blade is then inserted and fastened in the saw-frame, and the hole is cut out to the desired shape.

Avoiding Broken Blades

Care must be taken to keep the saw running true, for otherwise the blade is very easily broken. The saw must not be forced, and slow, easy strokes are necessary. For metal thicker than $\frac{1}{8}$ in. the process is extremely tedious and not to be recommended.

For cutting large pieces of sheet iron, copper, brass, and tin-plate the most useful tool is the shearing machine shown in Fig. 50. This consists of a fixed blade and a cropper, operated by a long handle so as to obtain the advantage of a long lever. The cutting edges of the blades are ground almost square (about 87 deg.), and are adjusted so that the two blades are perfectly parallel and the moving

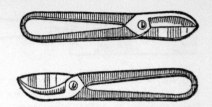

Figs. 51 and 52. Hand-shears or snips are used for shaping thin sheet metal. Straight snips or tinman's shears (*above*) are used for straight line work and large external curves; bent snips for small external and all internal curves.

blade or cropper just touches the face of the fixed blade in making the cut.

This type of shearing machine is not only capable of cutting sheet metal of fairly heavy gauges, but may be used to shear off bars and rods roughly to length. Such a machine with 8-in. blades and a handle about 4 ft. long will cut mild-steel rods up to $\frac{3}{8}$ in. diameter and bars $\frac{1}{4}$ in. thick. There is a considerable saving of time over the hack-saw method; the end, however, is not cut square, except on very thin material, so that it is not possible to work to accurate dimensions without filing.

Straight and Bent Snips

Hand-shears or snips are used for cutting thin sheet-metal to shape. They may be straight, as in Fig. 51, or curved, as in Fig. 52. Straight snips are used for all straight-line work, and for large radius external curves; bent snips are useful for cutting small external and all internal curves.

When cutting external curves with the curved shears, the shears should be held so that the curve of the blades is opposite to that of the cutting line on the metal. In dealing with fairly

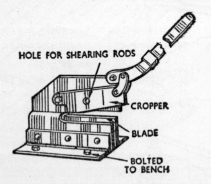

HOLE FOR SHEARING RODS

CROPPER

BLADE

BOLTED TO BENCH

Fig. 50. A light shearing machine such as is used for cutting medium-gauge sheet metal and rods up to about $\frac{3}{8}$ in. in diameter. The two blades are parallel, the moving blade just touching the fixed blade as it cuts.

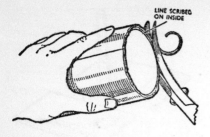

LINE SCRIBED ON INSIDE

Fig. 53. How curved shears are used for trimming a piece of cylindrical or conical work in sheet metal. The line to be followed is marked on the inside surface of the job.

heavy-gauge metal with hand-snips, the work is generally simplified if one arm of the snips is gripped in the vise so that greater force can be applied to the other arm. The not uncommon practice of using a short length of pipe over the free handle is a bad one, since the increased leverage is likely to damage the shears. If the metal cannot be cut with ease

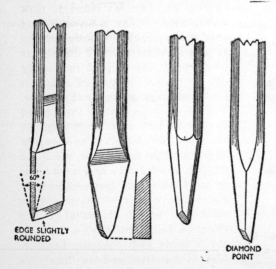

60°

EDGE SLIGHTLY ROUNDED

DIAMOND POINT

Fig. 55. Four kinds of cold chisel in common use: the flat, cross-cut or cape, round-nose or half-round, and diamond-pointed chisels.

without this addition, the work should be done on a shearing machine, or with a hack-saw.

In sheet-metal work, the ends of cylindrical or conical shaped jobs are

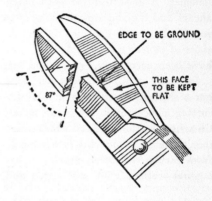

EDGE TO BE GROUND

87°

THIS FACE TO BE KEPT FLAT

Fig. 54. Details of the cutting blades of hand-shears. The edge is made at an angle of about 87 deg.

best trimmed, when this is necessary, by using curved shears. The line to be followed is marked on the inside, and the shears and work held as shown in Fig. 53.

The jaws of the shears are generally pivoted about a rivet, so that if they need sharpening it is difficult to re-grind them separately without drilling out the rivet. Unless they have become very badly damaged this is seldom done; the jaws are opened as wide as possible and the edges of the jaws reground, preferably on a wet grindstone.

The edge is made at an angle of about 87 deg., as shown in Fig. 54, and the burr taken off the face, care being shown not to grind any metal off the face itself.

If any space is left between the two jaws, the snips will not cut thin metal, especially near the edge of a sheet. The rivet must then be tightened slightly with a rivet set and a hammer. A good test for both hand-shears and the shearing machine is to see if they will cut cleanly a thin sheet of paper; they will do so if they have been accurately ground and set.

In many cases neither a hack-saw nor a shearing machine is suitable for cutting a piece of heavy-gauge metal. Chiseling is the method which must then be used. Cold chisels are made from carbon tool steel, usually of octagonal section. They are heated and

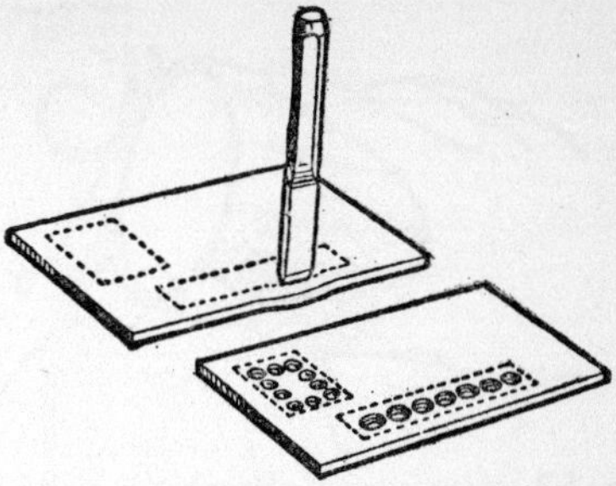

Fig. 57. When cutting out slots near the edge of a plate, the chisel will distort the edge of the sheet unless a series of holes, as near together as possible, (*right*) is previously drilled in it.

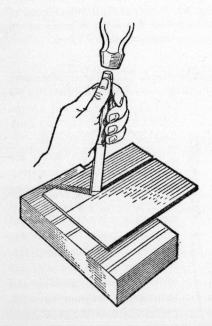

Fig. 56. When a flat chisel is used for cutting sheet metal, it is held at a slight angle to the surface of the metal so that when struck by the hammer it moves gradually toward the worker. The sheet is supported on a soft iron block.

hammered to the desired shape and finished more accurately by grinding. Next, they are hardened and tempered, and sharpened according to the particular job for which they are required.

There are four kinds of chisels in common use, and these are illustrated in Fig. 55. The flat chisel is most widely used. It has a broad cutting edge which should be slightly rounded to reduce the tendency of the corners to dig in. It can be used for cutting out sheet metal, cutting off rods and bars, and for chipping broad surfaces.

When used for cutting sheet metal it must be held at a slight angle to the surface of the metal, as shown in Fig. 56. This is so that when the chisel is struck by the hammer it tends to move along the line continuously toward the worker, at the same time as it cuts through the metal. If the chisel is held vertically, a separate cut is made each time the hammer-blow is delivered, and the "line" becomes a series of cuts. A block of soft iron is generally used to support the sheet metal while it is being cut.

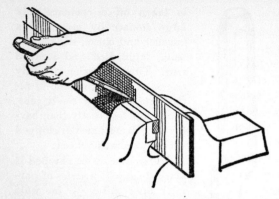

Fig. 58. Sheet metal held in a vise for cutting with a chisel.

Chiseling Sheet Metal

The same method is applied to the cutting of slots of various shapes and sizes in sheet metal, although the removal of the metal is often simplified by drilling a series of holes as near together as possible before the chisel is used. This is essential where the amount of metal left on the outside of the slot is small, for otherwise the chisel would distort the shape of the plate (Fig. 57).

Another method of cutting metal with a chisel is to support it in the vise, as shown in Fig. 58. Care must be taken that the line along which the cut is to be made is as near to the top of the vise-jaws as possible, so that the metal is not bent or the edge of the cut badly burred over.

Cold chisels are also used for a variety of purposes such as are found in repair work; for example, removal of rivet-heads, or the cutting of nuts and bolts which are rusted fast. In the absence of a shearing machine it is often useful to cut rods and bars to length with a flat chisel, although where they are of a heavier section they are usually heated in the forge and cut with a hot chisel and a sledge-hammer.

The cross-cut or cape chisel is forged so that its cutting edge is slightly wider than the body; this is to insure that the chisel does not bind in the cut when it is used for deep grooves. The width of the cutting edge varies according to the work from about $\frac{1}{8}$ in. to $\frac{1}{2}$ in. This type of chisel is used chiefly for cutting keyways and for cutting parallel grooves on a surface which is to be chipped.

A round-nose or half-round chisel is used for forming flutes and oil channels in bearings or pulley bushings. It is also used as described in the section on Drilling, for *drawing* a hole into correct position when it has been set out inaccurately. It will be noticed from Fig. 55 that the edge is formed by a single bevel.

The diamond-pointed chisel is drawn down to a square section at the end and then ground away to a single bevel, thus forming the diamond shape. It is used for chipping through plates, for cleaning out square internal angles, cutting V grooves, or for squaring up the corners of slots.

Other chisels may be designed for special jobs where occasion demands. For example, a chisel shaped as shown in Fig. 59 is especially useful for removing the metal from cotter ways or slots which have to be cut by hand.

Grinding and Re-Tempering

All the chisels described are usually sharpened by grinding, preferably on a wet grindstone. After frequent regrinding, however, the cutting edge becomes too thick, and the chisel then has to be heated, drawn down to shape, and re-tempered.

The correct thickness of the edge varies with the metal to be cut; the softer the metal the thinner the edge of the chisel may be, so that for zinc, lead, or aluminum the chisel may be only $\frac{1}{16}$ in. thick, while for harder metals it should be made progressively thicker, up to, say, $\frac{3}{16}$ in. for cast iron and mild steel. In the same way the cutting angle may be sharper for the softer metals. For copper and brass, for example, the angle of a flat chisel should be about 40 deg.; for wrought iron, 50 deg.; for cast iron and all general cutting purposes, 60 deg.; and for cast steel 70 deg. The grinding angle can best be tested by means of a mild-steel template in which V-shaped notches of the different angles have been made with a triangular file.

Correct tempering is also dependent upon the metal to be cut. Thus, it should be tempered to a medium straw color for steel, or to a dark purple color for brass or wrought iron. If the temper were correct for cutting soft metal, the edge would be too hard, and would easily chip when the tool was used on steel.

Chipping is a hand method of surfacing, whereby a fair amount of metal

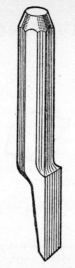

Fig. 59. A side chisel, used for removing metal from cotter ways or slots.

is taken off a comparatively large surface by means of a hammer and chisel, the surface being later filed and scraped true. This operation is only done at the present time in repair work and for small jobs, where it is less costly than having the job machined or chipped with a pneumatic chisel.

The surface to be chipped is marked out with a series of parallel lines about $\frac{3}{8}$ in. wide and no more than 1 in. apart. Grooves are cut along these with the cross-cut chisel, and similar grooves are then cut at right angles to them. All the grooves should be of equal depth. The remainder of the metal is then removed with the flat chisel.

The chisel is held lightly, mainly with the second and third fingers, the index finger being relaxed. With the chisel held at a constant angle, hammer-blows are delivered to chip away the surface metal. After the first cut the chipped edge will steady the edge of the chisel, which should not be allowed to draw back after each blow. The hammer is swung from the shoulder rather than from the elbow, and the body is allowed to swing slightly with the blow of the hammer.

Considerable skill is necessary to chip a surface quickly and accurately, and long practice is essential. A little oil will help the cutting action when chipping iron or steel.

RIVETING

RIVETING is a method used for joining together two or more pieces of metal. The rivets used are generally of the same metal as the parts to be joined, and are commonly made from mild steel, wrought iron, brass, copper, or aluminum; for tinplate work they may be obtained in *tinned iron*. They are made with heads of various shapes for different purposes; are specified according to their length, diameter, and shape of head; and are usually sold by weight.

Fig. 60 shows the types of rivets in general use. The button head is the most common form; the head is nearly a hemisphere, and the diameter is 1.75 times the diameter of the rivet. This type, along with the pan-head rivet, is most widely used for all ordinary jobs where the joint must be as strong as possible.

The conical or steeple head is the shape usually produced by hand hammering; the diameter of the head is twice the rivet diameter, and the height is equal to three-quarters of the diameter. This pattern is used extensively for small articles, since the head matches the shape most easily formed by hand hammering. They can also be used to produce a decorative effect.

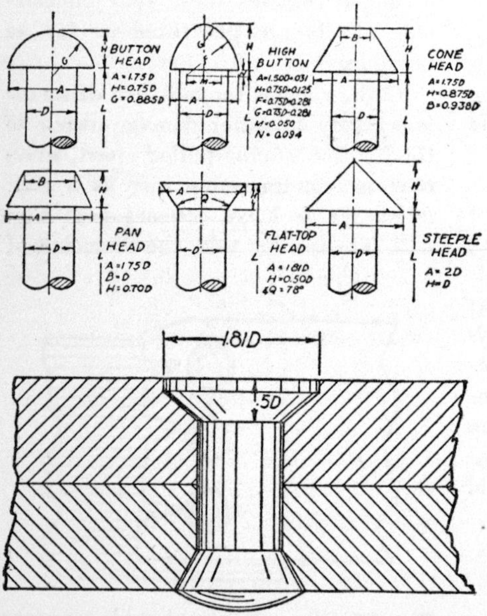

In the case of pan-head rivets, the head is 1.75 times the rivet diameter, and the height is .70 of the diameter. Pan-head rivets are very strong, and are therefore widely used for girders and heavy constructional engineering.

Countersunk rivets have a head that is 1.81 times the rivet diameter with the height equal to half the rivet diameter. There is some slight objection to the sharp edge of the countersunk head, since it is likely to spring away from the metal face after being riveted. Because of this, the other two types of countersunk head rivets are preferred, the advantage being that they do not project from the surface of the work. They are widely used for tool-making and other precision work.

Flat-headed rivets are usually made in copper, brass, or aluminum, and are used chiefly for light iron work, small tank construction, and the like, where the metal is

Fig. 60. Rivets in Common Use: 1. Button head, 2. High button head, 3. Cone head, 4. Pan head, 5. Flat top countersunk head, 6. Conical or steeple head, 7. Flat and round top countersunk head.

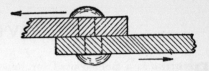

very thin and great strength is not necessary.

In addition to the head, a rivet has a shank and a tail, and the length is normally measured from the underside of the head. The countersunk-headed rivet is, however, an exception, since in this case the length is measured over the head.

Rivets are used chiefly for joining together metal plates. They are espe-

Fig. 61. If a rivet too small in diameter is used, the two holes may be pulled apart; to prevent this, rivets should be $\frac{5}{16}$ in. more in diameter than the thickness of the plates.

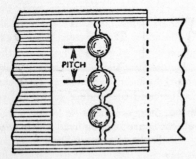

Fig. 62. *Tearing* caused by the plates being weakened by the rivet holes is avoided by correctly spacing or *pitching* the rivets, often at $1\frac{3}{5}$ times the plate thickness plus $1\frac{1}{4}$ in.

cially suitable in light construction for fixing handles or plates, for forming pivots, attaching hinges and other fittings to metal plates, and for joining the ends of metal formed into a cylinder or band. In heavier work, riveting is used for joining girders to stanchions, constructing heavy built-up girders for bridges, and in other constructional engineering where it would be impossible to use a welded joint.

Considerations of Design

Boiler construction is largely dependent on riveted joints for the connection of the various plates which have to be made steam- and watertight. In fact, metal sheets of all kinds,

after being bent to shape, are usually fixed together at the angles by riveted joints.

In designing a riveted joint, it must be borne in mind that it may fail in one of four ways; the rivets may be sheared off; the joint may suffer from being crushed; the plates may be torn around the rivet-holes; the plates may burst. Consequently the rivets are so arranged that all these four undesirable effects are prevented as far as possible.

If the rivet is too small in diameter it is likely to suffer damage owing to the two holes being pulled apart, when they act in the same way as a pair of shears or large scissors (see Fig. 61). To prevent this, the diameter of

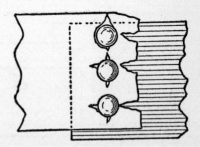

Fig. 63. When the rivet hold is too near the edge of the plate *bursting* may occur. To prevent this, the distance from the center of the hold to the edge of the plate should be $1\frac{1}{2}$ times the diameter of the rivet.

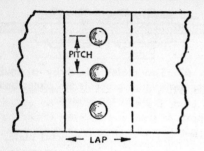

Fig. 64. The lap of two plates which are joined by a rivet should be three times the thickness of the plate, plus 1⅛ in.

of the plate. There should always be a distance equal to 1½ times the diameter of the rivet from the center of the hole to the edge of the plate. The amount of lap for the joint (see Fig. 64) is found by multiplying the thickness of the plate by three and adding 1⅛ in.

The rivets may be arranged in a single line as in Fig. 62, or they may be in two, three, or more lines, when

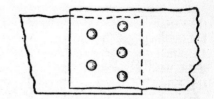

Fig. 65. Staggered riveting in which the rivets are spaced out alternatively in two (as here) or more lines.

the rivet should be equal to 1.4 times the square root of the thickness of the plate.

Failure of the joint due to crushing is generally attributed to the plates being too thin, or to the rivets being too small in diameter.

Tearing, as indicated in Fig. 62, is due to the plates being weakened by the rivet-holes. It is largely to avoid this trouble that correct spacing or *pitch* of the rivets is necessary. For simple jobs this is often arrived at by multiplying the thickness of the plate by 1.6 and adding 1¼ in.

Bursting of the plate (Fig. 63) is likely to occur when the rivet hole is drilled or punched too near the edge

the arrangement is known as chain riveting. Staggered riveting is shown in Fig. 65.

The joints are most frequently made by lapping one piece of metal on to the other, but they may be made with butt joints and a single cover-strap, as shown in Fig. 66, or a double cover-strap as in Fig. 67. In a single-lap joint, where there is considerable

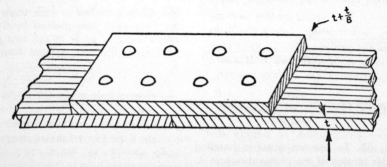

Fig. 66. Two plates joined together by means of a butt joint and a single cover-strap.

tension on the plates, there is a tendency to cause bending, and the joint is often set at an angle to avoid this, as shown in Fig. 68.

A double cover-strap could, of course, prevent this bending, but this may not always be convenient or satisfactory for other reasons.

Strong angle joints are made in constructional work by using angle irons riveted to each plate, as shown in Fig. 69.

The holes to receive the rivets in the various plates are generally drilled, but in thin plates they may be punched. In either case the rivet should be a tight push fit or light driving fit in the hole.

Unfortunately, punching is injurious to the plates, because it hardens the edge of the hole excessively. This fault may be obviated by punching the holes slightly smaller than required, and afterwards reaming or drilling them to the correct diameter. Or the plates may be annealed (i.e., softened) after punching. The only advantage of punching is that it is quicker and cheaper; also, a drill is often difficult to use in a corner, where a punch may be less awkward. Punches are made in different sizes, and the hole is often made simply by driving

Fig. 67. Two plates joined by a double cover-strap which prevents the plates bending under tension.

the punch against the metal plate, as in many sheet metal processes. A

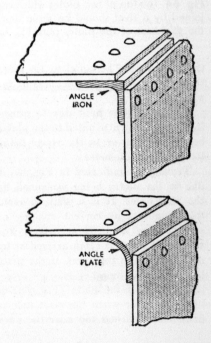

ANGLE IRON

ANGLE PLATE

Fig. 69. In construction work angle joints are frequently strengthened by riveting angle irons to each of the two plates forming the joint, as here shown.

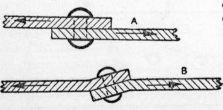

A

B

Fig. 68. To prevent possible bending under tension of the plates shown in A, the rivet joining them may be set at an angle, as shown in B.

cleaner hole is always made, however, by using a bolster, which, in effect, supports the metal about the hole. Fig. 70 shows an arrangement whereby the bolster is combined with a guide and is adaptable to fit thin sheet metal of varying gauges.

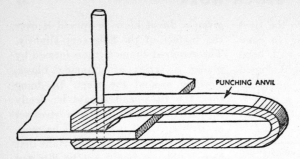

Fig. 70. A bolster, combined with a guide, is often used to support the metal about a rivet-hole while punching the hole, thus giving a cleaner hole.

When using this arrangement it is often difficult to insure correct positioning of the holes. On the other hand, the punched hole is always slightly tapered, and this is an advantage, in that the force holding the two plates together is not entirely confined to the heads, but by the rivet being spread into the tapered hole, when the shank takes some of the strain. This point is illustrated in Fig. 71.

Where plates are to be joined by the use of more than one rivet, it is essential that the holes in the plates be immediately opposite each other. To mark out the two plates and drill

a series of holes so that they will all coincide calls for skilled lay-out and accurate drilling. It is, therefore, much better practice first to drill all the holes in one plate and one hole in the second plate. The plates can then be held together by one rivet and a clamp while the remaining holes in the second plate are drilled by using the holes in the first plate as a guide (see Fig. 72).

Where a number of similar jobs have to be riveted, a jig or template may be used. This consists of a hardened-steel drilled plate which, when clamped

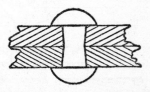

Fig. 71. Since rivet-holes are always punched with a taper, the shank, spreading into the tapered hole, shares the strain with the rivet-heads.

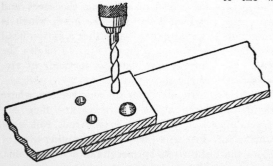

Fig. 72. So that the rivet-holes may coincide, it is best to drill all the holes in one plate and one hole in the second plate first, using that as a guide in drilling the second plate.

to the work, serves as an accurate guide for the drill.

After drilling, the burr formed at the lower edges of the hole should be removed by very lightly countersinking; if this is done to excess, the plates will be forced apart, owing to the rivet being spread out into the recess thus formed between the plates.

The amount of tail that is left projecting from the face of the plate, and which has to be formed into the rivet head, must not be too long (a common fault), or the rivet will bend over instead of forming a well-shaped head. If insufficient projection is allowed, a smaller and weaker head is formed. The length of rivet required to form a conical or a snap head is 1¼ times the diameter of the rivet, and an amount equal to the diameter for forming a countersunk head. In

given a direct blow to spread it over the surface of the hole very slightly. The required shape is then formed by giving a series of glancing blows, working around the rivet. In doing this, the rivet-head should be firmly supported, preferably on a rivet-set or riveting anvil, which will be mentioned again later. It is important that hammer-blows should not be directed vertically downward, since this has

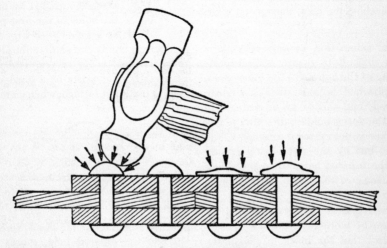

Fig. 73. Right and wrong methods of riveting. The hammer blows should be at an angle.

practice, these proportions are, of course, not measured, but are estimated by eye. Should the projection be excessive the rivet is cut off; if insufficient, a longer rivet is used.

Where rivets of ½ in. diameter or more are used, a steam or pneumatic riveting machine is generally used for clinching them, although odd rivets of such size can be clinched by using a hammer. For smaller rivets where the work is being done by hand it is correct to use the ball-peen of a hammer, or a specially designed riveting hammer, and to work round the edge of the rivet. First, the tail should be

the effect of splaying the rivet and making a flat *pancake* head, which is much weaker than either a button head or a conical head. Fig. 73 shows the correct and incorrect methods of riveting.

In all types of construction where large rivets are necessary they are first heated to bright red. Not only does this facilitate the paning-over of the rivet, but results in a firmer joint. This is because the rivet contracts on cooling, and so pulls the two members more closely together. In hot-riveting it must be remembered that the diameter of the rivet is increased by heating, and therefore that the rivets must be rather smaller initially than the holes. In practice, this allowance should be $\frac{1}{16}$ in. for rivets of $\frac{3}{4}$ in. diameter and over.

Although it is often sufficient in simple jobs to support the rivet-head

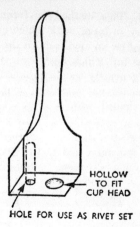

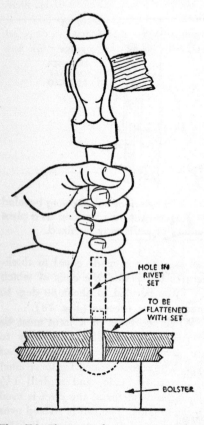

Fig. 75. The cup-tool, for forcing down the top plate over the rivet-shank, may be combined in a single tool with a set for holding the rivet head.

date the rivet-head. The bolster may take one of several forms. It may be designed to be held in a vise, or on a flat surface; or it may be of heavier construction and fitted with a handle, so that one person can hold it over the rivet-head while another peens over

Fig. 74. The use of a rivet-set as here indicated secures that the top plate will be forced down around the rivet-shank before riveting over.

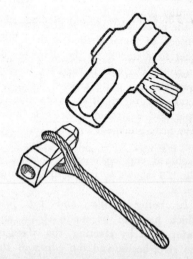

on an anvil or steel block, this is not always satisfactory, since a conical or button-head will be flattened to a certain extent. A bolster or rivet-set is therefore used. This is a block of mild steel with a hollow in it to accommo-

Fig. 76. Cup tool for large rivets, held in position by a wrench.

the tail. This method is frequently necessary in large work which cannot be placed on an anvil-set. In the same way, the tail which has to be riveted over is generally roughly shaped with the hammer as described, and then finally shaped with a rivet-set. The

in shape to a chisel, but with a flat end (Fig. 77). Caulking is a very skillful operation, and if done badly may tend to open the plates instead of closing them.

Fullering is a similar process, but is perhaps less difficult. The fullering

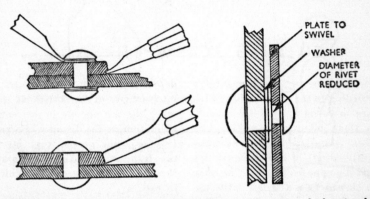

Figs. 77–79. *Left (above)* a caulking tool; *(below)* a fullering tool, showing beveled edge of the plate against which it rests. *Right,* how a rivet may be used as a pivot on which swiveling or revolving members or parts may be fixed.

term rivet-set is applied loosely to either the bolster used for supporting the head or to the cup-tool used for shaping the head formed from the tail of the rivet. The name is also given to a block of metal drilled with a hole equal in diameter to the diameter of the rivet. The hole is used for forcing down the top plate around the rivet-shank before riveting over; this is especially desirable where the holes have been punched. Fig. 74 illustrates the process, while Fig. 75 shows a combined cup-tool and rivet-set, and Fig. 76 shows a cup-tool for large rivets.

In boiler-making, and for jobs which have to be made steam and water tight by riveting, the edges of the rivet-heads and the edges of the plates are generally burred down with a caulking tool, which is very similar

tool has its end made equal in thickness to the plates, the ends of which are often beveled to about 80 deg. to facilitate the process (Fig. 78).

When the faces of a joint must be smooth and flush, it is necessary to use rivets of the countersunk-head type. The recess formed for these must be carefully made, and a drill $1\frac{1}{2}$ times the diameter of the rivet is used to countersink. The tail is riveted over so that it is left protruding slightly; it can then be filed off flush. Care must be taken not to strike the surface of the plate with the hammer when riveting over a countersunk head. The countersunk rivet is obviously not as strong as the button- or conical-headed type, and a greater number of rivets is necessary to insure strength.

Rivets are often used to act as pivots on which parts may revolve or swivel. The rivet between the legs of a pair of calipers is an example; it must not be hammered up too tightly or the parts will not revolve, although various degrees of stiffness may be imparted for different purposes. Thus, arms of a pair of calipers would need to be fairly stiff, while the faller of a gate-latch would need to be free in its action.

Where this type of rivet is required it is best to reduce the diameter of the rivet and use a washer against which to rivet the tail, as shown in Fig. 79. This allows the rivet-head to be well formed.

CUTTING SCREW-THREADS

SCREW-THREADS vary in form largely according to the purpose for which they are to be used, and also according to their country of origin. The American Standard is the one most frequently used in this country for all general engineering work. The form of the thread is a triangle with the angle between the sides 60 deg. The top and bottom are flattened to a width of one-eighth the pitch; the

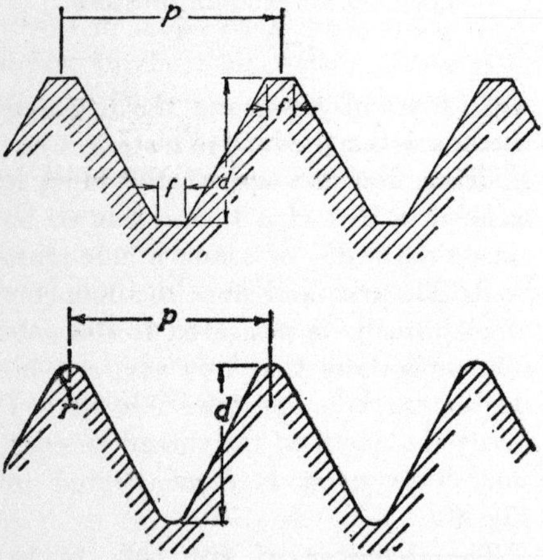

Figs. 80–81. *Above,* American Standard Thread Form. p = pitch of thread, d = depth of thread, f = width of flat at top and bottom of thread. *Below,* Whitworth Standard Thread Form. p = pitch of thread, d = depth of thread, r = radius at top and bottom of thread.

depth is .649519 of the pitch. The pitch or rise of any thread is the distance the nut travels in one complete revolution, or the distance between any two adjacent *crests.* Fig. 80 shows the form of the American Standard thread. Fig. 81 shows the Whitworth thread.

Other forms of thread which cannot, however, be readily cut by hand tools are the *square* thread, the *buttress* thread, and the *acme* thread, which are shown in Fig. 82.

The V thread is used chiefly where parts have to be securely fastened together. It is much stronger than the square thread and is very durable; on the other hand, the square thread has less friction to overcome, and is therefore preferred for transmitting motion. Square threads are usually found on clamps and vises. *Buttress* threads are useful when the pressure is always in one direction. *Acme* threads are used for lead screws on lathes, as the slight taper from the root to the point allows easy engagement with the half-nut.

Threads may be *left-handed* or *right-handed;* a right-handed thread is one where the nut is screwed on to the bolt by turning it to the right, or in a clockwise direction; the reverse applies to a left-hand thread.

Single and double threads are shown in Fig. 83. Multiple threads are necessary where a greater distance has to be traveled by the nut in one revolution than it would go were the thread single. A large, coarse thread of depth equal to half the pitch would weaken the bolt unduly, and so a double or triple thread is used, each pitch or lead being twice or three times that of the single thread.

Parts to be threaded together consist of an external thread and an internal thread, the external one being formed on the bolt and the internal one in the nut. It has been stated that usually only V threads are cut by hand, and of these it is normally satisfactory to cut them of 1 in. diameter or less. For larger screw-threads of the V type, and for most other forms of thread, a thread-cutting lathe is used.

The most satisfactory hand process consists of cutting the internal threads

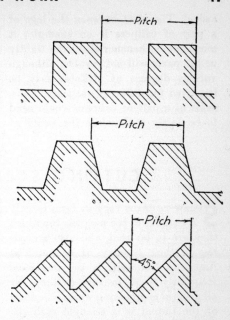

Fig. 82. Other forms of thread: Square, used for clamps and vises; Acme, used for lead screws on lathes; Buttress, used under one-directional pressure.

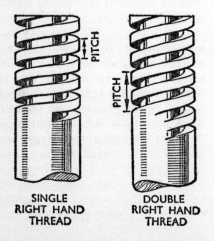

SINGLE
RIGHT HAND
THREAD

DOUBLE
RIGHT HAND
THREAD

Fig. 83. Single and double threads. The double or multiple thread is used where the nut has to travel a greater distance in one revolution than it would go if the thread were single.

with a set of taps, and the external threads with a die held in a stock. Considering first the use of the taps, it is obvious that if a thread has to be cut on the inside of a nut, a hole must be drilled first, and since the diameter of all threads is measured to the outside, it follows that for, say, a 1-in. thread the hole must be less than 1 in. by the depth of the thread on each side. This point is demonstrated in Fig. 84.

The diameter of the hole to be drilled is termed the tapping size.

A set of taps of the type used for cutting an internal thread is shown in Fig. 85. It will be seen that there are three taps in the set, all of the same maximum diameter. The taper tap is used first, and it will be seen that for some distance from its end there are no threads. This is to allow the tap to enter the hole, and to assist the user to hold the tap in line with the hole, which is very important.

The tap-wrench fits the square end of the tap, and forms a handle by means of which the tap may be turned gradually into the hole. If a tap is passed through the hole, a complete thread is cut; but if the hole does not go through the metal, no thread is cut near the bottom of the hole. To make a clean thread in such a *blind* hole, it is necessary to follow on with the intermediate or *second* tap which, as can be seen, has only a few threads ground away at the bottom end. Finally, the plug or bottoming tap is used to complete the thread to the bottom of the *blind* hole.

A less common form of tap is parallel. This type also is used in sets of three; the first tap, however, is not

Fig. 84. Diagram illustrating meaning of the terms tapping size, clearance size, and diameter as applied to screw threads.

tapered, but simply has a very shallow thread; the second cut is slightly larger in diameter and the thread is more nearly the correct size; the third tap is the correct diameter and has the correct, finished depth of thread.

When tapping a thread in thin metal it is often difficult to insure that the tap is kept upright. A simple method of overcoming this trouble is to place a nut of the same size and form as the thread to be cut on top of the hole, and to press this firmly against the surface of the metal. The tap passes through this before entering the tapping-size hole and is thereby supported.

Taps are made from high-class cast steel, and are hardened and tempered uniformly. They have to be extremely hard, so that their threads may have as long a life as possible. In consequence they are extremely brittle and are easily broken by the inexperienced user. Great care is required in use, especially with those of smaller diameter. Equal pressure must be applied with both hands on the tap-wrench; it is usual to press harder with the right hand, but this must be avoided. Incidentally, an excessively long tap-wrench increases the danger of unequal pressure being applied and of excessive force which might cause the tap to be broken by being twisted off.

The tap must not be turned continuously, otherwise the chips are not removed and the tap becomes wedged tightly in the hole. It should be turned forward about a quarter of a turn, back a quarter-turn, forward a half-

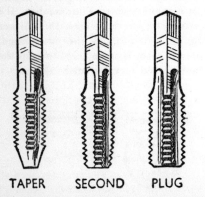

TAPER   SECOND   PLUG

Fig. 85. Set of three taps of the most widely used type. All have the same maximum diameter, but the taper and second taps are tapered off at the ends.

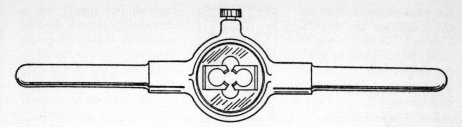

Fig. 86. Die-stock.

turn, and so on. The speed of tapping may be increased when the operator becomes used to the feel of the job, and he knows from experience just how much pressure may be applied before the tap jams and is liable to break.

It is best for the beginner to use a tap of more than ⅛ in. diameter, so that there is less danger of breakage. Any tap which may be broken can be extracted by unscrewing it with pliers if there is any part projecting, or by making a piece of steel with *fingers* to fit the flutes if the tap is broken below the surface. In cases of extreme difficulty it is necessary to heat and soften the tap and then to drill it out (as described for broken drills).

The oil-can should be used freely when tapping iron or steel, to prevent the tap from overheating and losing its correct degree of hardness. Without special equipment it is difficult to re-grind taps that have become worn, and excessive grinding should be avoided, because this results in a reduction of the diameter of the tap, and therefore its cutting size.

For cutting external threads, stocks and dies are used. These may be of several different designs, the most common form being shown in Fig. 86. The die takes the form of a hardened steel nut cut in two halves. Both parts have V-shaped grooves along their edges which fit over a corresponding projection on the side of the rectangular hole in the stock. The two halves are thus capable of sliding along, and are adjusted to the correct size by means of a set-screw. The dies are accurately fitted to the slides on the stock and are marked 1 and 2 to insure their correct position every time they are used.

The stock is usually designed to hold three sizes of dies (¼ in., ⅜ in. and ½ in., for example). For the next three sizes a larger stock is used. A notch is cut out of the center of each half of the die, to allow for the disposal of the metal cut off. This also provides additional cutting edges, and at the same time reduces friction and prevents binding. The smaller the amount of screw surface, the quicker the die will cut. On the other hand, a large screw surface helps to keep the die true and forms a better thread.

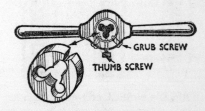

Fig. 87. Stock with split die, the die of which is shown in greater detail inset. This type of die is more generally used for smaller diameter threads.

Fig. 88. Hexagonal and square die nuts, both of which are used for cleaning up threads that cannot be reached with dies held in a die-stock.

Before beginning to cut the thread with the stock and die, it is essential that the rod should be of correct diameter. A perfect thread may be cut on a rod which is either too small or too large; but in the former case the nut will be loose, and in the latter case will not go on.

It is therefore best where tapping and threading have to be done to tap the hole first, as this is of fixed size, and then to cut the bolt-thread to fit. The rod should be slightly tapered near the end to give the die a start, and the dies should then be adjusted to fit the rod and the two halves tightened sufficiently to hold the stock and dies in position. Care must be taken to see that the stock is at right angles to the rod which is to be threaded.

The stock is then turned until a shallow thread of the required length has been cut. Next, it is turned back to the end, the dies are tightened up a little more, and the process repeated until the thread has been cut to the

Fig. 89. Die plate. A convenient tool for making screw-threads on rods up to about $\frac{1}{8}$ in. in diameter. There are three dies for each diameter, and these are used in order, starting with that having the shallowest threads.

correct depth. This is tested by using the nut previously tapped. If the nut will not go on when the thread has been cut fully on the rod, it means that the rod is too large in diameter, and part of the threads must be filed off before the dies are run down again. It is unwise to follow the bad practice of some workers of using the dies to reduce the diameter of the rod. Besides injuring the die, it is almost certain that the thread will be damaged or completely stripped; if the rod is of small diameter it will probably be twisted off.

Using Dies

In using the die, care must be taken to keep the clearance notches free from the waste metal cut off and, when threading iron or steel, to keep the rod well lubricated with light machine oil to prevent the dies from becoming overheated.

After the dies have been run down the required length of thread, they must be turned back again without tightening, since they are designed for cutting the thread in one direction only.

Another common type of stock and die is shown in Fig. 87. This is perhaps a more convenient form than that shown in Fig. 86, but is suitable only for smaller sizes of thread. The stock is designed to take a larger number of dies than the larger type. As may be seen, the circular split die is held in the stock by three small set-screws, and some slight adjustment in the diameter of the die is possible by tightening up the center screw first. This opens out the cut, and so increases the effective diameter. This type of stock and dies is very commonly sold in sets conveniently arranged in a polished hardwood case, and is extremely useful for the smaller diameter threads.

A die nut (see Fig. 88) is similar in shape to an ordinary square or hexagonal nut, and may be obtained in all sizes of standard threads. Its main use is for running down an existing thread that has become burred or damaged. It may be turned with an ordinary wrench, and is particularly useful for restoring bruised threads on studs such as those in cylinder covers or valve chests, where the ordinary stocks and dies cannot be manipulated.

Where threads have to be cut on rods of ⅛ in. diameter and under, it is common to use a screw-plate of the type shown in Fig. 89. This is a hardened steel plate with a series of holes tapped for various-sized threads. Usually there are three holes for each size of screw, so that the thread is cut gradually by running the plate down, using the holes in turn. The third hole cuts the thread to the correct depth. These holes are slightly enlarged on one side of the plate, and care must be taken to see that the screw-thread is always started from this side.

The tapped holes in the plate have notches cut in them to provide clearance for the waste metal and to provide cutting edges. The thread is formed very largely by pressure, however, the metal on the rod being pressed out of the hollows to form the ridges. This has the effect of increasing the diameter of the rod, and tends to lengthen it slightly. The small thickness of the screw-plate makes it difficult to cut a thread which is true, and special care must be taken to keep the plate square with the rod. Also, the plate is frequently unbalanced when in use, since it is impossible to have all the holes at the center, and this adds to the difficulty of keeping the plate square to the rod.

Hand-Chasers

Hand-chasers are shown in Fig. 90. These are made in pairs—one for internal work, and the other for external

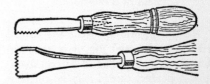

Fig. 90. Internal and external screw chasers. Although these are hand tools, they are used on metal mounted in the lathe. A good deal of skill is necessary for their successful operation.

work. The teeth in the chaser are the counterpart of the screw-thread to be cut. In forming external threads, the rod is turned to the correct diameter and fixed in the lathe, the chaser then being held firmly against the work and moved along at a uniform rate. This is an operation which is extremely difficult, and success depends largely on the skill of the worker. If the chaser is moved along too slowly, a number of parallel rings are formed, and if it is moved too quickly, the pitch is wrong and the screw is irregular. The chasers, therefore, are generally used only for small threads on brass, or for rounding-off the tops and bottoms of threads previously formed by the V tool in the screw-cutting lathe.

Pitch Gauges

It is often necessary to cut a new thread either to match or to fit an existing thread, and the number of threads per inch or pitch is best measured by using one of the many screw-

TABLE OF MORSE TWIST-DRILLS
LETTER AND NUMBER SIZES

	SIZE IN IN.		SIZE IN IN.		SIZE IN IN.
Letter Z	.4130	No. 11	.1910	No. 46	.0810
" Y	.4040	" 12	.1890	" 47	.0785
" X	.3970	" 13	.1850	" 48	.0760
" W	.3860	" 14	.1820	" 49	.0730
" V	.3770	" 15	.1800	" 50	.0700
" U	.3680	" 16	.1770	" 51	.0670
" T	.3580	" 17	.1730	" 52	.0635
" S	.3480	" 18	.1695	" 53	.0595
" R	.3390	" 19	.1660	" 54	.0550
" Q	.3320	" 20	.1610	" 55	.0520
" P	.3230	" 21	.1590	" 56	.0465
" O	.3160	" 22	.1570	" 57	.0430
" N	.3020	" 23	.1540	" 58	.0420
" M	.2950	" 24	.1520	" 59	.0410
" L	.2900	" 25	.1495	" 60	.0400
" K	.2810	" 26	.1470	" 61	.0390
" J	.2770	" 27	.1440	" 62	.0380
" I	.2720	" 28	.1405	" 63	.0370
" H	.2660	" 29	.1360	" 64	.0360
" G	.2610	" 30	.1285	" 65	.0350
" F	.2570	" 31	.1200	" 66	.0330
" E	.2500	" 32	.1160	" 67	.0320
" D	.2460	" 33	.1130	" 68	.0310
" C	.2420	" 34	.1110	" 69	.0292
" B	.2380	" 35	.1100	" 70	.0280
" A	.2340	" 36	.1065	" 71	.0260
No. 1	.2280	" 37	.1040	" 72	.0250
" 2	.2210	" 38	.1015	" 73	.0240
" 3	.2130	" 39	.0995	" 74	.0225
" 4	.2090	" 40	.0980	" 75	.0210
" 5	.2055	" 41	.0960	" 76	.0200
" 6	.2040	" 42	.0935	" 77	.0180
" 7	.2010	" 43	.0890	" 78	.0160
" 8	.1990	" 44	.0860	" 79	.0145
" 9	.1960	" 45	.0820	" 80	.0135
" 10	.1935				

WHITWORTH SCREW-THREADS

OUTSIDE DIAMETER IN INCHES	THREADS PER INCH	TAPPING SIZE DRILL	CLEARANCE SIZE DRILL
$\frac{1}{16}$	60	No. 56	No. 52
$\frac{3}{32}$	48	No. 50	No. 41
$\frac{1}{8}$	40	No. 40	No. 30
$\frac{5}{32}$	32	No. 31	4 mm.
$\frac{3}{16}$	24	$\frac{9}{64}$ in.	No. 12
$\frac{7}{32}$	24	No. 18	No. 2
$\frac{1}{4}$	20	No. 11	$6\frac{1}{2}$ mm.
$\frac{5}{16}$	18	Letter D	Letter O
$\frac{3}{8}$	16	Letter N	Letter W
$\frac{7}{16}$	14	Letter S	$11\frac{1}{2}$ mm.
$\frac{1}{2}$	12	Letter X	$\frac{33}{64}$ in.
$\frac{5}{8}$	11	$\frac{33}{64}$ in.	$\frac{41}{64}$ in.
$\frac{3}{4}$	10	$\frac{5}{8}$ in.	$\frac{49}{64}$ in.
$\frac{7}{8}$	9	$\frac{47}{64}$ in.	$\frac{57}{64}$ in.
1	8	$\frac{27}{32}$ in.	$1\frac{1}{64}$ in.

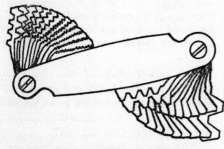

Fig. 91. Set of thread gauges.

pitch gauges which can be obtained. A useful type is shown in Fig. 91.

Clearance Sizes

The tapping or clearance size for a certain thread is usually obtained from a set of tables such as those just preceding. It will be noted that in some cases the correct sizes for the drills to be used are given as a letter, sometimes as a number, and sometimes as a fraction of an inch. The letters and numbers are what are known as the Morse twist-drill sizes. The drills are of standard diameters to provide the correct tapping and clearance sizes for various diameters of screw-threads for several different thread forms, including Whitworth. The Morse twist-drill table shows the decimal equivalent of the number or letter of the drill.

Another type of drill in use is the *jobber's* drill. These are twist-drills for holes from $\frac{1}{16}$ in. upward, advancing by 64ths of an inch, and are denoted by their actual size in inches and fractions of an inch. The size is generally stamped on the shank.

VISES AND VISE WORK

IN ALL types of metal work, a vise, firmly attached to a bench, is the first requirement. Of the many different makes and patterns of vises there are two main types; the leg-vise, and the parallel-jaw vise. The leg-vise, shown in Fig. 92, is the older type, and is often preferred to the more modern parallel-jaw kind. It is usually made from mild steel or wrought iron, the jaws being faced with cast steel. It is more solid to work on than is a parallel-jaw vise, and will better withstand hard use. This type of vise is used generally for gripping work that has to be chipped or hammered, or for work which has to be gripped very firmly, such as when cold bending heavy metal.

It is fixed to the bench by bolts through the strap, which is keyed to the leg (see Fig. 92). The leg, or staple, is let into the floor or supported in a wooden block firmly attached to the floor, and this helps to give the feeling of rigidity which is sometimes

lacking in other types fixed only to a bench-top. The shorter jaw is fixed to the leg by a hinge arrangement, and a square-threaded screw is passed through this shorter jaw into a nut or box in the long leg. By turning the long handle provided, the shorter jaw is tightened up to the other. As this is unscrewed the jaws are opened by the pressure of a strong, flat spring between the two.

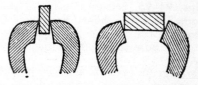

Fig. 93. An objection to the leg-vise is that the jaws do not meet squarely since one jaw is pivoted about the hinge; they therefore grip narrow work between the points of their upper edges and wide work between their lower edges.

The construction of the leg-vise whereby one jaw is pivoted about the hinge makes the jaw work in an arc of a circle, and the jaws do not therefore remain parallel (see Fig. 93).

This is a serious disadvantage when the work has to be gripped squarely for accurate filing or scraping. It also means that work, if it is to be held securely, must be gripped very tightly, because the jaws are frequently only gripping the work at the top or the bottom. This may mean that the work may be distorted or marked, where a parallel grip would hold the job as firmly without being tightened excessively. The chain vise overcomes this disadvantage.

The parallel-jaw vise is now very widely used for all classes of metal-

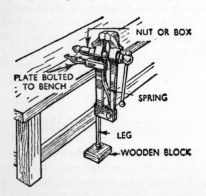

Fig. 92. A leg-vise, showing the principal parts and how it is fixed to the bench by bolts through the strap which is keyed to the leg.

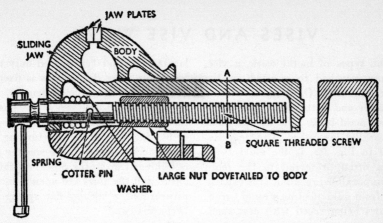

JAW PLATES

SLIDING JAW

BODY

A

B SQUARE THREADED SCREW

SPRING

COTTER PIN

WASHER

LARGE NUT DOVETAILED TO BODY

Figs. 94–95. Section through a typical parallel-jaw vise, showing the various parts. The saddle-shaped fixed body allows the sliding jaws, of which a section is shown in Fig. 95 (*right*) to pass through it, over the large nut dovetailed to the base of the body through which a square-threaded screw works.

working. An example is shown in Fig. 94. The body and sliding jaw are of cast iron, and the jaw-plates, which are usually renewable, are of cast steel, and are fixed to the casting by set-screws. The fixed half or body is of saddle form, and allows the sliding jaw to pass through it. The slide is shaped as shown in Fig. 94, and thus is able to pass over the large nut which is dovetailed into the base of the body through which a square-threaded screw works. This is shouldered against the front of the sliding jaw and cotter-pinned behind it, so that the jaw is moved inward or outward as the screw is turned. This will be more clearly understood by referring to Fig. 95. The sliding jaw is accurately fitted into the fixed body, and, being of a substantial section, it allows a rigid parallel motion of the jaw.

Mounting a Vise

In fixing to the bench it should first be fitted so that it beds down level, and then it is bolted through the bench.

A less satisfactory method is to make use of lag screws.

The vise top should be about 3 ft. 4 in. from the ground; a more accurate method of positioning is insured by making the top of the vise equal to the height of the worker's elbow from the floor when the arm is bent. (This is explained in the section on Filing.) It is better to have the vise fixed too high rather than too low, since a small platform is easily made to bring a person up to the correct height, while if the work is too low the worker becomes tired more quickly through stooping, and his command over the tools, especially files, is not as good.

Quick-Release Arrangements

Parallel vises are frequently designed to have an *instantaneous grip*. This means that the jaw can be moved in or out quickly by pressing a small lever and pulling or pushing the sliding jaw to the required position. The ordinary screw arrangement is then

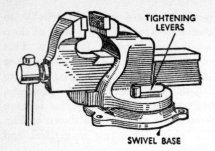

TIGHTENING LEVERS

SWIVEL BASE

Fig. 96. Parallel-jaw vise with swivel-base, enabling the whole vise to be turned in a complete circle. Such vises are much used in fitters' work.

engaged, the vise works in the ordinary way.

The half-nut can be renewed, but nevertheless this type of vise will not stand the hard wear that the fixed type of nut allows in the ordinary vise. The quick grip is popular among fitters, where the chief need is for gripping work to be filed or scraped.

Specially-designed parallel vises are made for very heavy work in railway and machine shops, foundries, etc. These are cast in tough steel with extra deep jaws, and all the parts of heavy section.

Other types of parallel-jaw vises are made with one jaw to swivel so that tapered work may be gripped conveniently. Fig. 96 shows a type where the whole vise may be swiveled in a complete circle and firmly locked in any position by tightening two screws. This is a very useful feature, especially for fitters' work, where, by swiveling the vise, an awkward corner may be filed without taking the job out of the vise and gripping it again. Long work is often more conveniently fixed by swiveling the vise, so that the work does not interfere with other

applied to give the usual grip. The quick release is worked by means of a buttress-threaded screw working in a half-nut, which may be engaged or disengaged with the screw by means of a bar pivoted on one edge, and which fits into a slot in the shank part of the half-nut. As the lever actuates the bar, the half-nut is raised or lowered, and is thus engaged with or disengaged from the thread (see Fig. 97).

When disengaged, the sliding jaw may be pulled out to any desired gap, thus saving considerable time. When

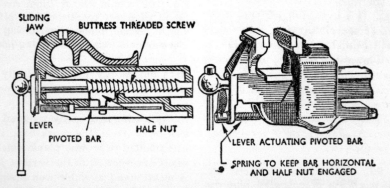

SLIDING JAW   BUTTRESS THREADED SCREW

LEVER
PIVOTED BAR   HALF NUT

LEVER ACTUATING PIVOTED BAR

SPRING TO KEEP BAR HORIZONTAL AND HALF NUT ENGAGED

Fig. 97. Parallel-jaw vise with instantaneous grip; the sliding jaw can be moved quickly in and out by pulling or pushing it to the required position after pressing the small lever indicated. *Left*, section through the vise, showing how the pivoted bar disengages the half-nut from the thread.

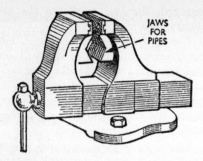

JAWS
FOR
PIPES

Fig. 98. Special combination vises, such as this, are made with unusually high parallel jaws, below which are special jaws for gripping pipes; the latter may be detached if desired.

vises in the same line, or with a wall or other possible obstruction.

There are vises designed especially for gripping pipes, so that they may be threaded or cut off to length. Fig. 98 shows an ordinary parallel-jaw vise with the addition of pipe-jaws arranged below the parallel jaw-plates. These have to be made of tool steel, carefully hardened and tem-

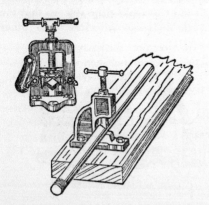

Fig. 99. Steam-fitters, plumbers, etc. make much use of a special pipe-vise with vertical screw and a movable jaw that works vertically. Two types are shown above. Such a vise is often bolted to a loose plank for easy transport.

pered, and are easily detachable so that they are not in the way of deep work fixed between the jaws. This combination vise is useful where pipes and rods have to be threaded or cut to length. For steam fitters, plumbers, electricians, it is more useful to have a pipe-vise of the type shown in Fig. 99, where the screw is vertical and

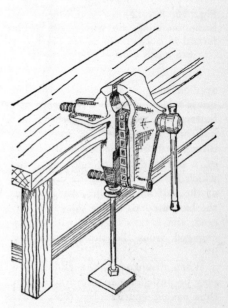

Fig. 100. Chain-vise. A chain run between sprockets keeps the jaws of this vise in parallel planes, overcoming objectionable features of the leg-vise.

the movable jaw works vertically instead of horizontally. This type is usually bolted to a bench-top, although, being frequently required for use away from the workshop, it is often bolted to a loose plank which is easily transported to the various jobs. A metal stand of angle iron designed for carrying a pipe-vise is also frequently used, and this may be either of the collapsible or non-collapsible type (see Fig. 101).

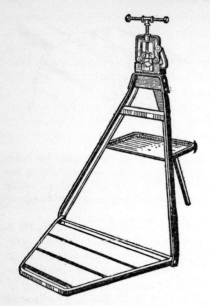

Fig. 101. Pipe vises may also be mounted on angle-iron metal stands which, as demonstrated in the example, may be collapsible.

Small vises are made to hold work which is being drilled or shaped, and these have slots or holes in the base by means of which they may be bolted to the bed of the shaping machine or drilling machine. Such a type is shown in the section on Drilling; see page 10.

A small toolmaker's vise is shown in Fig. 102. This is used for small, del-

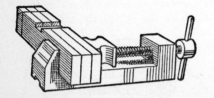

Fig. 102. A small toolmaker's vise is used for small, delicate work which must not be screwed up too tightly. It is convenient for pieces of metal of rectangular section.

icate work which might easily be damaged by being screwed up too tightly. It is usually of mild steel, and the jaws are not serrated, but merely case-hardened. It is useful for holding small work for filing or drilling, and may conveniently be used in the hand for small jobs which have to be ground, drilled, polished, or set out.

The jaws of all machinist vises are of hardened steel, and are cut in a similar way to a file, so that they may obtain a firm grip on the work. They

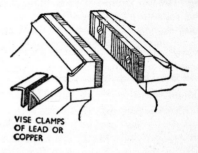

VISE CLAMPS OF LEAD OR COPPER

Fig. 103. Fiber-faced steel vise clamps of this kind, with the steel lugs bent round the vise jaws to hold the clamps in position, prevent the cuts from marking the work. (See also Fig. 14)

will, however, seriously damage any light or finely polished work. To prevent the cuts from marking the work, clamps are used, as explained under Filing (see page 1). They may easily be made from soft metal, but vise-makers can also supply specially-made fiber clamps of the type shown in Fig. 103. The usual practice is to have an iron mould into which lead is poured to form clamps; worn-out clamps of lead are melted and recast.

For holding small bars or tubes for threading, a clamp of the type shown in Fig. 104 is often used. A hole is chosen which is slightly smaller in diameter than the pipe, since this allows the pipe to be gripped firmly without marking.

Another type of vise-clamp is also shown (Fig. 105), and this will grip round work, but tends to mark it, so

Fig. 104. In clamps such as this pipes and rods may be gripped in a pair of holes slightly smaller than their own diameter to avoid marking.

that it is used more as a substitute for a pipe-vise than as a protection for gripping polished work.

A third type of vise-clamp useful for holding bars or spindles horizontally in the vise is shown in Fig. 106.

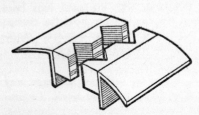

Fig. 105. Clamps of this type can easily be improvised for holding pipes and other similar work in a vise.

When the jaws are slack the rod is still supported, and may be revolved easily to any position before the vise is tightened again. It is therefore useful for gripping spindles in which key-ways or slots have to be cut.

The hardened-steel jaws on parallel-jaw vises are invariably held in position by means of set-screws which are countersunk flush with the face

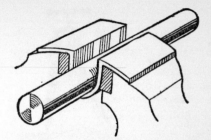

Fig. 106. Type of clamp used for holding bars or spindles horizontally in the vise; the bar may be revolved easily when the vise-jaws are loosened.

of the jaws. These jaws rest on a shoulder in the casting, which prevents any undue stress being put on the small set-screws. They may, however, be broken if heavy hammering of a piece of work is done in a horizontal direction. They may also become worn with heavy use, and consequently they are fitted so that renewal is possible. Some difficulty may be experienced in extracting the set-screws, since they are inclined to rust in or become slightly bent. A small improvised screw-driver is placed between the open jaws of the vise, and the vise tightened to give the necessary thrust. The screw-driver is then turned with a wrench as indicated in Fig. 107. The vise-jaws have to be opened gradually as the screw is withdrawn, but as it is the first eighth of a turn which loosens the screw, an ordinary screw-driver used over the top of the vise-jaws is

Fig. 107. How the set-screws of a parallel-jaw vise may be loosened.

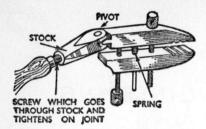

Fig. 108. This parallel-jaw hand-vise for holding small work has two screws and a spring which presses the jaws apart.

generally sufficient to remove the screw once it has been loosened.

Parallel vises are usually specified according to the width of jaws; these vary from about 2½ in. to 8 in., and 4½ in. may be taken as about the average size.

The depth of the space between the jaws is also specified (that is, the distance from the top of the jaws to the top of the slide), and in a 4½ in. jaw vise this is about 3 in. The weight is also given, so that of two makes equal in all other respects, the heavier type could be judged as being suitable for heavier work, being made from metal of thicker section.

Hand-vises are used for gripping screws, rivets, small tools, and work which cannot be conveniently held in the bench-vise or hand, but which requires the same manipulation as if held by hand.

A common type of hand-vise in general use is similar in construction to the leg-vise, and the jaws are closed by tightening up the wing nut. This type is often fitted with a small C-clamp arrangement which allows it to be fixed to a light bench or table. Hand-vises may also be of the parallel-jaw type. A useful pattern is shown in Fig. 108.

This works with two screws, while the central rod helps to keep the jaws rigid and carries a spring which presses the jaws apart. One jaw is pivoted to the stock, and the handle has a projecting screw which, when tightened, fixes the jaws in any position. One jaw has V cuts in it to facilitate the holding of small rivets, rods, etc. The type is often described as a toolmaker's clamp.

A pin-vise useful for holding wire or small-diameter rods which have to be filed or threaded is shown in Fig. 109. It consists of a chuck and a handle; the jaws grip the work when the handle is turned, and the rod may be passed right through the handle if necessary. This type is often used to hold small files of the needle type, or to hold small drills which are being reground.

Benches for metal-working are usually about 2 ft. 9 in. high, and vary in width according to the work for which they are intended. The front board of the bench-top should be very substantial—say 2½ in. to 3 in. thick and 15 in. wide. This makes a solid bed for holding the vise. The remaining width of the bench is often just filled in with 1-in. boards.

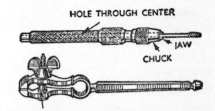

Fig. 109. Two types of pin-vise, used for holding rods, wire, files, drills, and other jobs of small diameter which have to be filed, threaded, or ground.

CHAPTER 2

METALS IN ENGINEERING PRODUCTION

METALS AND THEIR USES. HEAT RESISTANCE. TENSILE STRENGTH. ALLOYS. CAST IRON. CARBON CONTENT. NICKEL IRONS. CHROMIUM AND SILICON. WROUGHT IRON AND STEELS. DEFINITIONS. MILD AND MEDIUM STEELS. NICKEL CHROME STEELS. NON-FERROUS METALS. USES OF BRASSES. MANGANESE BRONZE. USES OF COPPER. CUPRO-NICKEL ALLOYS. PROPERTIES OF ALUMINUM.

MATERIALS used in the manufacture of machines is a question of increasing importance. On the one hand greater demands are being made as to the performance in service and on the other, competition forces the question of cost to the front. The cheaper a part can be made to meet given performance specifications, the more profitable its manufacture, and quite often the materials from which the part is made will largely determine its ability to stand up in service.

Many manufacturers produce their own special raw materials, so as to control the quality but manufacturers of special metals are growing rapidly. Better quality and lower cost are the results.

Metals and Their Uses

Metals, comprising broadly iron, steel, copper, bronze, brass, aluminum and certain nickel alloys, are judged, by their physical properties, the principal of which are the tensile strength, compressive strength, ductility, and hardness.

The specifications regarding these properties are often furnished the supplier of the raw materials although it may pay the user to adopt certain standardized raw materials, which may be had at a lower price than to pay the cost of special production.

They cover, almost without exception, materials suitable for any specific purpose, as, for instance: cast iron to withstand high temperatures or exceedingly hard wear; steel suitable for casehardening or having extremely high strength of 200,000 lbs. per sq. in. or more, or with an ability to resist corrosion (stainless steels); brass suitable for screw machine work or for drawing operations such as cartridge cases; bronze of high tensile strength, etc.

Restricting Impurities

The specifications may restrict the content of certain elements such as phosphorus and sulphur in iron, for instance, which are regarded as impurities. They specify the carbon content of iron and steel, and they indicate the content of nickel, chromium, copper, or molybdenum in the various alloy irons and steels, the copper, tin, zinc, nickel content, etc., of bronzes, and the silicon and copper content of aluminum, etc. While there are no hard-and-fast rules, there are general ones governing the suitability of any material for any specific purpose.

With the normal equipment of the plant laboratory, samples of material are tested to prove that they conform to requirements, and when parts such as castings prove to be faulty during machining, or steel parts harden badly, or parts have been found to fail in service or under inspection or test, it is the function of this department to determine if the raw material is at fault.

Thus the shop worker is not immediately concerned with the material he is working with, but will certainly be better equipped for his work if he has a general knowledge of the underlying principles.

Choosing Material

It must be assumed that the material from which a part is made has been carefully selected for the purpose. The relatively heavy base and main castings of an engine—the frame of a pump or machine tool or gear casing for instance—will usually take the form of an iron casting, because cast iron, being high in compressive strength, is good for support. It is also true that many machine bases can be produced by welding up plates and angles, and this construction is being adopted because it is lighter and cheaper. A steel casting may be used

because it is tougher and can stand shock better. Locomotive frames are often cast steel. Stainless-steel castings may be used for hydraulic machinery, and of course aluminum castings usually replace iron for aircraft and other work where lightness with strength as well as resistance to corrosion is important.

Heat Resistance

If the part has to withstand heat, the material can be alloyed to resist high temperatures: an iron casting may be alloyed or chilled in certain parts to give a hard-wearing surface, or it can be alloyed to be almost the equal of stainless steel in resisting corrosion. Samples of the melts generally go to the laboratory to check up on all this. Cast iron, while high in compressive strength, is relatively weak in tension; cast aluminum is strong enough for certain classes of casting such as crankcases and gear casing—but is also weak in tension. Neither of these materials is, in general, suitable for parts subjected to repeated stress, which sets up *fatigue* in the metal. The breaking of a piece of wire by bending back and forth is a simple example of fracture by fatigue. The pull on a chain is continually setting up fatigue which necessitates annealing at times to restore the nature of the material. This is also one of the reasons for the annealing of parts between shop operations.

Specification Details

Among the principal specifications of any material are the tensile strength, yield point, the elongation, and the hardness. The first, usually expressed in pounds per sq. in., is the direct measure of the load that any part made of such material can stand. The more important is the ultimate tensile strength.

Tensile Strength

Most cast metals, when a piece is tested for tensile strength, will fracture suddenly, but in the case of wrought materials, and especially steel, they will stretch appreciably before breaking, which is shown by the difference between yield point and ultimate tensile strength and by elongation. This elongation is an important property, as it is a measure of the ductility of the material, which for certain work may be of more importance than mere tensile strength.

With the present-day knowledge of materials, metals can be given fairly definite values of tensile strength, elongation, hardness, and resistance to impact, either by alloying or by heat-treatment, or both. The nature of the heat-treatment necessary to bring out any particular property usually forms part of the specification.

Alloys

An alloy consists of two or more metals mixed by melting together, one usually being in much larger proportion than the others. Steel may be alloyed with nickel, manganese, chromium, tungsten, molybdenum, vanadium, or cobalt. The effect of these will be discussed later. Copper may be alloyed with zinc to form brass or with tin to make bronze. Aluminum with a small amount of copper, gives duralumin, which has the strength of steel but the lightness of aluminum. Small amounts of other metals added to cast iron give the alloy valuable properties.

The moving parts of most machines are made of steel because of its high strength, which in the case of certain alloy steels may reach 200,000 lbs. per sq. in. Also most steels are relatively cheap; they can be machined by average equipment in the annealed or normalized condition, and then hardened by methods to be described later. The moving parts of a modern locomotive carry a high stress in working, hence they are made of alloy steel, but the reason for an aero-engine connecting rod being made of aluminum alloy is that the alloy is lighter. Some aluminum alloys such as duralumin, have the strength and other good properties of the high-tensile steels.

Crankshafts and camshafts are usually made from steel forgings, but this requires many costly machining operations. For certain uses, such as tractor engines, such parts can be made equally well, and much cheaper from high-strength alloy cast irons or cast steels. Such metals and methods are often used for certain gears.

Cost of production today is quite as important as quality of manufacture, with certain exceptions in the case of war material. Thus, complicated shapes may often be cast in iron and then made the equal of good commercial steel by being made malleable.

All these materials are dealt with in the following pages, together with brass, bronze, copper, aluminum, and other metals commonly used. Brass, generally in the form of bar or strip, is used principally for the mass-production of small parts for the electrical and instrument trades, for light ordnance such as fuses, and for practically all pieces, such as shell cartridge cases, which are produced by blanking, cupping, and drawing. High-tensile brass (manganese bronze) is often used for bolts, pump parts, etc., as it is much stronger than ordinary brass.

What may often be mistaken for, and spoken of, as brass castings are usually bronze castings. Brass, which is a comparatively cheap alloy of roughly 60 parts of copper to 40 parts of zinc (described as 60/40), while entirely suitable for that class of work, is a weak material, whereas bronze, which is an alloy of copper and tin in various proportions with nickel, lead, or aluminum is stronger, has better wearing properties, and casts better than brass.

CAST IRON

CAST iron, except in the case of malleable casting, cannot be bent. From 1.7 to 4.5 percent carbon is usually present and in most cases an important percentage of silicon. The four general classifications are: (1) Pig iron, (2) White cast iron, (3) Malleable cast iron, (4) Gray cast iron. The chips, when cut by a cold chisel or machine tool, are small brittle *crumbs,* and the skin of a casting may be so hard in parts as to resist filing or to take the edge off a tool. This may be due to a *chill* in the mold for the purpose of giving the casting a very hard surface to resist wear. Such a surface would be finished by grinding, but in most cases local hardness is the result either of bad material or of faulty molding.

During machining, the metal may show up soft or spongy with blow holes (gas pockets), and must be rejected. Thus, while cast iron can be alloyed to give a very hard metal, or rendered specially soft for ease of machining, it is in general a moderately hard metal sufficiently brittle to be broken readily by a hammer blow, by too tight a gripping in the vise, or by dropping. The worker should always treat an iron casting with respect.

Completely annealed gray iron molded in a metal mold is the most readily machined. Sand castings are frequently found containing burned-in sand, which must be removed by making a heavy first cut to get the tool cutting edge under the sand. Chilled or white iron is extremely difficult to machine.

Although cast iron is weak in some respects, a good iron casting made for machine work may be entirely satisfactory for the purpose for which it was designed. An examination of a cylinder casting will reveal the fact that iron can be cast into intricate shapes, and the polish which can be imparted to a cylinder bore indicates that it is a material that will stand wear.

In the case of steam engines, pumps, valves, and other hydraulic equipment, there is a natural tendency for cast iron to rust, but it is not so readily attacked by corrosion as are commercial steels. It can be alloyed to be highly resistant to corrosion. Gray iron is also commonly used for agricultural machinery, machine tool frames and beds, flywheels, water pipe, soil pipe, and hardware. Common uses of chilled and white iron castings are plow shares, chilled car wheels, pulverizing balls, stamp shoes, dies, and various types of wearing plates.

Iron is reduced to pig iron from iron ore by intense heat in the blast furnace. Pig iron has two principal uses: conversion into steel, and for use by the founder for remelting. The foundry may decide to add silicon, ferro-manganese, nickel, copper, and chromium in varying amounts, according to whether a hard, soft, heat-resisting or a corrosion-resisting casting is called for.

Uses of Wrought Iron

At one time a large amount of wrought iron was produced, this being virtually a reduction of cast iron to a permanent malleable form by a process known as *puddling,* but today there are few uses in engineering production for wrought iron, as commercial mild steel serves the same general purposes and is very much cheaper. It is the purest form of iron. On the other hand, cast iron is a complex material of which only about 95 percent is actually iron. There is, in the average run of close-grained iron suitable for

machine work, about 3 percent of carbon in the form of graphite, ¾ percent of carbon combined with the iron, and 1–2 percent of silicon, which improves the iron in certain ways. A small percentage of manganese is also regarded as an essential constituent, as it controls the sulphur and phosphorus which most specifications require to be limited to small amounts.

Buying Pig Iron

The pig iron as used by the founder is bought, according to the nature and purpose of the castings to be made, with definite percentages of these elements. Sometimes they are classified as refined irons, mine irons, and cold blast irons, and sometimes as *synthetic* irons.

The following are typical examples of some of the various chemical compositions which are used on typical applications.

CHEMICAL COMPOSITION OF CAST IRON

	C	Si	Mn	P	S	Ni	Cr	Mo	V
Cylinder blocks, automotive	3.25	2.25	0.65	0.15	0.10	0.75*	0.30		
Pistons, automotive	3.25	2.25	0.65	0.15	0.10			0.50*	
General machinery parts	3.25	1.85	0.50	0.35	0.10				
Locomotive cylinders	3.45	1.50	0.50	0.50	0.10				0.15
Brake drums	3.30	2.00	0.65	0.15	0.10	1.25	0.50		
Pipe for water mains	3.60	1.75	0.50	0.80	0.10				
Chilled plow shares	3.60	1.25	0.55	0.40	0.10				
High strength iron	2.75	2.25	0.80	0.10	0.10	1.00*		0.35*	
Rolls for steel mills	3.50	1.10	1.20	0.20	0.10	4.00	1.85		0.35
Steel ingot molds	3.50	1.00	0.90	0.20	0.05				
Car wheels	3.35	0.65	0.60	0.35	0.15				
Dies for forming, stamping, etc.	3.00	1.25	0.60	0.20	0.10	2.75	0.80		
Grate bars	3.70	1.75	0.50	0.40	0.10				0.15
Forging dies	3.10	1.50	0.60	0.20	0.10			1.00	
Valve parts	3.30	2.00	0.50	0.35	0.10				

* Indicates this element is optional.

Importance of Carbon

Carbon is the important element. As will be seen later, the initial procedure in steel-making is to include a definite percentage of carbon by addition, whereas in cast iron, reduction of the carbon content is in order. Certainly the small amount which can be carried in solution by the iron, known as combined carbon, is a source of both strength and hardness. The free carbon in the form of graphite, while useful for making a soft, easily machinable iron for general-purpose castings, is the cause of softness and porosity in the heavy sections of machine casting.

The Hard Spot

Casting against a *chill* prevents the formation of free carbon near the chilled surface, which therefore becomes hard; this is one recognized means of imparting a good wearing surface to a casting in a very simple manner, but the familiar *hard spot* is a local steely area which may result from mixing steel with the iron to reduce the carbon. This is a condition which the foundry must avoid.

Between the ordinary run of foundry irons for general-purpose castings and the alloy cast irons which will be dealt with later, there comes a class of iron generally alluded to as *high strength* iron, which for all practical purposes could be regarded as iron produced from the best ores and under strict metallurgical control. Its total carbon content is below 3.0 percent, as against the average of 3.3 percent for ordinary cupola iron. In the latter case, the hardness and strength are largely controlled by silicon, but when the total carbon is less than 3 percent the silicon ceases to have much controlling influence.

High Strength Iron

High strength iron usually indicates cast irons ranging above 40,000 lbs. tensile strength. To produce these, a considerable quantity of steel is often used in the charge. Alloys are often added for machinability and strength. Nickel, or nickel and chromium, or molybdenum are most commonly used as alloys for this purpose. These types of iron are frequently produced in the electric arc furnace for better control of the composition.

The Meehanite Process

Meehanite is a trade name, applied to cast irons of various analysis, usually containing a large portion of scrap metal to which is added calcium silicide, while the iron is melted. This produces a fine graphite structure. These Meehanite irons, which can be given heat-, abrasion-, and corrosion-resisting properties, can also be chilled and heat-treated. An important feature is that the chilling can be carried to any depth and to a Brinell hardness from 300 to 500 as required, but differing in nature from the chill of ordinary iron. It is much tougher and will resist spalling. With an ultimate strength of about 60,000 lbs., these irons stand up to shock loads well, and are therefore suitable for cams, gears, and dies, and especially in the production of inexpensive gearing for rough machinery.

The high-nickel-content irons are sometimes used to obtain special qualities of expansion in the finished part. At about 14 percent nickel with some copper and chromium, they are practically free from *growth* and will not scale excessively at temperatures up to 1500 deg. F. These also resist acids, salts, alkalis, etc., better than ordinary iron.

Why Nickel Is Used

In modern foundry work the average good cast iron contains 1 to 2 percent of nickel. Besides the effect in eliminating hard spots and giving added density to the metal in the thicker and softer sections, it makes the metal more fluid and easier to cast. Although the through hardness is greater than that of ordinary cast iron, it is easy to machine. These low-nickel irons, while not corrosion-resistant in the accepted sense of the term, have a greater resistance to corrosion than ordinary irons. Again, owing to the improved density and soundness of the metal, they resist heat fairly well without the brittleness associated with low-silicon irons.

Medium-Nickel Irons

Another effect of the addition of small percentages of nickel, is the high degree of polish that the iron takes, this being very important in cylinder bores and wearing surfaces in general. Graduated additions of nickel to low-silicon white iron first tend to harden it, then, as it becomes graphitized, it becomes softer. With nickel additions up to 5 percent, there is a general increase in hardness, and these medium-nickel irons are somewhat difficult to machine. A further addition of nickel, however, produces a metal which once more becomes commercially machinable.

An average analysis of low-nickel iron suitable for general work would be total carbon 3.05 percent, silicon 1.4 percent, manganese 1 percent, phosphorus 0.18 percent, sulphur 0.10 percent and nickel between 1 and 2 percent. The average tensile strength of such irons is in the neighborhood of 40,000 lbs., and iron of this kind is readily produced in any foundry by the addition of nickel to the melt as it is tapped from the cupola, or by the addition of nickel ingots to the cupola charge or use of nickel-bearing pig iron.

Chromium and Silicon

There is often .50 percent of chromium in the high strength low-nickel irons, principally to neutralize the silicon as an alternative to reducing it. Silicon must be present in low-carbon irons to give density of structure.

In the harder irons there is about 4 percent of chromium. They are white or chilled cast irons alloyed with nickel to give hardness without loss of toughness. Suitable compositions will give a hardness up to 300 Brinell with a strength 50 percent above that of ordinary iron. They resist impact conditions fairly well, cast well into intricate shapes, and are suitable for surface-hardening by the nitrogen process. While still retaining the total carbon at about 3 percent, the corrosion-resisting irons are usually produced in the foundry by the addition of nickel-chromium-copper pig to a base iron with 1.5 percent of chromium. Their main purpose is to stand up under heat or corrosion, as they lack both strength and hardness.

Corrosion-resisting metals can be made harder by adding more chromium, a 30 percent nickel and 10 percent chromium alloy being almost the equal of stainless steel in its ability

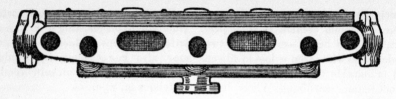

Fig. 1. A Diesel-engine exhaust manifold in nickel-chromium heat-resisting cast iron. A nickel-chromium alloy resists corrosion and takes a high polish almost as well as stainless steel. It is easily machined and can be temper-hardened.

to resist corrosion and to take a high polish. Iron with 2 percent total carbon, 5 percent silicon, 1 percent manganese, 18 percent nickel and 2–5 percent chromium is a heat-resisting metal which is easily machined and can be temper hardened.

Silicon is an important element in iron because of its action on the carbon. It promotes the formation of graphite. Thus by changing white iron to gray iron, it makes the production of commercial gray iron possible.

Manganese has little effect on the mechanical properties of iron, as used in the ranges of 0.50 to 0.80 percent.

Sulphur exerts little harmful effect on iron when present in amounts of less than 0.18 percent provided there is sufficient manganese present to prevent chill.

Phosphorus is usually present in the range of 0.10 to 0.90 percent. Such amounts have no harmful effect.

Molybdenum increases tensile strength and hardness. It is the most effective of any element used as alloy in these characteristics, and also increases wear resistance in some applications. It is often used in combination with other alloys such as nickel or chromium or both, and it promotes structural uniformity in heavy sections of the castings.

Vanadium is also used to increase tensile strength and hardness.

There are nickel alloy pig irons, which are manufactured to various specifications. They contain anything from 2 to 25 percent of nickel, with silicon, manganese, and phosphorus to suit. They are available in sand-cast or machine-cast pigs, and are often refined by a degassing process. The same applies to nickel-chromium irons. Refined chromium pig iron, however, is also available for the purpose of making chromium additions to nickel or other alloy iron. A chromium content of about 8 percent and 3.5 to 3.75 percent total carbon produces a pig iron of specially-low melting point, and this is generally the best for making chromium additions to foundry mixtures. When an addition of molybdenum is called for, molybdenum-bearing pig iron is recommended.

Copper is one of the elements which assist in giving iron corrosion-resisting properties, although the copper content is not large, usually being in the neighborhood of 2 percent. These ingots are suitable for re-melting without any other addition.

High-silicon acid-resisting irons come as ingots suitable for direct re-melting either in the cupola or electric furnace. They are manufactured to give a silicon content, when re-melted, of from 14 to 16 percent, and they are sometimes sold as *acid-resisting* iron. It is a chromium-bearing pig iron used principally for furnace parts. The average chromium content is 0.75 percent, the iron being available in two grades. The white iron is low in silicon and is suitable for those parts which do not require machining. Where, however, this is called for, white iron is too hard, and a softer grade with a higher silicon content is used. Most furnace parts, however, are simple rough castings which require little machining, although drilling is sometimes necessary.

As a substitute for non-ferrous castings or steel forgings, alloy cast irons offer boundless possibilities, as was the case in the early days of alloy steels which came into prominence principally during the first World War. Fig. 3 shows one of the most remarkable examples of the use of alloy cast irons. Instead of heavy machining a costly drop forging, the whole work on this crankshaft, which is typical of Diesel and gas-engine work of the present day, can be finished to the grinding stage with comparatively light cuts from the casting. Camshafts are being made in a manner similar to this. Though not suitable for aero-engine work, these cast-iron crankshafts and camshafts have proved the equal in every way of those made from alloy steels, though they are heavier. For tractor engines and marine motors that is no great objection.

Fig. 5 shows some typical castings from corrosion-resisting iron for centrifugal pumps. Machine-cut gears may also be economically produced from a high-strength nickel-chromium-molybdenum iron.

Heat Treatment of Cast Iron

Cast iron is comparable to steel in its reaction to heat treatment.

For relieving internal stresses, normalizing, or mild annealing, heat to 800 to 1000 deg. F. and hold at that temperature from $\frac{1}{2}$ to 5 hours according to the size. Cool slowly in the furnace. This causes only slight

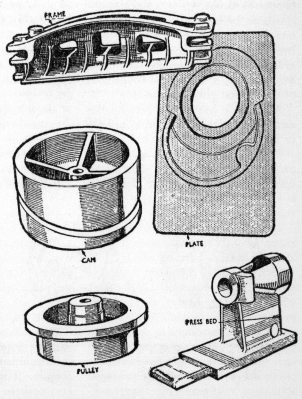

Fig. 2. A group of high strength castings, including a cam, a plate casting, a pulley and a press bed. This material can be heat-treated to increase its toughness.

Fig. 3. An engine crankshaft casting in high strength in the rough state (*above*) and machined state (*below*). The whole work can be finished to the grinding stage with comparatively light cuts from the casting.

reduction of the hardness and strength of the material.

For softening for machinability, heat to 1400 to 1500 deg. F. and cool slowly in the furnace. Some alloys require higher temperatures for complete annealing. This generally reduces the hardness to 120 to 130 Brinell for ordinary irons and 130 to 180 Brinell for alloy irons. Strength is also reduced.

An increase in wear and abrasion resistance may be obtained by heating to 1450 to 1550 deg. F. slowly and thoroughly and then quenching in oil. Water may be used on some limited types and simple sections. Air cooling will harden some alloys. This reduces the strength somewhat, but this may be restored by suitable drawing. This is usually done at about 300 deg. F. for two or three hours.

Flame hardening is frequently applied to castings such as machine beds, etc., where hard surface is desired, but the part is not adaptable to ordi-

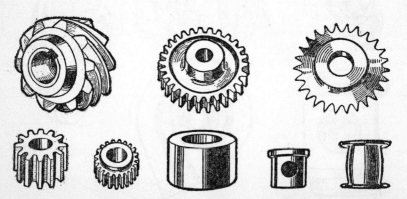

Fig. 4. Typical components manufactured from alloy cast iron in bar or rod form, specially prepared for the production of small parts of this kind. Such alloy cast iron parts are fully equal to those made from alloy steels.

nary heating and quenching method of hardening.

Special types of iron containing aluminum may be nitrided. This process consists of producing an exception-ally hard surface, only a few thousandths of an inch deep by exposing the finished part to anhydrous ammonia gas at about 1000 deg. F. for 20 to 90 hours.

WROUGHT IRON AND STEEL

At one time all cast metals were limited in use by the fact that their shape was confined to that in which they were cast. This led to the introduction at a very early date of a means of altering the nature of iron

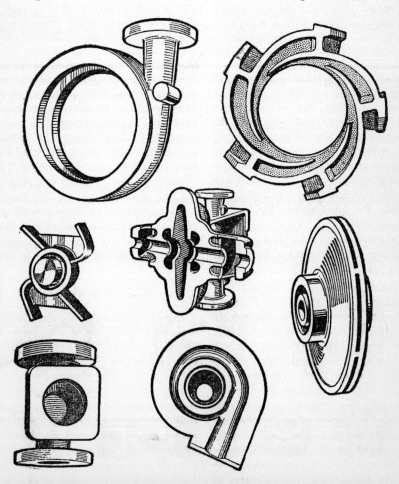

Fig. 5. Some typical castings for centrifugal pumps in an alloy cast iron which possesses considerable corrosion- and heat-resisting properties.

as it was cast so that it could be worked. As the hard, brittle nature of cast iron is due to the contained carbon, removal of the carbon is the essential process.

Prior to the introduction of steel, cast iron was converted into the malleable condition by complete annealing or graphitizing. The resultant metal is virtually pure iron, often referred to as *ingot* iron. That produced by the old-time methods of the iron-workers is a metal with a distinctly fibrous structure, caused by the inclusion of a certain amount of slag in the semi-molten iron, which is removed by the hammering and subsequent rolling operations. Good average wrought iron has a tensile strength of about 50,000 lbs.

Lacking the strength of most steels and being very much more expensive to produce, it has now only a few special applications, such as blacksmiths' work in general, chains, bolts, and nuts, and work mainly constructed of sheet and plate where resistance to corrosion is of more importance than strength. For the less-important parts of machinery and metal-work in general, mild steel—that is, steel with a low carbon content—is by far the most commonly used material.

Easy to forge or produce in bars or tubes, parts can be produced, especially from the free-cutting steels manufactured for the purpose, on automatic and semi-automatic machines at very low cost. This also applies to relatively complicated shapes produced by milling operations, and hollow parts originating in plate or strip and formed by blanking and cupping operations. Much of this work is also done in harder steels which are, in general harder to work. But the usual procedure is to soften or normalize such steels during the shop operations and bring them to the required degree of hardness later. This heat-treatment may also increase the strength of the steel.

Cast Steel

Cast steel is usually low in carbon, as compared to cast iron, sometimes as low as 0.10 and up to 0.80 percent carbon. Cast steel is always given at least one type of heat treatment and often more than one. It may also be alloyed with chromium, nickel, vanadium, molybdenum, or copper, or a combination of these elements, in addition to the manganese and silicon which are generally present.

After normalizing or annealing, and hardening, and tempering, cast steel develops a tensile strength of at least 60,000 lbs. and with some alloys is as high as 120,000 lbs.

This is important where high stresses are encountered and where reduction in weight is important. Some typical applications are: caterpillar treads, stone crusher jaws, shovel teeth, locomotive frames, etc.

Definitions of Steel

Steel is spoken of in various terms, some of which relate to the process of manufacture and others to the carbon or alloy content. What is collectively referred to as *mild* steel is generally a cheap material used for structural work and general purposes. Sometimes it is designated as Bessemer steel, by reason of the fact that it may be made by burning out the carbon from the pig iron in a Bessemer converter. The carbon content of all mild steel is low, and it cannot be hardened. Those grades used in the machine shop are usually refined in a manner to make them *free-cutting*.

Open-hearth steel is made in a furnace by what is for all practical purposes a boiling process. Unlike Bessemer steel, which is always made from molten pig iron, open-hearth steel can be made from steel scrap as well as pig iron. Both these processes produce steel from iron by removing carbon.

Crucible steel, which is sometimes called *cast* steel, was the most common type for producing tool steels and other high quality steels for many years. Today these steels are almost always produced in electric furnaces. The crucible method consists of placing the iron, carbon, and other alloys in specific proportions in a small pot or crucible, which is heated as one unit of a large number in a large flat gas fired furnace; when melted, the hot crucible is lifted by hand, the seal broken, and the molten metal poured into ingot molds. Each crucible usually holds about 100 lbs. of steel.

The electric furnace, as used today, is of the basic, acid, or induction type. The basic type is the more common. It is made in sizes to produce from 1 ton up to 100 tons at each heat. Here a cold charge of scrap and alloying materials, all of known chemical and physical properties is melted by passing heavy currents of electricity through the steel. When melted, burned lime and fluorspar or sand is added which forms a basic slag in combination with the oxides from the molten metal. Chemical analysis is made several times during melting to check the desired elements and additions are made to secure the analysis required. The molten metal is poured by tilting the entire furnace. It flows into a ladle and thence is poured into the ingot molds.

The acid electric furnace is similar in appearance, but is lined with an acid mixture such as ground ganister and silica brick. It is generally used for producing cast steel, because the melting time is shorter and lining maintenance is lower. Good fluidity is easier to obtain and the slag is easy to handle. However there is little reduction of sulphur and phosphorus by this method, and it is therefore not practical for the highest quality steels.

The coreless induction furnace is generally built in the smaller sizes from 100 lbs. up to 2 tons capacity, but some have been made up to 8 tons capacity. Here the charge is held within close limits of the desired product, as there is little loss or change during the melting. The heat is applied by induced currents of high frequency passing through the metal from a primary coil. The result is fast melting, sometimes a charge of 1000 lbs. being melted in less than 1 hour. This type of furnace is especially adapted to producing small steel castings of special alloys, for low carbon stainless steels, and high speed steels. It is higher in operating cost, which limits its use in high tonnage production. The majority of machinist's tools, other than those made from alloy steels, are made from tool steel with a carbon content of from 0.85 to 1.35 percent, according to the final hardness wanted.

These high-carbon steels, however, are not often used for machine parts, as softer steels are cheaper and easier to work, and the necessary hardness is attained by causing the surface to absorb carbon in the *case-hardening* process.

None of these terms, including alloy steel, must be considered as having too great importance, as they are

Mild and Medium Steels

In general, when the carbon content is under 0.25 percent the steel can be regarded as *mild* and not capable of being hardened. Between 0.25 and 0.5 percent carbon content steels are *medium* and of a harder nature. They are sometimes used for work requiring hardening. Between 0.5 and 0.75 percent carbon are steels which harden well and have a tensile strength of about 80,000 lbs. or more. When the carbon content approaches 1 percent, the steel has a high temper value and the tensile strength may reach 200,000 lbs. or more, with corresponding lower toughness.

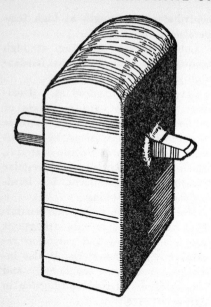

Fig. 6. A nickel-steel cold chisel can be driven through a 2½-in. block of mild steel, as above, without damaging the tool's edge or head.

often used loosely. The actual carbon content is the principal criterion of carbon or tool steel, while alloy steels, although the majority contain nickel, may contain also tungsten, vanadium, chromium, molybdenum, etc.

The main difference in steels lies in the carbon content, and the percentage inclusion of nickel, chromium, vanadium, molybdenum, tungsten, etc., which they contain for the purpose of giving definite strength and hardness values in the final condition, after such heat-treatment as may be specified. The substance made from cast iron, by the Bessemer process, the open-hearth furnace, or in an electric furnace is for all practical purposes carbon-free iron, and to this is added the required amount of carbon and other elements.

Grain of Steel

To the user of medium carbon alloy steels, alloy carburizing steels, and tool steels, grain size is of some importance. In most applications, the fine grain steels (Austenite grain size 5 to 8) are deeper hardening, tougher, have less distortion in hardening, are

Fig. 7. Top and bottom halves of a pump-casing cast in stainless steel, including nickel and chromium.

less apt to develop quenching cracks, less susceptible to grinding cracks, and have lower internal stresses. This same material is more difficult to machine, but gives better machining in fine cut finishes. The opposite is true of the coarse grained steels (grain size less than 5).

In tool steels, the grain size is usually rated on the standards of Shepherd fractured specimens. These agree approximately with Austenite grain sizes. Hardened tool steels usually show a fracture grain of $8\frac{1}{2}$ or finer (10 is the finest size). These fine fractured grains are often referred to as *silky* fractures.

The *flow lines* of steel grain are determined by the direction of working of the steel during hot rolling or forging.

It is generally considered that greatest strength is located in the direction of grain lines. Therefore for maximum strength, it is considered advantageous to use upset forging blanks for highly stressed tools such as milling cutters, heavy duty die blocks, and also for severe service as gears and other machine parts. Parts made from rolled bar stock can be laid out so that the points of maximum stress are across the flow lines of the bar. The addition of various elements to steel is for precisely the same purpose as they are added to iron; that is, to increase the strength of the metal and add to its toughness.

Effects of Alloying Elements in Steel

Aluminum is used as a deoxidizer. Also is present in steels made specially for nitriding.

Chromium increases hardenability, abrasion resistance, especially when in compositions with high carbon and contributes to strength at high temperatures.

Cobalt resists softening at high temperatures and decreases hardenability.

Manganese is required as a deoxidizer, offsets the harmful effects of sulphur, and gives moderate increase in hardenability. At about 12 percent it provides a hard, ductile material, which will not harden under regular quenching heat treatment, but hardens from cold working.

Molybdenum increases hardenability considerably, increases strength at high temperatures and corrosion resistance in stainless steels. It also increases ductility, toughness, and strength and can replace tungsten in high speed steels.

Nickel promotes high toughness in composition with other elements and develops good hardenability. In stainless steels, combined with chromium, it causes good corrosion resistance and is not hardenable by quenching treatment but does harden by cold working. Very high nickel alloys have special thermal and magnetic properties.

Phosphorus improves machinability in high sulphur steels, but must be limited to less than 0.05 percent to obtain plasticity. It contributes to hardenability, strengthens low carbon steels, and adds some corrosion resistance.

Silicon is a general purpose deoxidizer and increases strength, especially in combination with manganese. Universally used in magnetic sheet steels, where it aids in crystallization and increases electrical resistance.

Titanium is a good deoxidizer, prevents grain growth at high temperatures in stainless steels, and reduces hardenability in medium chromium steels.

Tungsten resists softening at high temperatures, increases hardenability, and forms hard, abrasive-resisting carbide particles. It is almost always present in high speed cutting tools.

Vanadium produces fine grain and increases hardenability.

Case-Hardening

All but a few of the mildest steels can be case-hardened, and steels having a low carbon content are generally used for parts which have to be case-hardened, 0.2 percent carbon being usually the maximum allowable. The carbon is generally about 0.15 percent contents lower than 0.1 percent, leading to machining difficulties.

The soft, low-carbon case-hardening steels are easy to machine, and are often used for parts which need not be case-hardened. This softness, however may increase the difficulty of obtaining the fine finish needed for certain parts, especially when final grinding to exact size is difficult, owing to the shape of the teeth or the design of a gear.

The nickel steels, without sacrificing any of the toughness, give just that slight increase in hardness and fineness of structure which make for the smooth surface which is essential for parts intended for case-hardening.

Hardening Carbon Steel

Steels used in engineering may be grouped for all practical purposes under five main headings:

(1) Plain carbon and machinery steels of ordinary quality not intended for case-hardening.

(2) Alloy steels of medium carbon content intended for hardening and tempering to attain high physical properties.

(3) Case-hardening steels, including both plain carbon and alloy types.

(4) Tool and other similar high quality steels.

(5) Stainless Steels.

Of these, steels with lower carbon range have the widest application to the formation of the moving and smaller stationary parts of machinery. It is easy to form them to rough shape by forging and stamping, and in the soft condition they are easy to machine. They are strong enough for most work and wear fairly well.

Alloy Steels

Good quality alloy steels contrast favorably with the plain carbon type. Greater care is taken in manufacture, and impurities are lower, so that the combined values of tensile strength and ductility are greater. However, they cost more to buy and machine than the plain carbon steels.

The only practical drawback to the use of these steels in machines is that the surface is never thoroughly hard. The Brinell hardness numbers on quenching range from 444 to 600 against about 653 for carburized steels.

The more common alloys, such as manganese, chromium, and molybdenum, in addition to nickel, are all very effective in facilitating hardening. They reduce the critical cooling velocity necessary for complete hardening to be obtained. If sufficiently alloyed, hardening may be obtained with even slow rates of cooling, such as are associated with the normal cooling of large masses in air.

The following tables are the standard series of analyses, established by the Society of Automotive Engineers and represent the types most commonly used.

S. A. E. STEELS (Revised 1938)

Carbon Steels

S.A.E. No.	C.	Mn.	P. (max.)	S. (max.)
1010	0.05–0.15	0.30–0.60	0.045	0.055
1015	0.10–0.20	0.30–0.60	0.045	0.055
X1015	0.10–0.20	0.70–1.00	0.045	0.055
1020	0.15–0.25	0.30–0.60	0.045	0.055
X1020	0.15–0.25	0.70–1.00	0.045	0.055
1025	0.20–0.30	0.30–0.60	0.045	0.055
X1025	0.20–0.30	0.70–1.00	0.045	0.055
1030	0.25–0.35	0.60–0.90	0.045	0.055
1035	0.30–0.40	0.60–0.90	0.045	0.055
1040	0.35–0.45	0.60–0.90	0.045	0.055
X1040	0.35–0.45	0.40–0.70	0.045	0.055
1045	0.40–0.50	0.60–0.90	0.045	0.055
X1045	0.40–0.50	0.40–0.70	0.045	0.055
1050	0.45–0.55	0.60–0.90	0.045	0.055
X1050	0.45–0.55	0.40–0.70	0.045	0.055
1055	0.50–0.60	0.60–0.90	0.040	0.055
X1055	0.50–0.60	0.90–1.20	0.040	0.055
1060	0.55–0.70	0.60–0.90	0.040	0.055
1065	0.60–0.75	0.60–0.90	0.040	0.055
X1065	0.60–0.75	0.90–1.20	0.040	0.055
1070	0.65–0.80	0.60–0.90	0.040	0.055
1075	0.70–0.85	0.60–0.90	0.040	0.055
1080	0.75–0.90	0.60–0.90	0.040	0.055
1085	0.80–0.95	0.60–0.90	0.040	0.055
1090	0.85–1.00	0.60–0.90	0.040	0.055
1095	0.90–1.05	0.25–0.50	0.040	0.055

S. A. E. STEELS (Revised 1938) (cont'd)

Free-Cutting Steels

S.A.E. No.	C.	Mn.	P.	S.
1112	0.08–0.16	0.60–0.90	0.09–0.13	0.10–0.20
X1112	0.08–0.16	0.60–0.90	0.09–0.13	0.20–0.30
1115	0.10–0.20	0.70–1.00	0.045 max.	0.075–0.15
1120	0.15–0.25	0.60–0.90	0.045 max.	0.075–0.15
X1314	0.10–0.20	1.00–1.30	0.045 max.	0.075–0.15
X1315	0.10–0.20	1.30–1.60	0.045 max.	0.075–0.15
X1330	0.25–0.35	1.35–1.65	0.045 max.	0.075–0.15
X1335	0.30–0.40	1.35–1.65	0.045 max.	0.075–0.15
X1340	0.35–0.45	1.35–1.65	0.045 max.	0.075–0.15

Manganese Steels [1]

S.A.E No.	C.	Mn.	P.(max.)	S.(max.)
T1330	0.25–0.35	1.60–1.90	0.040	0.050
T1335	0.30–0.40	1.60–1.90	0.040	0.050
T1340	0.35–0.45	1.60–1.90	0.040	0.050
T1345	0.40–0.50	1.60–1.90	0.040	0.050
T1350	0.45–0.55	1.60–1.90	0.040	0.050

Nickel Steels [1]

S.A.E. No.	C.	Mn.	P.(max.)	S.(max.)	Ni.
2015	0.10–0.20	0.30–0.60	0.040	0.050	0.40–0.60
2115	0.10–0.20	0.30–0.60	0.040	0.050	1.25–1.75
2315	0.10–0.20	0.30–0.60	0.040	0.050	3.25–3.75
2320	0.15–0.25	0.30–0.60	0.040	0.050	3.25–3.75
2330	0.25–0.35	0.50–0.80	0.040	0.050	3.25–3.75
2335	0.30–0.40	0.50–0.80	0.040	0.050	3.25–3.75
2340	0.35–0.45	0.60–0.90	0.040	0.050	3.25–3.75
2345	0.40–0.50	0.60–0.90	0.040	0.050	3.25–3.75
2350	0.45–0.55	0.60–0.90	0.040	0.050	3.25–3.75
2515	0.10–0.20	0.30–0.60	0.040	0.050	4.75–5.25

[1] Silicon range of all S. A. E. basic open hearth alloy steels shall be 0.15 to 0.30 percent. For electric and acid open hearth alloy steels the silicon content shall be 0.15 percent min.

S. A. E. STEELS (Revised 1938) (cont'd)

Nickel-Chromium Steels [1]

S.A.E. No.	C.	Mn.	P. (max.)	S. (max.)	Ni.	Cr.
3115	0.10–0.20	0.30–0.60	0.040	0.050	1.00–1.50	0.45–0.75
3120	0.15–0.25	0.30–0.60	0.040	0.050	1.00–1.50	0.45–0.75
3125	0.20–0.30	0.50–0.80	0.040	0.050	1.00–1.50	0.45–0.75
3130	0.25–0.35	0.50–0.80	0.040	0.050	1.00–1.50	0.45–0.75
3135	0.30–0.40	0.50–0.80	0.040	0.050	1.00–1.50	0.45–0.75
3140	0.35–0.45	0.60–0.90	0.040	0.050	1.00–1.50	0.45–0.75
X3140	0.35–0.45	0.60–0.90	0.040	0.050	1.00–1.50	0.60–0.90
3145	0.40–0.50	0.60–0.90	0.040	0.050	1.00–1.50	0.45–0.75
3150	0.45–0.55	0.60–0.90	0.040	0.050	1.00–1.50	0.45–0.75
3215	0.10–0.20	0.30–0.60	0.040	0.050	1.50–2.00	0.90–1.25
3220	0.15–0.25	0.30–0.60	0.040	0.050	1.50–2.00	0.90–1.25
3230	0.25–0.35	0.30–0.60	0.040	0.050	1.50–2.00	0.90–1.25
3240	0.35–0.45	0.30–0.60	0.040	0.050	1.50–2.00	0.90–1.25
3245	0.40–0.50	0.30–0.60	0.040	0.050	1.50–2.00	0.90–1.25
3250	0.45–0.55	0.30–0.60	0.040	0.050	1.50–2.00	0.90–1.25
3312	0.17 max.	0.30–0.60	0.040	0.050	3.25–3.75	1.25–1.75
3325	0.20–0.30	0.30–0.60	0.040	0.050	3.25–3.75	1.25–1.75
3335	0.30–0.40	0.30–0.60	0.040	0.050	3.25–3.75	1.25–1.75
3340	0.35–0.45	0.30–0.60	0.040	0.050	3.25–3.75	1.25–1.75
3415	0.10–0.20	0.30–0.60	0.040	0.050	2.75–3.25	0.60–0.95
3435	0.30–0.40	0.30–0.60	0.040	0.050	2.75–3.25	0.60–0.95
3450	0.45–0.55	0.30–0.60	0.040	0.050	2.75–3.25	0.60–0.95

Molybdenum Steels [1]

S.A.E. No.	C.	Mn.	P. (max.)	S. (max.)	Ni.	Cr.	Mo.
4130	0.25–0.35	0.50–0.80	0.040	0.050	…….	0.50–0.80	0.15–0.25
X4130	0.25–0.35	0.40–0.60	0.040	0.050	…….	0.80–1.10	0.15–0.25
4135	0.30–0.40	0.60–0.90	0.040	0.050	…….	0.80–1.10	0.15–0.25
4140	0.35–0.45	0.60–0.90	0.040	0.050	…….	0.80–1.10	0.15–0.25
4150	0.45–0.55	0.60–0.90	0.040	0.050	…….	0.80–1.10	0.15–0.25

[1] Silicon range of all S. A. E. basic open hearth alloy steels shall be 0.15 to 0.30 percent. For electric and acid open hearth alloy steels the silicon content shall be 0.15 percent min.

S. A. E. STEELS (Revised 1938) (cont'd)

Molybdenum Steels (cont'd)

S.A.E. No.	C.	Mn.	P. (max.)	S. (max.)	Ni.	Cr.	Mo.
4320	0.15–0.25	0.40–0.70	0.040	0.050	1.65–2.00	0.30–0.60	0.20–0.30
4340	0.35–0.45	0.50–0.80	0.040	0.050	1.50–2.00	0.50–0.80	0.30–0.40
X4340	0.35–0.45	0.50–0.80	0.040	0.050	1.50–2.00	0.60–0.90	0.20–0.30
4615	0.10–0.20	0.40–0.70	0.040	0.050	1.65–2.00	....	0.20–0.30
4620	0.15–0.25	0.40–0.70	0.040	0.050	1.65–2.00	....	0.20–0.30
4640	0.35–0.45	0.50–0.80	0.040	0.050	1.65–2.00	....	0.20–0.30
4815	0.10–0.20	0.40–0.60	0.040	0.050	3.25–3.75	....	0.20–0.30
4820	0.15–0.25	0.40–0.60	0.040	0.050	3.25–3.75	....	0.20–0.30

Chromium Steels [1]

S.A.E. No.	C.	Mn.	P.(max.)	S.(max.)	Cr.
5120	0.15–0.25	0.30–0.60	0.040	0.050	0.60–0.90
5140	0.35–0.45	0.60–0.90	0.040	0.050	0.80–1.10
5150	0.45–0.55	0.60–0.90	0.040	0.050	0.80–1.10
52100	0.95–1.10	0.20–0.50	0.030	0.035	1.20–1.50

Chromium-Vanadium Steels [1]

S.A.E. No.	C.	Mn.	P. (max.)	S. (max.)	Cr.	Vanadium	
						min.	desired
6115	0.10–0.20	0.30–0.60	0.040	0.050	0.80–1.10	0.15	0.18
6120	0.15–0.25	0.30–0.60	0.040	0.050	0.80–1.10	0.15	0.18
6125	0.20–0.30	0.60–0.90	0.040	0.050	0.80–1.10	0.15	0.18
6130	0.25–0.35	0.60–0.90	0.040	0.050	0.80–1.10	0.15	0.18
6135	0.30–0.40	0.60–0.90	0.040	0.050	0.80–1.10	0.15	0.18
6140	0.35–0.45	0.60–0.90	0.040	0.050	0.80–1.10	0.15	0.18
6145	0.40–0.50	0.60–0.90	0.040	0.050	0.80–1.10	0.15	0.18
6150	0.45–0.55	0.60–0.90	0.040	0.050	0.80–1.10	0.15	0.18
6195	0.90–1.05	0.20–0.45	0.030	0.035	0.80–1.10	0.15	0.18

[1] Silicon range of all S. A. E. basic open hearth alloy steels shall be 0.15 to 0.30 percent. For electric and acid open hearth alloy steels the silicon content shall be 0.15 percent min.

S. A. E. STEELS (Revised 1938) (cont'd)

Tungsten Steels [1]

S.A.E. No.	C.	Mn. (max.)	P.(max.)	S.(max.)	Cr.	W.
71360	0.50–0.70	0.30	0.035	0.040	3.00–4.00	12.00–15.00
71660	0.50–0.70	0.30	0.035	0.040	3.00–4.00	15.00–18.00
7260	0.50–0.70	0.30	0.035	0.040	0.50–1.00	1.50– 2.00

Silico-Manganese Steels

S.A.E. No.	C.	Mn.	P.(max.)	S.(max.)	Si.
9255	0.50–0.60	0.60–0.90	0.040	0.050	1.80–2.20
9260	0.55–0.65	0.60–0.90	0.040	0.050	1.80–2.20

Corrosion and Heat-Resisting Alloys

S.A.E. No.	C.(max.)	Mn. (max.)	P. (max.)	S. (max.)	Si. (max.)	Nickel	Chromium
30905	0.08	0.20–0.70	0.030	0.030	0.75	8.00–10.00	17.00–20.00
30915	0.09–0.20	0.20–0.70	0.030	0.030	0.75	8.00–10.00	17.00–20.00
51210	0.12	0.60	0.030	0.030	0.50	....	11.50–13.00
X51410	0.12	0.60	0.030	0.15–0.50	0.50	....	13.00–15.00
51335	0.25–0.40	0.60	0.030	0.030	0.50	....	12.00–14.00
51510	0.12	0.60	0.030	0.030	0.50	....	14.00–16.00
51710	0.12	0.60	0.030	0.030	0.50	....	16.00–18.00

[1] Silicon range of all S. A. E. basic open hearth alloy steels shall be 0.15 to 0.30 per cent. For electric and acid open hearth alloy steels the silicon content shall be 0.15 per cent min.

Tool Steels

Tool steels are produced today in a wide variety of analyses and under many trade names. They may be classified in general into a few general types.

Carbon or water hardening tool steel is the oldest and most common type and has the outstanding characteristic that it usually hardens with a very hard outside or *chill case* and with a comparatively tough and softer core which give the strength necessary for high impact jobs such as cold heading dies used for making nails, pins, etc., and in most jewelry dies and punches. It is also generally used for blacksmith and hand tools. Small additions of vanadium or chromium give steels of similar general characteristics, but finer in grain, deeper hardening, and sometimes tougher.

Low carbon and low alloyed tool steels are used for jobs requiring high strength and medium hardness such as dies for metal die castings, tough chisels, punches, etc.

Highly alloyed, high carbon-high chrome steels are used for very long wearing operations such as lamination dies, can making dies, and punches, etc. They are in general difficult to machine and grind. They may be hardened in either oil or air.

Oil hardening tool and die steels are usually medium in manganese, with tungsten, chromium, and vanadium optional. They are generally considered as the non-deforming types and retain size well during hardening. They wear sufficiently for the average tool steel application and are today the most popular type of tool steel.

Air hardening steels for applications similar to those of the regular oil hardening material are developments of recent years and are outstanding in their freedom from distortion and cracks during hardening.

High speed steels are generally used as cutting tools, tool bits, drills, milling cutters, etc. They are characterized by their ability to hold their hardness and a sharp cutting edge even at dull red temperatures. Tungsten and molybdenum are required elements with chromium, vanadium, cobalt giving additional properties as already mentioned. They are also used at times for hot working dies and sometimes for regular cold working tools, dies, etc.

Hot working steels are a distinct group, devoted usually to the forming or working of hot metals. Various types are especially adapted for heat resistance, wear resistance, toughness, and hardness characteristics.

Stainless Steels

When some of the nickel is replaced by chromium, marked corrosion-resisting properties are obtained, the chromium sometimes reaching 18 percent, along with 8 percent of nickel in steels of the stainless group. These steels are extensively used for castings of hydraulic machinery, as shown in Fig. 7, while some typical aircraft fittings made from stampings are shown in Fig. 8.

Heat-resisting steels are called for in practically all furnace work, though principally for the smaller parts of mechanical stokers in conjunction with heat-resisting iron castings for the larger ones. Other examples are found in such work as aero- and Diesel-engine valves and steam superheaters, where not only is the material required to possess high strength, but what is more important, to maintain that strength and to avoid scaling at high temperatures. The breakage of a valve in any over-head valve engine would probably wreck it. Chromium and nickel are the principal alloying elements of these steels, which have an average tensile strength of 100,000 lbs. at high temperature. When cast they are rather softer and weaker.

Corrosion-resisting steels are popularly known as stainless, though they actually fall into several different classes for different varieties of work. Strength and hardness are comparable with the heat-resisting steels, but they are hardened and can give considerably greater strength by appropriate heat-treatment. The carbon content averages about 0.30 percent, and the principal alloy is about 13 percent chromium. These steels can be softened for machining. Parts for hydraulic and pumping machinery and equipment for the chemical and allied industries are made of them. All high-nickel-chromium steels are high cost and call for very careful handling, so that for the most part forgings and castings come direct from the steel-makers, whose directions in regard to heat-treatment and handling must be followed closely.

Although airplane engine valves may be working for several hours of merciless hammering at temperatures which would destroy any ordinary steel, a high nickel-chromium steel will stand up. There is no possibility of hardening occurring in cooling down from the high temperature at which the valve may often function. The resistance to scaling at high temperatures, is also a very valuable property.

Valves

Valves made from such steels are used in airplane engines and in the engines of automobiles and trucks.

In acid-resisting steel there is 18 percent of chromium and 8 percent of nickel in addition to some other alloys. It makes strong castings, and it will resist most acids and sea-water, but under conditions which might induce inter-crystalline corrosion there is another grade known as *Staybrite F.D.P.* available, which is also a heat-resisting steel, while *Staybrite F.M.B.*, which is 18/8 chro-

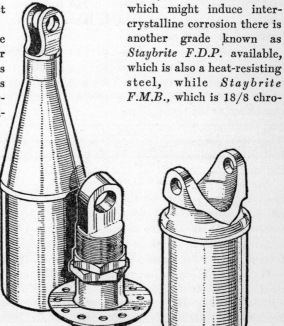

Fig. 8. Typical parts in stainless steel such as these, machined from steel stampings, are largely used in modern aircraft manufacture: they are particularly noteworthy for their high corrosion-resisting properties.

IRON & STEEL INSTITUTE TYPE NUMBERS FOR STAINLESS STEELS

TYPE NO.	CARBON	CHROME	NICKEL	OTHER ELEMENTS
301	.09–.20	16.00–18.00	7.00– 9.00	Mn. 1.25 Max.
302	.08–.20	18.00–20.00	8.00–10.00	Mn. 1.25 "
302–B	.08–.20	18.00–20.00	8.00–10.00	Mn. 1.25 " Si. 2.00–3.00
303	.20 Max.	18.00–20.00	8.00–10.00	S. or Se. .07 Min., or Mo. .80 Max.
304	.08 "	18.00–20.00	8.00–10.00	Mn. 2.00 Max.
308	.08 "	19.00–22.00	8.00–10.00	Mn. 2.00 "
309	.20 "	22.00–26.00	12.00–14.00	
309–S	.08 "	22.00–26.00	12.00–14.00	
310	.25 "	24.00–26.00	19.00–21.00	
311	.25 "	19.00–21.00	24.00–26.00	
312	.25 "	27.00–31.00	8.00–10.00	
315	.15 "	17.00–19.00	7.00– 9.50	Cu. 1.00–1.50, Mo. 1.00–1.50
316	.10 "	16.00–18.00	14.00 Max.	Mo. 2.00–3.00
317	.10 "	18.00–20.00	14.00 "	Mo. 3.00–4.00
321	.10 "	17.00–20.00	7.00–10.00	Ti (Min.) 4 x Carbon
325	.25 "	7.00–10.00	19.00–23.00	Cu. 1.00–1.50
327	.25 "	25.00–30.00	3.00– 5.00	
329	.10 "	25.00–30.00	3.00– 5.00	Mo. 1.00–1.50
330	.25 "	14.00–16.00	33.00–36.00	
347	.10 "	17.00–20.00	8.00–12.00	Cb. (Min.) 10 x Carbon
403	.15 "	11.50–13.00		Turbine Quality
405	.08 "	11.50–13.50		Al. .10–.20
406	.15 "	12.00–14.00		Al. 4.00–4.50
410	.15 "	10.00–14.00		
414	.15 "	10.00–14.00	2.00 Max.	
416	.15 "	12.00–14.00		S. or Se. .07 Min., or Mo. .60 Max.
418	.15 "	12.00–14.00		W. 2.50–3.50
420	Over .15	12.00–14.00		
420–F	" .15	12.00–14.00		S. or Se. .07 Min., or Mo. .60 Max.
430	.12 Max.	14.00–18.00		
430–F	.12 "	14.00–18.00		S. or Se. .07 Min., or Mo. .60 Max.
431	.15 "	14.00–18.00	2.00 Max.	
438	.12 "	16.00–18.00		W. 2.50–3.50
439	.50–.65	8.00		W. 8.00
440	Over .12	14.00–18.00		
441	" .15	14.00–18.00	2.00 Max.	
442	.35 Max.	18.00–23.00		
446	.35 "	23.00–30.00		
501	Over .10	4.00– 6.00		Often Mo. .50 Max.
502	.10 Max.	4.00– 6.00		Mo. .50 Max., Cb. .50 Max.

mium-nickel steel with the addition of 3 percent of molybdenum, will resist high acid concentrations and elevated temperatures. Heat-resisting steels as such, however, are plain chromium steels of the *ferritic* type, and at ordinary temperatures they tend to be brittle, but at the elevated temperatures at which they are intended to be used they become ductile, so that this condition disappears.

It is sometimes possible for certain parts of a machine to be produced equally well from an alloy iron casting, a steel casting, or a steel forging, the final choice being decided after estimating the cost of each method and the facilities available for the necessary machining.

Steel is generally used for cast parts where an iron casting of reasonable weight would lack the necessary strength and where a forging would be too costly or impracticable to machine.

Steel casting, as shown in Fig. 9, is much more difficult than iron casting, and is seldom undertaken by any but specialists. This applies particularly to alloy steels. A limited amount of work is done in manganese steel, which is both strong and tough.

Except for stainless-steel castings for hydraulic machinery foundry steel has a carbon content of about

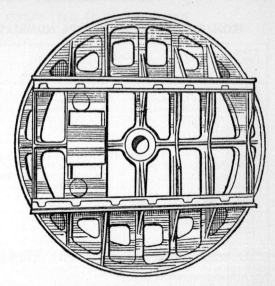

Fig. 9. Cast-steel turn-table for a 6-ton mobile crane. Casting such parts in steel is much more difficult than iron casting.

0.3 percent and usually 2–3 percent of nickel, and the tensile strength may be anything from 30 to 90 tons and the B.H.N. 200–450, though the strength and the more important property, toughness, depend to a very large extent upon the foundry work and subsequent heat-treatment to bring out the properties of this material to the fullest extent.

The addition of chromium gives the metal corrosion-resisting properties without its being *stainless,* and adds hardness and tensile strength to the toughness and ductility imparted by the nickel, the ratio of nickel to chromium being about 2½ to 1. The addition of a small percentage of vanadium gives ductility.

APPLICATIONS OF CAST NICKEL ALLOY STEELS

REQUIREMENTS.	TYPICAL APPLICATIONS.	RECOMMENDED STEEL.
Highly Ductile Steels, Resistant to Shock and Fatigue at Atmospheric and Low Temperatures.	Locomotive frames, castings for mining, excavating and steel mill machinery, ship castings.	Low Carbon 2% Nickel Steel.
With somewhat higher carbon than A, increased elastic properties and strength can be obtained.	Miscellaneous railroad castings, large gears not subjected to severe abrasion, crusher frames, tractor and power shovel frames.	Medium Carbon 2% Nickel Steel.
Moderate Cost with Strength and Ductility Superior to Carbon Steels. These steels replace carbon steels when the mechanical properties desired do not warrant the use of higher nickel steels.	For stressed members of tractors, motor trucks, road building machinery, electrical machinery, etc.	Pearlitic Nickel-manganese Steel.
Superior Mechanical Properties in Normalised Steel Castings. For light and medium sections.	Oil well tools, sheaves, sprockets, tractor shoes, gears, cams, etc.	Nickel-Chromium Steel. Nickel-Molybdenum Steel.
For medium and heavy sections.	Castings for locomotives, rolling mill machinery, highly stressed gears, power shovels and other machinery subjected to rugged service.	Nickel-Chromium-Molybdenum Steel. Nickel-Molybdenum Steel.
Quenched and Tempered Steel Castings with High Strength, Hardness and Wear Resistance. For light and heavy sections.	Hardened gears, cams, rollers, sprockets, conveyor chain links, etc., oil well tools, sheaves (these castings are sometimes differentially hardened).	Nickel-Chromium Steel. Nickel-Chromium-Molybdenum Steel.
For medium and heavy sections.	Highly stressed gears, pinions, racks, rollers, sprockets and miscellaneous machine parts.	Nickel-Chromium-Molybdenum Steel.
Abrasion-Resistant Castings. For light and medium sections.	Particularly adapted for castings which are to be differentially hardened, for example: power shovel teeth, impact hammers. Ball and tube mill liner plates, ore chute liners and other parts not subjected to high impact.	Nickel-Chromium Steel. Nickel-Chromium-Molybdenum Steel. Nickel-Chromium-Molybdenum Steel.
For medium and heavy sections.	Crusher jaws, dredge pumps, impact hammers, dipper teeth, etc.	Nickel-Chromium-Molybdenum Steel.
Resistance to abrasion under heavy pressure and/or impact. Retention of ductility after exposure to temperatures up to 1100° F. (600° C.). Weldability. For light, medium or heavy sections.	Hot bed run-out tables, forming dies for lap welded pipe, draw bench chain for butt weld tube mills, heavy crusher rolls, jaws and liners, railroad crossings.	Austenitic Nickel-Manganese Steel.
Strength and "Creep" Resistance at Elevated Temperatures.	Valves and fittings, return bends, superheater and heat exchanger heads, cement clinker chain.	Nickel-Chromium-Molybdenum Steel with Carbon .30–.40.

NON-FERROUS METALS

BRASS, bronze, and aluminum are all commonly used in engineering work. Aluminum castings are sometimes quite large; bronze castings, except for certain parts of hydraulic machinery, comparatively small. Brass, except in the form of high-tensile brass, commonly known as manganese bronze, is usually produced as bar stock for screw machine work, or strips for drawing operations. The cartridge case is a familiar example. Brass suitable for this class of work is often designated as *cartridge* brass. Copper may be produced as bar stock chiefly for switch gear and other electrical work. It is also produced as extruded sections.

In the shop, copper is used principally as strips and sheets for fabrication by welding and brazing into equipment for the chemical and allied industries. Some small parts are also made of nickel, though the more important use is as a cupro-nickel alloy, which is dealt with later.

Brass is an alloy of copper and zinc roughly in the proportions of 70 copper and 30 zinc. Commercial brasses are used for a wide variety of small components of machines, electrical equipment, wireless apparatus, fuses, and ordnance work.

Brass is a weak material, and the properties of the more generally used brasses are summarized in the table on page 82. Alloyed with a small percentage of tin, a 60:40 basis metal is often referred to as naval brass. Practically all these metals are produced to standard specifications, and a great deal of light brass production can be done from extruded sections by simply cutting off the required length and drilling and tapping one or two holes.

The more essential particulars of the brasses used for the general run of production work are given in the table on page 82, but in connection with all drawing and similar operations it is important to note that even though the metal be supplied specially for this work, any cold working on brass, whether by rolling, pressing, stamping or drawing, will harden it. If this is the final condition, it may be of some advantage, but when there are several operations on the one piece, it is nearly always necessary to anneal the metal between operations. This is generally done by heating to a dull red and allowing to cool slowly.

For press work the risk of defects from cold working no longer arises. Like steel, the desirable property is free cutting; without it, brass, essentially a soft metal, is by no means easy to machine. The remedy is a small percentage of lead. Care must be taken that material for rapid machining is of the correct hardness, because, while the resistance to cutting increases with the hardness, soft rod bends and causes chatter and digging-in of the tools; cold working may be necessary to give brass sufficient hardness before machining, also production depends to a large extent on the use of suitable tools.

Manganese Bronze

Although brass does not deteriorate rapidly if exposed to the atmosphere, it is not in a sense a corrosion-resisting metal, and it is therefore rarely used in marine or hydraulic

USES OF BRASSES OF DIFFERENT COMPOSITION

NAME OF ALLOY.	APPROX. COMPOSITION BY WEIGHT.			PRINCIPAL USES.
	Copper %.	Zinc %.	Other Elements.	
Gilding Metal	90	10	—	Architectural and other decorative metal-work.
Cartridge Brass	70	30	—	For drawn articles, deep pressings and applications where very high ductility allied with strength is required.
65:35 Brass	65	35	—	A ductile alloy for cold presswork.
Rivet Metal	63	37	—	A typical alloy for general cold presswork.
Yellow Metal or Muntz Metal	60	40	—	For brass sheets and articles which do not experience much cold work during manufacture. This alloy works well when hot.
Brass for Hot-stamping, Free Cutting, Casting, etc.	58	40½	1½% lead	Casts well and is easily hot stamped or extruded. Machines well.
High-tensile Brass ("Manganese Bronze")	58	38	Manganese, aluminium, iron, nickel, tin, approx. total 4%	High-tensile alloys for casting, extrusion or hot stamping.

work. The exception is manganese bronze, which casts quite well and makes good forgings and stampings. The percentage of manganese is relatively small, being as a rule between 2 and 4 percent, with about 2½ percent of aluminum added to a 60:40 copper-zinc base.

The forged material has a tensile strength of about 43 tons and a B.H.N. of 160–170. There is usually a small inclusion of iron, and this constituent is nearly always present in high-tensile brasses. The manganese has the effect of increasing the amount of iron which can be taken into solution. A small percentage of aluminum adds to the strength and resistance to corrosion, the latter being important in hydraulic machinery. Nickel is sometimes included, but it adds to the cost of the material without giving any very marked improvement in the physical properties.

Temper-Hardening

Nickel, zinc, and aluminum are alloyed with some brasses to give a property known as *temper-hardening*. A 72:6:1½:20½ copper-nickel-aluminum-zinc composition when softened by quenching from 850 deg. C. has a tensile strength of 23 tons, but heat-treatment at 500 deg. C. will increase this to 36 tons, and further heat-treatment after cold working will bring it up to 48 tons. These alloys are largely used for small gears and pinions. The effect of cold work on cartridge brass is shown in the table on this page.

As opposed to brass, which is used principally in bar or extruded sections for machining, and in sheet and strip for blanking and forming, bronze is an alloy of copper and tin which is usually cast. The castings are generally small, except for some parts of hydraulic machines. Owing to their great strength, resistance to corrosion, and resistance to heat, considerable use is now made of alloy bronzes. Various percentages of aluminum and nickel, with tin as a hardener are added.

High-strength bronze castings are made up from special formulas, but a commonly-used mixture is 88:10:2 copper-tin-zinc, commonly known as gun metal.

Up to 5 percent of nickel can be substituted for tin or added direct, and it improves the physical properties. For work which is subsequently plated, the fine grain of nickel bronze helps the coating to stick to the metal. Fig. 10 shows a good example of the highest class of work produced from bronze castings. The worm itself is of suitable alloy steel polished after grinding, while the wheel with which it mates is nickel bronze produced as a centrifugal casting to give it the maximum density.

Concerning alloy bronzes in general, if 5 percent of the tin content of gun metal, is replaced by 5 percent of nickel, the strength, toughness, and ductility are improved, and the tendency of this material to be brittle is removed. More important still, is that this simple alloy can, with quite simple heat-treatment, be raised in strength to a tensile strength of about 37 tons with a B.H.N. of 170, which is considerably harder than the average. This treatment consists of heating for two or three hours at 760 deg. C., followed by rapid cooling. This again is followed by a re-heat to 500 deg. C., and again rapid cooling, the properties of the metal being then comparable with high-tensile brass (man-

CONDITION.	PROOF STRESS (0.10%). TONS PER SQ. IN.	MAX. STRESS. TONS PER SQ. IN.	ELONGATION ON 2 IN. %.	BRINELL HARDNESS NUMBER.
Chill castings (*i.e.*, strip ingots prior to rolling)	6	16	60–70	60
Hard-rolled sheet	Over 25	30–40	10–15	150–200
Sheet annealed after rolling	6	20–23	65–75	60

ganese bronze). There are no practical methods of surface-hardening bronze.

Except for electrical work, where electrical conductivity is important, bronze is used for two main purposes: a wearing part such as a bushing for which phosphor-bronze is largely used; and parts of hydraulic machinery and marine equipment, where resistance to corrosion is the main consideration. Phosphor-bronze bushings are largely produced from rod, although bearing shells are generally cast. If they are lined with bearing metal, an 88:10:2 copper-tin-zinc composition serves very well, but where the shaft turns on the bronze, a leaded bearing alloy is required.

The low-nickel bronzes with a nickel content below 5 percent are suitable for most bronze castings as used in engineering, but when the nickel content is between 5 and 10 percent the full benefit of the nickel is developed only after the appropriate heat-treatment to bring about temper-hardening of the metal.

The high-nickel bronzes—that is, those with a nickel content of over 10 percent—are used in high-pressure steam fittings, and to resist the corrosive conditions of chemical liquors. These alloys, while they lack ductility, retain both their strength and hardness at high temperatures, and they are only surpassed in their corrosion-

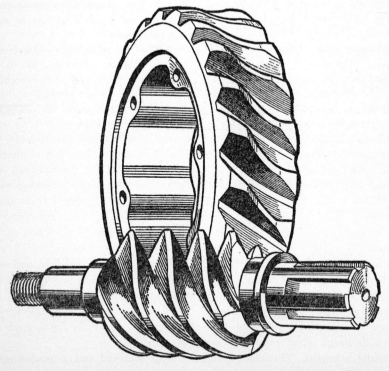

Fig. 10. An alloy bronze worm-wheel, a good example of high-class bronze casting. The worm itself is of polished alloy steel.

resisting properties by the cupro-nickel alloys such as Monel metal.

To cut costs, alloy cast irons are used in many cases in place of bronze. Silicon-copper, which is a tin-free bronze, is also extensively used. A copper-rich alloy of the solid solution class, with about 95 percent of copper to which is added silicon and manganese, combines the strength of medium carbon steel with the corrosion-resisting properties of copper, and casts very well. Its high tensile strength and, what is more important in this connection, its high fatigue limit, makes excellent bolts; and these, with the various rolled sections available, place an exceedingly useful material in the hands of the engineer, especially for any outdoor equipment.

Uses of Copper

Although copper has the corrosion-resisting properties of brass and bronze, it is generally too weak and soft for machine parts. Except for small tubing for which it is the best material, it is used in the form of plates and sheets for fabrication by welding or brazing into low-pressure steam apparatus and equipment.

Small parts for electrical apparatus are either machined from bar stock or worked from strips in the same way as similar parts are made from brass.

Arsenic raises the temperature at which softening upon annealing occurs, and it improves the strength of the metal at high temperatures. Hence the use of arsenical copper for locomotive fireboxes. Cast copper is low in tensile strength. The chief point to note in copper is the hardening that results from cold working, which calls

for annealing. In doing this it is essential to insure that the whole mass of metal reaches 500 deg. C., or just below dull red heat, before being allowed to cool slowly.

Cupro-Nickel Alloys

The cupro-nickel alloys are among the most costly metals used to any extent in engineering work, but they are exceedingly useful, as they combine the strength of good-quality steel with a practical immunity from corrosion under any conditions, or deterioration at high temperatures. So, in addition to being used for equipment in the chemical and food industries, they are found in the vital parts of high-pressure steam equipment, for turbine blading, pump parts, and condenser tubes for severe working conditions.

While the term cupro-nickel alloy implies a metal with roughly 30 percent of copper and 60 percent of nickel, the more usual commercial form is Monel metal, which is roughly a 70:29 nickel-copper alloy with small percentages of iron, manganese, silicon, and carbon. It is not a manufactured metal in the usual sense, as it is refined from copper-bearing nickel ores found in Canada by the International Nickel Co., and takes its name from a former president of that company.

It is available in rod, bar, and sheet, and is worked and machined much in the manner of mild steel, though it is hard on the dies in any cold-working operations, and calls for a good deal of annealing.

This material makes good forgings in any shape, but it is difficult to handle in the forge, as it is readily af-

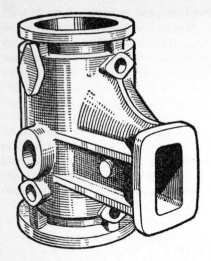

Fig. 11. An aluminum exhaust manifold for a marine engine: the lightness of the metal makes it a useful substitute for bronze in high-speed craft.

fected by scale, by too prolonged heating, or by excessive heat, the upper safe limit being 1180 dcg. C. Exceeding this is very likely to cause cracks.

Aluminum

Unlike most primary metals which are reduced from ore by simple smelting, the production of aluminum from bauxite is a complicated process, calling for large amounts of cheap electricity. Hence its reduction to the ingot stage is carried on where hydroelectric power is available and cheap, the principal plants in this country being at Niagara Falls, the Tennessee Valley, and in the Pacific northwest at Grand Coulee Dam. The sheet, tube, bar, and extruded sections are produced in rolling mills by more or less orthodox methods.

From these the smaller parts for the aircraft industry are produced by methods applicable to most non-ferrous metals. This grade of aluminum, in common with that used for domestic hollow ware, etc., is a pure, soft metal of no great strength, lightness being the primary consideration. Even lighter metal can be produced by means of alloying with magnesium.

In engine work, however, where the parts are sand-castings, die-castings, forgings, or stampings, the materials, while still basically aluminum, are of a wholly different nature, being alloyed for strength, resistance to heat, wear, or corrosion. In the latter use, aluminum has not the corrosion-resisting properties of suitably-alloyed bronzes, although it is sometimes used as a substitute for bronze on light, high-speed craft, because of its lightness (Fig. 11).

In the form of sand-castings, the commonest use of aluminum is seen in the automobile-engine crankcase (Fig. 12) though the present-day motorcycle crankcase is usually an assembly of two or three die-castings readily recognized by a smooth, satiny finish. For the average run of sand-castings the aluminum is usually alloyed with about 2½ percent of copper and as much as 13 percent of zinc. Aluminum alloyed with silicon is stronger and casts cleaner into intricate sections, but tends toward softness, and is difficult to machine by reason of its somewhat sticky nature. In common with other metals, aluminum for any particular work is bought by the purchasing department to definite specifications.

A very important part of the present-day work in aluminum, however, is in die-castings. Die-casting consists, briefly, of the pouring of molten metal into a hardened steel die shaped to the part and squeezing it down in the die by a plunger. The result is that a relatively complicated part like a piston can either be produced exactly to size, or so near it that the only machining required, other than drilling and tapping a few holes, is a light grinding operation. For this class of work silicon alloys are generally used.

A large amount of work is done in the silicon alloys with such additions as have been noted, but the copper alloys combine good machinability with good mechanical properties, and they can be improved by heat-treatment, which raises both the strength and the ductility.

Alloy 218 commonly designated as "Y" alloy, contains 4 percent of copper, 2 percent of nickel, and $1\frac{1}{2}$ percent of magnesium. Having good heat resisting properties, it is extensively used for pistons and cylinder-heads. It machines well, but it is not easy to cast, and is somewhat prone to porosity and lacks tensile strength.

Alloy 226 has better properties in this direction. It contains 4.5 percent of copper with small inclusions of silicon and iron. When heat-treated, the T-35 alloy is one of the strongest casting metals; it can be treated to increase its ductility and render it suitable for aircraft-engine crankcases, for which it is extensively used. For dense, pressure-tight castings it may be desirable to add as much as 12 percent of copper with small inclusions of silicon, iron, zinc, and tin, these being the alloying elements of Alloy 226, a very fluid metal which

machines and finishes extremely well.

Magnesium is the main inclusion of very light metals. Most of these, such as Alpax and Elektron, are proprietary metals produced under patents and by a process known to the trade as *modification*. Elektron is nearly half the weight of ordinary commercial aluminum, and, with a specific gravity of 1.81, is the lightest metal used in engineering work. The cylinder and piston shown in Figs. 12 and 14 are typical of present-day work in aluminum.

High-Strength Alloys

Although there is popularly supposed to be a good deal of mystery behind the high-strength metals of the aluminum group, they are really only a specialized product, as are the stainless steels. Their production here was of little importance till the introduc-

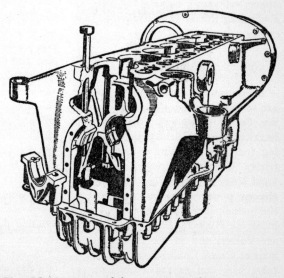

Fig. 12. An automobile engine crankcase in aluminum alloy in the form of a sand-casting. The alloy generally used is copper and zinc, though silicon is sometimes employed.

PROPERTIES OF ALUMINUM

ALLOY DESIGNATION.	CHIEF ALLOYING METALS.	FORM OF TEST SPECIMEN.	ULTIMATE TENSILE STRENGTH (TONS/SQ. IN.)	ELONGATION ON 2 IN. %.	BRINELL HARDNESS.
3L5	2½–3% Cu 12½–14½% Zn	Sand cast Chill cast	9.0–11.0 11.0–14.0	2.0– 4.0 3.0– 8.0	60– 65 65– 70
4L11	6–8% Cu	Sand cast Chill cast	7.5– 9.0 9.0–11.5	1.5– 2.5 3.0– 5.0	60– 70 65– 70
3L8	11–13% Cu	Sand cast Chill cast	7.0– 8.0 9.0–11.0	.0– 1.0 .0– 1.5	75– 90 80– 90
BA/40D	10–13% Si	Sand cast, modified Chill cast, modified	10.5–11.0 13.0–14.0	5.0– 8.0 8.0–15.0	50– 55 55– 60
BA/40J	7½–8½% Si	Sand cast Chill cast	9.0–10.0 11.0–12.0	6.0–11.0 13.0–20.0	42– 47 45– 50
CS/16	4% Cu, 3% Si	Sand cast Chill cast	8.0– 9.0 10.5–12.5	2.0– 4.0 6.0–10.0	55– 70 55– 70
"Y" alloy	4% Cu 2% Ni 1½% Mg	Sand cast, heat-treated Chill cast, heat-treated	14.0–15.0 18.0–20.0	.0– 1.0 2.0– 4.0	95–105 95–105
BA/23	1¼% Mg	Sand cast, heat-treated Chill cast, heat-treated	12.0–13.0 16.0–17.5	2.0– 3.0 12.0–20.0	70– 80 75– 85
BA/40M	12% Si .4% Mn .3% Mg	Sand cast, heat-treated Chill cast, heat-treated	15.5–18.0 19.0–22.0	.0– 1.0 .5– 1.5	95–105 100–115
BA/5	5–6% Cu	Sand cast, heat-treated Chill cast, heat-treated	14.0–15.5 19.0–21.0	2.0– 3.0 8.0–13.0	75– 85 80– 90

tion of a high-strength alloy, known as Duralumin, some 20 years ago.

While the specialized production of these alloys is comparable to the production of the alloy steels, in the main, it is adding the correct proportions of copper, silicon, nickel, iron, magnesium, and one or two other elements to produce material suitable for sand-castings, die-castings, forgings, etc. Duralumin, for instance, has 4 per cent of copper, 0.5 percent of manganese, 0.3 percent of silicon and 0.2 percent of iron in its composition. It must not be assumed that aluminum is mainly a casting metal. Both in pure aluminum and in the alloys there are strip, bar, sheet, and extruded sections for the production of small parts by the usual machining methods, and alloys for forgings and drop-forgings.

Some airplane engine crankcases which might, in the machined state, be assumed to have originated in a casting, are actually formed as a forging, as, in common with other metals, the forging is generally the denser and stronger form. A familiar example is the engine connecting-rod, which as an H-section drop forging (see Fig. 15),

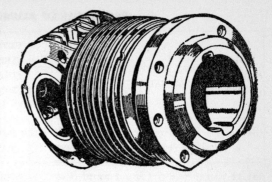

Fig. 13. This cylinder is a typical example of present-day work in aluminum alloy. Magnesium is the commonest inclusion for extra light weight aluminums.

can be produced actually stronger than one of steel. This makes possible a considerably longer connecting-rod to reduce the piston friction which results from a short rod, without adding to the weight of the reciprocating parts of the engine.

With the exception of Monel metal and nickel silvers, which have already been discussed, the only white metals which are of interest to the engineer are those used for the lining of bearing shells. These are often referred to as babbitt. This class of metal, of which a small amount is required to line a bearing shell, is sold in different grades suitable for specific purposes. With the exception of some new alloys of cadmium, they are, almost without exception, tin-base metals which are suitably hardened by a copper inclusion and toughened by an addition of antimony.

Their ability to withstand heavier loads than

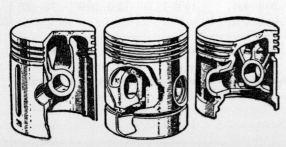

Fig. 14. Group of aluminum alloy die-cast pistons for automobile engines.

those for which the usual tin-base metals are suitable and to run under higher-temperature conditions are the reasons for the extending use of the cadmium alloys in airplane-engine work, as very light bearings for severe duty can be made by lining steel tube with cadmium metals.

POWDER METALLURGY

METALLIC or metal powder methods are used to make products which cannot be made in any other way or which cannot be produced as well or as cheaply by other methods, even when other methods are possible. Metal powders are used in the following ways:

1. In fabricating metals which have a very high melting point.

2. In producing combinations (these are not true alloys) which retain, to a marked extent, the individual characteristics of each of its constituent metals.

3. In combinations of metals and other materials—non metals.

4. To produce products of unusual structure.

5. To produce products of exact dimensions without elaborate machining operations.

6. To form a protective metal coating.

Powder metallurgy really goes back more than a hundred years to 1829 when Walloston showed that platinum powder could be pressed into a briquette and fused into a workable ingot, by subjecting it to temperatures several hundred degrees below the melting point of the metal, which permits hot forging and manipulation of the metal by rolling and drawing. The process was also applied to iridium which also has a very high melting point.

In the search for a really satisfactory filament for electric lamps during the early part of the present century, the method was applied to tungsten with very satisfactory results. The true melting point of this metal is 3400 deg. C. or 6152 deg. F. but sufficient welding together of the particles of the powdered metal was found to take place at much lower temperatures and the product could then be drawn into very fine wire which found extensive use in the form of lamp filaments. Other metals with very high melting points are molybdenum and tantalum. These metals, or rather products made from them, find extensive use in the chemical, electrical, and communication fields. Powder metallurgy methods are also applicable to them.

When two metals are melted together they form an alloy which frequently has characteristics different from either. A good example is the alloy of copper and aluminum called duralumin. Both copper and aluminum are soft and weak metals in their pure state and neither is hardened or toughened by heat treatment. In fact copper will harden from cold working and is softened by heating to a red heat and quenching. Yet duralumin can be successfully heat treated till it has the strength of steel. Brass has definite physical characteristics which differ from either of its constituent metals, copper and zinc.

On the other hand, metal powder combinations, curiously enough, often possess the original characteristics of the constituent metals in the direct proportions in which they make up the composition. This is true of powder combinations of copper and tungsten, or silver with nickel, tungsten, molybdenum, or graphite. The fusing and pitting of the copper electrodes of electric welders was overcome by using a powder combination of copper (because of its low cost and high conductivity) and tungsten (which resists the tendency to fuse). Another field which is being explored with very satisfactory results is that of the electric circuit breaker.

It is perhaps in the third field, mentioned above, that the machinist should be most interested—namely the use of powders for combining metals with 1 1-metals, to form some very useful products. Perhaps the most important commercially is the cemented carbon carbide such as *carbaloy*. These carbides are being used to an ever increasing extent in high speed cutting tools, which are doing so much to increase the productivity of machine tools and also, of course, the productivity of the worker who operates these tools. It is the productivity of this combination, tool and operator, which has enabled the American industrial system to support the high wages that prevail in this country.

Structurally the cemented carbides consist of tiny particles of tungsten carbide cemented together with cobalt. Tungsten carbide is one of the hardest materials yet produced by man, being almost as hard as the diamond. It has one disadvantage, however, and this is its brittleness, which causes it to break, under shock, very easily. For the machining of metals, where the tool is subjected to severe punishment, this is a serious drawback. By a powder combination of the carbide and the cobalt, the hardness of the former is nicely supported by the toughness of the latter to produce a very valuable product.

Grinding wheels made by a combination of diamond dust and powdered brass are used to make and keep sharpened these same hard carbide cutting tools.

The fourth field of powder metallurgy is of great interest to the machinist as its development forecasts great changes in machine shop practice. The employment of metal powders permits the formation of unusual structural effects which are impossible to get by the conventional methods of casting or forging.

As an example of this use of powders, one of the most interesting is that of the porous metal bearing. The bearing consists of copper and tin to which has been added a small percentage of graphite. These are combined as powders with a lubricant and pressed into the shape wanted. Heat treatment or sintering under suitable conditions brings about a diffusion and alloying of the copper and tin and produces a porous structure which has proved to be of great advantage in bearings. Later they are brought to exact size in dies and impregnated with lubricant. The performance of these bearings in actual use is truly remarkable. The oil is carried to the bearing surface directly through the pores of the metal. In some cases it is possible to impregnate the bearing with oil sufficient to last during the life of the bearing.

Another product incorporating the porous structure idea is the porous metal filter. Electric motor brushes made from flake copper and flake graphite have especially good conducting properties in the direction of their length.

The forming of machine and other parts directly to shape and size without machining is also possible with metal powders, and this should be of great interest to the shop man. At present, due in part to the great cost of the dies and presses required to mold them, the parts are all relatively small, but it seems safe to predict that improvements will be made and cost reduced so that larger and larger products will be manufactured—molded to exact size and form much as are the great variety of plastics.

An excellent example of products now made and used is the oil pump gear used in the Oldsmobile automobile. The steel powder is placed in a mold, subjected to a heat treatment under a pressure of some fifteen tons, and the gear is finished ready for use. Contrast this with the usual method of forging or casting the blank and machining it into the finished product. Besides, the pressed gear seems better in every way.

The use of metal powders in producing protective coatings is not new. The use of red lead, white lead, zinc oxide, copper, and aluminum, all in powder form as ingredients of paint, is quite well known. Also the cementation process used in calorizing (with aluminum) and sherardizing (with zinc) are not new. Here the powder coating diffuses into the underlying metal, forming an alloy bond integral with it.

A third method of coating metals as well as other materials with a protective covering makes use of the metal spray gun. The feed metal may be a powder or solid wire either of which becomes liquid as it leaves the gun and solidifies on the sprayed article in the form of a coating.

A fourth method, of course, is the plating by electricity of a protective metal coating onto the article. Nickel, copper, silver, and gold have been used for a long time. Cadmium and chromium have more recently been found adaptable to this method.

WEIGHT OF IRON AND STEEL SHEETS

No. of Gage	THICKNESS BY BIRMINGHAM GAGE			No. of Gage	THICKNESS BY AMERICAN (BROWN & SHARPE'S) GAGE		
	Thickness, Inches	Weight per Sq. Ft.			Thickness, Inches	Weight per Sq. Ft.	
		Iron	Steel			Iron	Steel
0000	.454	18.16	18.52	0000	.46	18.40	18.77
000	.425	17.00	17.34	000	.4096	16.38	16.71
00	.38	15.20	15.50	00	.3648	14.59	14.88
0	.34	13.60	13.87	0	.3249	13.00	13.26
1	.3	12.00	12.24	1	.2893	11.57	11.80
2	.284	11.36	11.59	2	.2576	10.30	10.51
3	.259	10.36	10.57	3	.2294	9.18	9.36
4	.238	9.52	9.71	4	.2043	8.17	8.34
5	.22	8.80	8.98	5	.1819	7.28	7.42
6	.203	8.12	8.28	6	.1620	6.48	6.61
7	.18	7.20	7.34	7	.1443	5.77	5.89
8	.165	6.60	6.73	8	.1285	5.14	5.24
9	.148	5.92	6.04	9	.1144	4.58	4.67
10	.134	5.36	5.47	10	.1019	4.08	4.16
11	.12	4.80	4.90	11	.0907	3.63	3.70
12	.109	4.36	4.45	12	.0808	3.23	3.30
13	.095	3.80	3.88	13	.0720	2.88	2.94
14	.083	3.32	3.39	14	.0641	2.56	2.62
15	.072	2.88	2.94	15	.0571	2.28	2.33
16	.065	2.60	2.65	16	.0508	2.03	2.07
17	.058	2.32	2.37	17	.0453	1.81	1.85
18	.049	1.96	2.00	18	.0403	1.61	1.64
19	.042	1.68	1.71	19	.0359	1.44	1.46
20	.035	1.40	1.43	20	.0320	1.28	1.31
21	.032	1.28	1.31	21	.0285	1.14	1.16
22	.028	1.12	1.14	22	.0253	1.01	1.03
23	.025	1.00	1.02	23	.0226	.904	.922
24	.022	.88	.898	24	.0201	.804	.820
25	.02	.80	.816	25	.0179	.716	.730
26	.018	.72	.734	26	.0159	.636	.649
27	.016	.64	.653	27	.0142	.568	.579
28	.014	.56	.571	28	.0126	.504	.514
29	.013	.52	.530	29	.0113	.452	.461
30	.012	.43	.490	30	.0100	.400	.408
31	.01	.40	.408	31	.0089	.356	.363
32	.009	.36	.367	32	.0080	.320	.326
33	.008	.32	.326	33	.0071	.284	.290
34	.007	.28	.286	34	.0063	.252	.257
35	.005	.20	.204	35	.0056	.224	.228

Specific gravity.................................Iron 7.7 Steel 7.854
Weight per cubic foot........................... " 480. " 489.6
Weight per cubic inch.......................... .2778 " .2833
As many gages differ, and even the thicknesses of a certain specified gage are not assumed the same by all manufacturers, orders for sheets and wires should always state the weight per square foot or the thickness in thousandths of an inch.

CHAPTER 3

THE LATHE

MECHANISM OF THE LATHE. SPEED ADJUSTMENT. GEARING. THE HEADSTOCK. MAINTENANCE. CENTERING. TOOLS. TOOL ANGLES. ATTACHMENTS. CHUCKS. COOLANTS. LUBRICANTS. METAL TURNING. AUTOMATICS. AIR-CHUCKS. TOOLS FOR AUTOMATIC LATHES.

THE most essential and universally used machine tool is the lathe. This is due to the fact that while the ordinary lathe is rarely built for a specific purpose, its versatility is so great that, with proper equipment, an endless variety of work can be machined at low cost. In addition to this feature, the ease of operation of a modern lathe is such that it can often compete with more expensive and complicated machines specially designed for mass-production purposes.

General Construction

Before considering any particular lathe in detail, it should be realized that the greatest amount of work is in the form of cylindrical parts. To turn this kind of work, it is merely necessary that conical holes be drilled in the middle of each end so that the work can be supported and revolved on pointed, hardened-steel centers. On the other hand, some work, generally of odd shape, does not lend itself to being supported in this way, and must be bolted or gripped directly to the face-plate or chuck which is mounted on the spindle. The methods are generally similar to those used for wood-turning, but whereas the chisel for wood-turning does the cutting by hand movement, the tool for turning metals is supported mechanically and moved along by power, except in certain hand operations.

Two alternative methods are employed for revolving the work. The first is by a cone pulley belt-drive, and the second by a geared head drive turned either by a belt or by an electric motor. Since a belt running over a single pulley would permit of only one speed being used for all diameters and types of work to be turned, therefore, three or four pulleys of different diameters made in one unit are driven from a similar unit on an overhead motion, known as a countershaft. Thus the belt can be moved from one size of pulley to another, to obtain a different speed. This arrangement is known as a cone-pulley drive. In the alternate method, the work speed is controlled by a cluster of gears in a gearbox, or headstock, which is made to engage in different speeds, in the same manner as the various speeds of a motor-car are obtained (see Fig. 1).

Just as various speeds are required to revolve the work at different speeds, the cutting tool must also move along. This movement is known as the *feed*, and is often obtained through a gear-drive by changing the position of the gears in a feed box (Fig. 1). On simple lathes a cone-pulley is employed for this purpose.

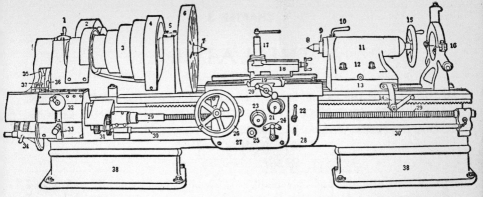

Fig. 1. Parts of an engine lathe: 1, rear bearing; 2, back gear case; 3, cone pulley; 4, face rear guard; 5, front bearing; 6, face plate; 7, live center; 8, dead center; 9, footstock spindle; 10, footstock spindle lock; 11, footstock; 12, footstock locking bolts; 13, footstock base; 14, arrangement for moving tailstock; 15, hand wheel for moving dead center; 16, steady rest; 17, tool post; 18, compound rest; 19, cross slide; 20, cross feed control handle; 21, power cross feed knob; 22, half nut engagement handle; 23, longitudinal power feed knob; 24, feed reverse handle; 25, gear stud; 26, longitudinal hand feed; 27, front apron; 28, rear apron; 29, lead screw; 30, power feed drive shaft; 31, change feed gears; 32, change feed box; 33, change gear handle; 34, change gear handle for compound gearing; 35, change gear handle; 36, change gear handle; 37, change gear handle; 38, bed.

To distinguish between the movement of the cutting tool along the bed, for turning a long bar, and that of the tool moving across the bed, the first movement, or *traverse*, is known as turning and the cross-bed movement as *facing*. Because both are power-operated they are designated as self-acting feed motions, and can be started or stopped by knobs which actuate friction clutches or similar devices in the *apron*.

The apron is another geared unit which slides on the ways of the bed with the *saddle*, this being a casting spanning the bed and carrying the cross-feed and *compound rest* to which the tool post and cutting tool are clamped.

In addition to revolving the work held in a chuck or against the face-plate, in the case of long bars, the work is supported on the *dead* and *live* centers of the lathe which are held respectively in the headstock and tailstock spindles.

Principal Parts of the Lathe

Referring now to the engine lathe shown in Fig. 1, the driving headstock will be seen bolted on the left-hand end of the bed; at the opposite end is the tailstock capable of being moved along the ways of the bed and clamped in any position, so that varying lengths of work can be accommodated between the centers. The tailstock can also be used for drilling operations when the work is held in a gripping device, known as a chuck, or bolted on the face-plate indicated in the reference.

Between the headstock and tailstock is the apron and saddle unit, while the feed gearbox is shown bolted to the

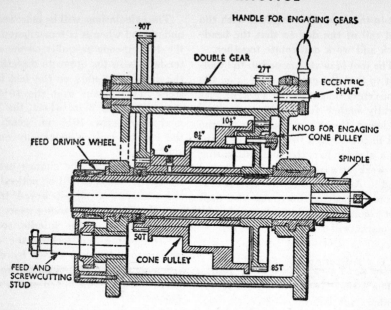

Fig. 2. Section through a representative headstock. Three fast speeds are given by movement of the belt on the cone, and these speeds may be reduced by making use of the back-gearing as explained in the text.

bed end, below the headstock. This box receives motion from a train of gears at the end of the headstock and transmits the various rates of feed by a long shaft at the front of the lathe called the *feed rod*. On most lathes a separate drive shaft for the feeds and another for the lead screw, retained exclusively for screw-cutting, are mounted along the front of the bed, but in the illustration, the splineway is cut into the screw, so that this one component serves both as a feed rod and a lead screw combination drive.

As a simple preliminary example of a lathe operation, assuming that the operator received a steel bar to turn, the first procedure is to move the tailstock along the bed into a position suitable for the length of work. The tailstock is then bolted to the bed and the bar located on the headstock cen-

ter, while the tailstock center is adjusted by the hand-wheel to support the opposite end of the bar. As this center does not normally revolve, care must be taken that it is not screwed up too tightly into the bar end, otherwise it will be burnt off or otherwise injured by the expansion and friction of the revolving bar against it. In addition, oil or grease must always be applied to the tailstock center before starting the lathe and in between operations.

It will be apparent that starting the lathe headstock spindle to revolve will not take the bar around with it unless there is some connection between the two parts, and for this purpose, previous to mounting between the centers, a crank arm called a *lathe dog* is clamped at the end of the bar adjacent to the face-plate of the headstock. A slot in the face-plate engages with the bent tail of the dog so that the headstock and work can rotate together.

The tool is next clamped in the toolpost so that the cutting edge is on the same center height as the work, or just slightly higher for finishing. If it is set lower, there is a tendency for the tool to chatter and in the case of turning a slender bar, the tool will spring the work upward and dig into it and bend it. Another thing to watch is that the tool does not overhang the toolpost excessively, or vibration and chatter marks will result on the work.

Adjusting the Speed

The lathe is now set up ready for turning, but before running the machine some instruction on the mechanism is required to prevent damage through inexperience of the various functions.

Fig. 2 shows a typical cone-pulley drive, giving a series of three fast speeds by step-by-step movement of the belt on the cone, and a means of reducing these speeds to a slower series by utilizing the back-gears, which will be more fully explained later. Thus, if the overhead countershaft is running at 200 r.p.m. and the diameter of the pulleys are respectively $10\frac{1}{2}$ in., $8\frac{1}{4}$ in., and 6 in. then the three fast speeds would be: $200 \times \frac{10\frac{1}{2}}{6} = 350$; $200 \times \frac{8\frac{1}{4}}{8\frac{1}{4}} = 200$; and $200 \times \frac{6}{10\frac{1}{2}} = 114$ r.p.m.; and the three slow speeds using the back gear ratio: $350 \times \frac{50}{90} \times \frac{27}{85} = 62$; $200 \times \frac{50}{90} \times \frac{27}{85} = 35$; and $114 \times \frac{50}{90} \times \frac{27}{85} = 21$ r.p.m.

The calculations will be more readily understood when it is remembered that the driving-cone assembly on the countershaft is in the opposite direction to the driven assembly on the fast headstock. This means that the $10\frac{1}{2}$ in. gear drives the 6 in. wheel, the 6 in. gear drives the $10\frac{1}{2}$ in. gear, and the $8\frac{1}{4}$ in. gear is driven by one of similar size.

To understand the change over of the speed range, it will be noticed that the cone-pulley is not keyed to the spindle. The front driving gear, however, is keyed on the spindle, so that by connecting and locking the cone-pulley to this gear, either by clamp screw or a spring-plunger, the spindle rotates at the same speed as the cone-pulley.

Back Gearing

When the fast range of speeds is in operation, the back gears are swung out of mesh with the spindle gears by means of an eccentric, but to effect a substantial speed reduction and increase the driving power of the lathe, the back gears are brought into engagement with those on the spindle, while the cone-pulley is disconnected from the front driving gear. This is necessary, for otherwise the two series of speeds will be locked together and this will throw the belt off the cone-pulley or countershaft and possibly injure the gears. The pinion on the spindle is attached to the cone, so that the drive now follows from this pinion to the large back gear and its pinion, to terminate at a reduced speed on the spindle gear, that is $\frac{50}{90} \times \frac{27}{85} = \frac{3}{17}$, or a speed ratio reduction of 5.7 to 1 for each speed obtained by moving the belt on successive steps.

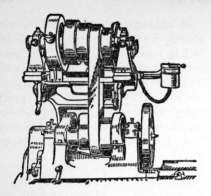

Fig. 3. A motor-driven countershaft such as this may be used to make a lathe self-contained, and to save space.

One of the drawbacks of the ordinary cone-pulley drive is the necessity of mounting a countershaft adjacent to some line shafting (or primary shaft driven by means of a motor or engine) to obtain motive power. This often involves difficulties of installation, is wasteful of floor space and introduces light-restricting overhead belts. There are, then, many advantageous features, if, while retaining the cheapness and simplicity of a cone-pulley drive, these drawbacks can be eliminated. Figs. 3 and 4 indicate means to this end and show how a lathe can be made self-contained by either mounting a motor-driven countershaft on a bracket above and behind the headstock (Fig. 3), or utilizing the cabinet foot of the lathe to house the countershaft and electric motor (Fig. 4). This makes a neat totally-enclosed unit drive. A V belt is used to insure a smooth connection between the motor and countershaft, while a lever conveniently located on the foot allows the belt speeds to be changed in a manner more mechanical than the dangerous hand or belt-stick shift usually employed with overhead countershafting.

The cone-pulley drive suffers from the defect that the available speed range is usually narrow, and that the least power is available when it is most needed; that is, in turning large-diameter work when the belt is on the small step of the countershaft cone.

To increase the speed range by adding more steps to the cone is unsatisfactory, for a further reduction in the cone diameter means still less power, so that when a cone-pulley drive to cover a wide speed range is essential, the best solution is the incorporation of double back-gearing and a two-speed countershaft, thereby obtaining eighteen speeds with only a three stepped cone-pulley.

This arrangement still suffers from the defect of a varying power factor with each change of speed whereas the initial high belt motor speed of a geared drive insures that practically

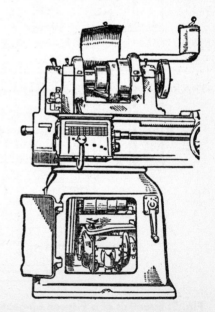

Fig. 4. The lathe base may be used to house the countershaft and electric motor in a self-contained lathe.

the full power is available for all speeds. There may be as many as eighteen or more speeds, obtained by clutches, tumbler gears, sliding keys, or sliding gears, or combinations of these systems in almost endless variety; but for all-round efficiency, general reliability and number of changes of gears obtainable, the sliding-gear type is superior to the rest.

A nine-speed lathe headstock with sliding gears is shown in Fig. 5, and will be seen to comprise only nine gears on three shafts. The speeds are obtained by sliding the two cluster gears on the pulley-shaft and the spindle respectively, by actuation of two levers which give the various gear combinations shown at the top of the following page.

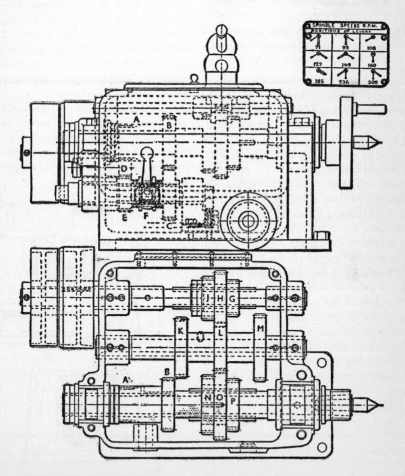

Fig. 5. Essentials of a 9-speed all-geared fast headstock. *Below,* plan of the headstock with cover removed. There are 9 gears on three shafts, and the speeds are obtained by sliding the cluster gears on the pulley-shaft and the spindle, by actuating two levers which give the combinations shown on page 100.

$$\frac{G}{M} \times \frac{L}{O}, \frac{J}{K} \times \frac{L}{O}, \frac{G}{M} \times \frac{K}{N},$$

$$\frac{G}{M} \times \frac{K}{N}, \frac{J}{K} \times \frac{M}{P}, \frac{H}{L} \times \frac{L}{O},$$

$$\frac{J}{K} \times \frac{M}{P}, \frac{H}{L} \times \frac{K}{N}, \frac{H}{L} \times \frac{M}{P}$$

A small hand-wheel on the front of the headstock is used for starting or stopping by moving the belt on fast or loose pulleys or actuating a friction clutch if a single pulley is fitted. Alternatively, if the lathe is driven direct by a motor, a push-button box can be mounted on the headstock and duplicated on the saddle, so that the lathe can be conveniently controlled from any working position of the operator.

The feed motion of a lathe is driven from a gear on the spindle to connecting gearing which includes a reverse motion, generally on the fast headstock, but sometimes in the feed gearbox, or even in the apron. This last arrangement is convenient for or-

dinary turning, but for screw-cutting purposes a reverse motion is desirable previous to the lead screw, so that the mechanism is duplicated. There are also some simple types of lathes driving the feed motion by cone-pulleys, in which case the reverse motion is obtained by the crossing of the belt. With other small lathes, the introduction of an intermediate gear in the gear train is necessary to reverse the feed direction, but the modern method is to incorporate a permanent reversing arrangement actuated from some position which is convenient for the operator.

Where space is limited, the tumbler device (Fig. 6) is often employed to give a straight-through reverse. The construction comprises a tumbler plate A which carries pinion gears either of which can be engaged with the spindle wheel B (Fig. 6a), or, if neither gear is in mesh, the feed motion is disengaged.

The method of reversing the driven wheel can be followed by considering the diagram in the position shown where the drive from the spindle is $\frac{57}{25} \times \frac{25}{57}$, so that if the spindle gear is rotating in a clockwise direction, the tumbler-plate gear also rotates in the same direction. If, now, the bolt clamping the tumbler plate is released and the pinion 22 teeth swung into mesh with the spindle gear, then the drive follows $\frac{57}{22} \times \frac{22}{25} \times \frac{25}{57}$, so that the tumbler-plate gear will move in the opposite direction to its previous rotation.

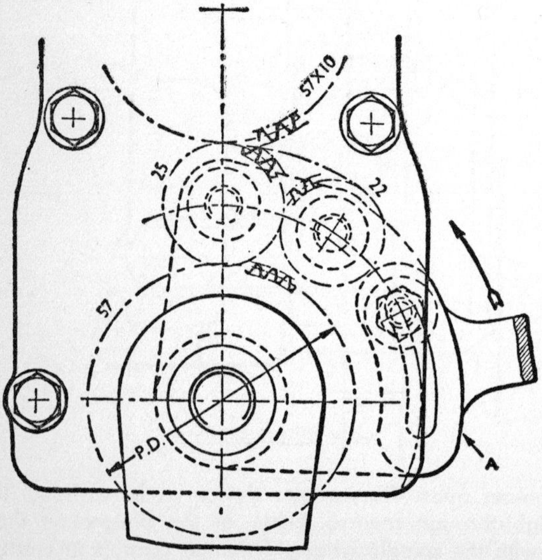

The construction permits

Fig. 6. Tumbler device for straight-through reverse.

a free motion of the tumbler plate around its axis, and is accomplished by making the distance between the center of driver and driven gears equal to the pitch diameters of the large tumbler pinion, plus one-half of the pitch diameters of driver and driven gears. The pitch diameter is the diameter across a gear-wheel to the centers of the teeth; this is the effective diameter when two gears are running together. This is shown in Fig. 6 and 6a.

A difference of three teeth in the tumbler pinions will usually be sufficient to give clearance to both driver and driven gears, and care must be taken to select such diameters as will allow clearance when the tumbler gears are entirely disengaged from the driver. When the center of the smallest pinion is selected, it is necessary to make it such that a circle struck from the driven-gear center will be tangential to the pitch-circles of both the large and small tumbler pinions. This explanation will be more readily followed if

reference is made to the chapter on Gears and Gear-Cutting.

One recognized trait of this type of reverse gear is its resistance to being engaged in one direction and its equal resistance to being disengaged in the opposite direction. The spindle gear tends to help it into mesh in the direction indicated by the arrow and to push it out of gear when moved in the opposite direction.

Economizing Effort

By way of comparison, one may calculate what effort would be required at the handle with 4 in. diameter gears arranged as shown in Fig. 6. With a tooth pressure of 500 lb., the resultant load on the tumbler plate tending to

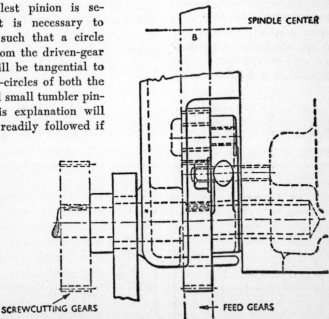

Fig. 6a. Reverse motions of tumbler gear. The tumbler device as here shown is frequently used to give a straight-through reverse. Either of the pinions on the tumbler plate can be engaged with the spindle wheel; if neither gear is in mesh, the feed motion is disengaged. (See also Fig. 6 on p. 100.)

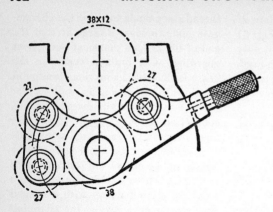

Fig. 7. This type of lathe reverse gear is found in practice far superior to the ordinary type, for it requires only about one-sixth as much effort to turn when the gears are fully loaded.

turn it in a clockwise direction is exactly twice the pressure on the teeth, the pressure angle of the teeth having no effect in this case. This load, acting on the stud of the intermediate gear, the center of which is 4 in. from the pivotal center of the tumbler plate, gives a turning moment of the plate of $1,000 \times 4 = 4,000$ lb. in., so that the effort required on the 10 in. long handle will be 400 lb. when the gears are fully loaded. This is nearly six times as much as with the arrangement shown in Fig. 7, and explains why it is so difficult to operate the ordinary type of reverse mechanism when the machine is running. In practice the arrangement shown in Fig. 7 is found to be far superior to the ordinary type, which, excepting cheapness, has nothing special to recommend it.

An alternative method of reversing a lathe feed motion is by two gear trains and a dog-clutch. This arrangement is shown in Fig. 5 (top), and comprises a cluster gear on the spindle with teeth at A and B. The latter connects with a wheel C on the feed driving shaft located directly below the main spindle, while gear A meshes with an intermediate pinion D, this in turn driving the feed wheel E. Thus wheels E and C run in different directions on the feedshaft, but being bushed, transmit no motion until connected to the clutch F. This is keyed to the feed-shaft, but, being clear of the wheels E and C in the intermediate position, can be used to disengage the feed motion, this being a convenience at the high spindle speeds when polishing work or performing other hand operations. To engage the feed in either direction, the ball handle is turned to the right or left, and, by an eccentric shaft and brass die, the clutch-teeth engage with those on either gear E or C.

Bevel-Gears

The same result can be obtained by using three bevel-gears and a clutch, but the cost of a bevel-gear is approximately double that of a spur-gear, and it rarely runs as quietly, so that unless constructional details favor the use of bevel-gears, a spur reverse motion is preferable.

To connect from the lathe headstock to the feed gearbox requires either a single train of gears which is used for both feeding and screw-cutting, or a separate train for each motion. This latter arrangement is shown in Fig. 8, the train for the feed motion being indicated at A and that for the screw-cutting motion at B. To connect the gear on the tumbler plate of the headstock reverse motion (Fig. 6) with the feed gearbox (Fig. 10), only one intermediate gear, C, is required, this being free to revolve on a stud in the bed. A suitable guard is provided to enclose the mechanism.

The method of selecting the gearing for screw-cutting is explained later, but the arrangement comprises a change-gear plate D, swinging freely on the tumbler-plate shaft of the headstock, but capable of being locked in position when the change-gears are assembled and connected up. Two gear-studs are available, these sliding in a slot to accommodate either single or compound gear trains as required.

With this arrangement, while the feed-gearing can be neatly guarded, the range of sizes of wheels required for screw-cutting over a wide range of thread sizes tends to cause the change-gear plate to cover a large area of the end of the bed, so that neat permanent guarding of a built-in type for the gears is difficult. From this standpoint of appearance alone, as well as for more important details discussed later, connecting gearing which serves the dual purpose of feed and screw-cutting motions can be much more neatly housed at the end of the bed, as shown in Fig. 6, where the change-gears are protected by a housing with a hinged door giving easy access for changing when required.

Following the mechanism now to a feed gearbox of the type shown in Fig. 10 giving three changes: this comprises two centers, one for the lead-screw and the other for the feed-shaft. Actually, however, the lead-screw passes through the box but has no ro-

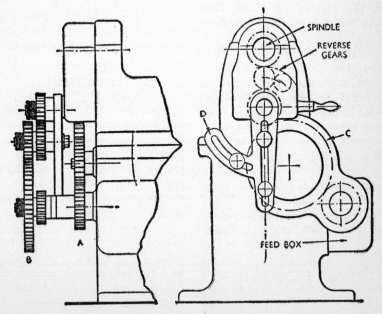

Fig. 8. Arrangement of gearing connecting headstock and feed-box. A. Train for the feed motion; B. Train for the screw-cutting motion; C. Gear connecting tumbler plate gear with feed gearbox; D. Change-gear plate for screw-cutting.

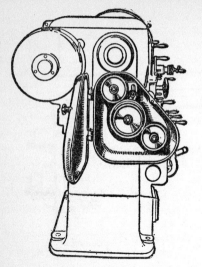

Fig. 9. Representative change-gear drive; the change-gears are protected by a housing with hinged door.

tary connection with it, simply receiving its motion from the change-gears at the end of the bed and utilizing the box for bearing purposes only. The feed-gears are either cut out of a socket, as in the case of the left-hand pinion gear or keyed to it.

The socket receives motion from the gear train at the end of the bed, via the end gear on the socket, and rotates the three gears on the feed-shaft. Of these, the center gear is the only one keyed to the feed-shaft and transmitting the motion, but is capable of being moved along the shaft out of engagement with the center socket gear and into clutch engagement with either the right- or left-hand gears on the feed-shaft. Normally, these gears run loosely, but when engaged with the sliding-clutch gear, transmit motion to the feed-shaft at a rate approximately double or half of that of the center gear. The feed change is actuated by the lever shown acting through rack and pinion to a fork spanning the sliding gear. This can be followed in Fig. 10.

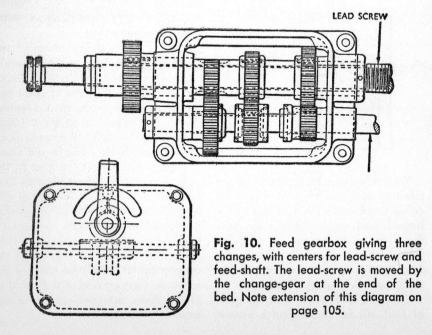

LEAD SCREW

Fig. 10. Feed gearbox giving three changes, with centers for lead-screw and feed-shaft. The lead-screw is moved by the change-gear at the end of the bed. Note extension of this diagram on page 105.

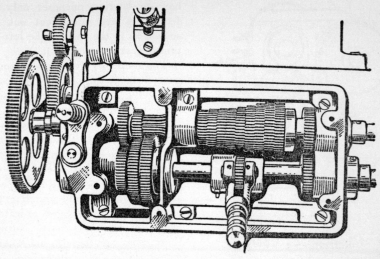

Fig. 11. Gearbox with cover-plate removed. With this type 27 changes can be obtained by hand-lever, three for each of nine variants obtained by the cone of gears and the tumbler pinion on the bottom shaft.

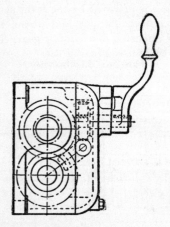

number of screw-threads, so that by supplying a few change-gears only, instead of a full set, a wide range of threads can be cut with only a limited amount of gear-setting on a much smaller change-gear plate.

Fig. 11 shows an extension of the idea giving twenty-seven changes obtained by hand-lever. Nine changes are obtained by the cone of gears and a tumbler pinion, shown on the bottom shaft. This pinion is given a longitudinal and part-rotary movement on the bottom shaft as it is moved along to engage each successive gear in the cone. For each of the nine speeds thus obtained a further three choices can be made to give the full twenty-seven. This triplication is made by the left-hand lever, which, by a three-position movement, slides a key into one of the three gears on the bottom shaft of the left-hand compartment of the box, thus giving three rates of speeds to the tumbler pinion gear.

While the above arrangement is satisfactory and cheap where only occasional screw-cutting is required and a limited feed range suffices, the tendency is to incorporate a feed-box wherein the gears serve not only for feeding purposes, but are applicable to the rotation of the lead-screw as well. Thus, a feed-box with six rates of feed can be used to cut a similar

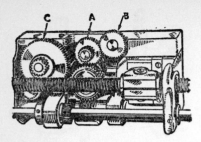

Fig. 12. Rear view of lathe apron, which carries the mechanism for the turning and facing motions and for screw-cutting. An interlocking device prevents the mechanism for one operation interfering with the other.

Multi-Change Gears

The lead-screw is directly connected to the cone of gears, while the right-hand pair of gears connects to the feed-shaft, so that the full range of speeds are available for ordinary turning operations. This is by no means the limit of changes obtainable with multi-change screw-cutting gearboxes, and very often a cone of twelve gears is employed which, with an outside four-speed change, will give forty-eight rates of travel; even this figure is often exceeded on many lathes. In any case, however, some removable change-wheels are usually supplied for special threads not easily obtained in a standard box.

The function of a lathe-apron is to carry the mechanism for the turning and facing operations and screw-cutting. Thus, for the first traverse motion, the gearing must terminate in a rack-pinion to move the tool along the bed, and for the second must connect to the cross-feed screw of the saddle. The screw-cutting requirements are a disengaging split nut, hand operated, and some provision to prevent the possibility of conflicting gears being engaged at the same time.

Referring to Fig. 12, which shows the rear view of a lathe-apron receiving motion from the gearbox shown in Fig. 11, the feed-shaft carries a pinion which meshes with a similar pinion gear adjacent to a worm in mesh with a worm-gear. Connected to the worm-gear is a spur-gear which meshes with gear A. This gear and a connected pinion gear are located on an eccentric stud, so that gear A may mesh with B, which connects to a pinion on the cross feed screw, or may be disengaged by a hand-lever which rotates the eccentric stud so that the pinion connected to gear A may be moved to mesh with gear C, which is keyed on the rack pinion shaft, and so engages the sliding motion. For rapid engagement or disengagement of both motions a cone friction clutch is fitted in the worm-gear and operates by turning a knurled knob.

Nut-Box Mechanism

The split nut mechanism to engage or disengage the lead-screw for thread-cutting comprises a pair of half-nuts capable of sliding in vertical guides, in or out of mesh with the lead-screw. This is effected by pins in the back of the half-nuts fitting into cam-grooves of a circular disc attached to a hand-lever, so that by lever movement the disc is rotated and the cam-grooves raise or lower the half-nuts in their guides. To prevent engagement of the sliding and surfacing motions when screw-cutting is in operation, and to insure proper engagement at other times, an interlocking device is fitted between the hand-lever for engaging the feeds and that for the screw-cutting, so that movement of the one is impossible unless the other is in the neutral or out-of-mesh position. The mechanism is completed by a hand-traverse along the bed by a hand-wheel attached to the bottom pinion in mesh with gear C.

Tool-Posts

The methods of supporting the cutting tool or tools are many and varied, but as some method of swiveling the tool is advantageous, a so-called compound feed-rest is generally mounted on the saddle.

Another type of tool-post is shown in Fig. 13, and comprises the usual compound feed, indexed and turning on a central stud before locking. The saddle screw and the top slide screw are both fitted with micrometer-graduated collars to read in $\frac{1}{1000}$ in. for regulating the depth of the cut. While this type of tool-post, with its one clamping screw, may lack the rigidity of the previous type, it has several advantageous features: the tool may be set in any angular position relative to

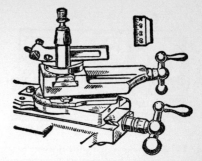

Fig. 13. Compound tool-posts of this type are in common use. Note the graduated swivel.

the top slide, clamping is simplified, and the concave washer and convex *rocker* allow the tool to be adjusted for height without the usual trial-and-error method of using several pieces of packing picked up at random.

A very rigid type of tool-holder is illustrated in Fig. 14. Two clamping screws for the tool are provided, and a good feature is that the central bolt around which the post swivels is not entirely depended on for clamping,

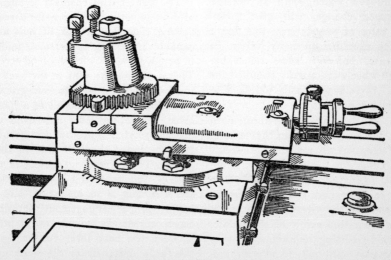

Fig. 14. Swivel tool-post of very rigid type, in which the central bolt is supplemented by a locking device consisting of a hardened steel wedge acting against a tool segment on the base of the tool-holder.

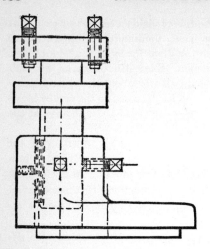

Fig. 15. Swivel tool-post with height adjustment effected by two screws acting on the shank of the tool-post.

screws acting on the shank of the tool-post, which is also prevented from rotating in the base by means of a key.

Adjustable Tool-Posts

When required, two tools can be set in the tool-post and brought into operation for consecutive machining operations. The screws for clamping both the cutting tools in the box and those for locking on the shank are of the same size, so that one wrench only is required for both settings, while it will be apparent that the tool-post is easily removable, so that the base can be used to fit other rests, such as chaser bars, hand-turning, or polishing rests.

Rapid Tool-Setting

For quantity production of work pieces, the tool-setting becomes a most important feature, and any device which will facilitate bringing the tools into rapid action is worthy of consideration. One means of accomplishing this is the fitting of a turret on the swivel slide so that four or more tools may be ready set for any operation at once.

Fig. 16 shows a typical square turret consisting of two main parts: a cast-iron base fitting on the saddle swivel slide and a malleable iron turret located and swiveling around a pivot on the base. A spring-loaded plunger is fitted in the base, and by its taper end locates the turret in any one of four positions by entering taper holes in the turret base. To index the turret, the ball handle is revolved and the screw lifts the turret clear of the locating plunger, so that it can be rotated to the next or any indexing position, and then locked in position.

but is backed up by a locking device which comprises a hardened steel wedge acting against a tool segment on the base of the tool-holder. A drawback of many lathes is the smallness of the index collar on the screws, making the reading of the micrometer dials a difficult matter. The one shown is an exception to this, the clarity of the indexing on the large collar being very pronounced and an inducement to the operator to use the facilities provided for accurate setting or machining.

For a wide variety of operations involving turning, boring, recessing, and screw-cutting, the matter of height adjustment of a range of tools of widely varying sections becomes increasingly important, and a useful type of adjustable tool-holder is shown in Fig. 15. The base is located on the lathe swivel slide in the usual way, so that it can be rotated to any desired position, but the chief feature is that the tool-post can be elevated to any desired height and clamped by two

While such a turret is a useful attachment on any lathe, it is possible to improve on the design in regard to time-saving and handiness of operation, and to this end a single lever movement can be used to give a quick action which cannot well be obtained by screw operation. The actual movements required are to unlock, lift clear of the plunger, rotate, and re-lock.

Handle-Operated Turrets

On one type of square turret, fitted on a well-known make of lathes, rotation of the handle in an anti-clockwise direction unbinds the turret when, after turning through 90 deg., it is automatically indexed. The handle is then brought back in the reverse direction to the bind position. One good point which requires emphasis in this design is that the turret is not lifted from its seating while being rotated, thus protecting the seating from shavings which have a tendency to fall under the base or clog the index plunger during rotation.

The seriousness of this happening is reflected in the character of the work produced, for any lack of accuracy in the control of the locking mechanism means that the position of the tool is affected in relation to the work; so that if the tool fails to locate properly or yields to an uncertain extent under the stress of the cut, uniform work cannot be obtained from the lathe. The variation is greater with chuck work than bar-work, for the tool has less chance to get a riding contact on the work, but in either case if the turret yields a matter of only .001 in. (one thousandth), the work will vary in diameter by at least double this amount. Excessive overhang of tools should also be avoided, for any looseness in the bearing on the center locating pivot tends to be multiplied at the tool-point.

Having previously dealt with the matter of spindle speeds, and now traced the transmission from the spindle drive to the tool-point, some information on the subject of feeds is required.

By feeds are understood the advances of a lathe-tool, either in line with or across the bed, in relation to the revolutions of the headstock spindle. Feeds may be expressed in inches per minute or inches per revolution of the spindle. For example, 40 cuts per in. indicates that while the tool has traveled 1 in., the spindle has made 40

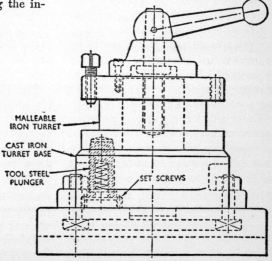

MALLEABLE IRON TURRET

CAST IRON TURRET BASE

TOOL STEEL PLUNGER

SET SCREWS

Fig. 16. Square turret fitted on the swivel slide enabling four or more tools to be set up for any operation.

revolutions; this could be stated as a feed of 5 in. per min. if the spindle is rotating at 200 r.p.m. But for lathes the feed is generally given in cuts per in.

It is not generally realized that the selection of a correct feed may be of greater importance than choosing the most advantageous speed, for a change in speed does not mean in general a correspondingly great change in the efficiency of a lathe, whereas a change in feed does; for the best results in quantity of metal removed per hour are obtained when the cross-section of the chip is the maximum, even though this entails a comparatively low speed.

Thus, an operator should be able to take the heaviest cut which work and machine will allow. There are, of course, many cases where but little metal is to be removed, and in such cases the depth of cut is practically fixed, so the operator is left with only speed and feed to adjust. If two cuts will complete the turning, and a good finish is required on the work, one roughing cut with a coarse feed followed by a finishing cut at a reduced feed will probably suffice, but if the work is to be finally finished by grinding, the coarse feed can be maintained throughout both cuts.

Varying Feed Rates

The wide choice of cutting materials now available has caused an extension in feed rates which a few years ago were covered by, say, three feeds ranging from $\frac{1}{8}$ in. to $\frac{1}{32}$ in. per revolution of the spindle for a heavy lathe, or $\frac{1}{16}$ in. to $\frac{1}{64}$ in. for smaller machines working exclusively with tools of high-speed steel. More recently, the great increase in cutting speeds has, owing to the brittleness of some types

of cutting tools, been accompanied by a finer feed range—for example, six feeds ranging from 50 to 200 cuts per in., and in cases where a lathe must use a wide range of cutting materials, no less than 24 feeds from 8 to 310 cuts per in. are listed.

The minutes required to turn 1 in. =

$$\frac{\text{Turns per in.}}{\text{r.p.m. of spindle}}$$

Example: Find the time required to turn 1 in. at 80 cuts per in. Spindle speed 125 r.p.m.

Minutes = $\frac{80}{125}$ = .64 min. or, extending this:

$$\frac{\text{Length of traverse in in.} \times \text{Feed cuts per in.}}{\text{Spindle speeds, r.p.m.}}$$

= Time in minutes.

In the event of a lathe-saddle overrunning the limits of its movement because of inattention by the operator, meeting with an obstruction on the slides, or due to excessive feed, there is danger of breaking or straining shafts and gearing if the drive is by gears throughout. At some point in the transmission, then, a safety device is often established to slip at a desired torque and prevent breakdown.

Safety Devices

In some cases this is nothing more than a soft steel pin passing through the boss of a connecting gear and shaft. This is made of such a diameter as to be capable of driving under normal conditions, but small enough to shear in an emergency. The pin should be recessed at the junction of the shaft and wheel to prevent the pin continuing to drive, owing to the broken ends wedging after shearing.

A better device is in the form of a slipping clutch (Fig. 17). The driving gear is loose on the shaft and has a single tooth-space of the shape shown, milled across its boss. A clutch, keyed on the shaft, with a similar projecting tooth, is kept in engagement by a square-section spiral spring. This can be adjusted as required to take the maximum load, but will allow the tapered sides of the clutch to slip out of engagement should it be subjected to severe strain.

Another device is a copy of the Weston friction coupling, where a series of soft steel washers attached to the driving and driven parts, respectively, are clamped together and operate on the same principle as a plate-clutch.

Function of the Tailstock

The function of the tailstock is two-fold: first, to provide a support to the end of the work, usually a shaft; and secondly, to feed a drill or similar tool toward the work when boring castings

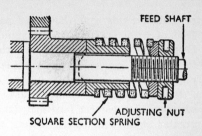

Fig. 17. Safety slipping clutch device for feed motion to prevent breakdown from over-running of lathe saddle.

or forgings. For this reason it is usually fitted with a non-rotating spindle, which is advanced or withdrawn by means of a screw and nut, and locked in position by a suitable clamp. The work, therefore, rotates on a dead center, except at high speeds, when a special ball bearing center may be used.

The use of a dead center allows a minimum of play, and it is possible to obtain more accurate work than when rotating upon live centers. Neverthe-

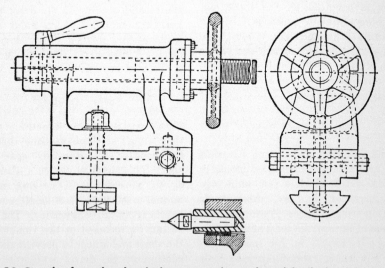

Fig. 18. Details of a tailstock, which supports the work and feeds the drill or other tool toward it when boring castings or forgings. Detail of the spindle end is shown inset.

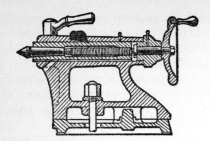

Fig. 19. Another type of tailstock, with small-diameter friction-reducing screw.

less, the small bearing surface of the work upon the fixed center, with its high bearing pressure, its relatively small rubbing speed, frequently causes seizing unless there is frequent lubrication and constant observation. For this reason ball- or roller-bearing centers are essential when using carbide tools to full capacity.

Referring to Fig. 18, the general construction comprises the base-plate, fitting between the bed-shears, and the tailstock casting carrying the spindle. This passes straight through the bored hole, and is threaded at one end to receive the nut attached to the hand-wheel. To prevent rotation of the spindle and give it a lengthwise movement, a keyway is cut on the underside for it to slide along a key at the front end of the bored hole. The front end of the spindle is bored out to a standard Morse taper to accommodate the center or taper shank-drills, chucks, reamers, etc.

It is important that the spindle should be a good fit in the bored hole and not distorted by the locking-bolt. In the arrangement shown, clamping is by the locking-bolt and split lug of the bored hole.

A second type of headstock, Fig. 19, is fitted with a short spindle having a nut fixed in one end. A small-diameter screw to which the hand-

wheel is attached passes through the nut and the recessed spindle bore, the main feature being, in contrast to the previous example, that a reduction of friction is obtained by means of the small-diameter screw, and thereby ease of operation when feeding the spindle.

A different method of clamping the spindle is also employed, instead of the split lug. Two hollow bushings are shaped with their ends to fit around the spindle, which is clamped by pulling these bushings together. Both arrangements given are designed for taper turning, a single casting tailstock being all that is required for straight work. The taper-turning device comprises a nut in the tailstock casting and a screw in the base-plate, so that rotation of the screw traverses the top casting across the base plate to throw the spindle center out of alignment with that of the headstock center.

The problem of locking the spindle without moving it out of alignment has been the subject of much thought, and a third arrangement is shown in Fig. 20. The spindle is advanced in the usual way by hand-wheel and screw, but the clamping action of the spindle is obtained through the concentric taper-bushing at the front and the split conical sleeve fitting therein. To clamp the spindle, the locking lever partially rotates a nut on the threaded end of the sleeve, which is thus drawn tightly and concentrically into the taper-bushing. A movement of the locking lever in the opposite direction allows a free traverse motion of the spindle.

The tailstock is clamped to the bed by bolts which pull a plate on to the underside of the shears. On some lathes separate guides are used for the tailstock, so that any wear on the bed occasioned by the continual traversing of the saddle does not affect the alignment of the two centers. On heavy lathes, movement of the tailstock along the bed is facilitated by providing a bracket and a pinion meshing with the rack, so that rotation of a hand-lever provides ease of movement. As many as four bolts are often provided for clamping to the bed, these sometimes being supported by a pawl fitting into a rack cast in the bed.

The advantages of a self-contained and separate motor-drive for a lathe are very pronounced and need no emphasis. Nevertheless, the types of drives and control methods vary widely, so that the subject is one of great and continually increasing importance.

The motor used may be one of the alternating-current type, of constant speed and controlled by push-buttons, or may be a pole-change motor giving up to four definite speeds, again push-button controlled; or, alternatively, a direct-current motor can be fitted. The ability to obtain speed changes on the motor means a considerable simplification of the gear train, but the introduction of the grid system of electric supply has resulted in a great reduction of D.C. motors, and while variable-speed A.C. motors are available, they are both large and expensive, so that their use is restricted to large lathes.

Pole-change motors are useful, but it should be realized that they, too, are comparatively large, with a characteristic that the output factor is one of constant torque, the output being proportional to the speed, which is a disadvantage when heavy cuts are required at a low speed. In addition, the speeds must always be definite pole-speed ratios, such as 1,500, 1,000, 750, and 500 r.p.m.

In some cases it is even possible to dispense with gearing altogether and mount a motor directly on the lathe-spindle. Such applications are, of course, very restricted, but the great increase in cutting speeds, particularly when machining non-ferrous metals of small diameter, has made this arrangement quite possible.

When not directly connected to the headstock gears, the connection between an electric motor and a lathe may be by either leather belt, V belt, chain, or noiseless pinion gears. As shown in Figs. 21 and 22, the motor may be mounted either on a base-plate

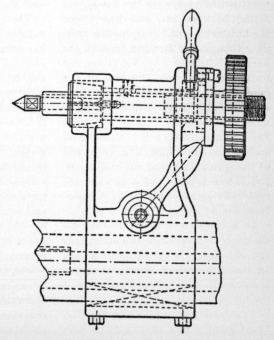

Fig. 20. Tailstock with special clamping device to lock the spindle without moving it out of alignment.

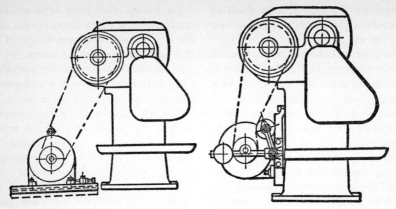

Figs. 21 and 22. Arrangements of drives for the electric motor of a lathe. *Left,* the motor is mounted on a base-plate; *right,* it is mounted on the side of the bed. Provision is made for the necessary belt adjustment in both cases.

or on the side of the bed, with provision in both cases for belt adjustment. Of the various driving methods given, that by V belt has achieved great prominence and success in recent years. The main features include: quiet operation, efficiency at short center distances, and freedom from vibration.

At the high speeds of present-day practice, the problem of vibration is a serious one, and many designs are brought forward to isolate the motor and gearing from the lathe-spindle. This necessitates mounting the motor in a cabinet foot and connecting by V belt to a gearbox in the foot, thence from the box to a pulley on the lathe-spindle via further V belts or an endless leather or silk belt. Actually the pulley is not mounted on the spindle, but on a socket with keys driving the spindle, the object being to relieve the spindle of all belt-pull.

A pioneer and patented development is shown in Fig. 23. The drive is by a flanged motor bolted low down on the bed end, and transmitting the drive through a multi-plate clutch operated by a lever situated on the bed at the foot of the headstock and on long lathes operated from the saddle as well. By this lever, the spindle is started, inched, stopped, and a brake applied.

Insuring Stability

The fast headstock carrying the spindle is fitted to the bed without overhang, and all driving shafts and gears are below the spindle and carried on ball bearings in a gearbox within the bed, giving great stability to the lathe. The speed changes are through sliding gears and an internal tooth-clutch on the spindle giving a range of twelve speeds. The gears are of nickel-chrome steel, heat-treated and ground. Oil is continually supplied from a trough above the gears by a pump from a sump within the headstock. This arrangement insures that vibration is not transmitted to the spindle, for the mounting of the flange motor insures great stability and a low center of gravity, which is not obtained when the motor is flange-mounted on the first driving shaft of the headstock in an overhung position, as is the usual practice.

The electrical control gear is housed in the bed-casting under the headstock, and is easily accessible upon removing the inspection door. When a D.C. motor is fitted, the starter is manually operated by lever or hand-wheel on the enclosing door. The A.C. starter is operated by push-button fitted with warning lights, and in this case the control gear consists of an isolating switch by which the current is cut off before the inspection door can be opened.

On lathes with long beds, another small motor is often fitted on the saddle for the rapid traverse motion. This is a good time-saving feature, which also prevents fatigue of the operator. Push-buttons are fitted to give forward and reverse motions; these must be continually depressed by the operator to cause the saddle to travel, a necessary safeguard to prevent damage to the lathe through the saddle running quickly against some obstruction when the attention of the operator is diverted elsewhere. At the same position on the saddle, the headstock start and stop push-buttons are often du-

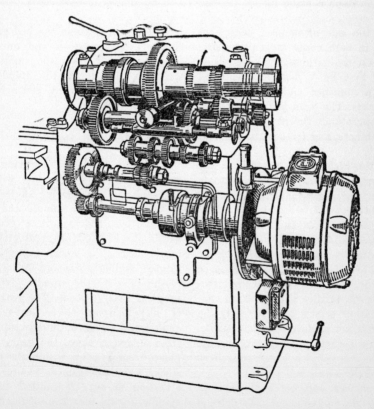

Fig. 23. Motor-drive and headstock gearing on one type of lathe. The flanged motor is bolted low down on the bed end; driving shafts and gearings are below the spindle, carried in a gearbox within the bed.

plicated so that remote control is available from the operating position. In many cases, a separate small motor is used for the coolant pump, while self-contained lighting equipment completes the electrical installation on other lathes.

Lathe Lubrication

A considerable number of lathe breakdowns are directly traceable to two causes: first, lack of lubrication, and second, the use of an unsuitable lubricant.

During the last few years most manufacturers of medium and heavy machine units have improved the oiling arrangements of their various machines, so that neglect on the part of the operator is to some extent overcome by more generous pumps containing a reserve supply of lubricant lasting a much longer period without attention than hitherto. Automatic pump-fed lubrication has also been developed, and on most machines the need for daily attention has disappeared, and a weekly review of the lubrication system should be all that is required.

On smaller machines, not having the amount of mechanism necessary on the larger sizes, the adoption of oil-gun nipples insures that oil will reach the surfaces for which it is intended with a minimum of trouble.

All high-grade lathes are subject to rigid inspection during every stage of manufacture and to final alignment and running tests before leaving the plant. For these alignment tests, precision spirit-levels and dial indicators are used in conjunction with accurate test-bars. The full range of tests may be very comprehensive, but in general they include a test to see if the

center line of the spindle is parallel to the bed-top and to side of the bed.

For this test a stiff bar is mounted in the spindle end and a dial-indicator gauge (see chapter on Measuring and Testing) in the compound rest to contact with the bar, first above the bar and then on the side of it. Any inaccuracy is indicated on the dial as the saddle is traversed along the bed.

For a similar test of the loose head-spindle, a long bar is mounted between the headstock and tailstock and the dial indicator traversed along as before. For testing the cross feed slides, a face-plate is mounted on the spindle nose and turned in position. The tool is then replaced by a dial indicator, which is traversed across the bed. A limit of .001 in. concavity is allowed, but no bulging roundness. Chuck-jaws are tested by a similar mounting of a dial indicator in the compound rest and bringing each jaw successively into position against the pointer.

Running Tests

There are, in addition, tests of the lead-screw accuracy and the actual running of the machine at all the speeds and feeds to insure proper gear-changing and that lubricating systems are functioning. But despite all the tests of the maker, the production of accurate parts on any lathe is largely dependent upon the care with which the machine is installed.

Careless slinging when lifting, so that parts are unduly stressed, may mitigate all previous accuracy, but assuming that a lathe arrives safely on its foundations, the method of setting up indicated in Fig. 24 can be followed with advantage:

1. Level up the lathe with an accurate spirit-level placed on ground

blocks X and Y in positions indicated at A and B.

2. Check off by the actual turning of a test-bar with a keen tool, and an extremely light cut on the collars C and D.

3. Measure the collars C and D with an accurate micrometer. These two collars should both be exactly the same diameter. A preference (if any) is given to collar D, the diameter of which may be .0003 in. larger than that of C.

4. Should you not obtain the readings as stated in 3, wedge the cabinet leg on the side required until you obtain the necessary accuracy, after which take another light cut over the collars C and D.

5. When readings are obtained as in 3, you will know that you have the built-in accuracy on alignment that the machine had originally.

Compared with its predecessors, the modern lathe is quite a complicated piece of machinery. At the same time, the introduction of forced lubrication, anti-friction bearings, protected and heat-treated slide-ways, and improved materials has reduced actual wear to a great extent and assure long life to the machine. In fact, after many years of running by a careful operator, a lathe with the above advantages will show scarcely any signs of wear on either slides or bearings.

Adjusting the Bearings

Maintenance of lubrication is, of course, essential, but is frequently neglected, and this is the prime cause of most breakdowns. In any case, after long running some adjustment will be required on plain bearings, and is easily performed on lathes with parallel headstock bearings and loose caps, as shown in Fig. 2. Such bearings, with

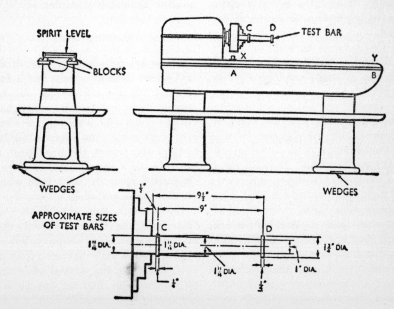

Fig. 24. Illustrating the procedure, explained on page 116, for setting up and testing a lathe, to obtain complete accuracy of alignment.

split bushings, readily lend themselves to scraping and re-bedding, while end play is taken up by lock nuts against ball thrust washers. Taper-bearing headstocks are fitted with adjusting nuts for taking up wear, and as a rule the main front bearing should be adjusted first, followed by the rear bearing. These taper bearings are often a source of trouble after adjusting, and should be well lubricated and carefully watched for overheating. Ball- and roller-bearing spindles are generally of the pre-loaded type and require no further adjustment, and lubrication only over long periods.

At present only a few center lathes are fitted with covers over the bed, and wear takes place by shavings falling on the slideways. Cast-iron dust and chips also find their way under the saddle and grind away the slides by abrasion. As the majority of work is performed close up to the headstock, it is this section of the bed which wears first, and if it becomes pronounced, the only cure is to rescrape the full length of the bed. Any slackness between the bed and saddle is easily taken up by adjusting the taper-strip or holding-down plates. Similarly, wear or slackness developing between the saddle and swivel slide, or between the top slides can be taken up by the strips and adjusting screws. A frequent cause of inaccurate work is backlash between the saddle cross-feed screw and nut. In this case, a new nut is the only cure.

Another factor affecting the accuracy of work is the proper maintenance of the centers in good condition. The head center, revolving with the work, does not suffer as much from rough usage as the one in the tailstock. Lack of lubrication, tightening the work between the centers, and failure to realize that expansion of the job takes place, often result in the center end burning off. This not only holds up production, but, as the center is hardened, considerable time is required to soften, turn it to shape again and re-harden. Moreover, the burnt-off center end is often fused in the center end of the work, which, if the work is of practically finished size, may be scrapped in the attempt to remove the obstruction and re-center.

Some partial protection from chips falling on the lead-screw and feed-rod is afforded by mounting them adjacent to the bed side, partly under the front slide, and covered by a short guard. Nevertheless, the lead-screw should be often cleansed and lubricated, for metal shavings left between the threads cause much damage to the bronze half-nuts.

In general, then, these are the main points of maintenance requiring attention; but damage to the slides and equipment is often caused by thoughtless operators using the bed for shaft straightening, constantly dropping work on the slides, leaving tools to be trapped between the saddle, headstock, and tailstock, and the unnecessary use of force by fitting a length of pipe on a wrench or chuck-key, this resulting in the stripping of screw-threads. It may be considered that these delinquencies do not come under reasonable lathe operation; unfortunately, experience proves that they are almost unavoidable in common practice.

METAL TURNING

THE methods required in preparing work before placing it in the lathe differ according to whether it is to be mounted between the centers or gripped in a chuck. The first operation for bar work is to saw off a suitable length. This may be done by hand if the diameter of the work is small, but usually a power hacksaw is employed for this purpose. The material must be about ⅛ in. longer than the finished length to allow for any inaccuracies in sawing and for preparing the bar ends for centering.

Special machines are available when a large quantity of bar work is being prepared. These machines revolve the bar, and while a cutter squares the end of the bar, a high-speed drilling spindle drills the center holes. An alternative method is to mark out the center of the bar and drill the center holes on an ordinary drilling machine. It is very important that the center holes in the bar end should correspond to the taper of the lathe centers, consequently a special drill is required.

These center drills are made in several sizes for large or small work, but all follow the same design, being double-ended, each end comprising a parallel portion and a 60-degree taper

part which gives the actual supported part of the center hole, the front parallel portion giving assurance that the point of the lathe-center is clear of work, and also forming a cavity for oil. It will be realized that if the lathe center point was touching the end of the center hole, the work would not be resting on the taper part of the center, and would therefore run out of true, besides damaging the center point.

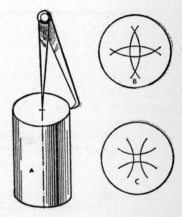

Fig. 26. How odd-leg calipers are used to find the center of a bar. The bar end is marked with chalk or red lead before using the calipers.

To find the center of the bar before drilling the center holes, several methods can be employed. The simplest of these, requiring no special tools, is shown in Fig. 26. Odd-leg or *jenny* calipers are set (A) so that arcs of circles can be scribed, either a little more or a little less than the center of the bar. Four arcs are generally struck as near right angles to each other as can be judged by the eye, so that a figure with either concave lines B or

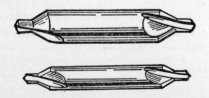

Fig. 25. Two types of combination center drill and countersink. Each end has a parallel portion and a 60-degree taper portion giving the actual supported part of the center hole.

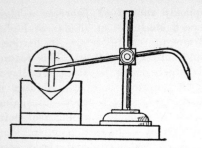

Fig. 27. Centering bars with a scribing block or surface gauge. The bar is mounted on V blocks, and marked with two pairs of parallel lines at right angles forming a small square in the center.

convex lines C is formed. The center of the figure determines the position of the center hole, which is marked by a blow on a center punch. To assist in giving clear scribed lines, the bar end should be covered with chalk or red lead preparatory to using the odd-leg calipers.

Another method is to use a scribing-block or surface gauge (Fig. 27) in conjunction with V blocks upon which the bar is mounted. The pointer of the scribing-block is set approximately to the height of the bar center and a line drawn across the bar. The bar is then turned through half a revolution, and another line drawn parallel to the first. These two operations are repeated with the bar now at right angles to its first position, so that a small square covering the center of the bar is formed. The center of the square represents the center of the bar, where a punch-mark is struck as before.

Assuming, then, that the bar has been centered and drilled, if not previously squared at the ends, it may now be mounted between the lathe-centers and this operation performed.

After squaring one end, the bar is reversed for operation on the other end.

For the bar to revolve between the centers, a dog must be clamped on it and engage with the face-plate. Fig. 28 shows several types, these generally being drop forgings made with various sizes of holes to accommodate different bar diameters. Hardened steel screws with square heads are provided to tighten on to the bar, or, alternatively, a safety screw can be fitted as in the left drawing. For heavy duty another pattern, shown at the right, has two safety screws which insure that the carrier does not slip around the bar when heavy cutting is in progress. This allows a drive at two points, and insures steadiness and an equal drive on light work, tending to prevent vibration, while on intermittent cutting the same advantageous features are available to prevent shock and inaccurate work.

If a bar is long, when placed between the lathe-centers and revolved it may be found to be bent to such an extent as to make it difficult to turn, or even to prevent it from being machined to the required dimensions. Various machines or attachments are available to correct this lack of alignment, some being heavy tools, power operated, and others applied by hand, either on the lathe itself or external to it.

Remarkable developments have taken place in the types and capabilities of cutting materials during recent years, resulting not only in a vastly increased production of engineering parts, but introducing problems in the operating of the lathe itself. In general, four types of cutting media are available: high-carbon steel tools, high-speed steel, Stellite, and cemented-carbides. The first type is rarely used today for high production, but is still used in some general machine shops for special tools, drills, and various cutters, for it is comparatively cheap, and hardens at low temperatures, but cutting speeds are low, being only about 25 ft. per minute.

High-Speed Steel

High-speed steel is used to an enormous extent, the advantage over a carbon-steel tool being its ability to machine ferrous metals (iron and steel) at considerably higher speeds and with longer life before re-grinding. When a carbon-steel tool becomes heated by the work to its temper color it softens, and the cutting edge is quickly rubbed off, whereas a high-speed steel tool at similar or higher temperatures still retains its hardness and cutting capabilities. This feature is largely due to the steel being alloyed with tungsten; hence the abilities of high-speed steel to stand up against the heat generated at the tool point as a result of the cutting action.

When annealed, high-speed steel can be easily machined or forged to shape, and is much simpler to harden than carbon steel, being brought up to a white heat, approximately 2300 deg. F. and cooled in oil or air, then drawn or tempered at about 1050 deg. F.

While there are many different shapes of lathe tools, depending on the purpose for which they are made, there is also a variation in the shape of the

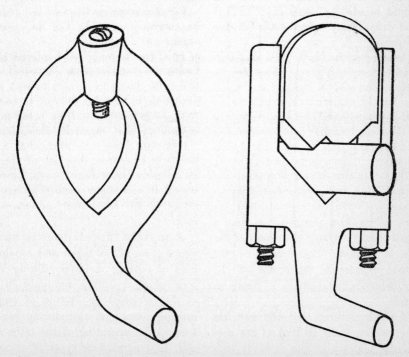

Fig. 28. Types of lathe dogs. These are generally drop-forgings with holes of varying sizes to take bars of different diameters.

cutting edge on tools performing the same duty, but in different materials. This is because the behavior of metals during cutting varies considerably and no standard set of tool angles can be given to cover all conditions. Mild steel is an easy material to cut, being free-flowing during turning, owing to the formation of a crack in advance of the cutting edge. This allows the cuttings to come off the work in long spirals if the tool is correctly ground with a keen cutting edge, whereas cast iron has a much greater blunting action, due to the metal being broken off more in crumbs. The hard sandy surface of a casting is also detrimental to tool life, so that in beginning to turn iron castings, the tool should always be set to cut deep, and never be allowed to rub on the surface. This also applies to turning brass articles, while hard steel should be machined with a tool having a more obtuse angle than that for mild or soft steel, so that the cutting edge has better support against the greater severity of the cut.

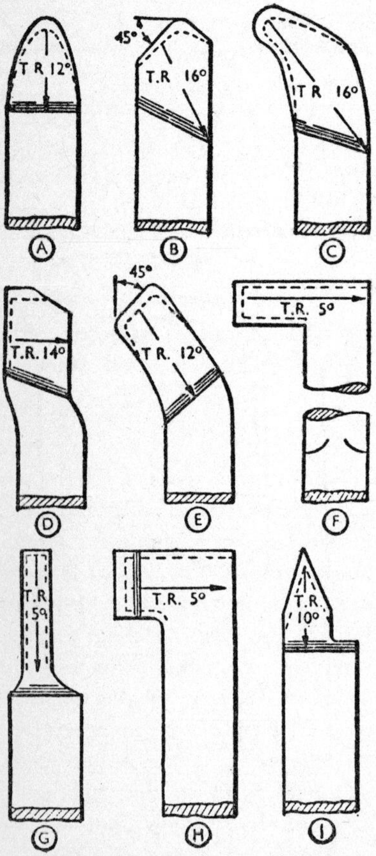

Cutting Angles

For maximum results tool bits must be correctly ground. The following angles are recommended: (A) *Angle of point clearance*—should be just sufficient to clear the work. Obviously it will vary according to the position of the point in relation to the axis of the work. In general, from 6 to 10 degrees is ample. (B) *Angle of top back slope* —may vary from 0 on very hard materials to 10 degrees on soft materials. (C) *Angle of top side slope*—may vary from 2 to 22 degrees, depending upon the character of the material to be cut. (D) *Angle of side clearance*—should be just sufficient to keep the side of the tool from rubbing against the work. It may vary from 6 to 10 degrees. Except in very rare cases, this angle should never exceed 10 degrees. (E) *Contour or radius of cutting edge* —Use all the radius possible, short of causing chatter. (F) *Recommended top side slope angles*—Very hard, tough, or abrasive metals, such as cast iron or cast steel, from 2 to 6 deg. Hard

Fig. 29. A selection of lathe tools. *A*, round-nose bore; *B*, a better shape; *C*, a roughing tool; *D*, knife tool; *E*, tool for sliding and surfacing motions; *F*, square-nose boring tool; *G*, parting tool; *H*, recessing tool; *J*, screw-cutting tool.

and tough metals, for example heat treated SAE 4140 and 6150 from 6 to 12 deg. Medium hard and tough metals, such as tool steels, bearing steels, stainless steels, heat treated machinery steels, from 12 to 16 deg. Soft metals such as cold rolled steel, bronze, brass, aluminum, screw stock —from 16 to 22 deg.

Grinding

On unground bits it is good practice to grind off sufficient material on the portion which will form the cutting edge to insure the edge being at least $\frac{1}{32}$ in. below the surface. This is not necessary on ground tool bits. A free cutting wheel, either wet or dry, should be used. Avoid undue pressure or bluing of the steel in this process, since this condition will develop strains and grinding cracks which will probably result in breakage.

The actual shape of the tool depends on the purpose for which it is to be used, but a general selection is indicated in Fig. 29. The round-nose tool, A, is one of the most commonly used for plain turning and gives good results, yet a better shape is that shown at B, where the straight cutting edge gives an even chip section, as against a varying one obtained by the curved edge of A, which tends to generate heat. For facing purposes, a bent tool, either right- or left-hand, is employed. For roughing-down material, the shape C can be used and then followed by a finishing or knife-tool D. Sometimes a single tool can be used for both sliding and surfacing motions, such as turning a pulley or flywheel over the rim and then down the face. Such a tool is shown at E and, when applicable, can be a means of saving production time by reducing the setting-up time.

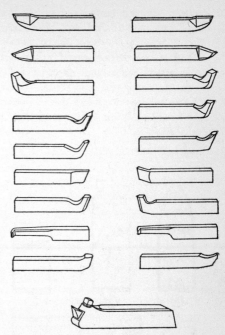

Fig. 30. A further selection of lathe tools, showing the great variety they may have.

Boring tools are made in a variety of shapes, one type F, being shown with a square nose; alternatives are a round nose, or V shape for screw-cutting purposes. The tool G is used for parting or cutting off work-pieces, or for necking down between the various diameters of a shaft prior to grinding. An alternative to the boring tool for internal purposes is the recessing tool H, this being made either right- or left-hand. Screw-cutting tools are made in a variety of shapes, the one shown at J for the external cutting of V threads being a representative example.

A material having greater cutting-speed capabilities than high-speed steel is a non-ferrous alloy of cobalt, chromium, and tungsten, known as

Stellite. It is a cast material, and possesses a valuable feature in that it can be welded. In small section Stellite can be used as a solid too, but it is more usual to use it in the form of tips brazed to a suitable shank, or in some cases to apply it direct to a tool-shank by melting Stellite rod with an oxy-acetylene flame, which causes the molten material to adhere to the shank without any flux. To obtain the necessary support against the cutting action, the front clearance angle should be about 6 deg. and the side-rake 6 deg. for cast iron and 10 deg. for steel. In general, the conditions for efficient use are very similar to those necessary for the latest cutting materials, known as cemented-carbides, which have revolutionized cutting speeds and the operation of machines using them.

Tungsten-Carbide

Although tungsten-carbide has been known for over 40 years, it was not until the 1914–1918 war that a practical use in engineering was discovered for it. In composition, the material comprises a cutting medium of either tungsten, tantalum, titanium, or molybdenum carbide interposed in a matrix or bond of cobalt. It is first powder-ball ground and mixed with 15 percent of cobalt, until, after heat-treatment, a material is obtained with a hardness only 5 percent less than the average diamond, so that it is impossible to alter it in shape by any other means than grinding on special wheels.

Despite many advantages, there are certain limitations, and tools of cemented-carbide require very careful handling. The material is expensive, and possesses a tensile strength only half that of high-speed steel, so that rigidity of mounting and a complete absence of vibration are essential during cutting. In general, the best results are obtained by using a very fine feed, and under proper conditions the metal removed may amount to five times that of a high-speed tool in the same time.

The tools are supplied under various trade names, some of them being capable of standing up to heavy and intermittent cutting. Others are more suitable for operating on cast iron than on steel, which has a high affinity for tungsten-carbide, so that the cuttings tend to build up and weld themselves on the tooltip. Upon breaking away, the tooltip is damaged, so that for operating on steel the pure tungsten-carbide requires an alloy such as tantalum which has a low affinity for steel.

Brazing Cemented-Carbides

Apart from the difficulties of manufacture, the cost of the material necessitates its use in the form of tipped tools, and Fig. 31 indicates a method of brazing the tips on to the toolshank. An electric furnace with a hydrogen atmosphere or a gas furnace with an excess of gas to prevent oxidation is commonly used for this process. Manufacturers of cemented-carbides usually give instructions for the brazing of their products, and this should be followed with care, for the failure of a tool is quite an expensive matter.

The correct grinding of all lathe-tools is of importance, for upon the proper angles depends the manner in which the cuttings leave the workpiece. Tools of carbon or high-speed steel are usually ground by hand on machines of the two-wheel type, one abrasive wheel being used for roughing and the other for finishing. Sandstone or emery wheel—these being natural abrasives—have been largely replaced by wheels of special compositions, which give more rapid removal of the metal.

When using abrasive wheels, there is some possibility of danger to the eyes from the flying particles of grit, so goggles should always be worn when tool-grinding. In addition, care should be taken to see that the wheel-face is in good condition and that the tool-rest is close to the wheel-face, for many accidents occur from a space being left between the wheel and the tool-rest. The average wheel speed is about 5,000 surface ft. per min., so that a tool drawn down between the wheel and the tool-rest can be a source of great danger.

In the grinding operation, only light pressure should be used against the wheel, while the tool should be reciprocated across the full face of the wheel to insure even wear. Inexperienced workmen often leave the tool in one position, with the result that a deep groove is formed in the face of the wheel, rendering it useless for accurate grinding, and necessitating the removal of a considerable part of the wheel-face to get it true again. Not only does this take up considerable time, with the machine out of use, but it also results in a short life for an expensive wheel.

One of the chief dangers to the tool through heavy grinding is that of overheating the cutting edge, which becomes cracked or softened. The solution to this difficulty is to use a continuous and abundant supply of coolant to prevent a high rise in temperature, and not to follow the practice of many tool-grinders, who grind a tool dry and plunge it into water when it becomes inconveniently hot to hold. This has the tendency to develop fine

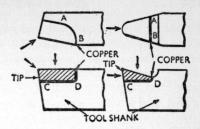

Fig. 31. Method of brazing a cemented carbide tip on to a tool shank.

cracks in the cutting edge, with the result that the tool is soon destroyed.

Carbide tools must be ground on special wheels, using the front face of the wheel, since grinding on the periphery has a tendency to produce a concave surface in the tool-face, and so weaken the cutting edge. Only moderate pressure should be used, for the application of undue force, combined with the extreme hardness of the material, results in rapid wheel wear with possible cracking and chipping of the cutting edge of the tool.

When hand-grinding on pedestal-type machines, the use of special rest and angle fixtures is recommended to obtain the correct angles in a simple manner. To minimize the risk of chipping, the tool should be ground so that the points of the wheel travel from the tip to the body of the tool, the front and side faces being ground first, and lastly the top. There are schools of thought, one of which recommends dry and the other wet grind, but the main point to emphasize is that if wet grinding is employed, a copious supply of coolant must be used.

Lapping

For the finishing cuts, lapping is advisable, and a quick means of lapping is obtained by the use of bakelite-bonded wheels impregnated with diamond dust; a good quality of thin oil should be used with them when lapping. A similar material is also supplied in the form of hand-laps to enable the operator to touch up the cutting edge of the tool without disturbing the setting of the latter in the machine. This is an important precau-

and which are not appreciably work-hardened by the cutting operation, need smaller rakes. Little or no rake is used for hard brass, phosphor-bronze, and similar metals.

The following recommended angles may be used as a guide, with the individual requirements of any job being developed by experience.

	CLEARANCE	SIDE SLOPE	TOP SLOPE
Aluminum	8–12°	12–16°	20–40°
Other non-ferrous metals	6–12°	5–15°	0– 6°
Cast irons	4– 6°	3–10°	0– 4°
Steels	6– 8°	10–20°	4–10°
Non-metallic materials	8–10°	5– 5°	3– 6°

tionary measure, which should be carried out at frequent intervals in order to preserve the cutting edge by removing any particles adhering to it.

Tool angles vary with the nature of the operation, the material to be machined, the quality of finish, and other variables. For cemented-carbide tools, clearance angles should be just great enough to allow of a free cutting action. From 4 to 6 deg. is common for steel cutting, but larger values are generally used for soft metals; and for certain non-metallic substances, such as vulcanite, bakelite, etc., the angle is usually about 12 deg.

A large top-rake gives an acute cutting angle and reduces the component forces acting on the tool. For the softer metals comparatively large rakes are used, but these cannot be employed when cutting steels, as the latter offer a greater resistance to penetration. In this case, a larger cutting angle is required to enable the cutting edge to enter the work without being snipped or broken and to sustain the cut when the tool has entered. Brittle materials such as cast iron, which leave the work in short independent chips,

To utilize cemented-carbide tools to their full extent radical alterations in lathe design have been made. In the first instance the speed range of the fast headstock has been raised considerably, while a much finer range of feeds has been provided. To prevent vibration, electric motors are isolated from the headstock, and the final spindle connection is made by V belts or by some similar flexible means.

Owing to the high speeds of work revolution, the fixed type of loose-head center would be rapidly destroyed, so that a live center must be fitted to revolve with the work. Two general types are employed, one fitted with a taper shank, as shown in Fig. 32; this simply replaces the standard center in the spindle. Ball bearings are fitted to take end-thrust, and care is required to see that all end-play is eliminated. The second type is more suitable for large lathes, for it will be realized that excessive overhang will be fatal to successful running; so that for heavy lathes the center is better if built into the spindle, as shown in Fig. 33. The advantage of this design is that the center proper can be removed without disturbing the bearings, an advantage when replacement is required. The end-pressure is taken on the center ball-thrust washers and journal loads on front and rear roller bearings.

Another problem is the disposal and control of cuttings, which in the case of steel turnings flying from the work at high speeds constitutes a real danger to the operator and anyone near the machine. A solution is to both mount the tool and run the lathe in the reverse direction to normal, so that the long curling cuttings flow from the cutting zone downward to the back of the machine.

Disposal of Cuttings

Several machines are made with this feature, but, more generally, a less satisfactory solution by means of a chip-breaker is employed. One attempt to overcome this difficulty is to grind a step in the top of the tool, the side rake extending for only a short distance behind the cutting edge and leaving a portion of the tip as a shoulder parallel to this edge. The object is to form a barrier which will cause the shaving as it flows across the tool-face to form into close coils and break. Unfortunately the form of shaving varies with the dimensions of the cut as well as with the metal ma-

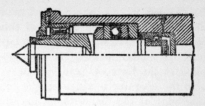

Fig. 33. Another type of revolving center for a large lathe, built into the spindle so that the center proper can be removed without disturbing the bearings when replacement is necessary.

chined, so that although a tool ground in this way may give good results with a given material, cut, etc., it may not do so when one or other of these variables is changed.

A second method which is capable of adjustment is to use a separate deflector which may be clamped down along the top of the tool. The deflector may be made of carbon steel faced with Stellite. The front face of the deflector is set at a steep angle, and the arrangement has the advantage that the deflector can easily be adjusted in relation to the cutting edge of the tool. Good results have been claimed for this device, although chip-guards may be necessary as an additional precaution.

It is difficult to give a tabulated list of suitable cutting speeds for cemented-carbide tools, due to the various grades of carbide and the conditions of cutting. Ordinary cast iron and mild steel is regularly machined at speeds ranging from 250 to 1,000 ft. per min. when a machine is in first-class condition and a feed of $\frac{1}{100}$ in. is used. The light non-ferrous metals (not containing iron) are machined at speeds limited only by the machine range and the ability of the operator to control it. These speeds may reach as much as 6,000 ft. per min.

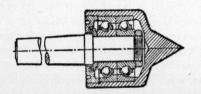

Fig. 32. Revolving type of lathe-center fitted with taper shank, which replaces the standard center in the spindle.

The necessary range of lathe-spindle speeds depends on the variation of the work diameters, the nature of the material to be machined and the type of cutting tools in operation, whether carbon steel, high-speed steel, or cemented-carbide. Thus, a lathe for turning shafts of a fairly constant diameter requires but a few speed changes, whereas a general-purpose machine fitted with a gap-bed to accommodate large diameters and cutting with various grades of tools on widely divergent metals needs sufficient speeds to cover all requirements.

Speed Changes

The speeds themselves should increase in a geometrical progression range, as 2, 4, 8, 16, or 3, 9, 27, etc., by increments obtained by multiplying each successive speed by a common multiplier, known as the progression ratio, which is generally 1.26 to 1.

The reason why these speeds should bear a certain relation to one another can be seen by assuming that four shafts are to be turned in a lathe, the respective diameters being 1, 2, 5, and 10 in. To keep the surface or peripheral speed the same in each case, the 1-in. shaft must revolve at twice the speed of the 2-in. shaft, and the 10-in. shaft at one-tenth the speed of the 1-in. shaft.

An addition of 1 in. to the diameter of the 1-in. piece then reduces the speed 100 percent. If 1 in. is added to the 2-in. shaft, the speed is reduced 50 percent, while 1 in. added to the diameters of the 5-in. and 10-in. shafts reduces the speed 20 and 10 percent respectively. Thus, the speed must vary inversely with the diameter for any given surface speed, and differ by small increments at the slow speeds,

the increment gradually increasing as the speed increases. In practice, the operator is soon made aware if the cutting speed is too high by the work glazing, and the necessity for frequent re-grinding of the tool. On the other hand, there is nothing to indicate too low a cutting speed, which merely results in a loss of time, unless the operator becomes aware of the capabilities and characteristics of the various cutting materials.

The Best Speeds

The actual cutting speed in ft. per min. varies for different materials, and also with the shape and rigidity of the work. For work taking up the full machine capacity, difficult to hold, or of fragile material necessarily means a restriction of cutting speed or feed and a decreased depth of cut. Moreover, the maximum permissible speed may not always be the most economical if frequent tool-grinding is required, but for general practice the following speeds are suitable for turning on lathes using cutting tools of high-speed steel.

Mild steel.........100 ft. per min.
Cast steel......... 50 ft. per min.
Aluminum ....300 ft. per min.
Cast iron.......... 70 ft. per min.
Malleable iron.....100 ft. per min.
Soft brass ....200 ft. per min.
Bronze .... 70 ft. per min.

The above speeds can be increased by 10 to 30 percent when light finishing cuts of only .002 to .010 in. are made. If used with cutting lubricants, both of these can be increased 25 to 50 percent. With tungsten-carbide tipped cutting tools these may be increased 100 to 800 percent.

With these cutting speeds as a basis, the operator, knowing the diameter of the work to be machined, now must find the most suitable spindle speed in revolutions per minute, and this can be obtained from:

Revs. per min. of spindle =

$$\frac{\text{Cutting speed (ft. per min.)}}{\text{Circum. of work in ft.}}$$

or

Cutting speed (ft. per min.) =

$$\frac{\text{r.p.m. of spindle} \times \text{circum. work. in.}}{12}$$

As an example, let it be assumed that a shaft 10 in. in diameter is to be machined at 100 ft. per min., then

$$\text{r.p.m.} \quad \frac{100}{.26 \times 10} = 38,$$

where .26 is a constant obtained by dividing π by 12, and 10 is the diameter of the work in inches.

The spindle speeds of the lathe are usually given on a plate fixed on the headstock, and the operator may find that the exact required speed is not listed, so that a compromise selection must be made. This is a drawback not only of cone-pulley drives, but of many geared headstocks, for the next higher speed given on the plate may be 30 percent increase on the one required. Obviously, the tool would not stand up to this speed without frequent re-grinding, so that the next lower speed must be selected with, say, a loss in production of 25 percent. The solution is, of course, an infinitely variable speed range, to enable the exact, and therefore most economical, cutting speed to be obtained for all conditions.

Another way of reducing the cost of expensive cutting tools is by the employment of tool-holder bits, as they are termed in the trade. These are short sections of high-speed or similar cutting steels made to fit into tool-

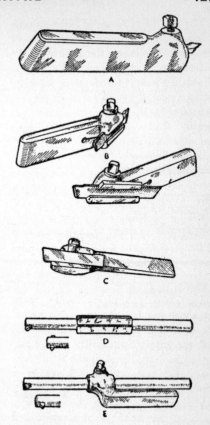

Fig. 34. Various types of tool-bits, interchangeable for fitting into a single holder. A, B, and C are used for straight and side turning; D and E for boring and recessing operations.

holders of various sizes and types to cover practically all turning operations as well as boring and screw-cutting. These small tool sections can be set at various angles so that forging is not required, while grinding is simplified to a great extent, for the position of the tool in the holder is generally such that the most important cutting edge exists naturally. Thus the minimum amount of grinding is required for sharpening, while the only piece wearing out is the small

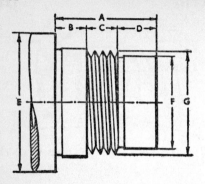

Fig. 35. Improved type of spindle nose; the length of the threaded portion C is such that when the chuck is put on the spindle end, the two locating parts F and G must register before the threaded portion is reached.

tool-bit, easily replaced when worn too short for further use. The useful life of the holder itself is indefinite, and the interchangeability of a number of tool-bits in any one holder reduces the number of holders to a minimum.

Several patterns are shown in Fig. 34. The one at A is of drop-forged steel, hardened, and machined on top and bottom true with the sides. The tool enters the holder at an angle, and is held in position by the square-headed screw. Similar holders are available, but with the front end bent partly round, either left- or right-hand, for side turning, whereas the one illustrated is for straight turning. Other types of this design are shown at B, with a knife or side tool-holder at C. Similar tool-holders are available for boring or recessing operations, two different designs being indicated at D and E. These are of the extension type for long boring if required, the bar being adjustable for length in the holder, which in the case of D is simply a bored and split

rectangular bar, the boring bar holding by clamping action of the lathe-tool straps on the split holder. One useful feature of these tools is that any required cutting edge can be presented to the work, simply by partially revolving the boring bar. Thus, again, grinding of the small bits is of the simplest nature.

The principal lathe attachments are either for driving the work, supporting it during machining or, in some cases, performing both functions. Many of these attachments, such as catch-plates, face-plates and chucks of various types, are screwed or bolted on to the fast headstock spindle nose, and as the true running of these components depends on the accuracy of the spindle nose, it assumes an importance worthy of consideration and care.

The usual type of lathe-spindle is made with a flange end and a nose partly threaded along its length, but leaving a plain portion up to the flange for locating purposes; see Figs. 2 or 5. An improved design is indicated in Fig. 35. The threaded portion C is between two locating diameters F and G, and is of such a length that when the chuck or face-plate is being put on the spindle end, the two locating parts must register before the threaded portion is reached. This is an advantage in assembly, preventing damage to the threaded portion by cross-threading, which often necessitates several attempts to fit a chuck or other driver on to the ordinary type of spindle nose. All types of threaded spindle noses, as well as the mating parts, should be carefully cleaned and lubricated before assembly, for chucks and the like have a tendency to seize fast against the spindle flange when these precautions are neglected, and attempts at removal may result in permanent injury to the spindle and bearings.

Although the action of cutting is to tighten a chuck or face-plate on the spindle nose, there is danger of loosening if the spindle is pulled up quickly at high speed. Thus, a large spindle flange can with advantage be used for bolting chucks and face-plates direct to the spindle, although a short threaded portion is provided to which face-plates of light chucks can be attached. This direct bolting without a back-plate to which chucks are generally fitted is a big advantage, in that it prevents overhang of the chuck and considerably reduces vibration during machining. Owing to the large variety of chucks and variation in size of spindle noses, it is not feasible to obtain a chuck to screw direct on to the spindle nose, hence the need for a back-plate, usually provided by the user for his own particu-

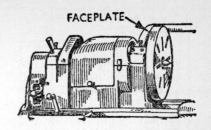

Fig. 37. Face-plate with slots to which work is bolted for machining.

lar lathe, to act as an intermediary between the chuck and the spindle nose in the manner shown in Fig. 36.

Some indication of the use of the spindle attachments is required, and for turning between centers a catch-plate is used. The sole purpose of this unit is to revolve the work by means of a projecting peg catching against the dog on the work. A face-plate, shown in Fig. 37, may be used for the same purpose, but is larger in diameter and provided with slots to which work may be bolted for machining purposes.

Lathe Chucks

A chuck provides the best and simplest method of holding and rotating work which is not suitable for mounting between the centers owing to its short length or large diameter. The device comprises a circular body with slots in which jaws slide to grip the work, these jaws being made of tough steel with three steps on each to accommodate various diameters of work. The face of each step is grooved or serrated to facilitate holding the work without it slipping under cut and damaging the part held. The movement of the jaws onto the work is by the use of a long-handled spanner rotating in a clockwise direction, so that the full strength of the operator is available to

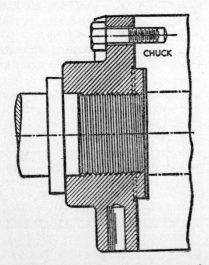

Fig. 36. Back-plate to act as intermediary between chuck and spindle nose. This is usually fitted by each lathe-user for his own particular lathe.

effect the gripping action of the jaws on the work to be held. Many operators supplement this effort by fitting a length of piping on to the handle of the box spanner, but such means of increasing the work-holding power of a chuck are to be discouraged, for they merely result in early destruction of the working parts.

Power-Operated Chucks

Where great holding power is required, special chucks with auxiliary power such as compressed air or oil pressure are available, and, on the other hand, where simplicity of chucking is the first consideration, magnetic chucks can be employed, the effort of the operator in this case being only that of holding the work on the face of the chuck and switching on the current. But this type is suitable only for light duty, and the standard lathe is generally fitted with two accepted types which cover the majority of turning operations. These are the independent-jaw and the self-centering types. There are, of course, variations in design, particularly as regards the number of jaws or gripping parts, and the shape of these jaws, while in some

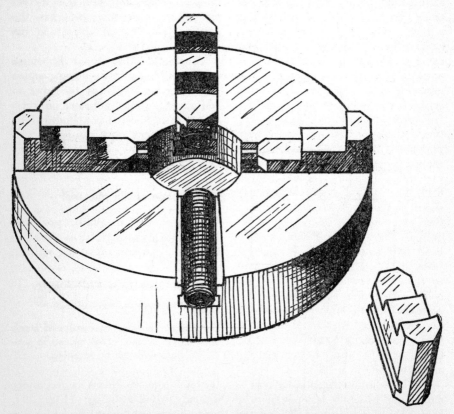

Fig. 38. A 4-jaw independent chuck, each of the jaws having its own movement by screw-action down on to the work. This chuck has great gripping power and can hold irregular-shaped work of various types.

cases chucks are made to combine all the advantages of both types, being either self-centering or independent as desired.

While the operator should become familiar with these types as they sometimes provide a solution to what might otherwise be a difficult piece of machining, it is first necessary to become accustomed to using the more general kinds of chuck, such as is represented by Fig. 38, which shows a section view of an independent chuck. As the name indicates, each of the four jaws has a separate movement by screw action down on to the work-piece; thus, some skill is required in setting work to run true. This is accomplished by holding a piece of chalk, or dial indicator, against the revolving work, and tightening or slackening the various jaws until the work runs satisfactorily true, although some assistance is given by scribed lines at intervals around the front face of the chuck. The main feature of this type of chuck is great gripping power and the fact that irregular-shaped work, such as brackets and various castings or forgings, can be held. The jaws are reversible in the slides, so that work can be gripped either externally or internally as required. The drawing shows the left-hand half as a section between the jaws, and T-slots are shown machined so that, by removing the jaws, the body castings can be used as a face-plate, or, if additional holding facilities are required with work difficult to hold satisfactorily by the jaws, additional support can be obtained by means of bolts in the T-slots.

The standard self-centering type is more rapid in action, less powerful by having three jaws instead of four, and is restricted to holding cylindrical work. The jaws are not reversible, and two sets are required to grip internal or external work. In the general design a scroll is revolved by bevel pinions and traverses the mating jaws in or out as required. The design is somewhat weak, and accuracy is soon lost, so that frequent regrinding of the jaw-faces is required for precision work; or, alternatively, soft jaws are fitted, these being useful for holding work already partly machined, and easily trued by a turning tool to regain accurate setting. In changing the jaws, care should be taken to see that the numbers on the jaws and the slides coincide, that jaw number 1 is the first to engage the scroll, and that the remainder follow in order, otherwise the jaws will not be concentric and the work will run out of true.

There are other types of chuck which combine a self-centering action with an adaptability of the jaws to setting at various positions in relation to each other; thus cylindrical- or irregular-shaped work can be gripped by the pre-setting of the jaws to any of the required position.

Use of the Mandrel

After a wheel or similar work has been bored in a chuck, it is often finished on a mandrel supported between

Fig. 39. A mandrel of hardened steel, such as the above, is often used to support work during finishing.

the lathe-centers. This is an accurately ground cylindrical bar (Fig. 39), made in various diameters and lengths and slightly below standard size at one end, but tapering upwards .0005

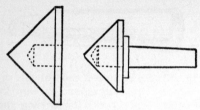

Fig. 40. Pipe centers, used to support the end of a pipe or of any overhanging work with a large bore. End-pieces are fitted in turn to the single taper shank as required.

per in. along the length. Thus, a mandrel of suitable diameter can be driven with sufficient force into the bore of the work to withstand the cutting action without slipping when the mandrel is mounted in between the lathe-centers. At each end the mandrel is reduced in diameter and provided with a flattened portion, upon which the driving dog grips. For special diameters expanding mandrels are sometimes used, these being adjustable for diameters within a small range.

As the accuracy of the work machined depends on the mandrel running true between the lathe centers, any damage to its center ends should be avoided. If a mandrel is driven into the work by a hand hammer, a pad should always be placed over the end of the mandrel to receive the force of the blow, but an arbor press for the purpose is more satisfactory and a surer preventive of damage. Arbor presses are made in a variety of types and sizes, ranging from power-operated machines worked by screw or hydraulic means to give pressures of many tons, to those hand-actuated.

Special Centers and Shaft Supports

There are many lathe operations on which special centers can advanta-geously be employed. Mention has already been made of revolving centers. To support the end of a pipe or any overhanging work with a large bore, pipe centers (Fig. 40) are employed. Only one taper shank to fit the tail-stock is required, and then a set of end-pieces can be fitted in turn on the one shank as required. In the diagram, the end-pieces are of cast iron to revolve on the steel shank, but ball bearings are often introduced to reduce friction. Sometimes a cone-center can be employed to fit over the end of a work-piece. This is the reverse of the pipe-center, being one of a set of hollow cones mounted on a support in the same manner.

When turning long, slender shafts between centers there is a risk of chatter-marks appearing on the work, or even of the shaft becoming bent or in-

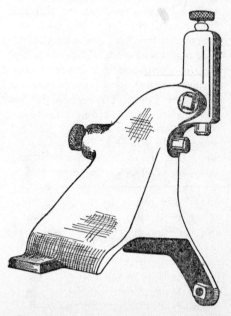

Fig. 41. Follower steady rest used in machining work of small diameter that is likely to spring if it has no support.

accurate, if some support is not given as the tool travels along. For this purpose a traveling stay or steady rest (Fig. 41) is attached to the lathe-saddle. Before commencing a long cut, two adjustable jaws are brought down on to some true running part of the shaft, one jaw immediately behind it facing the tool, the other being on top of the shaft. There are variations in this arrangement: sometimes the jaws are placed in angular positions, and occasionally three jaws are fitted; but the object is the same in every case— that of preventing the shaft from lifting and flexing during the course of the cutting operation.

The same result can be obtained by fitting a stationary rest (Fig. 42) but as the attachment is fixed to the lathe-bed, the saddle traverse is limited. For this reason the main use of the stay is to support the end of a shaft overhanging from a chuck so that the end

Fig. 43. Morse tapers such as this are made in sizes corresponding with the standard holes bored on drilling machine spindles.

can be bored or turned. Three jaws are fitted, two in the bottom part of the stay and one in the top part, which can be swung open to allow the work to be placed or removed from the chuck without removing the bottom part.

While the main function of the tailstock is to support one end of the work, it is not restricted to this function, but can be used to perform other machining operations, chiefly drilling and boring. The spindle end is bored with a taper hole, the size being one of a series known as Morse tapers. These taper holes are standard on drilling machine spindles, so that any attachment used for drilling operations can be fitted on a tailstock if of sufficient size. The various tapers are numbered 0 to 6, and made so that sleeves, as in Fig. 43, can be used to fit inside and outside of each other, and by reducing or building up, any attachment with a Morse taper shank can be accommodated. Thus, taper-shank twist-drills can be fitted either direct into the spindle end or fit into sleeves. The tailstock can then be brought along the bed until the drill-point is close to the work, and the headstock clamped down. Drilling is then carried out by rotating the hand wheel in order to feed the spindle forward.

Sometimes extension sockets (Fig. 44) are used to obtain a longer reach forward for deep holes; or boring bars

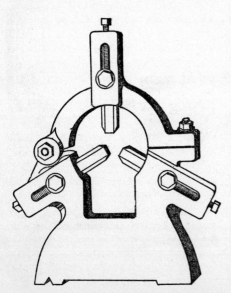

Fig. 42. Steady rest used to support the end of a shaft overhanging from a chuck so that it can be bored or turned.

Fig. 44. Extension shank for a Morse taper, used to obtain a longer reach forward when drilling deep holes.

and cutters as shown in Fig. 45, are used for larger holes, in which case several cutters may be in operation together. This type of bar requires some support at the end, and a pilot bushing should be fitted in the end of the headstock spindle to support the bar as it is fed forward. After boring, a hole may require reaming to give an accurate size, so that drills or boring bars may be replaced by the finishing tool (Fig. 46). Reamers are not meant to be used as cutting tools, and should remove only a small amount of metal to insure size. In order to follow the hole previously drilled, they should be allowed a floating action, which requires a special holder to fit into the tailstock.

It is now proposed to consider the procedure involved in preparing and machining certain components. Let us assume that the operation required is to produce a shaft and collar, as shown in Fig. 47. Commencing with the shaft, the first operation is to saw off a length of bar one-eighth more than the finished length and diameter, and to center the ends. The bar is now fitted with a dog and placed between the lathe-centers and each end faced in turn, using a knife-tool for cutting. The turning tool is mounted in the compound rest to turn the diameter A from one end of the bar close up to the dog. The same tool can be used to turn down the diameter B, the metal removed being shown sectioned. The work is now reversed in position, with the dog on the end B, so that the diameter C can be turned to size. It will require several cuts or traverses to remove all the metal, and if a round-nose tool has been used, a knife or parting tool will be required to square out the corners.

Fig. 46. A hole made by the drill or boring bar is finished off accurately by a machine reamer or finishing tool of this kind. It requires a special holder.

The piece of steel for the collar, having been sawn from the bar, will be gripped in a self-centering chuck, and faced with a knife-tool on edge A. The next operation is to bore the hole B by means of a twist-drill in the tailstock, care being taken to insure a true start. More than one drill may be required, depending on the size of the hole, or alternatively, the drill may be followed by a reamer to make certain of accurate size.

The remaining operation will be performed between the lathe-centers, so that the collar is driven on a mandrel for this purpose. The knife-tool already in position in the compound rest may be used to face the side D to give the correct thickness of the col-

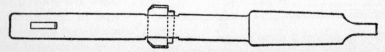

Fig. 45. Boring bar and cutters such as this are used for boring larger holes. The bar is supported at the end, as it is fed forward, by a pilot bushing in the end of the headstock spindle. Several cutters may be in operation together.

lar, and then be replaced by a turning tool to machine over the top of the collar D. To improve the appearance, a file and emery cloth are generally used to polish the work, remove sharp corners or obtain final size. In filing work revolving in a lathe there is a certain amount of danger, particularly from clothes being caught by the dog so that loose overall sleeves or even neck-ties should be watched, and on no account should a file be used without a handle.

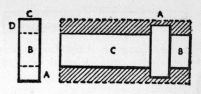

Fig. 47. Method used in turning a shaft and collar. A piece of steel ⅛ in. more than the finished length and diameter is sawn off the shaft to make the collar, and the ends are centered.

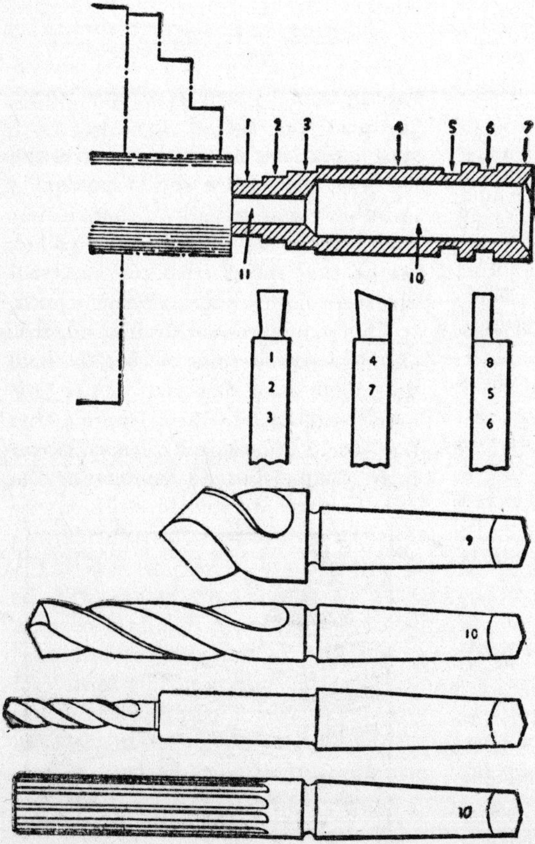

These two components, although simple parts, may be regarded as typical of the procedure employed in work performed on center lathes. Occasionally work out-of-balance must be machined, and in such a case it is bolted on to a face-plate and balance weights are attached to the face-plate in such a position as to neutralize the out-of-balance and mitigate the danger which may arise as a result of high speeds of revolution.

Again, there is a vast amount of machine work which can be completed at one setting in a chuck; this is shown by Fig. 48, a bronze pump plunger. The hollow spindle of the headstock is used to accommodate a bar, which is gripped in a three-jaw chuck and allowed to extend out sufficiently for machining. Eleven operations are required for the job, necessitating the use of three tools in the compound rest and four in the

Fig. 48. The parts of a pump plunger, and the tools used in turning it. The numbers marked on each tool correspond with the numbered parts of the plunger on which it is used. Eleven operations in all are necessary (see text).

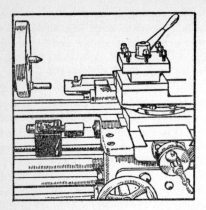

Fig. 49. Distance blocks can be inserted on a lathe between the trip stop and the slide stops to trip the feed at the lengths or diameters required.

tailstock. The various parts of the plunger requiring tooling are numbered with the same figures as the tools performing the operation; these would be used in the following sequence.

(a) Turn diameter 7 full length.

(b) Turn diameter 4.

(c) Square out 5, 6, and face end 8.

(d) Cut shoulder 1, 2, 3.

(e) Center and recess end of bore 9 from tailstock.

(f) Drill main bore 10 with twist-drill.

(g) Drill small bore 11 using extension socket.

(h) Ream main bore.

(i) Cut off to length using tool 8.

The bar would then be loosened in the chuck and brought forward for another part to be made. The changing of various tools takes up as much time as the machining, so the advantages of a square turret with the tools always ready for the work will be realized.

Shoulder Turning

In turning a part with several diameters and lengths like that just de-scribed, the operator must stop the machine after each traverse to check the work. This is frequently inconvenient and time-wasting, and leads to inaccuracies due to errors in reading from the measuring tool or in the tool itself. Loss of time is increased by the fact that the operator applies a number of small cuts, and sizes the work at each cut, before reaching finished size. Such methods are unnecessary on lathes where feed-trip stops can be accurately set to limit positively the movement of the slides. The procedure in such cases is as follows:

A stop is set approximately, and securely fixed by screws. Accurate adjustment for the longitudinal feed-stop is obtained by a fine-thread screw having a micrometer scale, and for the cross-slide movement by a similar stop, which can be set by the graduated collar on the traversing screw, and has therefore no micrometer scale.

These stops positively trip the feed at the required time, with the result that numbers of like parts can be produced without any variation, and time that would otherwise be spent in carefully feeding-in and controlling the

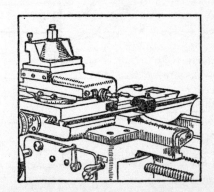

Fig. 50. A trip stop to limit the movement of the slides reduces stoppage of the machine when turning a part with several diameters and lengths.

traverse of the tool is saved. When machining parts with several shoulders, distance blocks (Fig. 49) can be inserted between the trip-stop and the stop on the slides to trip the feed accurately at the required length, or diameters, by stops (Fig. 50).

For such work a machine equipped with multiple tool-holders would be especially applicable, and would in many cases successfully compete with capstan, combination turret, and multi-cut lathes, particularly if arranged with front and rear tool-holders. When so arranged, the front tool-holders would be used for longitudinal turning and the rear for forming operations as in the case of multi-cut lathes.

Button- and Disc-Setting

There are accurate methods of locating work on the face-plate of a lathe for boring. The button method uses cylindrical bushings $\frac{1}{2}$ in. in diameter with holes $\frac{1}{8}$ in. larger in diameter than the screws passing through them. The principle is that end measurement with a micrometer can be more easily made than attempting to bore holes at centers which have been marked out on the work.

As an example, assume that a pump body is to have two bores at 4-in. centers (Fig. 51). The procedure is to mark out, drill, and tap two holes for the bushing-screws at approximately the correct center distance, and to clamp the bushings loosely on the casting. A micrometer is then set to measure 5 in. (4-in. centers and $\frac{1}{2}$ in. diameter of each bushing) and the bushing lightly tapped to give this dimension, at which distance they are clamped by the screws.

The casting is now bolted to the lathe face-plate with one bushing as near center as possible and revolved against a dial indicator, until by careful adjustment it registers dead true.

The bushing is now removed, and the tapped hole drilled away. It is important now that the hole be enlarged by a single-point tool, for the tapped hole was probably not central, and a twist-drill will always follow a previous hole. Boring then proceeds until size is attained, when the casting is released and the second button set in the same way as before. The same boring procedure is followed, with the assurance that the centers will be maintained to close limits.

The disc method is on similar lines to that described, except that discs are made to such diameters that when their peripheries are in contact, each disc center will coincide with the position of the hole to be bored; the centers are then used for locating the work.

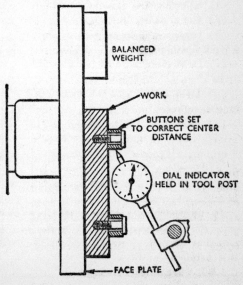

Fig. 51. A pump body with two bores, which serves as an example of the use of buttons.

Uses of Oil

The functions of oil for cutting compounds delivered to a tool may be conveniently presented under five headings:

(1) To cool the work and cutter.

(2) To wash away chips.

(3) To lubricate the bearing formed between the chip and lip of the cutting tool.

(4) To enable the cutting tool to produce a good finish.

(5) To protect the finished product from rust and corrosion.

Of these functions the cooling action is the most important. During the performance of any machining operation heat is generated between the tool and work, and if provision is not made for the removal of this heat, the temperature may become so excessive that the cutting edge of the tool breaks down. This, of course, results in loss of time for tool changing or regrinding. There is, in addition, the possibility of expanding the work during machining, so that the work measured at this stage may be found undersize on contracting.

In deep-hole drilling, such as boring lathe-spindles, ability of the cutting compound to wash away cuttings is of importance. The tool is ground in such a way that the chips are broken up into small pieces and the compound is delivered in sufficient volume and pressure to wash the chips out of the hole.

In the machining of cast iron, as well as aluminum, high-carbon steel and some grades of brass, the lubrication action is of little importance, as the chips break into small pieces; but it is very important when machining materials such as low-carbon steels, where long chips are produced that curl back over the lip of the tool. In such cases a bearing is produced in which the frictional resistance is severe, and unless the oil or cutting compound is a lubricant as well as a coolant, this friction will result in rapidly wearing out the tool.

Diversity of opinion exists concerning the possibility of oil affording a lubricating action for the bearing between the lip of a tool and the chip. It is fairly certain that metal-to-metal contact exists between the lip of a tool and the work, but as oils are less efficient cooling media than cutting compounds dissolved in water, it is assumed that the superiority of oil where long curly chips are produced is due to the lubricating action between cutting and tool-lip.

Supply of Coolant

A good finish can be obtained on certain classes of work whether the metal is cut dry or a compound is used, but when the latter condition is required, only a small film is actually needed at the cutting tool. In most cases, however, the fluid is necessary to enable a higher cutting speed, feed, or depth of cut to be maintained, so that a greater volume is used than would be necessary for finish alone.

Good cutting oils will prevent rusting of parts made from iron and steel, but lard oil with too high a percentage of free fatty acid will cause verdigris to form on brass parts, while vegetable oils often give trouble through gumming the bearings of small machines.

The method of applying lubricant or cutting compound to the lathe tool is often from a simple drip-can mounted at the rear of the saddle, this being fitted with a length of pipe to swivel to the most suitable position over the tool, and provision by means of a tap to regulate the flow of coolant. The only advantages of this method are those of cheapness and simplicity, so that a more efficient arrangement for supplying coolant is by a small pump driven by a belt from the machine (Fig. 52) or, as on many modern lathes, by a small electrically driven pump. The coolant is drawn by the pump from a sump in the trough under the bed, large cuttings being prevented from entering the sump by a covering plate, while a gauze filter surrounds the end of the suction pipe to prevent fine cuttings from being drawn into the pump and causing damage therein. In some cases a central distribution station is arranged so that one large pump will deliver coolant through pipe-lines to several lathes. With this system means are provided for returning the lubricant, along with filters, sterilizers, and means for purifying the returned oil. The four principal types of pumps used for this purpose are the geared, wing, plunger, and centrifugal types; the first and last are by far the most common.

The arrangement of piping to deliver lubricant from the pump is easily managed in cases where no adjust-

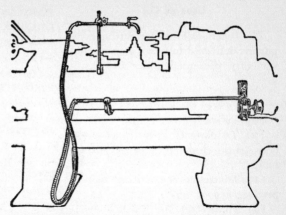

Fig. 52. An efficient method of supplying coolant to a lathe is by means of a small pump driven by a belt from the machine, or by a separate electric motor. The coolant is drawn from a sump in the trough under the bed of the lathe.

ment is required to suit movement of a machine-table or saddle, but in cases where, say, a lathe saddle has to travel a considerable distance, special means have to be provided to overcome this difficulty. Flexible metal tube connected to the supply pipe solves the problem in many cases, but becomes too long to be convenient on some machines, so that telescopic tubes are often used to furnish the compensation for the table or saddle traverse.

The efficiency of the results obtained in cooling and lubricating cutting tools is largely governed by the size and form of the nozzle through which the lubricant is delivered, as well as the direction, position, pressure, and volume of the supply of the coolant.

TURRET LATHES

THE chief object of an ordinary lathe is its general adaptability, but when mass production of parts is required, it is profitable to sacrifice adaptability

to specialization. Thus, when parts of large diameter and small width, such as gears, pulleys, or flywheels, are required in quantity, a machine as shown in Fig. 53 is called for. This shows the outline drawing of a boring and surfacing lathe. The main difference from an ordinary lathe is that the tailstock is omitted and a *turret* substituted for the tool-post. The possibilities of machining by the tools held in a turret are varied. Compounding is possible, so that one holder carries not one, but several, tools on each face, and every tool is capable of being brought into definite action against the work.

Fig. 54 shows a selection of holders for use in turrets, and comprises (at A) an extension slide to carry tools to turn large diameters or to carry a combination of tools. B shows the standard holder for this type of lathe. The round shank fits into a hole in the turret face and is clamped in any position suitable for the tools, which may be at right angles to each other, to reach the work. Another face of the turret may carry a drill-holder C, the

shank being the same size as that of tool-holder B, so that all equipment is interchangeable in any face of the turret and can be revolved to come into action in any sequence of operations. This drill-holder is bored out with a Morse taper hole to accommodate standard drills, but it may also be used to carry other similar tools.

At D is shown an extension drill or reamer holder, which is a casting bolted on to the turret face instead of fitting into a hole. A multiple toolholder is indicated at E, this allowing three tools to be set at suitable spacing and be brought into action together. In such instances, one tool is often set slightly in front of another, the first tool roughing and the second following with a fine finishing cut. At F is shown a floating reamer holder, fitting direct into the turret, while G is a straight shank-drill or bar-holder. H shows another type of single square-section tool-holder, and a boring bar-

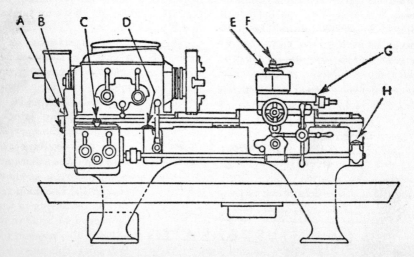

Fig. 53. Outline of boring and surfacing lathe, which differs from a center lathe in having no tailstock and a hexagon turret in place of a tool-post. The letters indicate oiling points for A and B, feed gearing; C, gear box; D, start and stop motion; E and F, hexagon turret; G, apron; H, shaft bearing.

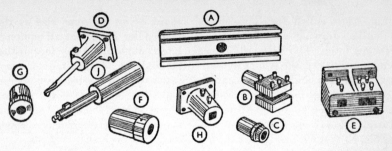

Fig. 54. Tools and holders used on the hexagon turrets of boring and surfacing lathes. Tools to turn large diameters, or combination sets of tools, can be carried in the extension slide A. For other references see text.

holder with a taper hole. It will be seen that a machine with a selection of this equipment always in position makes for high production without elaborate tools.

The limitations of a boring and surfacing lathe are that only one of these movements—sliding for boring or turning, and surfacing—may be in action at one time. There are, therefore, further possibilities for time-saving if, in addition to multiple tooling, several operations can be going on at the same time; hence the development of the capstan and turret lathes. The difference in terms may be illustrated by the diagram of a capstan lathe (Fig. 55), which shows that the capstan or turret is mounted on a slide having longitudinal movements in a saddle fixed to the bed, whereas a turret lathe (Fig. 56) has a similar turret on a saddle sliding directly on the bed. Generally capstan lathes operate on smaller parts than turret lathes, but both are fitted with an additional square turret close to the headstock, and if this is engaged with power traverses, then the machine is usually termed a combination turret lathe. The tool equipment may be arranged for chuck-work in similar manner to that described for boring and surfacing lathes, or be set up for bar-work.

The machining operations on a pump-plunger have been shown as performed on a center lathe using the tailstock and a square turret for carrying the tools (Fig. 48). If now a capstan lathe is available for the work, the same tools could be arranged on the square and hexagon turrets as shown in Fig. 57. The main feature is the saving in time by every tool being in position in the hexagon turret, so that as the turret is brought back after each operation, it automatically revolves and brings the

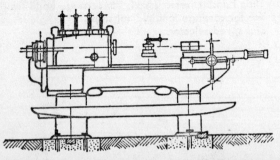

Fig. 55. In the capstan lathe, here shown, the capstan or turret is mounted on a longitudinally-moving slide in a saddle fixed to the bed.

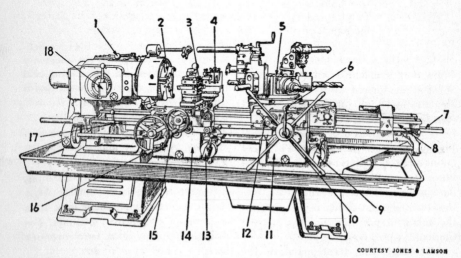

Fig. 56. Saddle-type Universal Turret Lathe: 1, start, stop, & reverse lever; 2, three jaw scroll chuck; 3, square turret; 4, tools on rear of cross slide; 5, hexagon turret; 6, two speed power traverse for saddle and power indexing of hexagon turret; 7, nine adjustable saddle stops; 8, hardened and ground steel bed ways; 9, single lever dial feed selector; 10, wheel for hand traverse of saddle and indexing hexagon turret; 11, turret saddle; 12, turret power feed lever; 13, single lever dial feed selector; 14, carriage; 15, cross slide hand traverse wheel; 16, carriage hand traverse wheel; 17, adjustable stop bar for carriage longitudinal stops; 18, single lever dial speed selector.

next tool into position for drilling, etc. In addition, stops are set to limit the forward movement of the tools, so that depth measurement is not required. This is in marked contrast to removing and replacing each tool separately in the tailstock and the careful measurement which is necessary after each traverse of the tool.

The amount of money spent on tool equipment depends entirely on the number of parts required or the chance of repeat orders. If it is assumed that the pump-plunger is required in large quantities, a somewhat more elaborate set-up could be employed, as indicated in Fig. 58. The main difference is that the tool 7 is taken from the square turret and used in conjunction with the drill 10, so that turning and drilling proceed from the hexagon turret at one traverse of the tool.

A comparison of the three methods shows:

Fig. 48.—Machining time, including

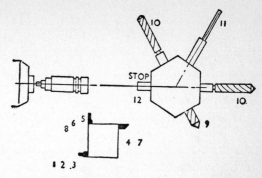

Fig. 57. If a capstan lathe is available for machining a pump-plunger (see Fig. 48) the necessary tools could be arranged on the square and hexagon turrets as here shown. As every tool is in position, time is saved.

trial cuts, moving tools, and tailstock: 60 min. per piece: 600 min. for 10 pieces.

Fig. 57.—Changing tools 15 min., setting up tools 17 min., setting stops 13 min. = 45 min. Machining time $25\frac{1}{2}$ min. $\times$ 10 pieces = 255 min. Total time 300 min. or 30 min. each per piece.

Fig. 58.—This arrangement is for a batch of 40 pieces, the machining time being 19 min. $\times$ 40 pieces = 760 min.; adding 180 min. for setting up gives $760 + 180 \div 40 = 23\frac{1}{2}$ min. per piece.

Thus the respective times per piece are, 60, 30, and $23\frac{1}{2}$ min.

To show the possibilities of production when a turret lathe is correctly tooled, two examples will now be considered, the first case being a small brass cover and the second an unusually large piston, both castings being machined on turret lathes.

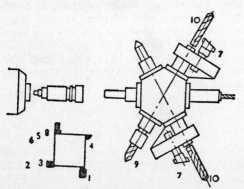

Fig. 58. Alternative set-up of the tools shown in Fig. 57 if a large output of pump-plungers is required. By using tools 7 and 10 in conjunction, turning and drilling proceed from the hexagon turret at one traverse.

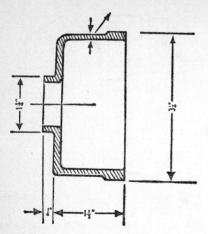

Fig. 59. This small brass cover can be machined on a correctly tooled turret lathe as described in the text.

The brass cover (Fig. 59) requires machining all over, so the first require-

ment is a three-jaw chuck for holding. Fig. 60 shows the casting thus held, with the various tools in position in the square turret and the hexagon turret. The reference letters near the tools denote the surface to be machined by corresponding letters on the work, and it is assumed that a finishing cut on exactly the same lines as the roughing cut will be required, so a face of the turret denoted by figure 2 is reserved for this equipment and shown by means of the dotted lines.

The sequence of movements, speeds, feeds, and times taken are tabulated below under the first operation.

With the exception of the top of the flange C, all the machining is inside the casting, and in practice the position of tool C is vertically above the

FIRST OPERATION					
	OPERATION	SPINDLE SPEED R.P.M.	SURFACE SPEED R.P.M.	FEEDS PER IN.	TIME IN MIN.
1	Chuck				.20
	Bring up 1				.10
	Rough turn and bore	250	200	80	.36
	Bring up 2				.10
2	Finish turn and bore	250	200	80	.36
	Bring up 3				.20
3	Rough face	250		Hand	.32
	Bring up 4				.20
4	Finish face	250		Hand	.32
	Remove work, etc.				.25
					2.41
For tool setting, changing, and fatigue, 25 percent					.60
	Total (approx.)				3 min.

boring bar, but it is now shown in a horizontal position for the sake of clarity.

Use of Soft-Jawed Chuck

The machining of the top of the flange provides a true surface for holding in the next operation (Fig. 61). A three-jaw chuck with soft jaws to prevent marking the work is employed, but to prevent the casting from being squeezed out of shape, it is put over a form.

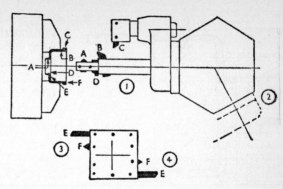

Fig. 60. Brass cover (Fig. 59) held in a three-jaw chuck, with the necessary tools in position in the square and hexagon turrets. The lettered surfaces on the work are machined by the correspondingly lettered tools.

SECOND OPERATION					
	OPERATION	SPINDLE SPEED R.P.M.	SURFACE SPEED R.P.M.	FEEDS PER IN.	TIME IN MIN.
	Chuck				.20
	Bring up 1				.10
1	Rough turn	250	200	80	.36
	Bring up 2				.10
2	Finish turn	250	200	80	.36
	Bring up 3				.20
3	Rough face	250		Hand	.32
	Bring up 4				.10
4	Finish face	250		Hand	.32
	Bring up 5				.10
5	Form neck, bevel, and radius.	250		Hand	.10
	Change speed, bring 6				.20
6	Thread	150	40	Hand	.10
	Remove work				.20
					2.76
For tool setting, changing, and fatigue, 25 percent					.69
	Total				3.45

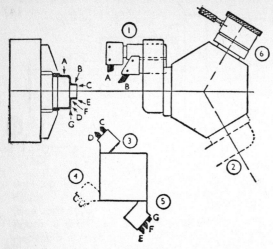

Fig. 61. For the second operation in machining the brass cover, the tool set-up is as here indicated. The operations are denoted by reference letters (see text).

The sequence of the second operation is tabulated on page 147.

Totaling the times from both operations gives 6.45 min. or $\dfrac{60}{6.45}$, approximately 9 pieces per hour. The setting-up time would be $1\frac{1}{2}$ to 2 hours, and this should be divided by the number of parts produced if the quantity is small. Owing to the short duration of operations performed with the hexagon turret, separate times have been given for operations with the square turret, but on larger work the procedure should be determined with the object of carrying out simultaneous machining with both turrets.

By way of contrast in dimensions, the tool equipment and the four operations involved in machining a large piston will now be taken up (see Figs. 63, 64, and 65). The size of the casting involves some special but comparatively simple equipment, and includes a good example of forming a convex face on the piston end, while the procedure for boring the wrist-pin holes

Another advantage of this is that it is also located at the correct distance from the chuck and square with the front face of the flange F.

The operations are denoted by reference letters as before, and in both operations it will be seen that several tools are required for very minor, but necessary, operations, such as chamfering corner D (first operation), E for beveling the front end, F for forming neck and G for radiusing (see second operation).

For threading the shank, a self-opening die-head, 6, is employed. This will be described in detail later, but to assist in this threading operation, it is well to leave plenty of stock on the end of the shank, because the first few threads are often slightly imperfect, and then to cut off the surplus length by a parting tool (not shown). It is not wise to try to thread right up to the shoulder, hence tool F for forming neck as shown detailed at F in Fig. 62.

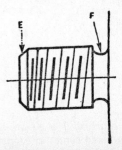

Fig. 62. Detail of the threaded shank for the brass cover in Fig. 59. The surplus length is cut off with a parting tool.

in the fourth operation should be carefully noted.

Double cutters are used to rough out the $3\frac{1}{2}$ in. diameter holes, and then an operation using single-point boring tools follows. This procedure should always be followed with cast or cored holes, or even after a twist-drill has been used. The reason is that double cutters or twist-drills will follow the cored hole or be deflected by blow holes in cast iron, whereas a single-point tool will true the hole practically to size, ready for finishing with a floating cutter or a reamer.

The complete machining operations are given in sequence, and, despite the size of the work, the production time for the whole machining is only 1 hour 50 minutes. The first operation is to hold the work by the head in a chuck fitted with special hard jaws shaped

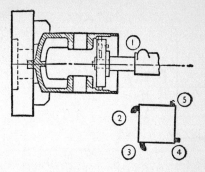

Fig. 63. Machining a large piston. First operation: 1, support as shown; 2, rough bore out open end and rough face end; 3, finish bore and face end; 4, rough form taper on end of outside diameter; 5, radius end of piston.

on the back locating face to suit the radius of the convex head. The open end of the piston is supported in a somewhat unusual manner, by a re-

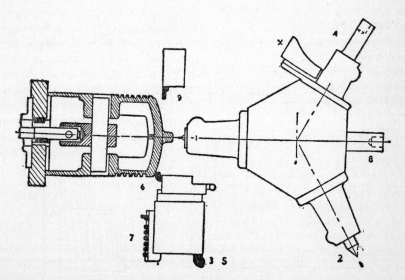

Fig. 64. Machining a piston. Second operation: 1, center spigot end with drill; 2, engage fixed center to support casting; 3, rough turn spigot; 4, engage support fitting over spigot; 5, rough turn outside diameter; 6, profile face convex end; 7, rough form piston-ring grooves and form end radius. Third operation: 8, support by hollow center over spigot; 5, finish-turn outside diameter; 7, finish-turn grooves; 9, cut-off spigot with parting tool in back cross-slide.

volving bushing fitted with a series of adjustable spring plungers. The revolving bushing is carried by the turret and is inserted in the bore as shown, any variation in diameter of the rough cored bore being overcome by the adjustable plungers.

When inserted, the plungers accommodate themselves to the bore, small set-screws at the side locking the whole arrangement in place. The compensating action of the support is very useful for work of this kind, an additional feature being that it leaves the open end free for a suitable distance, thereby enabling boring to be done in the first operation.

This bored end is used in the second operation for locating the piston on a short pilot on the lathe face-plate. A draw-back bolt holds the casting by a peg inserted through the cored wrist-

pin hole. The method of tooling includes a former slide application and a set of multiple tools for cutting the piston-ring grooves and forming the end radius.

Operation 4 shows the layout for boring the gudgeon-pin holes and facing the inside bosses to width. The operation is of interest in the method of chucking the casting. A face-plate fixture on which two V blocks are machined is used. These hold the casting by the outside diameter, by means of suitable clamps and bolts, while a short lug at the bottom end with a set-screw inserted serves as a locating point to position the casting endwise.

The productive capacity of this type of lathe is such that on many varieties of parts it is only a matter of a few minutes before the work requires resetting or replacing, this with the ordi-

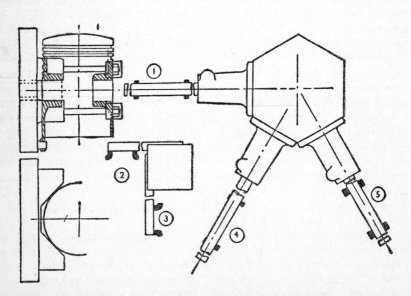

Fig. 65. Machining a piston. Fourth operation: boring wrist-pin holes and facing inside bosses to width: 1, rough bore holes with two flat cutters; 2, rough face inside bosses from square turret; 3, finish inside bosses from square turret; 4, finish bore holes with single-point cutters; 5, size holes with two inserted boring cutters. The machining time of the four operations is 1 hr. 50 min.

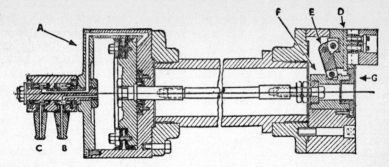

Fig. 66. Arrangement of air-chuck. A, cylinder containing piston; B, C, passages for air supply entry; D, slide-on jaw; E, hinged toggle links; F, slider attached to draw-bolt; G, adapter. See description on this page.

nary chuck necessitating considerable strength. In cases where frequent chucking is required, the fatigue of the operator can be considerably reduced by the use of air-chucks, while, in addition, the rapidity of loading is greatly increased.

With the hand-operated chuck, the clamping pressure effected before cutting commences may, by work-slip, become loose, whereas with power operation the holding effect is constant and it will not change during the operation. Air pressure at 70–80 lb. per sq. in. is usually employed, depending largely on the nature of the work in hand.

In the general design of air-chucks the central draw-bolt prevents the passage of long bars, so that usually it is better suited to actual chucking rather than long-bar work. Nevertheless, this difficulty can be overcome by a tubular draw-rod, or by incorporating the air cylinder at the front of the spindle to operate the collets directly without any intermediate connection.

Several devices have been designed to insure that the chuck will be self-sustaining in the event of the air pressure falling, for it will be apparent that a self-releasing device of this nature may fail, with serious conse-

quences to the operator or machine. Apart from mechanical devices, one arrangement is to connect the starting and stopping lever with a separate air cylinder to keep the lever in the starting position. Should the pressure fall, the lever returns to the stop position.

With an air-chuck (Fig. 66) either hand or foot operated, air supply can be arranged by valve operation to enter by passage B or C. The first supplies air to the rear side of the piston and forces it forward to open the jaws via the central rod. The passage C leads to the front of the piston to move it in the opposite direction and close the jaws. A reducing valve may be fitted to regulate the air pressure to that sufficient for holding the work without distortion.

The Chuck-Jaws

The chuck-body is of cast steel, designed to be dust- and dirt-proof, and carries three jaws, each with a slide D, so that they can be set to grip the work. They have a fairly wide range of movement, however, without the necessity of adjusting the loose jaws. This movement is obtained by the hinged toggle links E, applying the clamping pressure by the slider F attached to the draw-bolt. An adapter G completes the enclosure of the chuck.

Much of the work, such as bolts, studs, and short shafts produced on turret lathes, is machined from long rods passing through the headstock spindle and brought forward the distance required after each piece is com-

The lever is pivoted with a link to the headstock, and slides the sleeve D forked to operate the cone A, this in turn operating the toggles, tube, and chuck against the cap E. On releasing the toggles the elasticity of the chuck reacts and returns the tube. When the cone A is moved to the right, the screw in sleeve D draws the ratchet bar F in the same direction, but not immedi-

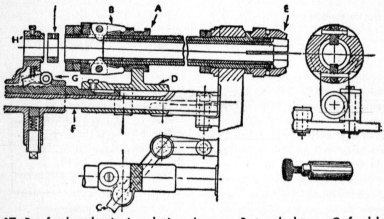

Fig. 67. Bar-feed and gripping device. A, cone; B, toggle levers; C, feed lever; D, sleeve; E, cap; F, ratchet bar; G, pawl; H, bar carrier; J, collar. The turret stop is shown bottom right. See text for detailed description.

pleted. For this class of work spring collets are largely employed, a set of collets being required for each diameter of rod used, these being removable by unscrewing the cap E (Fig. 67), which shows a typical arrangement. This comprises a sliding cone A at the tail end of the spindle, actuating toggle levers B which act upon the end of a tube inside the main spindle. The slight endwise movement given to the tube is sufficient to make the spring-chuck grip the bar. In some cases a weight is used to bring the bar forward, but in the arrangement shown, a positive feed is obtained by the lever C, which performs the double action of feeding and chucking.

ately, because of the slot in the bar, thus allowing the chuck to disengage before the bar-feed operates. A pawl G connects the rod carrier H with the ratchet bar, the pawl being lifted out of mesh when required to be moved to a new position. A spring-loaded pad F imparts an even pressure when the carrier is locked. To operate, a collar J is screwed to the rod, and this collar is pushed along by the front of the bushing in the rod carrier, bringing the stock along with it.

A stand carries the end of the shaft in which F is fitted and also supports the ends.

For power-feeding rollers are used, or, the ratchet bar F is replaced by a screw passing through the carrier. The screw carries a clutch intermediate between a spur reverse train of the three and two gear type driving from the spindle. The lever which operates the chuck also operates the clutch by a connecting lever, and by revolving the screw causes the stock to be fed forward against a stop located in the hexagon turret at some predetermined distance from the chuck, the clutch then automatically releasing itself.

Turret Lathe Tools

The high productive capacity of capstan and turret lathes is not restricted to castings or bar stock but includes machine spindles, stay-rods, or other long steel parts. As no tail-stock is available for supporting one end of the work, other means must be provided. In some cases support is by means of a center fixed in the hexagon turret and turning is performed from the square turret, but such a procedure should be avoided, if possible, for the machine then becomes an ordinary center lathe for all practical purposes, with the hexagon turret out of action for cutting.

The proper method for turning long bar stock is to equip the machine with tools specially designed for the purpose, and these generally include: an adjustable stop to regulate the amount of stock protruding out of the chuck; a roller box turning tool-holder for heavy-duty on steel; a flat, steady box-turning tool-holder for light-steel turning or for brass work; a self-opening die-head for threading; a centering and facing tool-holder; steady bushing to support work while forming; drill-chuck; releasing tap-holder; and parting tools for use in the square turret.

The most important of these is the roller tool-holder for supporting the bar while cutting. Fig. 68 shows a roller bearing steady in action on a rod, and it will be seen that the device comprises two rollers A mounted on roller bearings, these running on the studs C. The tool is bolted to a face of the hexagon turret and carries a turning tool Z set slightly in front of the rollers so that, when the bar end

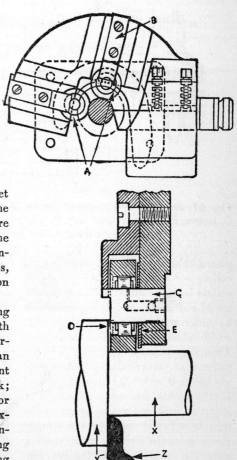

Fig. 68. Roller bearing steady turning tool, used for supporting a bar during cutting. Reference letters are explained in the text.

Fig. 69. The flat steady type of tool-holder used for supporting long bars during cutting usually includes a V support to act against the pressure of the cut.

The flat steady tool-holder on the lines of that shown in Fig. 69 is a simpler device. It generally comprises a V support to act against the pressure of the cut. Both roller and V supports are often built up as multiple tools, enabling different diameters of short stock to be turned to correct lengths at one traverse. This saves taking up several faces of the turret with separate tools and the necessity for setting stops for each and revolving the turret to bring each one into successive action.

Roller Steadies

Fig. 70 shows at A the kind of tool used for reduction with roller steadies. It is of the knife type, very suitable for deep cutting. The top-rake angle, given as 18–35 deg., varies with the material being cut, the softer the steel being machined, the greater the angle. There is some advantage in having the maximum rake at the cutting point with plenty of backing behind it. This

of original diameter Y is reduced to X, the rollers immediately support the work and insure adequate support as turning proceeds.

Adjustment of Rollers

The rollers are adjusted to the bar on the slides B, while entrance of cuttings is prevented by means of the plates D. A hardened washer E is provided at the opposite side to take end-thrust. By means of these tool-holders, a large reduction in diameter is possible, while a high finish, comparable with that of grinding, is secured. This finish is actually acquired by the burnishing action of the rollers against the pressure of the cut, and is more effective with heavy cutting than with light.

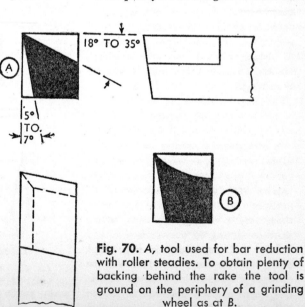

Fig. 70. A, tool used for bar reduction with roller steadies. To obtain plenty of backing behind the rake the tool is ground on the periphery of a grinding wheel as at B.

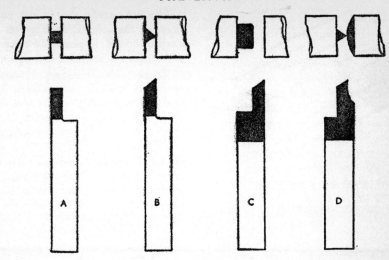

Fig. 71. Four types of parting tools used for cutting off a finished bar, showing their effect on the bar-end. *A* will cut close up to a shoulder or near to the chuck, but leaves a small pip that requires subsequent removal. *B* gives a clean face. *C* and *D* are double-cutting tools which form part of the bar left in the chuck.

can be obtained by grinding the tool on the periphery of a grinding wheel as at B, and additional advantage being that the curved lip produces a curling chip tightly rolled together. In grinding in this way the correct angle will be obtained if the chords of the arcs shown at B are at 5–7 deg. and 18–35 deg. respectively to the faces.

Parting Tools

The matter of cutting off a finished piece of bar-stock is of importance, for by correct grinding a parting tool can be used to perform additional operations on the end of the bar, other than simply cutting off, thus saving another setting of the work.

Four tools are shown in Fig. 71, A being the common type which will cut close to a shoulder or near the chuck, but leaves a small diameter or pip on the bar-end which must be removed.

There is an advantage, therefore, in grinding the cool-end as shown at B, so that the taper cutting edge insures a clean face being cut on the end of the piece being cut off. At C is shown a double-cutting or stepped parting tool, the object of the broad cutting edge being to reduce or form part of the bar on the next piece at the same time as the front edge cuts off, so that a good start can be made for the roller or box tool-holder which generally follows. A similar tool is shown at D, the main difference being the curved cutting face, which insures that the piece being cut has a rounded end, while the piece of bar which is still in the chuck is faced off square.

Threading Operations

The self-opening die-head, where many parts are to be threaded, is indispensable. The device, shown as tool

6 in Fig. 61, consists of a cylindrical body and shank which clamps in the hexagon turret. It requires a set of four dies for each diameter to be threaded, and these are numbered 1 to 4 and set in consecutive clockwise order in the body. Adjustment is provided to allow for cutting a deep or shallow thread, or to allow roughing and finishing cuts to follow each other.

Operating the Head

In operation, the head is partially rotated to close the dies and then fed on to the bar-end with a light pressure. On traversing the required distance, if the traverse handle is held, the effect is to allow the dies to move out of the cam holding them and fly open. This effect can also be obtained automatically by means of a suitable attachment which opens the dies at any predetermined point of the traverse.

Taper threads can be cut just as easily and rapidly as parallel threads. The taper is governed by a former bar held stationary by a stop in the toolpost, while the die-head travels for-

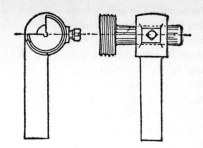

Fig. 73. Circular chasers are used for internal chasing of screw-threads. For right-hand threads the spindle is reversed in direction so that the chaser travels outward.

ward. The work is finished smoothly without the ridges left by taper dies where they stop cutting.

External threads too large to be produced by self-opening die-heads can be cut by chasing. Fig. 72 shows the tool, which is a long dovetailed blade clamped in a holder and arranged so that the cutting edge is inverted. When cutting right-hand threads the spindle of the lathe is run in reverse, so that the chaser travels away from the headstock, thus avoiding the danger of running into a shoulder. The teeth are chamfered so that the cut takes place on a number of threads, while the actual finishing of the full thread is done by the two end teeth. Due to the length of the chaser, its life is very long; it is also rapid in action.

Circular Chasers

Internal threads can be cut with circular chasers (Fig. 73). Again, when cutting right-hand threads, the spindle is reversed in direction so that the chaser travels outward.

Taps and dies can be used for threading on turret lathes, but should

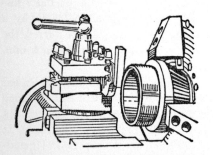

Fig. 72. External screw-threads can be rapidly cut by chasing with this tool: a long, dovetailed blade clamped in a holder with cutting edge inverted, and having chamfered teeth which cut on a number of threads.

be mounted in self-releasing holders. Actually very little threading is now done by circular dies, owing to the superiority of the self-opening die-head. Because of the danger of solid taps tearing the threads, large taps should be of the collapsing type.

The project shown in Fig. 74 is an armature spindle 15¾ in. long × 1⁵⁄₁₆ in. over the largest diameter. The first operation is to feed the stock out to the stop, which in this case is shown on the turret corner X. This operation is so simple that to use a turret face for this purpose is often a waste of valuable tool space. The next process is to turn the 1 in. diameter D with roller turning toolholder (1), then follow with the multi-roller toolholder (2), cutting the three diameters E, 1³⁄₁₆ in. F, ¾ in. and G, ⁹⁄₁₆ in. with forward roller steadies on the 1 in. diameter previously machined. The tapered portion is machined by toolholder (3), which has supporting bushings behind and in front of the tool to insure steadiness. The end is then finished by tool (4), which is a roller steady ending tool, center drilled by tool (5), and threaded by the self-opening diehead (6).

The diameters A, B, and C are machined simultaneously with those just described, by two tools in the square

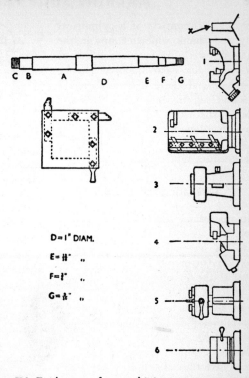

D = 1" DIAM.

E = 1¹⁄₁₆" „

F = ¾" „

G = ⁹⁄₁₆" „

Fig. 74. Tool set-up for machining an armature spindle. The stop is shown on the turret corner (5) and is threaded by the self-opening die-head (6). Diameters A, B, C are machined by two tools in the square turret. The time for the whole operation including grinding is 3¼ minutes.

turret. At this stage the partially finished stock is cut off to length by a parting tool in the square turret, the operations to this stage taking 2 min. 39 sec.

The stock is now re-chucked, ended to length, center drilled and threaded in 36 secs., giving a total time of 3¼ min. for the job to grinding limits. It is this subsequent operation of grinding which necessitates centering the bar at each end, otherwise the operations would be simplified and the time reduced.

AUTOMATIC LATHES

THESE automatics are essentially turret lathes in which the usual hand movements are entirely or partially performed by automatic means. In some cases, the work is chucked in the usual way by hand, the machine started, and machining proceeds until all operations are completed, when the machine stops for the work to be removed and another piece substituted. Other machines, generally for small parts, are self-loading from overhead hoppers. In this case the operator simply loads the hoppers and the work travels down a chute until stopped in front of the chuck. At this point the chuck opens and a finger pushes the work into the chuck, which closes on it and machining starts. At the completion of the operations the work is ejected and falls into a basket on the machine. Many of these machines are multi-spindled and turn out large quantities of work in a very short time, one operator attending to several machines.

Feeds on Automatic Lathes

The usual feed on automatic lathes is by a series of cams (Fig. 75), one set, A, feeding the turret forward at the normal cutting rate and then returning rapidly to save time on idle strokes, the turret revolves to present another set of tools to the work in readiness for the next operation.

The length of the stroke and rate of feed depend on the shape and position of the various cams on the cam-drum.

In most cases the cross-slides have automatic feeds in one direction only —that is, across the bed—so that the only operations possible from the cross-slides are facing and forming, but on some machines the cross-slides can be moved in a limited longitudinal direction to suit different lengths of work. The cams on drum B are used for feeding the cross-slide tools and can be arranged to operate at any point of the cycle; so that facing and turning can operate together or singly.

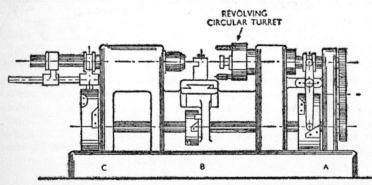

Fig. 75. Cams for feeding on automatic lathe. Set A feed the turret forward at the normal cutting rate with rapid return; those on drum B feed the cross-slide tools; those at C are needed for automatics, for opening and closing the chuck, and feeding the bar forward the correct distance. The shape and positions of the various cams on the cam-drum govern the length of stroke and the rate of feeding which can be given on this lathe.

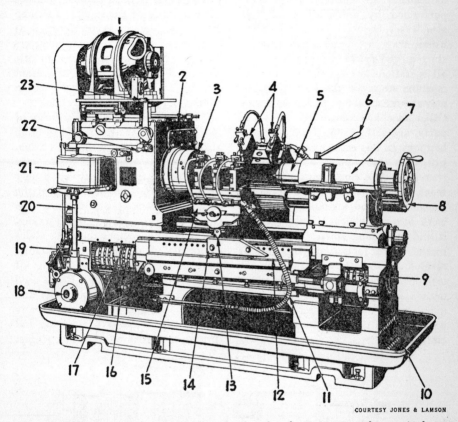

COURTESY JONES & LAMSON

Fig. 76. Fay Automatic Lathe: 1, motor; 2, headstock; 3, two jaw driver; 4, dovetail tool blocks on back arm; 5, tailstock ram and revolving center; 6, tailstock ram binder lever; 7, tailstock; 8, tailstock ram hand wheel; 9, cam drum tailstock end; 10, chip pan; 11, coolant pipe; 12, front former slide; 13, carriage former shoe; 14, carriage former; 15, carriage; 16, main cam drum; 17, cam; 18, worm shaft; 19, control drum and lever; 20, feed shaft; 21, feed change gear box; 22, hand trip; 23, starting lever.

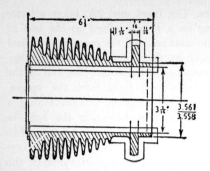

Fig. 77. Enlarged detail of motorcycle cylinder shown in Fig. 78, giving dimensions.

Automatic Screw Machines

A third set of cams is required for bar automatics, these being shown at C. The requirements include opening the chuck, feeding the stock forward the correct distance and closing the chuck. It will be seen that the success of automatic lathe operation depends on the setting of the various cams in the most suitable positions to obtain efficient working. It also depends, of course, on sufficient work of one type being available to warrant the expense involved in setting the cams and tools. These latter are practically identical with those used on standard turret lathes, and have already been described.

Lay-Out of Tools

As most automatic lathes are provided with wide cross-slides capable of carrying several tools, a four-face turret is found sufficient to handle most work. Fig. 78 shows the arrangement for machining a motorcycle cylinder. The cylinder is an iron casting gripped on the fins to insure concentricity, by means of a chuck which is

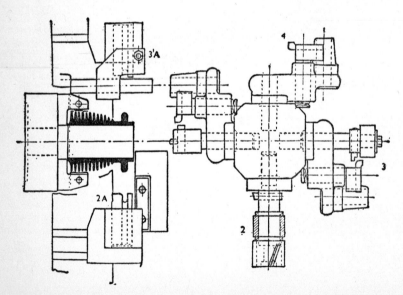

Fig. 78. Set-up of tools for first operation in machining a motorcycle cylinder on an automatic lathe. 1, tool for truing end of bore and facing end of casting; 2, tool for completing bore, 2A, 3A, forming tools for roughing out flange near end of casting; 3, tool for finish-facing end of cylinder and finish-turning spigot.

provided with special swiveling jaws.

Tool 1 trues the end of the bore and faces the end of the casting, while tool 2 completes the bore, being assisted by a rotating steady bushing at the rear of the tool. At the end of the boring operation, a second tool at the end of the bar bevels the end of the bore. For roughing out the flange near the end of the casting, two forming tools, 2A and 3A, move inward in turn. As this requires heavy cutting, to damp out vibrations, additional support is provided for the cross-slide tool-holders. The front one, 2A, takes a bearing on a bracket fixed to the bed of the machine, and the rear one is linked to an overhead support. The final operation is to finish-face the end of the cylinder and finish-turn the spigot. Tool 3 takes care of this machining, a roller support fitting in the bore in front of the cutting tools being used to insure accuracy and stability. The complete machining is performed in the floor to floor time of 8 minutes. The great advantage of the turret lathe for work of this type is evident from the above example.

CHAPTER 4

THREAD-CUTTING

SCREW THREAD STANDARDS. ACME THREADS. SQUARE THREADS. BUTTRESS THREADS. GEARING. SELECTING GEARS. PITCH AND LEAD. MACHINING. DIAL INDICATORS. MULTIPLE THREADS. ATTACHMENTS. AUTOMATIC THREAD-CUTTING. VARYING LEAD SCREWS.

AMONG the great variety of machining operations performed on lathes, the one requiring the most skill is that of thread-cutting. It is nevertheless a subject of great interest, and should be easily understood after a consideration of the general principles involved in trains of gears.

Before dealing with this aspect of the subject, some knowledge of the types of screw threads, their shapes and proportion, is necessary, otherwise a machinist can have no indication of the gear trains required nor the angles to which his tools should be ground.

A thread may be defined as being a cylindrical bar on which has been formed a helix or thread, this fitting a corresponding element termed a nut. The two together may be used for fastening purposes, as a nut and bolt, or may be used for traversing machine parts, such as the nut and screw of a tailstock or compound rest.

American Standard Thread Form

There must be some standardization in the form and number of threads per inch of screws. William Seller of Philadelphia studied the subject and proposed a form which was recommended by the Franklin Institute in 1864, and which is now known as the American Standard Thread. It has also been known by the names: the Sellers, the Franklin Institute, the U. S. Standard Thread and the American National form.

This thread is made with an included angle of 60 deg. (B, Fig. 1), the crest and root being flattened for one-eighth of the depth. This makes it easier to produce commercially than those with rounded parts but it weakens the thread at the root. The dimensions of this thread are given in Table I and are obtained from the following:

$$P \text{ (pitch)} = \frac{1}{\text{Number of threads per in.}}$$

d (depth) = P × .6495
f (width of flats) = P/8

Three common threads using this form are the coarse-thread series, the fine thread series and the 8, 12, and 16 pitch series, employing the symbols NC, NF and N, respectively.

The fine-thread series is used for parts subject to excessive vibration such as automobile parts, where an increase in resistance to loosening and allowance for fine adjustment is required. The reduced depth of this series allows a stronger core to be maintained in the body. Sizes of these bolts are given in Table I.

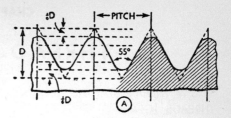

A. The Whitworth thread, triangular in section, has an included angle of 55 deg.; the thread is rounded off at top and bottom by one-sixth of its full depth. This thread is most suitable for locking purposes.

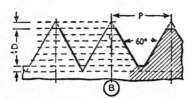

B. American standard Sellers thread with an included angle of 60 deg. and top and bottom flattened one-eighth of the full depth.

C. Acme thread, with included angle of 29 deg., and flat top and bottom; this is often used for transmitting motion in conjunction with a disengaging nut.

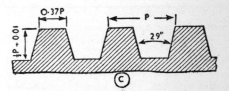

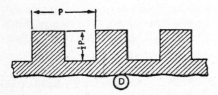

D. Square thread, in which the depth is equal to half the pitch; the friction is less than in a Whitworth thread.

E. Buttress thread, used when pressure acts in one direction only. In section, it shows a blunted triangle with an internal angle of 45 deg.

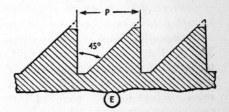

Fig. 1. Diagrams showing the principal varieties of screw-thread.

For general use in engineering work the coarse thread is recommended. Sizes of these are also included in Table I. Under $\frac{1}{4}$ in., for both the coarse and fine series, the threads are generally known as machine screw threads, and are numbered from 0–12.

The American Standard Pipe Thread

When putting threads on pipes a form similar to the American Standard Thread is used. This has an angle of 60 deg. and the crest and root are flattened an amount equal to .033 × P,

TABLE I

AMERICAN STANDARD THREADS

SIZE, NO. OR DIAM.	THREADS PER INCH.		PITCH DIAMETER IN INCHES.	
	COARSE THREAD SERIES.	FINE THREAD SERIES.	COARSE THREAD SERIES.	FINE THREAD SERIES.
0		80		.0519
1	64	72	.0629	.0640
2	56	64	.0744	.0759
3	48	56	.0855	.0874
4	40	48	.0958	.0985
5	40	44	.1088	.1102
6	32	40	.1177	.1218
8	32	36	.1437	.1460
10	24	32	.1629	.1697
12	24	28	.1889	.1928
1/4	20	28	.2175	.2268
5/16	18	24	.2764	.2854
3/8	16	24	.3344	.3479
7/16	14	20	.3911	.4050
1/2	13	20	.4500	.4675
3/4	10	16	.6850	.7094
1	8	14	.9188	.9536
1 1/4	7	12	1.1572	1.1959
1 1/2	6	12	1.3917	1.4459
2	4 1/2	12	1.8557	
3	4	10	2.8376	

the pitch of the thread. The depth of thread is $8/10$ of the pitch and the thread is tapered $3/4''$ per foot. Dimensions are given in Table II. It is important to remember that a 2 in. pipe has a bore of 2 in., the outside diameter being larger.

Acme Thread

This is a type of thread (C, Fig. 1) extensively used for transmitting motion in conjunction with a disengaging nut, as, for example, the lead screw of a lathe. It is of 29 deg. included angle, flat top and bottom, so that the taper sides facilitate engagement of the nut with the screw, and if wear takes place, adjustment is automatic by the nut moving deeper into engagement. (See Table III.)

The Whitworth Thread

The standard British thread is as shown in A, Fig. 1, the Whitworth thread. It is of triangular section, with

TABLE II

AMERICAN STANDARD PIPE THREADS

NOMINAL BORE OF PIPE OR TUBE INCHES.	NUMBER OF THREADS PER INCH.	OUTSIDE DIAM. AT SMALL END OF THREAD INCHES.	ROOT DIAM. AT SMALL END OF THREAD INCHES.
1/8	27	.393	.334
1/4	18	.522	.433
3/8	18	.656	.568
1/2	14	.816	.701
3/4	14	1.025	.911
1	11½	1.283	1.144
1¼	11½	1.627	1.488
1½	11½	1.866	1.727
2	11½	2.339	2.199
2½	8	2.820	2.620
3	8	3.441	3.241
4	8	4.434	4.234

an included angle of 55 deg. The thread is rounded off one-sixth of the full depth, top and bottom. Owing to the thread face being at an angle to the tightening force, there is a great friction between the threads, and therefore little tendency for the two elements to come apart by vibration. The thread is therefore most suitable for locking purposes, particularly

TABLE III

ACME STANDARD THREAD PARTS

NO. OF THREADS PER IN. LINEAR.	DEPTH OF THREAD.	WIDTH OF FLAT AT TOP OF THREAD.	WIDTH OF FLAT AT BOTTOM OF THREAD.	SPACE AT TOP OF THREAD.	THICKNESS AT ROOT OF THREAD.
1	.510	.371	.366	.629	.635
1½	.343	.247	.242	.503	.508
2	.260	.185	.180	.315	.320
3	.177	.124	.118	.210	.215
4	.135	.093	.088	.157	.163
5	.110	.074	.069	.126	.131
6	.093	.062	.057	.105	.110
7	.081	.053	.048	.090	.095
8	.073	.046	.041	.079	.084
9	.066	.041	.036	.070	.075
10	.060	.037	.032	.063	.068

when fine threads are used instead of those listed as standard. These fine threads are similar in section, but contain a greater number of threads per in. than those used for ordinary locking purposes.

Dimensions for various sizes are given in Table IV.

Square Thread

This thread is that most used for moving parts of machines, vise-screws, lifting jacks, valve spindles. The section is not as strong as a corresponding Whitworth thread, but friction is reduced. The depth is taken as half the pitch (See D, Fig. 1).

Buttress Thread

This type of thread is suitable for machine parts where the pressure acts in one direction only, such as on quick-acting vises and gun-breech mechanism. The modified triangular section gives a shearing strength for a given length of nut twice that of a square thread (See E, Fig. 1).

In order to cut threads in a lathe, some additional mechanism is required other than that for plain turning. This includes a train of gears connecting the headstock spindle to the lead screw along the front of the bed, a set of change gears to vary the connection for different threads to be cut, means to vary the center distances of the gears, and provision on the apron to engage or disengage a nut from the lead-screw to start or stop the tool movement.

Change Gears

These requirements will be considered in detail, beginning with the change gears. Examples have been given of magazine-type feed-boxes where gears nominally used for traversing the saddle for turning can also be used for thread-cutting purposes, so that only on rare occasions for special pitches need the connecting gears on the end of the bed be altered. This is a most advantageous feature, as few change gears are required, but regarding the general lathe a full set of

TABLE IV

BRITISH STANDARD WHITWORTH SCREW THREADS

DIAM. AT TOP OF THREAD INCHES.	NUMBER OF THREADS PER INCH.	DIAM. AT BOTTOM OF THREAD OR CORE DIAMETER INCHES.
¼	20	.1860
5⁄16	18	.2414
⅜	16	.2950
7⁄16	14	.3460
½	12	.3933
9⁄16	12	.4558
⅝	11	.5086
11⁄16	11	.5711
¾	10	.6219
13⁄16	10	.6844
⅞	9	.7327
1	8	.8399
1⅛	7	.9420
1¼	7	1.0670
1⅜	6	1.1616
1½	6	1.2866
1⅝	5	1.3689
1¾	5	1.4939
2	4½	1.7154
2¼	4	1.9298
2½	4	2.1798
2¾	3½	2.3841
3	3½	2.6341

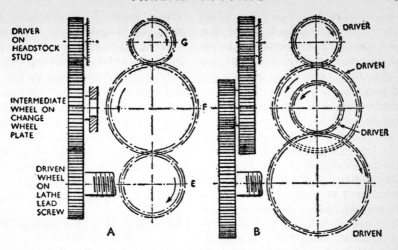

Fig. 2. Two gear trains for use when thread-cutting in the lathe. *A* shows a simple train where three wheels are in one plane; *B* shows a compound train which is necessary when cutting threads of much finer or much coarser pitch than the lead screw. A compound train has the advantage that it distributes the load of the drive over several wheels instead of concentrating on three.

change-gears is supplied, these being mounted as required. These gears commence with twenty teeth, and rise by steps of four teeth. Two gears of forty, or sometimes sixty teeth, for cutting threads of the same pitch as the lead screw of the lathe are included. Thus it should be remembered in setting out gear trains for thread cutting on lathes, that the number of teeth must be divisible by 4. Most of the lead screws on American lathes are either $\frac{1}{4}$ in. pitch or $\frac{1}{6}$ in. pitch.

Gear Arrangement

Referring now to Fig. 2, two methods of arranging the gear will be considered, that at A being termed a single-gear train, and B a compound-gear train. In many cases either arrangement can be used, but the compound-gear method is necessary when a large speed variation between the headstock spindle and the lead screw

is required, as, for example, in cutting threads of either much finer or much coarser pitch than the lead screw. In such cases the ratio cannot be obtained by a single train of gears, so that double, or compounding of the gears as shown at B, must be resorted to. There is also the advantage that a double-gear train distributes the load of the drive over several gears, instead of concentrating on three only, with the possibility of breaking the small gears or pinions, particularly if the pinions are driven gears, as occurs when speeding up the lead screw in relation to the headstock spindle.

Swing Frame

In order to be able to engage varying sizes of gears, some flexible connection between the lead screw and the spindle is required, and this feature is attained by the use of a change plate, shown at C, Fig. 2a. This plate pivots around the lead screw center on a boss on the supporting bracket, but has means for clamping in any desired positions. One or more slots are provided so that the change-gear studs can be slid into different positions, so that in the case of the single-gear train (A, Fig. 2) if gears G and E are placed in position on the headstock stud and lead screw respectively, then the intermediate gear stud F can be moved in its slot to engage gear G first, and then engaged with E by swinging the change-gear plate around its pivotal center until the teeth of E and F are in mesh. When they are in this position the plate is firmly locked to keep them in mesh.

It is important to realize that the intermediate gear F makes no difference to the gear ratio, but simply changes the direction of rotation and acts as a connecting gear, so that in a simple-gear train any intermediate gear of suitable size can be employed.

This change in the direction of rotation can also be effected by the headstock reverse gears previous to the change-gear arrangement, so that right- or left-hand threads can be cut without having to complicate the gear train by introducing extra gears to change the direction of rotation.

Replacing Change Gears

Some simple means of replacing the change-gears on the shafts is an advantage, and knurled nuts, as shown, save the use of wrenches; in other cases the nuts on the ends of the shafts are made less than the bores of the gears, so that these pass over the nuts and are retained by horseshoe-shaped washers between the two parts. Only a partial turn of the nut is then required to loosen it, remove the washers and slide the gear over the nut.

The screw-cutting stud is shown at D (Fig. 2a); this must be capable of being locked to the change-gear plate, and yet have means for one or, in a compound train, two gears to rotate together. The device then comprises a central stud, fitting in a slot in the change-gear plate and capable of being bolted thereto, and carrying

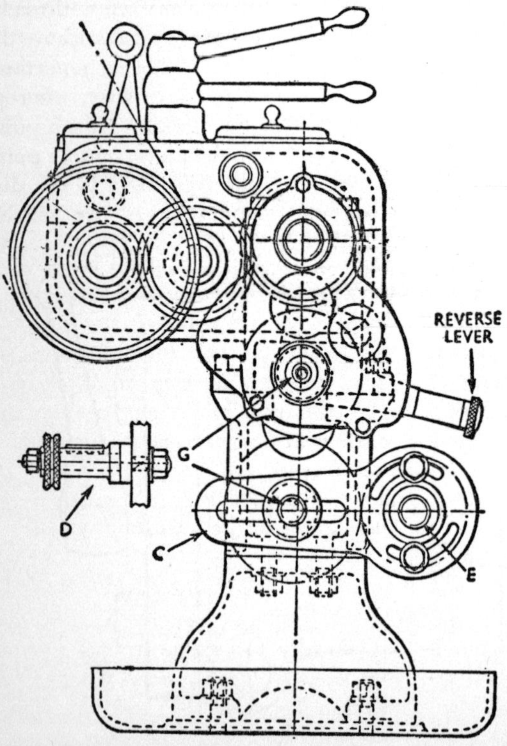

Fig. 2a. Thread-cutting mechanism and gear trains. C, change plate; D, detail of stud; E, G, gears.

a socket to revolve on the stud, this being keywayed so that two gears are able to rotate together when required for compounding.

Mechanism of Nut Box

The rotation of the lead screw is used to make the tool travel along the work to produce the thread helix, but as it would be inconvenient to be continuously starting, stopping, and reversing the lathe for the repeated cuts along the work and to bring the saddle back to the starting point, disengaging single or double half-nuts are used. The arrangement is located in the apron, and operated by raising or lowering a lever, this having the effect of engaging or withdrawing the half-nuts from the lead-screw. Fig. 3 shows the device in detail, from which it will be seen that movement of the handle rotates a plate with cam slots. Pins in the half-nuts engage these slots, and as the nuts are fitted in vertical slides

they are raised or lowered by cam movement as the plate rotates.

With a knowledge of the mechanism involved, the operator is now in a position to consider the selection of gears to cut a given thread. One turn of the lead-screw with the nut engaged moves the saddle a distance equal to the lead of the thread, and if the work and the lead-screw revolve at the same speed, the lead of the thread cut upon the work will be the same as that of the lead-screw. To do this the driving gear E and the driven gear G (see Fig. 2a) would be equal. The first step, then, is to find the ratio between the lead of the thread to be cut and that of the lathe lead-screw.

The term *pitch* was mentioned in connection with various screw-threads, but the last paragraph substitutes the word *lead* instead. This is important, and is due to the fact that, whereas pitch denotes the distance from a point on one thread to a corresponding point on the next, the term lead is the distance that a nut travels per revolu-

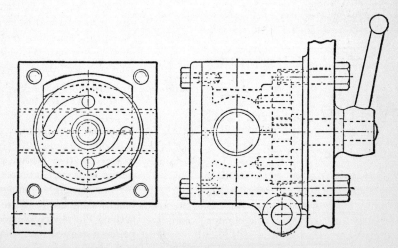

Fig. 3. Detail of lathe-nut-box. The handle rotates a plate with cam slots which are engaged by pins in the half-nuts; the nuts, fitted in vertical slides, are raised or lowered by cam movement as the plate rotates.

tion. With ordinary threads, such as bolts and nuts, the terms are the same, for the screw-thread is single and the nut travels a distance equal to the pitch for one revolution of the screw. There are, however, many screws and worms with multiple threads giving steep angles, so while the pitch is taken care of by the shape of the cutting tool, the change-gears must give a very different rate of travel to the saddle for the lead. This involves rather more complicated machining than can be discussed at present, but a knowledge of the difference in terms must be understood, and the term lead will be retained for movement of the saddle.

Thus, the ratio for the change-gears may be stated as:

$$\frac{\text{Lead of thread to be cut}}{\text{Lead of lathe screw}}$$

and some examples considered for a lathe with a lead-screw of $\frac{1}{4}$ in. lead.

(a) Find the gear ratio required to cut a thread of $\frac{1}{4}$ in. lead.

$$\text{Ratio } \frac{\frac{1}{4}}{\frac{1}{4}} = \frac{1}{4} \times \frac{4}{1} = 1$$

thus verifying the previous remark when work and lead screw are required equal.

(b) Find gear ratio to cut a thread of $\frac{3}{4}$ in. lead.

$$\text{Ratio } \frac{\frac{3}{4}}{\frac{1}{4}} = \frac{3}{4} \times \frac{4}{1} = \frac{12}{4} = 3$$

(c) Find gear ratio to cut a thread of $1\frac{1}{8}$ in. lead.

$$\text{Ratio } \frac{1\frac{1}{8}}{\frac{1}{4}} = \frac{9}{8} \times \frac{4}{1} = \frac{9}{2}$$

The next step is to select suitable gear-wheels to give the required ratio, bearing in mind that the numerator is the driving gear and the denominator the driven one, and in a single-gear train the first is on the headstock stud G, and the second on the lead screw E. Taking the three examples, a, b, c,

in order, the first ratio $\frac{1}{1}$ presents no difficulty, and as it was previously stated two equal gears of forty teeth were supplied with the change-gear set, then these two are mounted at G and E respectively and coupled up with any intermediate gear of suitable size—say sixty teeth—thus

$$\frac{E}{F} \times \frac{F}{G} \text{ or } \frac{40}{60} \times \frac{60}{40},$$

this showing that as the intermediate gear appears in both numerator and denominator it has no effect upon the speed ratio, and can therefore be omitted from the calculations.

(b) Ratio $\frac{3}{1}$, $\dfrac{\text{Driver}}{\text{Driven}} = \frac{3}{1}$,

or, multiplying to obtain suitable gears

$$\frac{3}{1} \times \frac{20}{20} = \frac{60}{20},$$

which are available.

(c) Ratio $\frac{9}{2}$, $\dfrac{\text{Driver}}{\text{Driven}} = \frac{9}{2}$

multiplied by, $^{108}\!/_{24}$, which are again suitable gears, but as there would be considerable strain in speeding up the small twenty-four tooth pinion, it would be better to try to select a compound train; thus, multiplying by $^{24}\!/_{24}$ gives:

$$\frac{9}{2} \times \frac{24}{24} = \frac{216}{48} = \frac{108}{48} \times \frac{2}{1}$$

again, multiplying by 12 to obtain suitable gears for the last pair gives:

$$\frac{108}{48} \times \frac{24}{12}$$

which fails by the twelve-tooth gear not being available, so a final multiplication by 3 gives correct gears as

$$\frac{108}{48} \times \frac{72}{36}$$

the arrangement being mounted on the studs as

$$\frac{\text{Driver}}{\text{Driven}} \times \frac{\text{Driver}}{\text{Driven}} \text{ or } \frac{H}{J} \times \frac{K}{L}.$$

Sometimes the pitch of a thread is given in threads per in.—say, 10

threads per in. To con-
vert to inches, or fraction
of an inch pitch, simply
divide 1 by the threads
per inch, this in the case
under consideration giv-
ing $\frac{1}{10}$ in. pitch or lead.
The ratio is then found
as before, and assuming
now that the lead screw
is $\frac{1}{4}$ in. pitch:

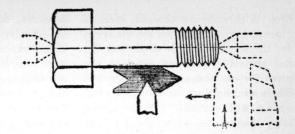

Fig. 4. For cutting a thread this tool is used. It is V-shaped to 60 deg., and should be accurately set in relation to the work with a thread gauge as shown.

(d) Ratio $\frac{\frac{1}{10}}{\frac{1}{4}} = \frac{1}{10}$

$\times \frac{4}{1} = \frac{4}{10}$ or $\frac{32}{80} = \frac{Driver}{Driven}.$

Having selected the gears for the gear train, a careful machinist should always check the correctness by simple calculation. The rule is to multiply the drivers together and the driven gears together, and divide the driving gears by the driven, then multiply the quotient by the lead of the lathe screw, thus:

$\frac{Drivers\ multiplied\ together}{Driven\ multiplied\ together} \times$ lead of lathe screw

Taking the case of example (c), required $1\frac{1}{8}$ in. lead, then

$\frac{108}{48} \times \frac{72}{36} \times \frac{1}{4} = 1\frac{1}{8}$ in. lead as required.

Where the lead-screw is given as, say, 4 per in. and the required screw as 10 threads per in., example (d), then the driven and driving gears change position as:

$\frac{Driven}{Driver} = \frac{80}{32} \times 4 = 10$ threads per in.

With a gear train selected and mounted, the next step is to check whether the required thread is to be right- or left-hand. If right-hand is required, then the lead screw, which is always right-hand, should rotate in the same direction as the work, so that the tool travels from the tailstock to

the headstock. If a left-hand screw is required, then the headstock reverse gear must be actuated to change the direction of rotation of the lead screw, and thereby cause the tool to travel from the headstock to the tailstock.

Threading an American Standard Bolt

Selecting the threading of a 1-in. bolt as a good exercise, from Table I it is seen that eight threads per in. are required. Treating this as $\frac{1}{8}$ in. pitch, then the gears required for a lathe with a $\frac{1}{4}$ in. lead-screw will be:

$\frac{Lead\ of\ thread\ to\ be\ cut\ \frac{1}{8}}{Lead\ of\ lathe\ screw\ \frac{1}{4}}$

or $= \frac{48}{96} = \frac{1}{8} \times \frac{4}{1} = \frac{4}{8}$

Checking to see if correct

$\frac{Drivers}{Driven} = \frac{48}{96} \times \frac{1}{4} = \frac{1}{8}$ in.

The next step is a suitable tool for the compound rest, this being V-shaped to 60 deg., as shown in Fig. 4. It is essential that it should be accurately set in relation to the work, and a thread gauge as shown should be used for this purpose. The required thread is to be right-handed, so the position of the tool at the start should be clear of the work, as shown in dotted lines, and just far enough forward to take a light cut when the lathe is started and the half-nuts engaged with the screw. When the tool has traveled the length required, the nut box-lever is pulled up, the tool withdrawn, and the saddle traversed by hand back to the starting-point. The tool is now fed a little farther forward, and another cut taken. This procedure is followed until, by repeated cuts, a full thread is formed. A thread gauge or, for a simple job, a hexagon nut can be used to test the thread.

When cutting threads the lead-screw nut can be engaged at any convenient

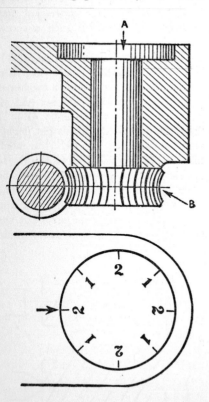

Fig. 5. A thread-cutting dial A is fitted on many lathes, rotated by the lead screw through a worm-wheel B.

place on the lead-screw and another cut taken along the work, only when the number of the work threads per in. is divisible by the number of threads per in. of the lead-screw. That is, if the lathe screw was made two threads per in., then the nut could be engaged at any point to cut four, six, eight threads, or any multiple of two. This is not the case, however, for odd numbers, and unless special precautions are taken, cross-threading and spoiling the work will result. One solution is to engage the nut, and take a cut along the work and reverse the lathe to bring the tool back to the starting-point without disengaging the nut. This method is good if the lathe has a reversing countershaft, but if not, another device is to bring the saddle to the starting-point by hand, engage the nut with the lead-screw and turn the spindle by hand to take up any lost motion, or backlash, between the nut and screw. Now put a chalk mark on the lathe-bed, close up to the saddle, or, if convenient, bring the tailstock up against the saddle. Also put a chalk mark on the spindle or spindle gear, and another on the lead-screw gear, and note the positions. After taking a cut, the saddle is returned by hand to the bed chalk mark or tailstock, and the nut is reengaged when the spindle and lead-screw chalk marks coincide as before. It will then be found that the tool will follow the first cut.

Unless care is taken, this latter method is not always trouble-free for sometimes the marks are a good distance away from the starting position and not easily seen, so many modern lathes are fitted with a screw-cutting dial (Fig. 5), to overcome this diffi-

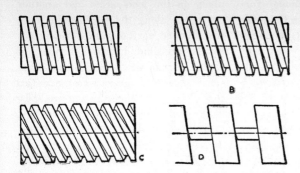

Fig. 6. Examples of multiple-start threads are shown at *A* and *D*, while *B* is a two-start and *C* a four-start thread.

the thread is cut. In such cases multiple-thread screws are used where the pitch is small, but the lead is increased to give the required movement. Examples are shown in Fig. 6, (A) being a single-thread, (B) a double-thread, and (C) a four-thread screw. The pitch is the same in each case, but the distance a nut on the screw would travel varies in the ratio of 1, 2 and 4. The diagram (D) illustrates a single-thread screw which would give the same movement per revolution as (C), but such a screw would fail in practice.

If the pitch of the screws (A), (B), and (C) be assumed as ¼ in., then the designation from which a machinist would have to work would be: (A) ¼ in. pitch, single, right-hand; (B) ¼ in. pitch, ½ in. lead, double, right-hand; and (C) ¼ in. pitch, 1 in. lead, four threads right-hand, while (D) to give the same result as (C) would be 1 in., pitch, single, right-hand. The tool used for cutting (A), (B) and (C) would be the same size, but the gear ratio and the change-gears would be quite different.

culty. This consists of a graduated dial A connected to a worm-wheel B in mesh with the lead-screw, so that, if the saddle is stationary, the lead-screw, acting as a worm, causes the dial to rotate. When the nut is engaged and the tool commences its travel, the dial remains stationary, with one of the graduations opposite the arrow. After the cut is completed and the saddle is returned to the starting-point with the nut disengaged, the dial commences to revolve again, and when one of the graduated lines comes opposite the arrow, the nut can be re-engaged with the assurance that the tool will follow the same cut.

The principle depends upon the number of teeth in the worm-wheel being a multiple of the lead-screw; and the number of teeth, divided by the pitch of the screw, equals the number of graduations on the dial. In some cases it is not feasible to engage the nut at any graduation, but only at particular ones.

There are many examples in engineering where a fairly rapid motion is required and yet to use a single-thread screw of a suitable pitch would seriously weaken the shaft upon which

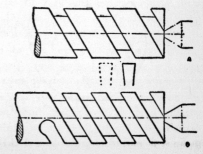

Fig. 6a. Method of cutting double-thread screw.

In some cases, instead of using the term, say, four threads, the word *start* is used—as, for example, ¼ in. pitch two starts. This is derived from the fact that, in cutting such a screw, the machinist does actually make two starts or separate cuts along the screw. Fig. 6a illustrates this, showing at (A) the first cut and at (B) the result of the second one, which should come central between the threads of the first cut. There are several methods of insuring that this takes place. First by an accurate dial on the screw of the compound rest, so that, after cutting one thread, the tool can be traversed the required distance to cut the next one, as shown by the dotted tool in Fig. 6a. Another method is to use an indexing faceplate in which the driving part can be revolved half a turn, or other fraction, this being equivalent to moving the tool; but the most-used method is to chalk-mark one of the teeth of the first driving gear and the space it occupies in the first driven gear. After cutting the first thread, the wheels are disengaged, and the lathe spindle turned to a position so that the gears can be engaged at a point half the number of teeth past the marked tooth in the driving gear. The result is equivalent to moving the spindle half a revolution, but the marked gear insures that exactly this distance is moved. It is essential that the number of teeth in the driving gear be divisible by two for a double-thread, or, for a treble-thread screw, that it be divisible by three; in the example given for the gears to cut 1⅛ in. lead where the gears are arranged $^{108}/_{48} \times \,^{72}/_{36}$, the first driving gear of 108 teeth could be chalked at each 36 teeth.

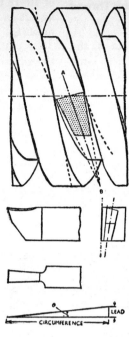

Fig. 7. *Above,* setting of tool and, *below,* tool used for cutting square-thread screw.

The procedure in cutting a square thread is similar to that for a V thread, with the exception of the tool setting, as shown in Fig. 7. The width of the tool point is equal to half the pitch of the thread to be cut, but, in addition, the cutting edge must be ground at right angles to the line AB, with equal clearance at each side, so that the action of the tool is alike on each side. A detail of a square-thread tool is given, and a method of finding the angle of the thread is also indicated. This angle depends upon the diameter of the screw and the lead of the threads. It can be calculated from the tangent

$$\text{angle} = \frac{\text{lead}}{\text{circumference}}$$

or drawn graphically as shown, and the angle θ measured by means of a protractor.

Unless the thread finishes in a groove, it is often difficult to withdraw the tool and disengage the nut simultaneously, and many broken tools or damaged work result. One way out of the trouble is to stop the lathe just before the end of the cut is reached, and to pull the spindle around for the tool to enter a hole drilled at the finishing point of the thread.

Example of Cutting an Acme Thread Screw and Nut

Selecting a suitable lead-screw, the work is shown mounted in a lathe (Fig. 8). Preliminary turning operations, after squaring the ends and centering, would include turning diameters A and B with the work in a reversed position to that shown, then placing the dog on diameter A and mounting as indicated to machine diameters C and D, this being done by repeating cuts down to within a few thousandths of an inch of finished size, when the shaft would be completed by filing as it revolved, and then polished with emery cloth. If, as is usual in modern practice, the shaft is to be finally sized by grinding, an allowance of 10–15 thousandths of an inch would be left on instead of filing for the final finishing.

In cutting either square or Acme threads, any vibration is fatal to a good thread and destructive to the tool, so the first essential is rigidity. This can be obtained by mounting a traveling steady rest on the saddle immediately in front of the tool as shown. It is advisable to rough out the thread with a square-thread tool having a front face equal to the width at the bottom of the Acme thread, and then to follow for finishing with a properly shaped tool with an included angle of 29 deg. A gauge as shown at A should be used for grinding to shape and then setting the tool in the correct position on the tool-rest.

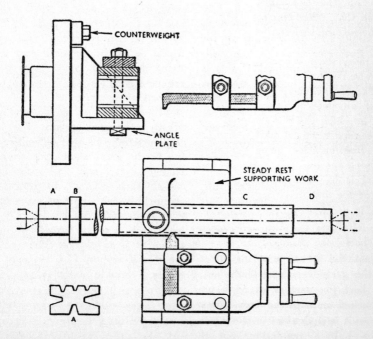

Fig. 8. *Bottom,* method of cutting an Acme thread-screw. After squaring the ends and centering, diameters A and B are turned with the work in reverse of the direction shown; then the dog is placed on diameter A and mounted to machine diameters C and D. *Top,* arrangement for cutting Acme thread nut.

Machining the Nut

Taking the half-nuts as shown in Fig. 8 as a practical case, these are of bronze, with the two halves cast as one, to facilitate machining, and then sawed in two parts after threading. The casting could be held in a chuck, but, as it furnishes a good example of the use of an angle plate, this will be described. The angle plate is first bolted on to the lathe face-plate and counterbalanced by a weight to insure safety. The outside of the nut will have been machined before reaching the turner, and the hole to be threaded marked out, so that the first operation is to set the work on the angle plate at the correct height and square with the sides. To get the correct height, the nut may be packed up or the angle plate adjusted before finally clamping the nut down ready for boring. Referring again to the lead-screw previously machined, if this is $\frac{1}{2}$-in. pitch, 2-in. diameter, then the depth of the thread cut would be from the tables of proportion, $.25 + .01 = .2600$. The dimension .01, however, represents the clearance between the top and bottom of the mating threads; so the bore of the nut must be 2 in. — (twice .25) $= 1\frac{1}{2}$ in. diameter; this, allowing the necessary clearance for the diameter of the bottom of the fitting screw, will be 2 in. — (twice .2600) $= 1.48$ in. diameter.

A rough hole of about $1\frac{1}{4}$ in. diameter would be already cast in the nut, so the boring operation would be of short duration, requiring, say, three cuts from a tool mounted in the compound rest. Inside calipers would be used to measure the hole, or, if available, a plug gauge of the *Go and No Go* type. No special difficulty would be encountered in the next operation of threading the nut, first by using a square-thread roughing tool, and then finishing by a bent tool of the Acme thread shape set in position by a tool-gauge. The manipulation of the lathe is the same for internal threading as it is for external—that is, by a series of repeated cuts, bearing in mind any special precautions for odd threads, multiple threads and the lead of the thread as outlined previously.

A worm may be regarded as a short, coarse-pitch screw of the same angle as the Acme thread, 29 deg., but of a different depth so as to gear with a worm-wheel, this depth being obtained from the linear pitch $\times .6866$, while the width of the tool at the front cutting edge equals the linear pitch $\times .31$. Thus the depth for a worm of $\frac{3}{4}$-in. pitch would be $.6866 \times .75 = .515$ in., and the size of the tool point $.75 \times .31 = .232$ in. A worm of these dimensions would be cut in the same way as an Acme thread, but coarse-pitch worms require a good many cuts and are often finished by separate cuts by left- and right-hand tools, as shown in Fig. 9. Multiple-threaded worms of a large lead sometimes present difficulties, owing to the great strain put upon the change-gears, and in such cases, rather than attempt to relieve the strain by a third pair of gears in the gear train from the headstock to the lead-screw, a coarse thread-cutting attachment is employed. The arrangement is shown in Fig. 10, and comprises a slidable pinion A, capable of meshing with either the cone pinion B or the spindle gear C. For ordinary thread-cutting the spindle gear C and the usual gear ratios are employed. With the lathe back gear of, say, 12 to 1 engaged, the cone-pulley makes twelve revolutions to one of the spindle, so that if gear A is moved to mesh with gear B, the change-gear stud is speeded up twelve times relative to the spindle and work. Thus, if the worm to be cut has a lead of 12 in., instead of having to obtain a ratio of $\frac{12}{\frac{1}{2}} = \frac{12}{1} \times \frac{2}{1} = \frac{24}{1}$, by the change-gears, a ratio of only $\frac{24}{12} = 2$ would be required. By such a method all heavy strain is taken from the change-gears, and not only coarse lead worms, but helical oil grooves can be cut with ease.

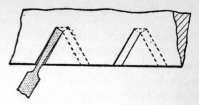

Fig. 9. Coarse-pitch worms, requiring many cuts, are often finished with separate left- and right-hand tools, as shown in the diagram.

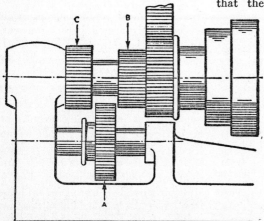

Fig. 10. Coarse thread-cutting attachment for multiple-threaded worms of large lead. The slidable pinion A meshes with either the cone pinion B or the spindle wheel C.

manner by the use of a translating gear of either 63 or 127 teeth. The reason for the use of this gear is that there are almost exactly 25.4 millimeters in 1 in., so that if a lathe had change-gears mounted $10\!\!/_{254}$ and a lead screw of 1 in., a screw of 1 millimeter of pitch would be cut. Such a gear would be too large for practical purposes, but a compound train with a gear of 127 teeth can be used. This gives great accuracy, and makes the fitting of a special metric screw unnecessary. Actually the error is only .008 of a millimeter, or .0003 in., so in many cases a more convenient-sized wheel of 63 teeth is used with sufficient accuracy for commercial screws.

A machinist must understand the procedure in dealing with metric threads or a lathe with a metric lead-screw because a great amount of work today is made to metric measurements.

These features call for no elaborate equipment to convert them into understandable measurements, and dealing first with the problem of cutting metric threads on a standard American lathe, this is solved in a simple

To find change-gears the rule is:

$$\frac{\text{Drivers}}{\text{Driven}} \frac{10}{127} \times$$

$$\frac{\text{Pitch of screw in millimeters}}{1}$$

or, as an example, if a 12 millimeter pitch screw is required to be cut on a lathe with a lead-screw of $\frac{1}{2}$-in. pitch, then the gears required would be,

$$\frac{10}{127} \times \frac{12}{1} = \frac{120}{127} \text{ or } \frac{60}{127} \times \frac{80}{40} \text{ com-}$$

pound train.

For lathes with lead-screws other than $\frac{1}{2}$-in. pitch, the following rule can be applied:

$$\frac{\text{Drivers}}{\text{Driven}} \times \frac{5}{127} \times \text{threads per inch of}$$

lead-screw $\times$ pitch in mm. of the required thread.

Example. Required the gears to cut 4-mm. pitch thread on lathe with lead-screw of 6 threads per in.

$$\frac{\text{Drivers}}{\text{Driven}} = \frac{5}{127} \times \frac{6}{1} \times \frac{4}{1} = \frac{120}{127}$$

$$\text{or } \frac{60}{127} \times \frac{80}{40}$$

The rule to find the change gears for cutting American standard threads with a metric lead-screw is as follows:

$$\frac{127}{\text{Threads to be cut} \times \text{metric thread}}$$
$$\text{mm.} \times 5$$

The 127 gear is the driver on the headstock, and the product of the numbers in the denominator gives the number of teeth in the gear to be mounted on the lead-screw.

Example. Required to cut a screw 2 threads per in. on a lathe with a metric lead-screw of 5 mm.

Then:

$$\frac{127}{2 \times 5 \times 5} = \frac{127}{50} \text{ or } \frac{127}{100} \times \frac{80}{40}$$

Screw-Cutting Attachments

It has been shown that the only serious difficulty in general screw-cutting occurs when the screw-thread must finish close to a shoulder or run out on a plain bar, instead of finishing in a recess or groove. Many devices are fitted to simplify these conditions; one is a quick-withdrawal attachment for the tool whereby, through the action of a double nut on the surfacing screw, the operator is enabled to feed in the tool for the repeated cuts at a fine rate, but a reversal of the operating handle withdraws the tool very rapidly. This gives him the opportunity of getting the tool out of the thread before it strikes an obstruction, but as the action of withdrawing the tool and disengaging the nut requires the simultaneous movement of both hands, it is still somewhat difficult unless the lathe is running slowly. For this reason, on turret lathes in particular, devices have been fitted in which the disengagement of the lead-screw nut simultaneously withdraws the tool from the work.

Withdrawing the Tool

Such aids are of value, but a more certain method is illustrated in Fig. 11. This shows the Holbrook one-position reverse clutch located in the headstock comprising gears A and B, running in opposite directions to drive the center clutch C, this in turn driving the gear D. This clutch can be engaged to the right- or left-hand gear in one position only, and this movement is effected by a rod located in front of the bed, adjacent to the lead screw. Automatic stops are adjustable along this rod on each side of the apron, and are available for the full travel of the apron, which, when it comes into contact with a stop, slides the clutch out of mesh. This obviates all danger of running into shoulders, so that the necessity of cutting grooves is avoided, or, rather, the tool makes its own channel as threading proceeds. The device also takes the place of reversing the drive, if required, for moving the rod in the opposite direction returns the tool without the neces-

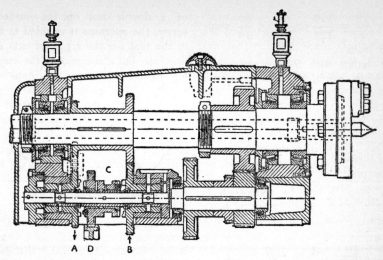

Fig. 11. A device for withdrawing the tool from the work simultaneously with the disengagement of the lead screw nut is the Holbrook one-position reverse clutch. Gears A, B run in opposite directions to drive center clutch C, which drives gear D.

sity of disengaging the nut from the lead-screw. In any case the relative position of the tool to the thread is never altered, no matter what pitch is being cut, or whether the thread is left- or right-hand.

It has been stated that after taking one cut along a shaft to cut a thread, the tool is returned to the starting-point and fed forward a little farther for the next cut. If any wear has taken place between the surfacing screw and nut there may be a tendency for the tool to *draw-in*, a very undesirable, but common feature. A simple device to eliminate this is shown in Fig. 12, and can soon be fitted to any lathe. Into the bottom slide of the compound rest a stud A is screwed and locked tight. On the outer end of the stud is a micrometer collar C with graduations, preferably indicating .001-in. movements of the tool. On the saddle front is a latch, pivoted upon and locked by a set-screw. When a cut is applied by the saddle-screw handle, the nut C is screwed up against the latch, but when the tool is withdrawn from the screw, the stud A, together with the micrometer nut, is moved bodily through the latch toward the handle, or hand-wheel. If next the micrometer nut is turned as many thousandths of an inch, the tool can be advanced into the work this amount and no more.

The usual way of cutting V threads is to set the tool square with the work and feed it in at right angles to the axis. With this method slow speeds and light feeds are the rule, because (1)

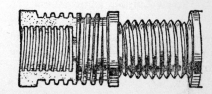

Fig. 11a. A sample of the kind of work made possible by the use of the Holbrook clutch shown in Fig. 11.

the cutting edges of the tool cannot have any top rake, therefore they are comparatively blunt, and not free-cutting; (2) the chips from the two sides of the tool interfere with each other, and have a marked tendency to choke, particularly at the point of the tool.

A better method is shown in Fig. 13, the tool point being set square to the work, but fed in the direction of the arrow B (approximately half the thread angle) by means of the compound rest. It will be seen from E (which is a side view of the tool looking in the direction of arrow D) that any amount of top rake C can be given to the cutting edge, with the result that heavier cuts can be taken and higher speeds used. The cut is all taken from one side of the thread, so that the chip has ample room to leave the point of the tool as it is severed

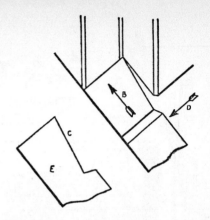

Fig. 13. For cutting V threads the best arrangement of the tool point, fixed in a swiveling compound rest, is that shown here.

from the bar. For roughing purposes the tool is a great time-saver, and some American lathe manufacturers specially arrange their compound rests to suit this method.

Automatic Screw-Cutting

Where considerable quantities of similar screws are required, some automatic means are preferable, and a type of lathe suitable for this purpose is shown in Figs. 14 and 15. Once the work is placed in position between the centers, the stops set and the cut started, no further attention from the operator is required until the screw is completed. To accomplish this the motions required are similar to those performed manually on an ordinary lathe, and, after the lathe has taken one cut, are as follows:

(a) Withdraw the tool.

(b) Return the saddle rapidly to the starting-point.

(c) Feed the tool to its original cutting position.

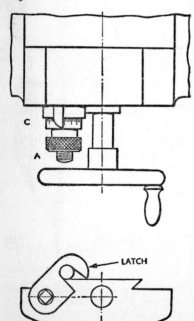

Fig. 12. A simple device to prevent draw-in of tool.

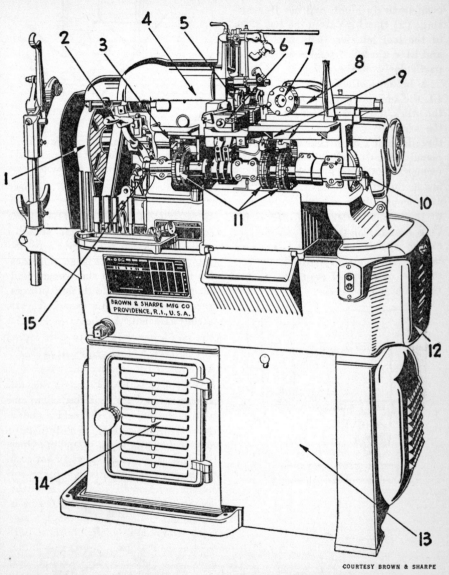

Fig. 14. Automatic Screw Machine: 1, driving shaft pulley; 2, driving shaft clutch lever; 3, trip lever; 4, spindle friction clutch; 5, spindle; 6, cross slide; 7, turret; 8, turret slide; 9, trip levers; 10, cam shaft; 11, trip dog carriers; 12, switch compartment; 13, driving motor; 14, spindle speed change pulley; 15, reversing shaft.

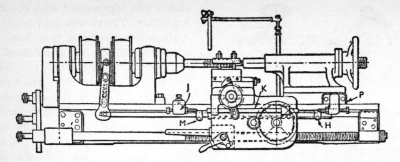

Fig. 15. For cutting considerable numbers of similar screws an automatic lathe is used as shown here and in Fig. 16; the screw then needs no further attention from the operator after placing the work between the centers, setting the stops, and starting the cut.

(d) Feed the tool forward a few thousandths for the next cut.

(e) The saddle traverse must reverse for the cutting stroke.

(f) At the final depth the in-feed of the tool must cease.

The lathe is driven from two belts, one for the cutting stroke and the other for the return at high speed. The work in question being the screws for lathe chucks, six or eight threads per in. left-hand, the tool starts from the headstock, and, when reaching the tailstock, to comply with the sequence of operations given, withdraws from the work. The arrangement for this is shown in Fig. 16, and comprises two adjustable brackets A and B, these

carrying steel plates with taper faces so that they can be set to strike a roller on segment C and give a partial rotation of pinion D, Fig. 16. This pinion is connected to a short screw $\frac{5}{12}$-in. pitch, $1\frac{9}{16}$-in. lead, five threads, right-hand, fitting in a bracket E, this acting as a nut. As shown in Fig. 17, the saddle screw is free to slide in and out of socket G as required, although keyed to it for feeding purposes.

With bracket A (Fig. 16) set, and having caused the withdrawal of the tool from the work, the next sequence is to return the saddle rapidly back to the starting-point, so collar H (Fig. 15) on the reverse rod must be set so that it is struck by the apron after

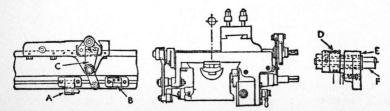

Fig. 16. The sequence of operations for thread cutting on an automatic lathe is similar to those performed by hand on an ordinary lathe, and is described in the text. The lathe is driven from two belts, one for the cutting stroke, the other for the return at high speed.

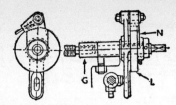

Fig. 17. When the correct depth of cut is obtained, the in-feed is stopped by lifting the pawl and no further cutting takes place. The machine can be left running for a period without damage to the work.

the tool is withdrawn, and, by means of the load-and-fire mechanism on the headstock, actuates the friction clutch between the two pulleys, for the reverse motion to commence and return the saddle for the next cut.

To feed the tool forward the requisite amount, the stop F (Fig. 16) must be set to strike rod K on the apron front, connected to the ratchet lever L as shown in Fig. 17, thus causing the pawl to feed the ratchet wheel, and thereby the saddle screw moves the tool forward .004 in. The tool is now ready for the next cut, which is started by the saddle moving against the stop M (Fig. 15) and moving the friction

clutch into engagement with the driving pulley. The various movements operate automatically in turn, until the correct depth of cut is obtained. At this point, the pawl (Fig. 17) is lifted out of engagement with the ratchet wheel by means of the segment N, which is previously set on the hub of the ratchet wheel in a suitable position to lift the ratchet pawl and stop the in-feed. So, although the lathe is still running, no further cutting takes place, and no damage to the work results if the machine is left running for a period; thus one operator can attend to several machines.

There are types of screw-threads in which the lead varies in different places; these require some means of moving the top slide of the compound rest, so that the movement of the tool is advanced or retarded relative to the motion along the bed, obtained by the change-gears. There is also a fairly common type of thread not yet described—that is, one cut on taper shafts—but before dealing with this, a knowledge of taper turning is required, so the subject is dealt with in the next chapter.

CHAPTER 5

TAPER-TURNING, KNURLING, AND OTHER USES OF THE LATHE

METHOD OF TAPER-TURNING. TAPER MEASUREMENTS AND ANGLES. USING TAPER GAGES. REAMING. FORMING. KNURLING. ECCENTRIC DIAMETERS. BACKING-OFF. BRASS WORK. SPINNING LATHES. GENERAL PURPOSE OPERATIONS. INDEXING FOR WHEEL-TEETH. SPECIAL TYPES OF LATHES.

ONE of the operations which a machinist is often called upon to perform is that of turning taper surfaces, and for this operation there are three main methods and two lesser known ones available.

The simplest method (Fig. 1) is performed by swiveling the compound rest to the required angle and traversing the top slide by hand. This method is limited to short taper parts, as for example the one shown of truing up a lathe-center, for the traverse of the tool on the top slide is limited to a few inches only.

Tool-Setting

When plain cylindrical work is being turned, the height of the tool has no effect on the accuracy of the work, although it may affect the finish on it, but the turning of conical surfaces requires special care in tool-setting, and it is of great importance that the tool should be exactly on the center line of the work, otherwise a true cone is not obtained. This can be seen in Fig. 2, which indicates that if the full lines represent the small and large ends of a taper surface, then the tool will have moved outward the distance A as it travels along the bar.

If, however, the tool had been set at the height B, touching the small end of the taper and then traversed along, it would still move outward the distance A, but terminate at the dotted-line position, making the large end of the taper much too small. In addition, in the operation of turning work to a fine point, like the lathe-center shown, it will be realized that if the tool was set either above or below the work-center it would leave the work before a point was produced; so that, in addition to making inaccurate work, it is impossible to produce a pointed article unless the tool is set correctly. One of the simplest methods of insuring this is to set it by comparing the height of the cutting edge with one of the lathe-centers before placing the work in the lathe. This method of turning tapers by swiveling the compound rest is applicable to short tapers on work mounted between the centers, or either turning or boring tapers on work held in a chuck.

Offsetting Tailstock

Another method largely used for long tapers is shown in Fig. 3. From previous illustrations of tailstocks it will have been noticed that this unit comprises two main castings, the part carrying the spindle and the base or shoe clamped to the bed. The reason for this construction is that it allows the spindle section to be moved by screw and nut in a cross direction, so that it can be set out of alignment with the center of the headstock. If work is now mounted between the lathe-centers, it will be turned tapering, be-

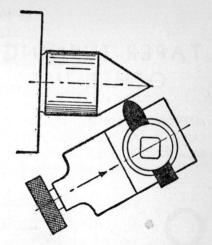

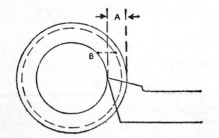

Fig. 1. The simplest method of taper-turning is by swiveling the compound rest to the required angle and traversing the top slide by hand.

cause while the axis of the work is diagonal to the lathe-bed, the tool still travels along its customary parallel path, and the amount of taper obtained, or the difference between the large and small diameters, depends on the amount that the tailstock has been offset from the central position.

The amount of offset is somewhat

Fig. 2. The tool point for taper-turning must be exactly on the center-line.

limited, and while available on either side of the center, only slight tapers can be produced on long shafts. Assuming that the tailstock is offset 1 in. and the work is 8 ft. long, then it will be turned 2 in. smaller at the tailstock end than at the headstock, which would give a taper of ¼ in. per ft., whereas if the shaft had been only 1 ft. long, it would have tapered 2 in. per ft. This method is reasonably accurate for long tapers, but reference to Fig. 3 will show the limitations, the chief one being that

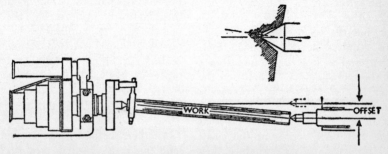

Fig. 3. Long tapers may be turned by offsetting the tailstock, the amount of taper obtained depending on the amount of offset. The position of the center in taper-turning is shown in the upper figure.

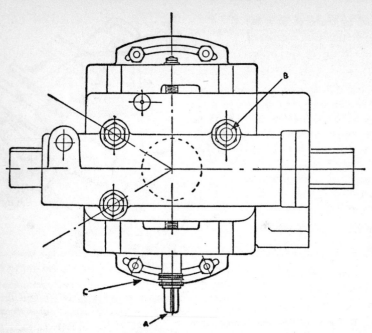

Fig. 4. For taper-turning this special headstock with a swivel slide C between the base and the spindle section is used. This is indexed in degrees, and the micrometer collar in thousandths of an inch, giving very accurate setting in two directions.

the centers do not point toward each other, and the second one, caused by the first, is that the center holes of the work cannot get a proper bearing on the headstock centers; this tends to cause excessive wear, and may throw the work out of true. The tailstock center is the chief sufferer, because this is a dead center around which the work revolves, whereas at the opposite end, although the work may not bear accurately on the center, as both revolve together the conditions are not so severe. In all cases the ends of the work must be faced perfectly square, or otherwise it is impossible to get the work running true. Where greater accuracy is required, a special headstock as shown in the plan view, Fig. 4, can be used with advantage. This arrangement necessitates a swivel slide be-

tween the base and the spindle section, so that previous to offsetting the tailstock, which is done by the screw A, it can be swiveled by loosening the bolts B and pulling the spindle around to the angle required. The front of the swivel slide C is indexed in $\frac{1}{2}$ degrees, while the micrometer collar on the transverse screw is graduated to read in .001 in., so that very accurate setting in two directions is possible. This arrangement takes all strain from the dead center, which bears fully in the end of the work, and while the live center still bears only on one side, it has been pointed out that the conditions are not severe at that end.

Many lathes are fitted with an attachment which permits the lathe-centers to remain in alignment just as if for cylindrical turning, but causes the tool to traverse in a tapering direction as compared to the setting of the lathe-centers. This is the best and most accurate method of taper-turning, and, as shown in Fig. 5, will be seen to comprise a device fitted to the back of the lathe-saddle and to the rear slide of the bed. A slotted bar is fixed to the toolrest, and can be clamped to a short slide on the swivel bar A. For plain turning the swivel bar is set in alignment with the slides of the bed, so that the tool follows a longitudinal path only when the sliding feed is engaged; but if the bar is swiveled, then the tool follows a tangential path, in or out as well as along the bed. The device is available on any length of the bed by clamping the bracket B at the required position, and fine setting for either boring or turning is obtained by the end graduation giving the inches per ft. taper. As drawings are often sent to an operator and give the taper in angles, or tapers

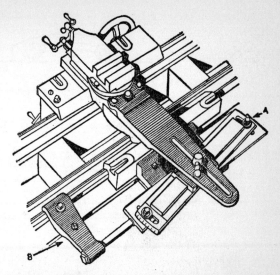

Fig. 5. With this graduated attachment, the lathe-centers remain in alignment, but the tool traverses in a tapering direction as compared with the setting of the centers.

per ft., while the converse would be more useful, the table on this page can

TAPERS PER FOOT WITH CORRESPONDING ANGLES

TAPER PER FT.	INCLUDED ANGLE.	ANGLE WITH CENTER LINE.
In.		
⅛	0° 36′	0° 18′
¼	1° 12′	0° 36′
⅜	1° 47′	0° 54′
½	2° 23′	1° 12′
¾	3° 35′	1° 47′
1	4° 46′	2° 23′
1½	7° 09′	3° 35′
1¾	8° 20′	4° 10′
2	9° 31′	4° 46′
2½	11° 54′	5° 57′
3	14° 15′	7° 08′
3½	16° 36′	8° 18′
4	18° 55′	9° 28′

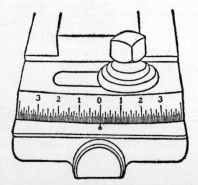

Fig. 5a. Close-up of the graduated scale, marked in inches per foot, on the attachment shown in **Fig. 5.**

be used to convert from one to the other.

Boring-Machine Spindle

A practical example of making a boring-machine spindle will now be explained. From the diagram (Fig. 6), it will be observed that there are six diameters to turn, including a short, steep taper hole in the spindle end. The spindle is cut off from a bar 5¼ in. in diameter and ¼ in. longer than the finished length of 3 ft. The ends are squared and the bar centered in the manner previously described, and a dog placed on the end A, so that the diameters B, D, E, and F can be roughed down at one setting. As a preliminary operation to grinding, the diameters B and E are left .015 in. over size, while at this stage the taper portions C, D, and F can be roughed down parallel to the diameters at the largest part and tapered later.

The dog can now be removed from A and a smaller one fitted on F, so that the bar can be reversed endwise and the diameter A roughed down to grinding size. To allow for clearance of the grinding wheels against shoulders, recesses just below the finished

size should be cut at the meeting point of each diameter, as at H, and while the recessing tool is in the lathe, after cutting H, the bar is again reversed on the lathe centers so that the remaining recesses can be cut.

In this position the steep taper C of 45 deg. can be cut by swiveling the tool-post to this angle, and by means of repeated cuts gradually obtaining the size required by hand operation of the tool along the top slide.

Trial Settings

Alternative methods of machining the taper portion D are either off-setting the tailstock or using a taper-turning attachment. Selecting the first method for this operation, the first thing is to remove the work from the lathe, loosen the tailstock bolts and traverse the spindle section of the tailstock towards the front of the lathe. To determine the amount of this offset, several methods can be employed. As the taper is 1 in 12, and 6 in. long, with the large diameter 4 in. the diameter at the small end will be ½ in. in 6 in. or 3½ in. diameter. A trial cut can be made along the bar and the two ends of the taper meas-

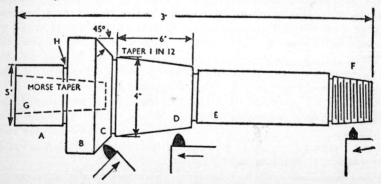

Fig. 6. The making of a boring-machine spindle as described in the text involves three methods of taper-turning. There are six diameters in all to turn. The first setting necessary is illustrated above.

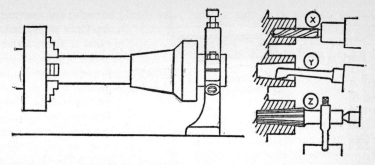

Fig. 7. Second setting of boring-machine spindle for boring taper hole in the spindle end. The work is gripped in the chuck at section *E* (Fig. 6) and supported at *A* by the tailstock center in the center hole.

ured. If the large end is found to be 4⅛ in. and the small end 3¾ in. in diameter, then it would show that the tool was taking too much metal from the large end and that the tailstock had not been brought far enough forward. Altering this until the correct taper is obtained, further cuts are taken by engaging the sliding motion, until the correct size is reached.

Using Taper Gauge

Some of these trial settings can be avoided if a gage of the correct taper is available. This is set between the centers, and the tailstock brought out of alignment until the taper edge of the gage is parallel with the slides of the lathe-bed. This is checked by traversing the tool along the gage and, if found equi-distant at all points, the tailstock would be clamped in this position with the assurance that the tool will produce a similar taper on the spindle.

If the diameter F should be a plain taper portion, it could be turned by offsetting the tailstock, but as it needs to be threaded, there is only one correct method of performing this, that is by the taper-turning attachment.

Drunken Threads

The reason for this is that the tool for cutting threads must be set at right angles with the axis of the shaft as shown, and not at right angles to the taper surface. In addition, if the tailstock is offset, there is a tendency for the angle between the dog on the work and the face-plate to rotate the work at a varying velocity and produce uneven or *drunken* threads, as they are termed. This effect is caused by the threads not advancing at an even rate, and if the amount of offset is fairly large, this trouble is accompanied by another one—that is, the production of a finer-pitch screw than that for which the lathe is geared. This is explained by treating the offset shaft as the hypotenuse of a triangle instead of the base. The tool travels a distance equal to the base, but as it is in contact with the hypotenuse, which is longer than the base, more threads than are required, or threads of a finer pitch, are cut on the shaft.

The taper-turning attachment is set to the angle obtained from the table and used at one setting for both turning and thread-cutting, completing all

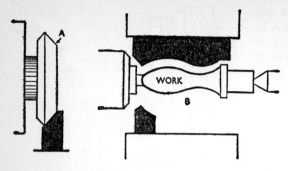

Fig. 8. *Left,* facing a bevel wheel by means of a single traverse of a taper-face forming tool. *Right,* forming shaped handles by using back and front tools.

the lathe operations except that of machining the Morse taper hole G in the spindle end. The operations have been given on the assumption that only one spindle is produced, but for quantity production, it is quicker to complete similar operations in sequence—that is, if the tool and machine are set to produce the taper portion D, machine this part of the spindle on every piece.

Setting the Attachment

Fig. 7 shows the next setting to bore the taper hole; this requires a chuck to hold the section E, and not on the finished end F, while the opposite end A is set to run true in a steady rest. To assist in this setting, the work is first gripped in the chuck and supported at A by the dead center in the center hole. This will insure true running, and if the three jaws of the stay are now adjusted to the work and clamped in position, the spindle will be found ready for boring when the dead center is withdrawn.

The first operation is to drill a hole of the same size as that of the small end of the taper, and for this purpose a twist-drill X is fitted in the tailstock

spindle and fed by hand. In the case of large tapers, other drills of larger size, fed shorter distances, could follow, giving a *stepped* taper, but the actual taper boring must be performed by the tool Y in conjunction with swiveling the tool-rest to the required angle, or using the taper-turning attachment as before. Thus the Morse taper would be machined within a few thousandths of an inch of size and then finished by the taper reamer Z. It should be realized that reamers are intended for the fine finishing only, and must not be used as cutting tools to remove a lot of metal. They are expensive, and should be handled carefully in the following manner. Place the reamer in the bore with a dog on the shank, so that the dog rests on the tool-post. Support the end of the reamer by the dead center as shown, and, while pulling round the driving belt, gently feed the dead center forward, taking care that the center does not leave the hole in the reamer end. Use plenty of lubricant, and when the reamer has gone in to the correct depth, a fine finish will result.

Use of Reamers

The use of a taper reamer insures that a correct taper is obtained, but to check a taper part, as section D, required to fit a bushing, the usual method is to rough the taper, and then chalk a few lines along the surface, place the bushing or a gage, on the taper portion and give it a few turns. The chalk marks will show whether the tapers correspond; if not, they will be erased at one end only. More accurate results can be had by the use of a smearing of Prussian blue or red lead, for these not only show the correct taper, but will denote high places due to vibration.

Forming

The operation of forming is that of turning intricate shapes by one traverse of a tool, instead of several movements. Thus the bevel wheel A, Fig. 8, can be produced by the taper-face tool at one cut, instead of by repeated cuts in the manner just described for taper turning. As every tool is suitable for one purpose only, there must be sufficient

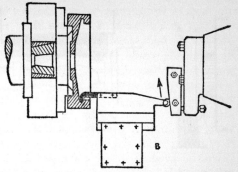

Fig. 10. Profiling a flywheel using a taper-bar and roller. The taper-bar is bolted to a bracket on the turret; a cutting tool and roller are carried on a slide clamped to the square turret B.

work to justify its making and sufficient rigidity on the machine to prevent vibration. A low finishing speed should be employed with a heavy lubricant such as lard oil, and if the cut is very heavy, it is better to machine from the rear cross-slide, if at all possible. This enables the cutting pressure to be transmitted to the headstock casting instead of to the cap; but if this method is not feasible, then the work should be supported against the cut by suitable steadies bearing against it, or, in the case of a turret lathe, by running the end of the work in a steady rest or on a dead center. Under such conditions cuts up to 8 in. wide can be performed on mild steel, providing sufficient power is available.

Forming can be usefully employed to produce many articles that were formerly turned laboriously by hand. Such parts include shaped handles and knobs, one shown at B being produced by two tools, mounted back and front. Another example is indicated at C, (Fig. 9), and it will be seen that in these last two cases the shape of

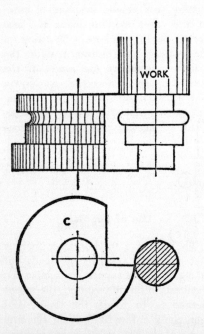

Fig. 9. Application of forming tool of circular type. The shape of the tool is a negative of that required in the work.

the tool is the reverse of the shape required in the work. To reduce the amount of high-speed steel required to make the tools, they are usually made to fit into holders, while for some classes of work the life of the tool can be extended considerably by making it of circular section as shown at C. Grinding is performed on the flat surface, and the tool partly revolved to produce the new sharpened cutting edge, which should always be located exactly on the height of the center, otherwise a true form will not be obtained.

Shaped surfaces of any great length on bar or castings cannot be machined directly with form-tools, so, to produce the same result, a single tool guided by a former can be used. A common example is that of *crowning* or forming a curved face on a pulley. Instead of the straight guide on a taper-turning attachment being used, if this is replaced by a guide having a radial slot, into which fits a roller on the tool-slide, as the saddle travels along the bed the tool follows a convex path, which is reproduced on the pulley face.

All tapers, of course, do not lie in the same plane of direction as the lathe-centers, but taper in a direction across the bed, so that, when profiling in this direction, the taper-bar must be supported either across the bed on the tailstock or, as in the case to be considered, by a taper-bar on the turret (Fig. 10). This shows the method of profiling a cast-iron flywheel on the inside web, the taper-bar being bolted to a bracket on the turret, which is kept rigid by clamping the turret slide on the bed. On the square turret B is clamped a slide carrying the tool-holder, which contains a cutting tool at one side and a roller at the other so that when the surfacing feed is engaged, the point of the cutting tool follows a path dictated by the angle of the taper-bar and reproduces the desired shapes on the flywheel. This method of profiling gives a good finish, and is particularly applicable on heavy work, where the attempt to form a shape at one cut is difficult.

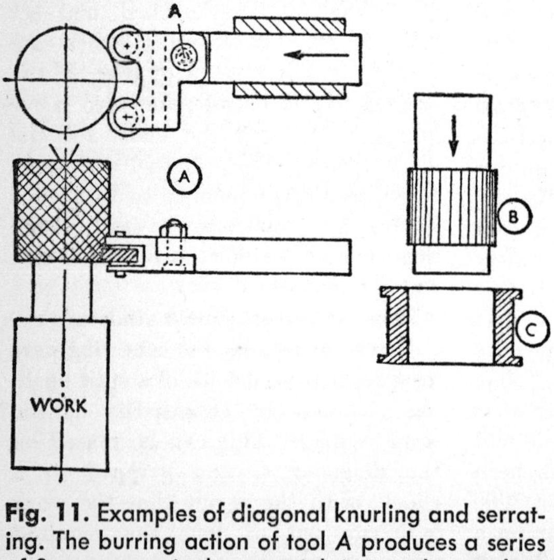

Knurling

The use of a knurled surface is either to facilitate handling or to replace keying or screwing light cylindrical pieces together. The process is one of producing a series of right- and left-hand grooves in the material by a burring action produced by

Fig. 11. Examples of diagonal knurling and serrating. The burring action of tool A produces a series of fine grooves in the material; it can also produce straight serrations along the axis of the work, as at B.

a tool A, (Fig. 11). The work to be knurled—for example, a plug gauge as shown—is mounted between the lathe-centers and driven by a dog in the usual way, while the tool is mounted in the tool-post, so that either of the knurling rollers is free to pivot and rest freely against the work. This floating action of the rollers is essential, otherwise a poor result will be obtained. The next step is to force the rollers with considerable pressure against the work, supply plenty of oil or coolant and engage the feed. Each roller under pressure cuts itself into the work, and as one is provided with right-hand and the other with left-hand grooves, a diamond-shaped pattern shown in the diagram is pro-

duced. Other effects can be obtained, and coarse, medium, and fine ridges made by varying the angle of the knurl helix. Sometimes six rollers are fitted on one holder, so that any two can be used as required, or, as an alternative, convex or concave knurled rollers are fitted on the tool to use on similar-shaped work. On short work no longitudinal traverse motion is required, and the tool can, if required, be used to produce ridges parallel to the axis of the work as at B. This type of ridge is often used to form a connection between two mating parts, the part B being hardened and pressed into the part C, cutting its own multiple splines during the operation and producing a cheap and rapid joint.

OTHER USES OF THE LATHE

A MACHINIST may be called upon to machine a shaft or stud in which all the diameters are not coaxial, but instead some of them may be eccentric to the others. One common example is that of the back-gear arrangement of a lathe where the back-shaft is either made with eccentric diameters or runs in eccentric bushings. Fig. 12 shows the eccentric shaft complete at A, while B shows the same shaft after the first operation. To arrive at this stage, the first procedure is to end and center the bar and rough-turn the ends to a diameter rather more than twice the distance X, to insure that the full diameter of the two ends will finish to size after the bar has been set eccentric in the lathe-center. The next operation is to lay the bar on a pair of V blocks as shown, and with a height-gauge or carefully held ruler, mark the position of the new center

holes to throw the bar out the required amount of eccentricity. Now drill new center holes where marked, and set between the lathe-centers, when the whole bar will run out of true. If the eccentricity is large, some care is required in turning the ends, for the work at first strikes the tool with some force, in similar manner to turning a square shaft, and may be easily bent; thus it is advisable to use a keen tool and a fine feed.

Where short eccentric studs are required in quantities, the centering part may be dispensed with if a split bushing of the same eccentricity as the work is made. This can be placed on the diameter C and gripped in a chuck, with the result that the work will run out of true the required amount to give the correct eccentricity when the ends are turned in the normal way.

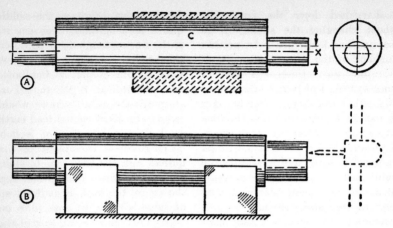

Fig. 12. To machine a shaft with eccentric diameters, after the bar has been ended and centered and rough-turned, it is laid on V blocks (*B*), the position of the new center holes marked and drilled, and set between the lathe-centers. The final result is seen at *A*, which shows the eccentric shaft complete.

Engine crank-shafts may be regarded as large eccentrics of a comprehensive type, a six-cylinder engine, as an example, having seven journals on the same center, and then the six cranks and webs and possibly balance weights to machine all at the same eccentricity, but in different angular positions. Special adjustable slides carrying the chuck or driving member can be fitted to insure that the correct eccentricity is obtained, but the throw of the cranks is usually so great that narrow toolboxes must be employed to fit between the cranks when turning the journals, or overhang of the tools will result.

Relieving

The purpose of relieving or backing-off, as it is termed, will be understood by reference to Fig. 13, which shows a gear-cutter and the saddle of a relieving lathe. In order that the cutter may present a cutting edge, and not merely rub on the work, some clearance is required, as indicated by the heavy line. This enables the cutter to

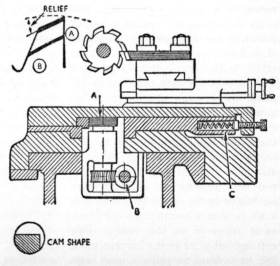

Fig. 13. Gear-cutter and saddle of a relieving lathe. The heavy line indicates the clearance of the cutter.

be sharpened down the front face without changing the shape of the work produced. In order to produce the shape of the heavy line, it is obvious that the lathe-tool must commence at the point A and terminate at B by either the cutter revolving onto the tool in an eccentric path, or the tool moving continually forward as the cutter revolves onto it and giving the same result. The procedure is complicated, however, because, unlike the machining of the eccentric just described, the operation may have to be completed not once for every revolution, but eight times or more per revolution of the work. The tool must therefore advance slowly for cutting, and before it is struck by the next tooth, be rapidly withdrawn and presented to the next tooth to commence another cut.

To accomplish this either a special lathe or an attachment on a standard lathe may be employed. The arrangement comprises a train of gears driven from the spindle gearing and terminating on a cam A in the saddle. The ratio of the gearing must be variable for different reliefs, or different-shaped cams can be employed, but the action is the same—that of giving a slow-cutting forward traverse and a quick withdrawal, this being determined by the shape and position of the lift on the cam. In the diagram the reciprocating movement of the tool to the work is obtained by the shaft B, which runs the length of the lathe-bed and imparts the correct rotary movement to the cam, which is of such a shape that a positive inward movement is given to the saddle while cutting, but after part of a revolution, the cam ceases to make contact with the saddle, which is rapidly returned clear of the work by the springs C.

In the example given, the saddle requires no longitudinal movement, but if the work was a hob, or spiral cutter, then movement along the bed would have to take place simultaneously with the infeed of the tool. For this purpose the lead screw would be geared up as if for thread-cutting— in fact, the relieving of a hob for worm-gears is equivalent to that of thread-cutting plus the additional mechanism for simultaneous reciprocation of the tool. Sometimes spiral-grooved cutters of irregular curved shape must be relieved, so still another motion is involved—that of the tool following the profile in addition to traversing and in and out for each tooth. For this purpose a device similar to a taper-turning attachment is employed, except that, instead of the straight slide, a grooved guide is used, so that the tool follows the correct contour, as described for forming the rim of a pulley.

For the production of brass work in quantities, while the ordinary turret lathe is often suitable, there are various alterations or additions which will add materially to its productive capacity. Moreover, as much of the work is of small size and easily machined, hand operations are largely employed. Thus the lathe shown in Fig. 14 comprises a turret head with six holes to bring the various tools for boring, turning, drilling, etc., into action as required. No power-feed is available, but the turret can be moved to any part of the bed and clamped in the most suitable position for the work which is to be machined. Hand-motions are provided for forward and surfacing operations, or the turret saddle can be swiveled for the taper work.

Chasing Arm

One of the important functions of brass finishing is that of being able to cut screw-threads rapidly, and to this end a special chasing arm A is fitted. This consists of a tool-slide carried on shaft B at the back of the lathe. At the headstock end of the shaft is a lever which carries a half-nut, which, when the chasing arm is in the working position shown, engages a short lead-screw C, which is driven from the headstock spindle by gearing, which is reversible for left- and right-hand threads. When the nut engages the screw, the rear shaft and the chasing tool are carried along in the correct pitch for producing the thread. At the required distance, the chasing arm is raised to withdraw the tool from the work and simultaneously disengage the halfnut from the screw C. At the same time the weight D returns the arm and nut back to the starting position for another cut if required. The depth of cut is set by a small hand-wheel at the top of the slide, and the arm carries a roller to run the short bar E on the bed-front, so that the same depth of thread is cut on each work-piece, or the bar may be adjusted for threading taper work. There is not a big variation in the pitch of threads used on brass-work, fine threads being usual, but whatever variation there is requires a separate lead-screw C and a corresponding half-nut in order to produce the pitch required on the work.

Many hand operations are performed on these lathes, so, if not required, the chaser arm can be swung out of the way over to the rear of the

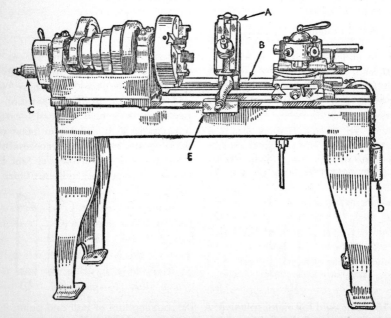

Fig. 14. This brass-finisher's lathe has a turret-head with six holes to bring the various tools into action as required. The turret can be clamped to any part of the bed most suitable for the work.

lathe and a hand-rest substituted. This is of the simple type fitted on wood-working lathes, and is used in the same way, with somewhat similar-shaped tools, for producing shaped handles, spherical ends, and ornamental designs on brass or non-ferrous alloys. These are easier to machine than steel, in which such shapes are better produced by forming tools as described. There are, however, certain steel parts, such as ball handles, for example, still produced by hand-turning. Similarly, in all metals fine screw-threads can be cut by hand-chasers (Fig. 15), either external by the upper, or internal by the lower tool. To start the thread the tool is supported on the hand-rest and the teeth are brought into contact with the work with sufficient force to strike the thread at the first attempt, otherwise a crossed thread will result.

Fig. 15. Hand-chasers as screw-tools, the upper for cutting external, the lower for internal screw-threads in all kinds of metals.

rest, thus causing injury to the worker. Hand-chasing tools are often used to finish quite large V threads after they have been first cut to almost finished size by the ordinary power screw-cutting method. It is preferable, however, not to attempt too much in this direction, for, by hand-chasing a large screw, it is easy to lose much of the accuracy obtained by the machine. Of course a separate chasing tool is required for every pitch of screw which is to be cut.

Hand-Finishing Threads

The first cut will not produce the full thread, but should be of sufficient depth so that the chasing tool will follow the first cut without difficulty and deepen the thread to the amount required. In all hand operations the rest should be set close up to the work, so that the tool has no opportunity of slipping between the work and the

Spinning

A process of forming shapes by revolving sheet-metal and applying pressure, competes with those producing shapes by the operation of power-presses, and possesses certain advantages so that, even on mass production, it can compete successfully. This arises chiefly from the fact that the lathe and tool equipment are of

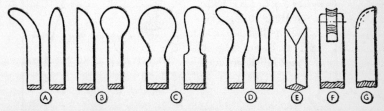

Fig. 16. Tools used for metal spinning. *A*, first spinning tool or ball and point; *B, C*, second spinning tools for finishing operations; *D*, inside tool; *E*, trimming tool; *F*, beading tool; *G*, skimming tool. These tools, including an 18-in. handle, are from 30 to 36 in. in length. They must have a high polish for efficient work.

the simplest types as compared with expensive dies and presses, and also because articles requiring tapered, beaded, or dome-shaped contours can be produced without wrinkles or cracks. In some cases the preliminary operations are carried out on power-presses and completed on spinning lathes.

The lathe itself is of the simplest possible type, while the material employed may be copper, zinc, aluminum, brass, white metal, and mild steel. Owing to the severe treatment which the metal receives in the process, annealing is necessary between various stages of production if deep steps or several curved surfaces are required in the work. By spinning sections of the unit and welding them together, large units may be produced.

Six or more tools are required to cover the range of spinning operations, these being generally made of tool-steel, but for tinplate work brass tools are used, or for simple shapes in the softer metals hard wood forms a suitable material. The complete tool and handle is of considerable length, being, with a handle of 18 in. long, no less than 30 to 36 in. in length. A selection of tools is given in Fig. 16, and comprises: (A) first spinning tool or ball and point, (B) and (C) second spinning tools for finishing operations, (D) inside tool, (E) trimming tool, (F) beading tool, (G) skimming tool. A high polish is maintained on the tools to insure a good finish on the work, and lubricant must be applied during use. This may be ordinary soap, tallow, or beeswax, and the work-speeds on non-ferrous metals up to 18 in. diameter range from 1,200 to 1,600 r.p.m.

Chucks and formers made from steel, lignum vitæ, beech or birchwood

are used, steel being the most suitable for quantity production, since wood-formers have a tendency to warp or shrink if left for long periods of disuse.

Method of Procedure

In order to produce a part as shown at D, Fig. 17, a former of the required shape is made and attached to the face-plate of the lathe. The blank is then centered as in view A and held against the end of the former by a plate whose shank revolves against ball-thrust washers in a bar extending from the tailstock spindle. The first operation is performed by a ball-and-point tool, which is located against a peg standing on the top of a T-shaped rest. In this position, with the handle of the tool under his right arm, the operator brings pressure to bear onto the work until the shape as at B is produced. At this stage the outer edge may require trimming by a diamond tool, and if annealing is necessary, each unit of the batch would be spun to this stage. The process would now be continued to that shown at C, when it would be again trimmed and smoothed by the second spinning or finishing tool. To bead the rim, the curl may be partly formed by a hand-tool and then pressed over by the roller tool to give the finished shape, as in diagram D.

Use of Back-Stick

The T-rest is provided with a row of holes so that the fulcrum peg may be moved to the most advantageous position as spinning proceeds from the center outward. The action of the operator is one of a series of short strokes, and as these proceed to shape the work, a back-stick is used in the operator's left hand to press on the metal and counteract the tool pressure when nearing the edge; for it is at this point that buckling or tearing of the metal starts if not carefully watched and annealed when becoming too hard.

The Lathe as a General Purpose Machine

Many operations other than turning are possible on a lathe fitted with a few attachments. Such equipment often enables work to be carried out that

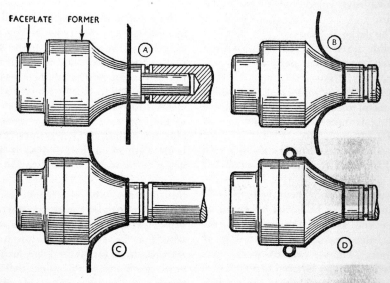

Fig. 17. To produce the part D, the blank is centered as at A and held against a former of the shape required, attached to the lathe face-plate. The operations explained in the text produce the final shape by way of B and C.

This is a simple example, but representative of a great range of similar work produced without elaborate equipment on any lathe. Where special tool set-ups are used, intricate shapes can be formed on domestic and other utensils, such as tea-pots, bottles, trays, and beakers. The process is one of much interest to the amateur lathe operator and well worthy of practice. In general, the heavier the gauge of the material used, the softer it must be to insure a successful result.

This is one instance in which lathe work can become an interesting as well as an instructive hobby.

would otherwise have to be done on separate and expensive machines of a specialized type. For example, flat surfaces can be produced by a milling cutter fixed in the spindle nose and a vise attachment fitted on the saddle in place of the compound rest. Fig. 18 shows the milling of a dovetail slide by this method, the surfacing motion of the saddle giving the automatic feed. Similarly, keyways can be cut by a suitable cutter in the same way.

To bore a casting or other work too big to be held in a chuck, advantage can be taken of the T-slots shown on the saddle top. These enable the cast-

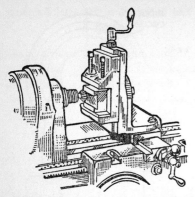

Fig. 18. Milling a dovetail slide on a lathe. The surfacing motion of the saddle gives the automatic feed.

ing to be strapped on the saddle, with the compound rest removed, so that if a boring bar is now fitted between the centers and driven from the headstock, the casting can be bored by engaging the sliding feed of the saddle. If several holes in line are required to be drilled, the graduated dial of the surfacing screw can be used to space each hole in turn accurately if the work is fastened to the bottom slide, or on a work-table which is taking the place of the slide.

If the work is of such a length that the travel of the cross-slide is insufficient for the job in hand, then in place of mounting a milling cutter in the spindle nose, extra length of travel can be obtained by fitting a separate drive to the milling cutter and using the longitudinal feed available on the full length of the bed. Such attachments, depending on the size, may be fitted either in the tool-post, or on the saddle slide with the tool-post removed. In either case, all adjustment previously obtainable in a cross-wise direction or angular is still available. The mode of drive may be from an extra pulley fixed on the counter-shaft, or from a

small counter-shaft, or from a small electric motor mounted on a separate bracket from the rear of the bed, or, alternatively, it can be a self-contained motor unit.

Grinding Lathe-Centers

Such units are extensively used for grinding purposes, particularly that of grinding lathe-centers in position. Unless the center is so much damaged that softening, reshaping, and hardening are essential, these time-consuming operations can be avoided if a device of the type shown in Fig. 19 is available for truing up. The electric motor is often direct on the grinding spindle, but a belt connection between the motor and grinding wheel enables a wider range of work to be ground because the pulleys can be changed to vary the wheel-speed and allow different-sized wheels to be fitted. This is a useful attachment on any lathe, because hardened work, such as steel bushings, gears and the like, invariably warps or closes in on the bores during the hardening process, and cannot be corrected by any process other than that of grinding, which not only insures a

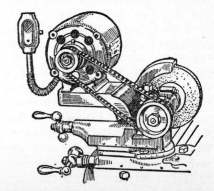

Fig. 19. Electric grinder for a lathe. The motor may be direct on the grinding spindle, or connected by a belt.

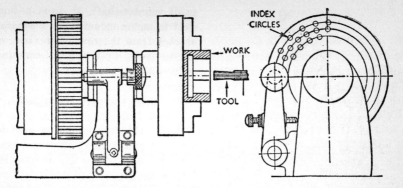

Fig. 20. For indexing or dividing work into accurate parts the spindle-wheel or cone pulley can be marked out by circles into various numbers, so that a spring plunger can engage into any hole while milling or slotting takes place.

fine finish, but great accuracy if done properly.

Dividing Methods

There are many advantages in being able to index or divide work into accurate parts to cut gears or slot keyways. As shown in Fig. 20, the spindle wheel or the cone-pulley can be adapted for this purpose by scribing and accurately dividing circles into various numbers, so that a spring plunger can engage any hole while milling or slotting takes place. Forty- and sixty-hole circles are very useful, as these figures have many multiples and allow both even and odd numbers to be obtained; for example, the cutting of four keyways in the work shown can be accomplished by traversing the tool forward until the first keyway is cut to the depth required, then indexing the spindle 10 holes in the 40-hole circle, cutting the next keyway, and repeating the movement until four keyways are cut. If three keyways had been required, then 20 holes in the 60-circle would have been used. This method is limited to numbers multiples of those in the circles, and a bigger range can be obtained by special attachments using indexing plates with worm and worm-wheel mechanism, as used on universal milling machines.

These plates enable practically all numbers to be indexed, but are expensive, so a simple method which can be used to cut gears needed as replacements is shown in Fig. 21.

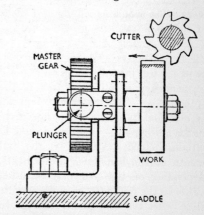

Fig. 21. In this simple set-up for cutting spur gears, blank and master gears are mounted on a stud on an angle-plate, and the gear-cutter fixed on a mandrel mounted between centers.

Gear-Cutting

An angle plate is fitted on the lathe-saddle with the blank and master gear mounted together on a stud. A spring plunger is fitted to engage a tooth space of the master gear, while a gear-cutter on a mandrel mounted between the lathe-centers operates on the blank. The surfacing motion of the saddle gives the cutting feed, and after the first tooth has been cut in the blank, the plunger is withdrawn from the master gear and engaged with each tooth-space in turn until the new gear is completed.

It will be seen that the lathe can be equipped with attachments so as to make it almost a universal machine. For example, a rapid slotting method

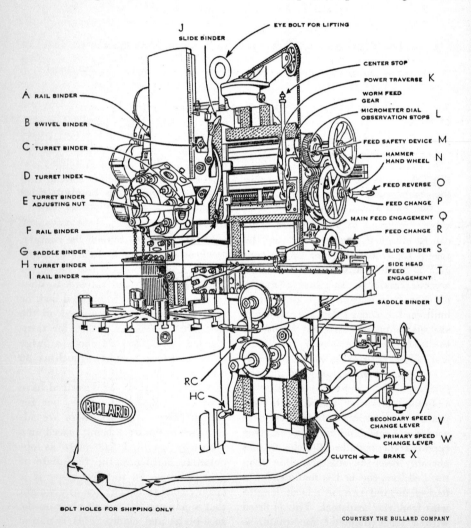

J SLIDE BINDER

EYE BOLT FOR LIFTING

CENTER STOP

POWER TRAVERSE K

A RAIL BINDER

WORM FEED GEAR

B SWIVEL BINDER

MICROMETER DIAL OBSERVATION STOPS L

C TURRET BINDER

FEED SAFETY DEVICE M

D TURRET INDEX

HAMMER HAND WHEEL N

E TURRET BINDER ADJUSTING NUT

FEED REVERSE O

FEED CHANGE P

F RAIL BINDER

MAIN FEED ENGAGEMENT Q

G SADDLE BINDER

FEED CHANGE R

H TURRET BINDER

SLIDE BINDER S

I RAIL BINDER

SIDE HEAD FEED ENGAGEMENT T

SADDLE BINDER U

RC

HC

SECONDARY SPEED CHANGE LEVER V

PRIMARY SPEED CHANGE LEVER W

CLUTCH → BRAKE X

BULLARD

BOLT HOLES FOR SHIPPING ONLY

COURTESY THE BULLARD COMPANY

Fig. 22. A vertical turret lathe, showing the main parts.

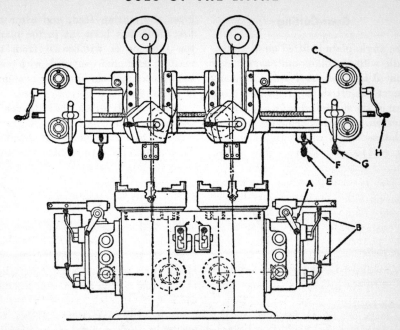

Fig. 23. In the Duplex boring and turning mill one table is used for turning and the other for boring, maximum speed being attained in both cases. Separate drive and feed-boxes are necessary on these machines. For explanation see text.

can be obtained by using a pin on the face-plate to work a crank motion and give a rapid reciprocating motion to a vertical slide. In other cases the spindle is extended to drive a drill press built on the end of the bed, which is shaped to provide vertical slides for the table.

Special Types of Lathes

Lathes differing radically in appearance from those described are used for heavy and large work. One type is known as a break-lathe, in that not only does the tailstock slide upon the bed, but the bed is mounted on a base-plate and can be moved lengthwise from the headstock. This is fitted with a large diameter face-plate, so that when work is not being turned in a normal manner between the centers, flywheels too large to swing over the bed or similar castings can be bolted to the face-plate and machined either from the end of the separated bed, or from a separate rest mounted on the base-plate. Similarly, lathes for turning locomotive wheels have a large swing and may weigh as much as 80 tons.

All the lathes so far described have been of the horizontal type, but for certain classes of work there are advantages in the work being placed on a vertically mounted face-plate as opposed to bolting to the face-plate of a break-lathe. In the first place it is much easier to chuck; for any weight that a man can lift he can place on the face-plate, and clamp. This is not so on an ordinary lathe, for he must retain his hold while clamping takes place. In addition, it must be carefully balanced and run at a slow speed, owing to vibration caused by the wear in the spindle bearings unless the machine is new; whereas with work mounted on a vertical spindle, all the weight is evenly distributed downward on the bearings, so that smooth running results and heavy cuttings are rendered possible.

These vertical machines are known as boring mills, vertical turret lathes, or vertical automatics, depending upon the construction. For medium to large work the type shown in Fig. 22 is used.

The main drive is by electric motor to a gearcase giving 18 speeds operated by the levers V and W, and thence to a large ring-gear fastened to the table. Feeds are available in all directions, these being controlled from levers indicated as P and R. The capacity of the machine shown is for work up to 4 ft. diameter, and operating on flywheels, car wheels, and similar work. Such a productive capacity is not equalled by any ordinary lathe of the boring and surfacing class.

Vertical turret lathes replace the two rams by a single turret head and side head on the right-hand upright. These machines compete most effectively with combination turret lathes on work of large diameter and small depth, but as both these machines suffer somewhat when simultaneously boring and turning, in that the speed of the machine must be set for the largest diameter, which is slow for boring, an alternative arrangement, as in Fig. 23 can be employed. Duplex tables on one machine are used so that if one table is employed for turning and the other for boring, the maximum speed can be employed in both cases.

This entails separate drive and feed boxes, the first being operated by the levers A and B and the double gearlever F, while the feed-changes are by levers F and E, the direction, vertical or horizontal tool traverse, being selected by the lever G. Hand traverses are by lever H, while the feed can be automatically tripped at any point of the tool traverses by setting the dogs C on the dial indicators.

Using the Turret

The tooling equipment on these machines does not differ from standard turret lathe practice, while the sequence of operations must be studied in the same way to insure that the best use is made of each face of the turret. Consider Fig. 24, which shows the machining of a tractor differential housing, this being selected on account of a spherical boring operation not previously described in any section on lathes. The casting is gripped in a three-jaw chuck, and for the first operation the top face is roughed down by the two tools cutting together. The turret is then turned so that the rim of the housing can be rough-turned by a vertical feed (operation 2). For small work, spherical boring can be done by a form-tool of the correct radius, but for the work in question, the size and accuracy necessitate special equipment. This comprises the holder A bored out to receive the steel bar B. The bar is a sliding fit in the holder, but is prevented from rotating by two keys. To save time, roughing and finishing cutters bore together, the rougher being set slightly in advance of the other. These cutters are carried in two arms which swivel on a stud passing through the bar, while connection between them and the holder

A is made by two links C as shown. The ball-handle on the holder is used to clamp the bar in the holder when the turret is being rotated.

How the Tools Operate

To operate the tool, the bar is lowered into the pilot bushing fixed in a central hole of the table, until it rests on a hardened steel washer. The turret is then raised until, through the action of the connecting links, the tools are extended in a horizontal position. The downward feed of the turret is now engaged to cause the tools to move downward in a radial path, and as the work is revolving around its own axis, the combined movements give a spherical cutting action on the work which is continued until the tools reach the bottom position. The pilot bushing has a series of drilled holes in order to facilitate the escape of cuttings down the hollow spindle to the floor.

Two tools operating singly are used to finish the face and rim respectively, while the last of the five faces of the turret is used to hold tools to complete the sequence of operations by chamfering corners of the bore and rim.

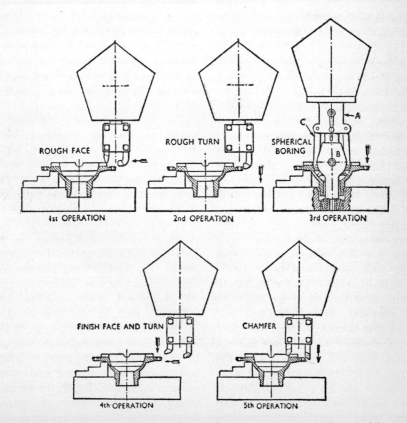

Fig. 24. Sequence of operations in the machining of a tractor differential housing. For full explanation see text.

Though generally used for chuck-work, the vertical automatic is adaptable to produce short bars between centers. Many of these machines have six small tables built to rotate around a central column which carries the tool-slides. The idea can be visualized by assuming that the work shown in Fig. 24 is not one casting, but five, on which separate operations are proceeding together, and as each one terminates, the tools are withdrawn simultaneously, the tables move to the next station and the tools move downward or sideways to commence another cut. The sixth station is reserved for loading and removing the work, so if the time-cycle is based upon one-minute intervals for cutting the work and indexing the tables, then a component would be completed every minute, each one taking six minutes to travel the complete circuit of the machine.

One operator can attend to several machines once they are tooled up and in operation, but for economical production it is necessary to insure that the operations on each table are of about the same length of time, for the time-cycle must be set for the slowest operation in the sequence. Instead of the six tables rotating around a column, they may be fixed vertically in line, as in the case of an automobile flywheel turning machine. Each table revolves by a separate motor, but the boring and turning tools, which are located above and in some cases below the work, approach and recede from the work together on a time-cycle of

four minutes. This feeding arrangement is actuated by a timing shaft along the top of the machine. The shaft carries a cam over every station and makes one revolution every four minutes, but all this period is not taken up with machining, but comprises time for inspection and the transfer of each flywheel to the next station. This transference is carried out by pistons operated by compressed air. These pistons push the flywheels from one table to the next one in line, when they are all gripped in air-chucks, except the last to leave the line, which being completed, is lifted by an electromagnet and swung on to a conveyor for transfer to another part of the workshop. Thus different machining operations proceed on each flywheel in turn, each taking 24 minutes to travel the length of the machine and one completed unit leaving the machine every four minutes.

All electric light and power are self-contained on the machine, which weighs 90 tons. Compressed air is available for cleaning as well as for clamping, a self-contained coolant and lubricating system is fitted, while cuttings fall down a V-shaped chute on to a screw conveyor which carries them away to a disposal station. This system may not have reached finality, but shows the great developments that have taken place in producing cylindrical parts on metal turning lathes since the days of the early pioneers, Whitworth and Maudslay, at the beginning of the nineteenth century.

CHAPTER 6

MILLING AND GRINDING

MILLING MACHINES. SPEED AND FEED. VARIETIES OF CUTTER. CLEARANCE ANGLES. SHARPENING CUTTERS. WORKING METHODS. CLIMB AND THREAD MILLING. CUTTING ANGLES. GRINDING. FLAT SURFACE WORK. CYLINDRICAL GRINDING. CHOICE AND GRAIN OF WHEELS. METHODS OF WORK.

THE processes of milling and grinding have assumed great importance during the past few years —an importance which continues to grow. In some instances the machinery employed is highly specialized and somewhat intricate, although the basic principles are not difficult to grasp.

It is obvious that in a book of this nature covering a very wide field, it is not possible to deal with the processes in detail, but the material which follows has been prepared in such a manner that the reader is able to get a picture of the main features. An attempt is made to present the subject in the manner which is best suited to the beginner and to the practical worker who has had little experience in the use of modern machinery of the kind dealt with. The information and instructions given are, therefore, a primer course, rather than planned for the experienced operator.

All the main types of milling machines and cutters are explained, along with the essentials of precision grinding as performed in a modern machine shop. But it is suggested that the reader should make himself thoroughly conversant with lathe practice before studying these processes.

MILLING

MILLING is a method of giving a specific shape or form to metal or other parts by cutting them with relatively slowly revolving tools, mostly known as milling cutters. Surface form can be more quickly and accurately given by milling than by the common operations of planing and shaping with the ordinary single-edged cutting tools. As a result, the use of milling is growing. The milling cutters can be generally described as discs or cylindrical tools usually made of high-speed steel and having serrations or teeth about their edges that constitute an exact counterpart of the sectional form it is desired to produce. A detailed description of the more generally used types of milling cutters and tools used in the milling machine will be found on pages 217–227. Work of virtually any shape can be produced with the aid of milling cutters. While it is feasible to use them in the lathe, it is customary and more efficient to work them in the milling machine.

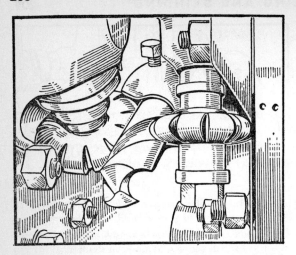

Fig. 1. The value of a milling machine consists largely in the uniformity of outline that can be given by its use to various similar parts. Here the flutes of a taper-shank drill are seen in the process of being milled in a machine.

both plain and irregular surfaces can be formed, and the value of the machine lies mainly in the uniformity of outlines that can be given to various similar parts. Nut faces, the flutes of twist-drills, taps and reamers, the teeth of circular saws, and other repetitive jobs in iron, steel, brass and other metals, are all produced on the milling machine (see Figs. 1, 2 and 3).

The machines are of various types, and can be grouped under four main headings: (1) universal milling machines; (2) plain milling machines; (3) vertical milling machines; and (4) manufacturing millers. We will outline briefly each of these four groups.

The milling machine itself can be roughly described as a machine in which the work to be milled is fastened to a movable table and passed under a revolving cutter. In this way

The universal milling machine (Fig.

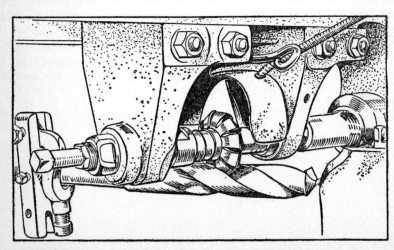

Fig. 2. The shaping of nut faces, drill flutes, circular saw teeth, and similar repetitive jobs in iron, steel, brass, and other metals are generally carried out on the milling machine. Above, a single cutter is fluting a large drill.

4) is so named because it is capable of handling a very wide range of jobs. It has a table that can be swiveled, and has, in most instances, a divided head for indexing and milling work between centers— for example, spur and spiral gears. This head also does angular work, such as milling the teeth of bevel and miter gears.

Plain milling machines resemble the universal type, but possess no swiveling table, and are not provided with a dividing-head attachment for indexing. (See Fig. 5.)

Vertical machines (Fig. 6) approximate closely the plain milling machines, but there is one important difference. The spindle or shaft carrying the cutter is vertical, and makes a right angle with the face of the table. They are used for numerous purposes, among which may be included the milling and boring of jigs and the machining of dies and other tools.

The manufacturing miller is a machine specially designed for repetitive work turned out in large quantities. It is of simple construction, and is employed principally in the production of automobiles, aircraft, typewriters, firearms, and sewing-machine parts.

Before we describe in more detail these various types of millers, it may be as well to outline simply the exact operation of milling, without specific reference to any one type of machine. Briefly, the milling cutter revolves on the spindle of the machine, to which it is fastened. It may be carried either by an arbor or a small separate spindle, which has a tapered end that fits into a tapered hole in the machine spin-

Fig. 3. Milling teeth in a circular saw blade by means of the action of an angular cutter.

dle, and is driven by the rotation of the machine spindle. The cutters may be of widely varying forms and dimensions, and the speed of the driving spindle will have to be adapted to the particular diameter of cutter used, provision for which is an essential feature of the milling machine. Furthermore, the bringing of the work into steady contact with the cutter (i.e., the *feed*) so that as each successive tooth-bite is finished the cutter does not revolve idly, but is given fresh metal to cut, is a function performed by the work-table. In the modern machines this is made automatic, so that the operator does not have to lose time by making the necessary continual manual adjustments.

The cutters have teeth, and as they revolve each tooth engages the work successively, removing a chip or shaving of metal. The teeth are of the desired form, and cut out of the piece being milled a shape or section of identical form. Sometimes in multiple or *gang* milling a number of cutters are mounted on one spindle, with the result that several surfaces can be machined at the same time.

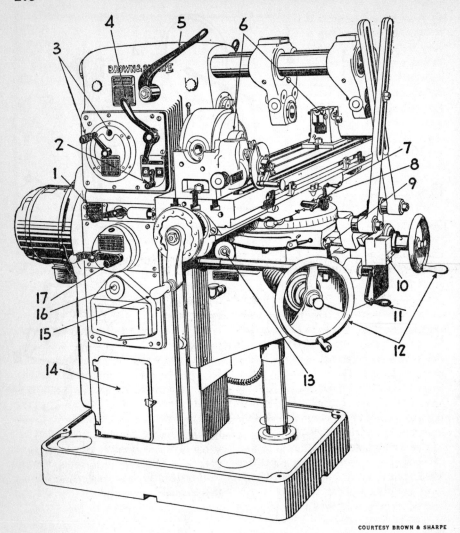

COURTESY BROWN & SHARPE

Fig. 4. Universal milling machine: 1, high-low speed series selective lever; 2, spindle reverse lever; 3, speed change lever; 4, spindle back gear lever; 5, adjustable starting lever; 6, universal spiral index centers; 7, directional longitudinal feed engagement lever; 8, table clamp; 9, transverse and vertical feed reverse lever; 10, control button for feed power; 11, knee clamped from operating position; 12, transverse and vertical adjustment handwheels; 13, sight indicator for automatic oiling system; 14, change gears for universal spiral index denters; 15, safety hand-crank for longitudinal adjustment; 16, sight indicator for lubrication system; 17, feed change lever.

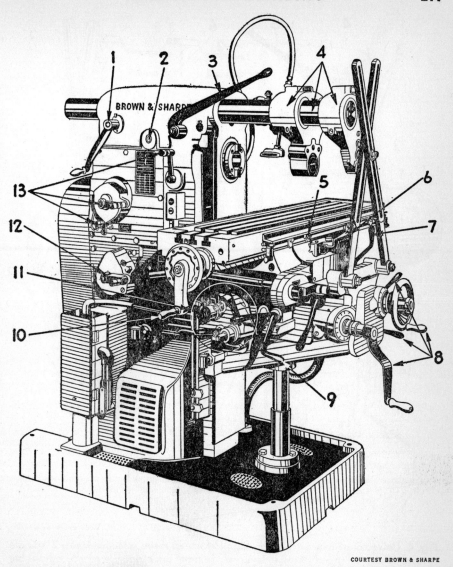

Fig. 5. Plain milling machine: 1, crank for endwise adjustment of overarms; 2, sight indicator for automatic lubrication system; 3, starting lever; 4, double overarm; 5, adjustable dogs; 6, longitudinal feed engagement lever; 7, lever controlling travel in all directions; 8, transverse and vertical hand adjustment and feed engagement levers; 9, transverse and vertical feed reverse lever; 10, safety handcrank for longitudinal adjustment; 11, rear-of-table transverse and vertical feed engagement levers; 12, lever controlling sliding gears for feed changes; 13, rotating lever and back gear lever control sliding gears for speed changes in two series.

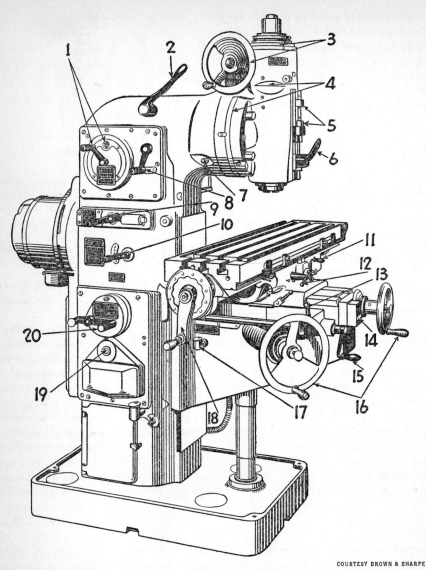

Fig. 6. Vertical milling machine: 1, speed change lever; 2, adjustable starting lever; 3, spindle feed handwheel; 4, spindle head; 5, fixed spindle stops; 6, spindle slide clamp lever; 7, lever operating locking plunger for exact vertical alignment of spindle; 8, spindle back gear lever; 9, high-low speed series selective lever; 10, spindle reverse lever; 11, directional longitudinal feed engagement lever; 12, table clamp; 13, transverse and vertical feed reverse lever; 14, switch controlling power fast travel; 15, knee clamp; 16, transverse and vertical adjustment handwheel; 17, filler cup for oil reservoir in knee; 18, safety handcrank for longitudinal adjustment; 19, sight indicator for lubrication system; 20, lever controlling change in feed.

The action of a milling cutter is very different from that of a drill or lathe tool, which both operate on the principle of a continuous cut, the cutting edge being kept continually in contact with the material. In milling, the cut starts at infinity and gradually picks up, as shown in Fig. 7. So that, the cycle of operations of each tooth is: first, a sliding action, then a crushing action, and finally a cutting action. In some metals this peculiar cutting action produces a surface-hardening effect called *work-hardening*, which complicates milling considerably, since it throws an increased strain on the teeth of the cutter.

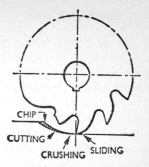

Fig. 7. Unlike a lathe, a milling cutter does not give a continuous cut, but begins with a sliding motion between the cutter and the work. Then follows a crushing movement, and then a cutting operation by which the chip is removed.

Types of Millers

While we have classified the milling machines into four main groups, it is well to bear in mind that a different and even simpler classification is possible—namely, into those of *bed* type in which the spindle is adjusted vertically, and those of *column-and-knee* type in which the work table is adjusted vertically. The *knee* is merely the projection of the table from the body of the machine, forming a knee on which the job rests. This means only that in one the spindle of the machine is adjusted to the height of the work, whereas in the other the work-table is raised or lowered to the cutter mounted on its spindle.

The universal milling machine is so constructed that the table on which the work to be milled is fastened can be swiveled to a fairly wide angle in a horizontal plane. This enables the operator to mill helical (spiral) grooves or slots. The work-table is raised or lowered by the knee, and can be moved either to left or to right when in position. The work can be fixed at any angle to the table, and rotated. Very complex movements are, therefore, possible.

The plain milling machine is a simpler form of the universal machine, but has no swivel-table and cannot be used for spiral milling unless provided with a special attachment. It has largely replaced the bed type of machine, and is a much more commonly used tool, because of its great rigidity.

The vertical milling machine differs from the plain miller in the position of its spindle, the vertical adjustment of which is usually accomplished by moving the entire head-frame carrying the spindle. Finally, the manufacturing miller is a simple machine of column-and-knee type and of rigid construction. In feeding, the operator can move the work forward as rapidly as he likes, and need not retard the forward travel of the table as it draws near the milling cutter, because in modern makes a special arrangement of the mechanism automatically takes over the feed of the table to the cutter as soon as the table reaches a certain point in its forward movement.

Speed and Feed

The two most vital factors for effective work are the speed of the milling cutter and the longitudinal feed of the work-table. A range of cutting speeds is ordinarily provided by a gearcase on the milling machine, while feed is automatic in three directions.

It is in the choice of speeds and feeds that success can often be assured in advance. It is not possible in a general book of this kind to lay down hard-and-fast rules for cutting speeds and feeds on various materials, for the reason that everything depends on shop conditions, the type of work, the age and condition of the milling machines in use, the quality of steel used for the cutters, whether these are of solid or inserted tooth type, the skill and experience of the operator, and so forth. With so many variables, as well as the wide variation in work to be done, it is impossible to give precise figures that will apply in every case. All that can be attempted is a rough guide, which will serve for the user until by trial and error he has established the best speeds and feeds for a particular job on particular metals, under his own conditions. (See table on page 215.)

Depth of Cut

The first error into which an inexperienced operator is liable to fall lies in believing that a heavy cut is the quickest way of finishing the work. Actually, it is much more effective to use a light cut with a fast feed. Unless the margin of material to be removed is very small, it is better practice to take numerous cuts with a fast feed than to take one heavy cut with a slow feed. Another common error is to run the cutter too fast, which shortens the life of the cutting edges and uses more power, while the finish will be inferior. It is usually possible to sharpen the teeth of milling cutters without causing them to lose their form, and frequent sharpening of the teeth before they have become noticeably dull is one of the essentials of successful milling.

It has been explained that a deep or heavy cut is not advisable for milling efficiency. The reason for this is that a heavy cut generates great heat at the cutting edge, and this heat will, if sufficiently great, draw the temper of the cutting edges of the tool. Even if the tool is made of the finest high-speed steel and will go on cutting steadily when at a red heat, it is probable that excessive vibration or chatter will occur, and this will damage the cutting edges. Furthermore, if the cutter is of the inserted-tooth type, in which the cutting blades or edges are of an extremely hard cutting alloy known as tungsten-carbide (which is formed of a powder sintered at great heat, let into the steel body of the tool) the vibration will almost certainly cause fracture, since this alloy is not proof against heavy vibration. Even if the cutter is run so that it takes only a slightly heavier cut than is desirable, the probability is that it will need much more frequent sharpening, with a consequent loss of time and higher tool costs.

Measuring Cutting Speed

So far we have referred loosely to the cutting speed of milling cutters. A closer definition is advisable. As the job is fed to the rotating cutter, the rate at which the metal shaving or

METAL.	TYPE OF CUTTER.	
	HIGH-SPEED STEEL.	TUNGSTEN- OR TITANIUM-CARBIDE.
	ft. per min.	*ft. per min.*
Aluminum	1300–1600	2600–4900
Brass	160–200	350–380
Bronze	130–165	250–330
Cast Iron	50–65	200–230
Duralumin	980–1300	1960–2450
Electron	980–1300	1960–2450
Malleable Cast Iron	60–65	200–230
Mild Steel	50–65	130–200
Nickel Chrome Steel	25–45	100–130

chip is removed is the cutting speed; the cutting speed is expressed in feet per minute of the tooth edge of the milling cutter as it removes a shaving. If the cutter measures 2 ft. round the circumference, and a speed of 40 ft. per minute is desired, it will take twenty revolutions of the cutter per minute to give this. In order to arrive at the correct r.p.m. of a cutter, therefore, it is necessary to divide the cutting speed by the circumference in feet of the cutter.

Actually, however, it is not customary in tool-rooms and machine shops to give sizes of cutters in terms of their circumference. The diameter is used instead, and the size given in inches. The practical formula for obtaining the r.p.m. (revs. per min.) necessary to produce the correct cutting speed is $\dfrac{CS}{\frac{1}{4}D}$ = R.P.M., where D is the diameter of the cutter in inches and CS the cutting speed.

Turning now to feed, it must be stressed here also that hard-and-fast rules cannot be laid down. (Feed, incidentally, is the distance the work advances against each successive tooth of the cutter.) It is governed by the depth and width of the cut, the type of cut (whether roughing or finishing) the size of the cutter, the number of teeth on the cutter, the proportion of thickness to diameter, the r.p.m. of the cutter, the manner in which the cutter is mounted, the condition and power of the milling machine, and the rigidity with which the work to be milled is held.

It will be seen that this is a long list of variables, and without a full knowledge of all these, no one can give specific recommendations. As a general rule, a roughing cut, which is intended solely to remove surplus metal before the final or finishing cut is taken, should have a coarse feed, but about $\frac{1}{64}$ in. should be left for the finishing cut.

The rate of feed has a noticeable effect on the surface finish. Slower feeds usually mean a smoother surface.

In setting up a job on the milling machine, the operator should have everything at hand before he starts the machine. While no great skill is required to operate a miller, extreme accuracy of setting is essential, and this depends on correct calculation. All figures should, therefore, be gone over twice, because one error, allowed to pass, will ruin a part. The keyway, for example, must not be out of center. The angle of the job must be exactly right, and the correct gears interposed. In indexing (see page 234), if the graduated sector is wrong by a single hole, the part will be ruined as soon as the second tooth is formed.

The cutters are threaded on to a shaft termed an *arbor,* whose extremity is inserted into a tapered hole bored in the driving spindle. It is prevented from slipping by a catch or *dog* near the end, and is firmly bolted to the spindle which drives it.

Holding the Work

There are numerous ways of holding the work. It may be fastened directly to the work-table; gripped in a special fixture; fixed to an angle-plate or other tool; held in a vise; held between centers; or held in a chuck. The accuracy of the holding arrangement should be tested before the job is begun. A clamp will damage a polished or finished surface unless something is interposed to protect the surface. Similarly, the job should not be pushed about without something being put down on which it can rest and which will prevent it from scratching the table-top. The threads of nuts and bolts should be oiled from time to time, and the right wrenches used in tightening or loosening them so as to prevent rounded corners of nuts. This will ultimately cause the wrenches to slip, and possibly injure the operator. More than one fatal accident has occurred as a result of a slipping wrench.

Wrenches must be used with care. Bolts of the right length should be used and not those too long or too short by a few threads. After the job is clamped down, care should be taken to see that nothing has been left lying about that will foul the machine or be swept off the table and cause injury, or do other damage. Thin pieces should be clamped down with care, to avoid distortion caused by excessive pressure. Rigidity of the work is essential, and, where necessary, support should be obtained from jacks or shims. Any tendency for the work to spring under the cutter should be avoided.

The table should be set as near to the machine column as possible. At the beginning of the set-up for the job, the clamping screws for knee and saddle should be loosened, but care must be taken to see that they are tightened before the actual milling operation begins, unless the job is a special one demanding a slight degree of looseness.

Adjusting the Cutter

The job is usually set up before the cutter adjustment is made, except when end-mills or face-mills are being used. In setting the cutter when the work has been clamped down correctly, complete cleanliness must first be insured by cleaning out the tapered hole in the machine spindle or collar and seeing that it is quite dry. The arbor shank must be cleansed of grease and dirt, which are always liable to cause slipping of the arbor in the spindle. A tight fit must be secured at all costs, or trouble will surely follow. The cutter faces should be thoroughly cleaned before the cutter is placed on the arbor. An occasional error by beginners is to run the cutter in the wrong, or reverse direction, which will smash the teeth. Proper direction of cutter rotation must be checked by first seeing that the driving spindle revolves in the correct manner in relation to the work, and that the cutter is properly mounted on its arbor and revolves likewise.

The cutter should be set as near to the spindle as the job allows. This lessens strain on bearings and knee, and brings the job closer to the body of the machine. If it is desired to change the cutter, whether for re-sharpening or because it is worn out, there is no need to take out the arbor, as long as the replacement cutter is of the same diameter. Cutters should never be given heavy or sharp blows with a hammer or other instrument, either to drive them on to the arbor or to remove them from it. This will certainly damage the teeth, and possibly crack the tool.

Examining the Machine

If the part to be milled is of small dimensions, it should be loosened a little on the work-table after the roughing cuts have been completed. This is to relieve the stresses caused by the clamping down, and so to prevent possible distortion. If the work is gripped in the milling-machine vise, the zero mark, at which the swiveling angle graduations begin, should be tested for accurate positioning by putting a long, straight edge in the vise, and, by means of a square on the work-table, swiveling the vise until the straight edge is parallel with the slots of the table.

If the part to be milled is delicate and has thin sections, the best practice is to employ a slow feed, even though the job necessarily will take longer. Success in milling will be found to depend, to no small degree,

on the condition of the milling machine. The operator should not neglect the regular examination of machine spindle, arbor and feed-screw, which, if allowed to become worn, will cause wobble or play and affect the work. The guides of the table must not be allowed to become loose, and the driving mechanism must likewise be kept in good running order.

If the job is one demanding a heavy cut, the greatest possible care should be taken to prevent chatter, with its injurious effect on the cutters. This can be done by bracing up the gibs of the knee-and-table-guides, while in horizontal millers the arm-braces can be employed. Considerable wear can be caused by bad mounting of the cutter on its arbor, with the result that the arbor is forced out of line under the pressure and blunts the cutter teeth. If any tendency for the arbor to deflect is observed, the cutter should be remounted close to the spindle nose; or, if it is already in this position, the arbor should be supported.

Choosing the Cutter

We may now turn to another important factor in milling efficiency: the choice of the right type of cutter for the job. The cutter must have the proper form of tooth, and be made of the most suitable material. Before this choice can be made, it is essential to know the difference between the various types of cutters. There are five main groups: (a) the plain milling cutters; (b) the spiral mills; (c) the face mills; (d) the angular or angle cutters; (e) the form cutters.

The plain milling cutter of normal type is a steel disc or cylinder with a hole bored through the center, with cutting teeth on the periphery. These teeth run parallel to the axis of the tool, which produces a flat surface parallel to its own axis. If the teeth run at an angle, the cutter is termed a spiral mill. If, on the other hand, they run radially across the ends of the disc or cylinder, the cutter is termed a face-mill. This type produces a flat surface at right angles to its own axis. An end-mill is simply a face-mill of smaller diameter and greater length. It is used for a wide range of milling jobs, such as making keyways and slots, milling the edges of fairly thin pieces, squaring the ends of smaller pieces, and sometimes forming a shoulder on a part or piece. The larger sizes (above $\frac{1}{4}$ in.) are generally provided with helical teeth.

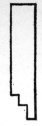

Fig. 8. Section through a fly cutter, the simplest milling tool —a piece of square-section steel filed to shape.

If the cutter has a conical form (with the top of the cone cut off), and the teeth are cut on the sides of this shortened cone, it is termed an angular or angle-cutter, which will form a flat surface at an angle to the cutter axis. If the outline of the cutter is irregular, it is called a form-cutter, and produces a surface of irregular outline.

All these types of milling cutters are usually made from solid discs of high-speed steel, although carbon steel is sometimes used where a fine degree of finish and accuracy is required and speed is not important. Cutters of very large diameter are often provided with detachable teeth of the cutting material, inserted and rigidly held in a body or blank made from a cheaper material such as carbon steel or cast iron.

These cutting blades or edges are of high-speed steel, but tungsten-carbide tips, brazed into position, are also used, mainly for milling cast iron and non-ferrous metals, as well as bakelite, and other plastic substances. They will cut these at high speeds and with reduced machining time, while giving a good surface finish. Tungsten-carbide will also cut hard steels if only short chips are formed, with a light cut at high speeds. It keeps its cutting edge for a long time, and does not suffer from loss of temper as a result of the heat generated at the cutting edge. It is, however, brittle, and will not withstand shock, as the brazed tips may snap off, particularly if the cutter is of incorrect design.

The five groups of cutters enumerated cover a considerable range of forms and types for various jobs. Over a hundred different kinds of cutter are manufactured. It is not necessary to give the names and specific functions of each of these. Here we will content ourselves with describing and illustrating those most commonly found in the machine-shop and the tool-room, a knowledge of which is important.

The simplest type of milling cutter is the fly-cutter (see Fig. 8), which is merely a portion of square steel, formed to shape by filing, or by some other method, hardened, and afterwards fixed, at right angles to the spindle, in a chuck or cutter-block held in the machine. It is, therefore, essentially a cutter with only a single revolving tooth. Fly-cutters are usually improvised tools designed to do a job cheaply, in a hurry, or experimentally, when a proper form-cutter is not available or would cost too much to make and use.

Helical or spiral mills have their ends flat and their teeth formed in a steep spiral around the body. The steeper the spiral, the smoother the cutting action (see Fig. 9). This tool shears rather than cuts the metal, and forces the chips away to the sides. It is particularly advantageous for milling thin metal, copper bars, boiler plates, and other springy jobs, because it does not spring away from the work. It is also good for heavy cuts.

Fig. 10. Two types of double-angle cutter for producing radial teeth. That on the left is used for taps, that on the right for reamers.

Two-lipped slotting end-mills or cotter-mills (see Fig. 9) are designed to cut slots and keyways. They have teeth not only on their sides, parallel to the axis, but also on one end. This arrangement enables them to mill deep slots in solid metal even if no starting hole has previously been drilled by a twist-drill, part of whose functions they are thus enabled to perform.

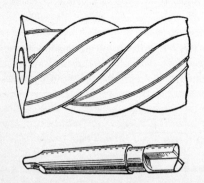

Fig. 9. *Above*, a helical or spiral mill, with teeth arranged in a steep spiral around the body; *below*, a two-lipped slotting end-mill or cotter-mill for cutting slots and keyways.

These tools should be run at high surface speeds with either a deep cut and a fine feed, or a rather shallow cut with medium feed. Ample lubrication is desirable.

Tap and reamer cutters (Fig. 10) are designed to produce a radial tooth in a tap or reamer. They belong actually to the double-angle cutters described on page 225, but the teeth are more rounded.

Corner-rounding cutters (Fig. 11) are designed for finishing the edges and corners of a part, and can be manufactured for any required radius. They are obtainable in either *hand*, and either single or double. Single cutters have top and side relief, as have the double cutters.

Plain milling cutters have the ends ground flat. The purpose of these tools is the milling of plain surfaces, and they can be used in either a right- or left-hand direction, by simply reversing the cutter on the arbor or shaft. In ordering them, a few points should be borne in mind. It is sometimes best to stipulate the *hand* of the spiral in order to get the thrust in the desired direction. The manufac-

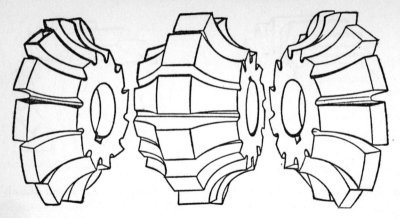

Fig. 11. Three corner-rounding cutters for finishing edges and corners: (*left to right*) left-handed single cutter, double cutter, and right-hand single cutter.

turers usually supply the type of cutter for ordinary work, as shown in Fig. 12, unless otherwise ordered, but it is recommended that, whenever possible, the type having a coarse tooth with a steep spiral should be used (see Fig. 12). The reason is that this type cuts more freely and uses less power. Staggered tooth- and inserted tooth-cutters of this type are also supplied.

Facing cutters have teeth on the periphery and one end, with the length of the cutting edges on the periphery equal to, or less than, half the diameter of the cutter (see Fig. 13). These cutters are not reversible on their arbors, so that it is necessary to indicate, when ordering, whether right- or left-hand cutters are required. The cutter shown at the left is a right-hand cutter. The coarse-type cutter as shown at the right should be used wherever possible, owing to the fact that it cuts more freely and takes less power.

The slotting cutter is one with teeth on the periphery only, and with the sides ground slightly concave to give clearance when cutting. It is used primarily, as its name implies, for milling slots accurately, and is generally made with straight-cut teeth up to ¾ in. wide and with spiral teeth above this thickness. Standard cutters

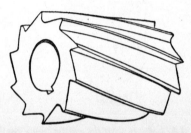

Fig. 12. Two varieties of plain cutter. That on the left, with smaller teeth, is for ordinary work; the coarser-toothed type on the right is for heavy work.

Fig. 13. Facing cutters with large teeth (*right*) cut more freely and absorb less power than the narrower-toothed variety (*left*).

are made with a thickness tolerance of plus or minus one-thousandth of an inch. The corners of the teeth of this type of cutter show signs of wear first, so that as soon as wear becomes noticeable, the cutter should be re-sharpened. Unless this is done immediately, a large amount of grinding will be necessary later to re-condition the cutter, and it may even be ruined altogether from the point of view of producing accurate and well-finished work in the future. Fig. 14 shows this type of standard cutter.

Side and face cutters (Fig. 14) have teeth on the face and both sides. They are generally used in pairs, for milling work with faces a definite distance apart. They are sometimes called straddle mills. Standard cutters are made with spiral cut teeth if over $\frac{3}{4}$ in. thick, and with straight-cut teeth below this thickness. For heavy work, the coarse-tooth type of cutter as shown in Fig. 14 is recommended. These cutters are supplied with a width tolerance of plus .005 in. and minus. 001 in. They can, of course, be used for milling slots, in the same way as the slotting cutter mentioned earlier, but are not designed for this type of work, and their suitability for it will depend on the accuracy

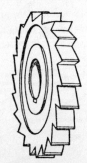  

Fig. 14. *Left,* a slotting cutter, with teeth on the periphery only and slightly concave sides. *Center and right,* two varieties of side and face cutter, which have teeth on both sides as well as on the face.

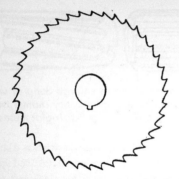

Fig. 15. Like a slotting cutter, this slitting saw has teeth on the periphery only and slightly concave sides.

required for the slots. This is clear if we compare the width tolerance of both types of cutters. It must also be borne in mind that side- and face-cutters are re-sharpened on the sides, whereas slotting-cutters are not, so that a side- and face-cutter taken from the toolroom may be considerably less than the thickness marked on the cutter, owing to previous re-sharpenings. Staggered-tooth and inserted-tooth types are also made.

The cutter for sawing metal, or metal slitting saw as it is commonly called, is a cutter with teeth on the periphery only, and with the sides ground concave to give clearance when cutting (see Fig. 15). It is used for a variety of work, from putting deep slots in heavy sections of steel to cutting through thin tubes. It will be realized that any one saw is not capable of covering this range of work satisfactorily, for while a fairly large pitch or spacing of teeth is required for solid work, it is of very little use for thin sections for tubes.

The importance of specifying, when ordering new saws, the class of work they will have to do, or of stating if a certain pitch or number of tooth has given entire satisfaction in the past, will be apparent. These saws are regularly made with $2\frac{1}{2}$ in. diameter and $\frac{1}{32}$ in. thickness ranging up to 8 in. diameter and not above $\frac{1}{4}$ in. thickness. For sawing off pieces from a larger body it is not economical to use the thinnest saw listed ($\frac{1}{32}$ in.), as it is a delicate tool and requires careful handling. Slitting cutters are also made with side chip clearance, but not below $\frac{1}{16}$ in. thick.

Shell-end mills have teeth on the periphery and one end, and are designed for mounting on an arbor. They can be readily confused with facing-cutters by the less experienced, but the difference is that shell-end mills have cutting edges greater in

Fig. 16. Shell-end mills, designed for mounting on an arbor, have teeth on the periphery and one end.

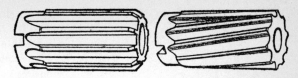

length than half the diameter of the cutter, whereas facing cutters, as indicated, have cutting edges equal to or less than half the diameter. As shell-end mills are not reversible on their arbors,

Fig. 17. Shell-reamers, used to enlarge deep or wide holes more cheaply than by an ordinary reamer, may have either straight (*left*) or spiral (*right*) flutes.

they are made to cut either left- or right-hand. In principle these tools are, of course, exactly the same as ordinary solid-end mills, but are marketed in the shell form for the larger sizes, simply to reduce expense. Manufactured with a diameter tolerance of plus .010 in. and minus .001 in., they are made (Fig. 16) for ordinary and also for specially heavy work.

Reamers of the ordinary type are designed to enlarge the diameters of holes already made by another tool, such as a twist-drill or punch, or by coring. A part is often cast with holes made by cores, inserted in the mold. The shell-reamer serves exactly the same purpose as the ordinary reamer, but was introduced to save expense in enlarging deep holes or holes of large diameter, where the cost of ordinary reamers would be excessive. This type

of tool is manufactured with a diameter tolerance of plus .0006 and plus .0012 in. for the smaller sizes and plus .0007 and plus .0014 in. for the larger sizes. They are made with either straight or spiral flutes (see Fig. 17).

The most commonly used type is that shown in Fig. 17, with spiral flutes and taper and bevel lead. They are, of course, made with straight flutes and exactly the same type of lead. The other type shown (left) has straight flutes and bevel lead only, and is termed a rose-shell reamer. This type has its advantages in that it will enlarge from a smaller diameter and is easy to re-sharpen. At the same time, it is not quite so adaptable to the same class of finish. Made with either parallel or taper hole, the taper being $\frac{1}{8}$ in. to the foot, these tools must not be confused with shell-end mills (Fig. 16), and are not made with the accuracy or the requisite lead to enable them to meet the same requirements as the shell-end mill.

This confusion can be overcome in an elementary fashion by remembering that standard shell reamers have flutes greater in length than the diameter, and have no teeth on the end.

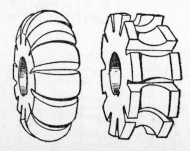

Fig. 18. Concave and convex milling cutters are used to produce concave slots or convex edges. The front faces only are ground when they are resharpened.

Concave and convex milling cutters, as shown in Fig. 18, are used on the milling machine in order to produce

Fig. 19. *Left,* an involute gear-cutter used for cutting gear teeth on the milling machine; they are roughed out with the cutter shown on the left and finished with that in the center. *Right,* a single-angle cutter with side teeth.

either concave slots or convex edges, as the case may be. They are almost always made of the same machine-relieved type, so that re-sharpening is simple, the front faces only being ground. This design also enables the cutters to reproduce the same profile, within very narrow limits, until worn out. The slight difference is due to the the fact that it has been found satisfactory to give special side clearance to the majority of these cutters. This slight alteration is not usually of great importance, but when accuracy is desired, an interlocking type of cutter is recommended. Used with suitable packing pieces, these enable the desired width to be constantly maintained.

Fig. 19 shows an involute gear-cutter used in the milling machine to produce gear teeth. There are usually eight cutters to a set, enabling gears with from twelve to any number of teeth to be cut, or a rack if necessary.

These cutters should always be kept well sharpened, as on the sides of some of the sizes only a small cutting clearance can be allowed. Unless they are kept in good condition, therefore, rubbing, or grinding in the cut, which is detrimental to cutter life, will soon take place. The teeth are of the form-relieved type, so that the cutters re-

tain their profile throughout their life. They must, of course, be sharpened only on the front faces, and care must be taken to see that this operation is correctly done. Otherwise the cutter will not produce the same outline after sharpening as before.

Both types of single-angle cutters are used to do the same work, the only difference between the two being that one, (Fig. 19) is made with side teeth, and the other with side ground concave. The latter is now seldom used. The type with side teeth is preferable, because it produces a better finish and gives a longer life per grind when cutting hard materials. Wherever possible the sharp corners of the teeth should be beveled off, as this increases the life of the cutters and at the same time enables a heavier feed to be employed. The angles of these

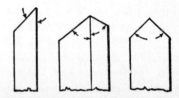

Fig. 20. This diagram shows how the angles of single-angle cutters, either right-hand or left-hand, are measured.

cutters are measured as in Fig. 20, and are either right-hand or left-hand. Fig. 19 shows a right-hand cutter. These cutters are made to any desired angle.

As their name implies, double-angle cutters differ mainly from single-angle cutters in that they incorporate two angles, one of which is usually 12 deg., and are used, for the most part, in cutting spiral teeth. The angles are measured as in Fig. 20, and the cutters are made either left-hand or right-hand. These also are made to any angle.

Equal-angle cutters (Fig. 21) are similar in design to the double-angle cutters, but in this instance both angles about the plane of intersection are of the same magnitude. The nominal angle of the cutter is the angle between the two conical sides, measured as in Fig. 20. This cutter can be made to all angles.

Before leaving types of milling cutters, some mention must be made of a method of relieving being rapidly adopted in many of the most modern machine shops. These cutters insure that the relief or beveling-off of the teeth is achieved in such a manner as to overcome one of the greatest disadvantages of form-relieved cutters—namely, their tendency to rub or failure to cut freely.

Form-relieved cutters made with this relief have increased cutting clearance with constant tooth form. Rubbing is entirely eliminated and a strictly constant tooth profile maintained. This combination means increased production and accuracy. Other advantages are reduced wear on the machine, less power required, greater feed and speed, and a minimum of strain.

In Fig. 22 it will be observed that this type of relief eliminates rubbing on the sides, while the good clearance angles will be noted. Compare the other type, showing how curved relief causes rubbing on the sides, and gives inadequate clearance angles. Similarly, Fig. 22 shows how the new type of relief eliminates rubbing on the back, as against Fig. 23 showing the rubbing on the back, unavoidable with curved relief.

The disadvantages of curved relief are: (a) rubbing on all the lateral surfaces of the teeth; (b) excessive generation of heat; (c) imperfect finish of the work unless speeds are reduced; (d) binding in the cut; (e) low production; (f) short cutter life as a result of rapid tooth wear; (g) excessive grinding; (h) high power consumption; (i) slow, arduous, and noisy cutting; (j) excessive strain on the machine.

By contrast, the new relief avoids all these drawbacks. The tool cuts more freely, because each tooth is cutting with line or point contact only. The teeth not only last longer, but will stand from two to five times more re-

Fig. 21. Two views of an equal-angle cutter, with both angles about the plane of intersection of the same size.

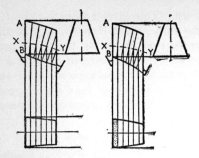

Fig. 22. A method of relieving adopted in many modern machine shops is illustrated *left*. This obviates side rubbing and gives good clearance angles. *Right*, curved relief which causes side rubbing and gives inadequate angles.

grinding. Clean, sharp-edged teeth with strictly constant profile or form and ample support behind the cutting edges eliminate rubbing on back and sides.

Except in a few instances where the length of tooth is comparatively short, cutters made on this principle have what is termed *double relief*. It will be observed from Fig. 24 that the front of the tooth is given approximately 17 deg. clearance, and that at a point approximately midway in the useful grinding zone of the tooth there is a change in direction of the relief, this again being so formed as to give approximately 17 deg. clearance to the teeth.

Not all cutters are made with exactly this 17 deg. angle of clearance. Some cutters call for a variation in this angle, and, in addition, a small margin is required in manufacture. While this relief gives a much greater clearance angle than ordinary cutters, maintaining at the same time a strong and robust tooth, the clearance angle is a diminishing one. As the front of

the tooth is ground back in re-sharpening, these relief cutters are usually made with double relief to prevent the angle from diminishing below satisfactory working limits, as mentioned above. This means a cutter with consistently good clearance angles throughout its life. It also facilitates the employment of a strong tooth, and one, moreover, having a very long life, the useful sharpening zone being a maximum as regards length. A large number of teeth in a cutter does not necessarily mean a long cutter life, the useful sharpening zone on any particular tooth being comparatively small. In general, the larger the tooth, the greater the number of re-grinds possible before the effectiveness of the cutter is destroyed.

This change in direction of the clearance angle on these cutters does not affect the form, which remains constant throughout the life of the cutter, if the teeth are re-sharpened radially. Fig. 22, being diagrammatic only, and used to illustrate a different point, is drawn with single relief only, but one should note that this has been

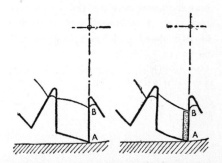

Fig. 23. *Left,* how the type of relief illustrated in Fig. 22 obviates rubbing on the back of the tooth. *Right*, the effect of the older curved relief, with the rubbing which the shape made inevitable.

done for the sake of clarity. It must be understood that, as a general rule, this type of cutter is given double relief (see Fig. 24).

We must now consider in closer detail the shape of the teeth of these various cutters, and their spacing. The benefits of double relief have been indicated above. Reverting to the standard tooth forms, it should be borne in mind that not all cutter teeth are form-relieved, but some remain *pointed* and have only a slight relief (approximately 5 deg.) to give clearance. This relief is provided by the grinding wheel when the tooth is sharpened. These pointed-tooth cutters are principally employed in milling flat surfaces. They cut freely, and with low power consumption.

Characteristic examples already described are the plain milling cutters and end-mills, the side- and face-cutters and the single- and double-angle cutters. They are lower in price than the form-relieved cutters, but the teeth lose contour sooner and have to be machined again before the tools can be put back into service. It should be understood, however, that each machining reduces the cutter diameter, and therefore reduces the spacing between the teeth, with the result that at a certain point they become too close to one another, and are unable to free themselves of chips or cuttings. They then produce bad work, consume more power, and have eventually to be discarded.

Improved Chip Clearance

At one time these cutters were made with closely-spaced teeth, but this practice has been largely abandoned, and the modern pointed-tooth cutter is made with coarse and widely spaced

teeth. This gives adequate room for the chips, which flow away from the grooves or flutes as the work proceeds. The teeth are stronger, and it is possible to give them a slight rake or undercut, which is an advantage in cutting. Furthermore, power consump-

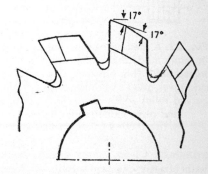

Fig. 24. Cutters of the new type are generally given double relief as indicated above, the clearance angle being usually 17 deg.

tion is decreased, because the freer cutting action reduces friction. Less heat is generated at the cutting edges, the cutters last longer, and need fewer re-grindings, while sharpening can be carried out with greater facility and rapidity.

Form-Relieved Cutters

Notches are often made at intervals in the cutting edges, with clearance on both sides, for the purpose of breaking up the chips. Side milling cutters often have their teeth staggered or set in zig-zag fashion, so as to raise their cutting efficiency. Form-relieved cutters need to be employed only when it is desired to mill a large number of irregular forms, accurate grooves, etc. The teeth of these tools have a radial face and are relieved eccentrically, in the form of logarithmic spiral curves, by means of a special machine provided with a suitable relieving attachment, and employing a tool of the correct form. This tool works on a reciprocating principle. As the hind part of each tooth of the slowly revolving cutter arrives at the correct point, the form tool darts forward, cuts away the surplus metal until adequate relief is given, then darts back to await the arrival of the hind part of the next tooth.

The point to be remembered is that form-cutters, however often resharpened, do not lose their tooth contour so long as the tooth face is ground radially.

Hand of the Cutter

The *hand* or direction of rotation of the cutter is termed left or right, according to the direction in which the cutter revolves when seen from the rear of a horizontal milling machine— with the cutter between the operator and the work. It should be noted that a left-hand end-mill will have teeth forming a right-hand spiral, while a right-hand end-mill will have teeth on a left-hand spiral.

To make this matter of hand clearer: as seen from the machine, the left-hand cutter will be seen to revolve in an anti-clockwise direction, whereas the right-hand cutter will revolve clockwise. If it is wished to determine the hand of a cutter used in a vertical miller, the cutter-spindle head should be regarded from above, and the left-hand cutter will then be that which revolves anti-clockwise and the right-hand cutter vice versa.

Sometimes it may be necessary to decide the hand of a cutter without reference to any particular machine.

The end thrust caused by the spiral lead of the cutter should be directed towards the cutter-spindle head. The hand of the lead is decided as with an ordinary screw.

The importance of frequent sharpening of the cutter has already been mentioned. The grinding of tungsten-carbide tools is dealt with on page 254, and the same rules apply to milling-cutter tips made from this material. The grinding of highspeed steel cutters demands somewhat different treatment. Is it preferable to grind high-speed steel wet or dry? Most manufacturers with experience, however, recommend dry grinding on a free-cutting abrasive wheel as the best all-round practice. To get the utmost out of a cutter, sharpening on a wet stone cannot, it is admitted, be surpassed, but, unfortunately, re-sharpening on this type of wheel is extremely slow compared with sharpening on an abrasive wheel and all too often speed is imperative.

The advantage of dry grinding is as follows. If a cutter tooth is being ground, when either of the faces is being ground there is close contact over the whole area between the wheel and the steel, so that even if a flood of water is employed, this flows only over the outer faces, and does not get to the point of maximum heat generation—namely, the center of the face being ground. Consequently, if a heavy pressure is used (and generally more pressure is used in wet grinding because the operator is deceived by the absence of any indication of heat into believing that it does not exist), the inside face of the tooth presented to the wheel becomes very hot. As soon as the tooth is withdrawn from the wheel, the water immediately strikes this hot spot, causing sudden contraction and cracking of the tooth. It is perfectly easy to raise the inside area to a straw, a blue, or even a red, heat under a flood of water without realizing that this is happening.

On the other hand, the rate of grinding with a dry free-cutting wheel is all that can be desired, and the operator is not led into a sense of false security, but is immediately warned of too heavy a cutting pressure by the fact that the edges of the tooth are discolored. No softening of a high-speed steel tooth takes place, even if it is slightly *blued,* although the practice of allowing a tooth to blue is to be condemned. Trouble generally arises from close grinding (with too great a pressure), and as many cutters are spoiled on the shop grinding wheel as in the hardening furnace, if indeed not more.

In grinding cutters no attempt should be made to finish off each tooth separately. It is much better to rough-grind all the teeth, using a roughing wheel, and then perform the finishing operation with a wheel designed for finishing. To prevent roughening or burring of the surfaces, the abrasive wheel should run toward the cutting edges. The cutter should be placed in the grinding machine, and set at an angle adequate to remove the whole heel of the blade.

How to Grind Cutters

A cup-shaped wheel is best for this work, and the cutter should be raised to a point at which the blade following that being ground will clear the wheel. The cutter should then be ground to the proper clearance. It is advisable to employ a setting gauge, unless the operator has sufficient skill and experience to judge the right angle.

Cutters with straight flutes are usually ground with the flat surface of the cup wheel, the convex or bulge side being used for the grinding of cutters with spiral flutes. A point to bear in mind is that not only must the cutting edges be kept sharp, but the tooth faces and backs must be maintained with a smooth polished surface to prevent friction and rubbing in the cut. This can be insured by attention with the grinding wheel.

Why Cutters Are Polished

Special equipment is obtainable for this purpose, but in the absence of this the same finish can be secured by passing the edges of the cutter slowly past the abrasive wheel during the last cut. For this work a wheel of rather finer grain is advised. Polishing after grinding is particularly beneficial for form-relieved cutters. The additional smoothness facilitates the passage of the chips and also gives a better finish to the work while prolonging the life of the cutter.

Tooth Contour

Gear cutters are of the form-relieved type, and must be radially ground so as to preserve the tooth contour. If this precaution is taken, the tool will not lose form however often it is re-sharpened. The cutter should be fed to the grinding machines. This means that grinding will always be radial, however much material is removed by one grind. The grinding wheel itself will, however, have to be kept true to form, and not allowed to wear to such an extent that it causes the cutter to lose its original tooth shape. Every tooth must be ground alike, or the teeth from which a less amount of material has been ground will have to do more than their fair share of the work and will therefore wear faster.

In grinding cutters with pointed teeth, the tooth-clearance angle is of great importance. This clearance is the amount of the tooth top, or *land* as it is called, removed or relieved to prevent rubbing in the cut. If this clearance is too large, rapid dulling occurs. If too small, there is rubbing and little cutting. The correct clearance angle is approximately 7 deg. for cutters below 3 in. in diameter, and approximately 5 deg. for those above this diameter. Approximately 2 deg. clearance should be provided on end teeth and side teeth, and to prevent drag and imperfect finish of the job, it is recommended that they should be ground one or two thousandths of an inch lower toward the center. The notes on pages 225 and 226 should be borne in mind in this connection.

There are many different methods of performing identical milling jobs. As one example, the milling of keyways may be mentioned. It is possible, for instance, to use no fewer than three different types of cutter for providing a shaft with a keyway: the plain milling cutter, the end-mill, and the cotter-mill.

Cutting Slots

A milling cutter of the staggered-tooth type can also be used for cutting slots if the design of the slot is suitable; it should have slightly rounded corners. Inserted-tooth cutters of special type are excellent for slotting nickel chromium steel, as long as the teeth are well spaced, so that each cuts away a chip representing only a portion of the width of the cut. Such

a cutter will cut freely and clear its chips without clogging and without the heat due to friction.

Lubricating Cutters

Lubrication of milling cutters is an important aspect of milling practice, because it has a considerable effect on surface finish, cutter consumption, and time lost in re-sharpening. Lubrication not only eases the task of the cutter tooth; it also cools the cutter by helping to conduct away the heat generated at the cutting edges. Stream lubrication is adopted on most of the modern milling machines.

A centrifugal pump in the machine base delivers as much as 10–12 gallons a minute to the cutter, and this large quantity continually streaming over cutter and work prevents excessive heat from being generated. The lubricant covers the surface of the table in a wide film, which also cools the job. The lubricant is delivered to the cutter by means of a flexible pipe and is returned by way of a flexible steel tube to the pump at the base.

A special type of cutter hood is often used for flooding the cutter. It restricts the coolant to the cutter and the job. It clears the chips from the cutter teeth, preventing their sticking or being carried back into the cut, where they will jam and cause trouble. It eliminates a large proportion of lubricant loss due to splashing, and acts as a safety device or cutter guard preventing injury to the operator.

The best form of lubricant combining the two essential functions of lubricating and cooling is an emulsion of soluble oil and water, in the ratio of ten to one, respectively. This is a better coolant than lubricant, but a small percentage of soda is desirable

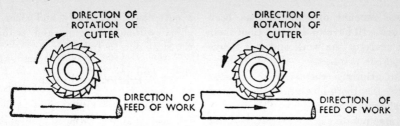

DIRECTION OF
ROTATION OF
CUTTER

DIRECTION OF
FEED OF WORK

DIRECTION OF
ROTATION OF
CUTTER

DIRECTION OF
FEED OF WORK

Fig. 25. In the standard milling operation the direction of the feed is opposite to that of the cutter; in *climb* milling the work is fed in the same direction as the path of the cutter teeth.

as an addition to eliminate a tendency to cause oxidation of the metallic surfaces. There are many extremely good cutting compounds on the market, and a reputable maker should be consulted as to the best lubricant for a particular type of operation. Lard oil is often used with good results. Cast iron must be milled without lubricant or coolant.

Climb Milling

Climb milling differs from the standard milling operation in that, instead of the job passing under the cutter against the rotation of the teeth (Fig. 25), it is fed in the same direction as the path the teeth take (at right). The teeth cut downward rather than upward. One advantage of this method is that play between feed-screw and nut is eliminated. Upward cutting tends to lift the job slightly from the table. A downward cut does not have this effect.

Climb milling is not suitable to every type of milling job. It is used when, for various reasons, a face-cutter cannot be employed, and when the form of the job or the way in which it is held in position makes a downward rather than an upward cut advantageous. The finish given by this type of operation differs from that given by ordinary milling, being rather like the

descaled finish of stainless steel as compared with the mirror finish of the same metal. So, if a bright polished finish is desired, it should not be used. It is necessary to reduce the rate of feed by about 50 percent per cutter tooth, with a corresponding faster speed, as long as proper lubrication is employed. The rake and clearance angles will also have to be greater, and it is necessary to use special cutters designed for the job, which cannot afterwards be used for ordinary milling. Less power is used in climb milling, since there is no need to drive the table against the cutter.

Milling Threads

Thread milling—the milling of threads on dies, screws, worms, etc.—both internally and externally, is

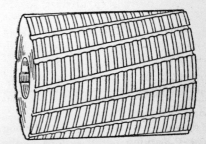

Fig. 26. A parallel-sided cutter with spiral flutes of the type here shown is used for milling short threads.

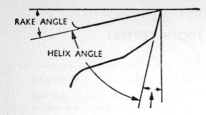

Fig. 27. The meaning of the terms used for the three vital angles of a cutter from the point of view of its efficiency will be clearly seen from this diagram. Choice of angle depends on material.

being more extensively used in modern machine shops as an alternative to the lathe. It offers speedy production with accurate threads and an excellent finish. Different types of cutters are used. Short threads are milled by means of a parallel-sided cutter (Fig. 26) with spiral flutes. Internal threads are milled with a straight-fluted cutter. Both machine-relieved and relief-ground cutters are used, according to the degree of accuracy required, the latter being superior in this respect, since the tool is given its hardening treatment in advance of grinding, and therefore remains undistorted after the relief has been given to the teeth.

Long threads are milled with disc-shaped cutters whose form repeats that of the thread contour to be milled. It is not possible to produce square threads by milling. The choice between lathe screw-cutting and thread milling is a matter of the rapidity with which the threaded parts have to be produced. It is possible to produce threads more rapidly and accurately by thread milling.

Varying Cutter Angles

There is one more aspect of milling that has so far been treated only incidentally: the cutting angles of the cutters. The three vital angles from the point of view of cutting efficiency are the clearance angle, the rake angle, and the helix angle (see Fig. 27). Choice of angle is governed by the material to be milled. Thus, a hard material requires smaller cutting angles. There are so many different materials to be milled in the modern machine shop that it would be impossible for the cutter manufacturer to stock cutters with the theoretically perfect angles for every metal. He therefore tends to concentrate on good average angles for cutting a range of kindred materials, such as cast irons, steels, and non-ferrous metals. The operator with a specific job before him, if he knows with accuracy the best angles for his particular material, can usually take the stock cutter and, by grinding, give it the slight modification necessary for his requirements. Cutters supplied are usually ground to a standard clearance, and this clearance is often too big for efficient work on a particular material.

The table gives some help in the choice of cutting angles, but must be regarded only as a guide.

Another point to be watched is the cutter arbor. This is the shaft on which the cutter is placed and on which it revolves. The size of these arbors must be as large as possible. If the job is heavy, they should be made more rigid and strong by means of an extra intermediate bearing. It is not advisable to use arbor supports fitted with pilot pins or centers unless the job is very light.

Choice of Machine

Great care must be given to the choice of a suitable milling machine.

ANGLES FOR COARSE TOOTH CUTTERS

TYPE OF CUTTER MATERIAL CUT.	CLEARANCE ANGLE.	RAKE ANGLE.	HELIX ANGLE.
Plain Milling Cutters			
Mild Steels	7	20	45
Cast Iron	6	15	45
Malleable Iron	5	20	45
High Tensile Nickel Chrome Steel	3	8	45
Cast Steel	5	15	45
Light Metal	8	25	45
Face Cutters			
Mild Steels	7	15	25
Cast Iron	6	12	25
Malleable Iron	5	12	25
High Tensile Nickel Chrome Steel	3	6	25
Cast Steel	5	10	25
Light Metal	8	25	40
Cutters With Staggered Teeth			
Mild Steels	7	15	20
Cast Iron	6	12	15
Malleable Iron	5	12	20
High Tensile Nickel Chrome Steel	3	6	10
Cast Steel	5	12	20
Light Metal	8	25	40
End Mills			
Mild Steels	7	15	45
Cast Iron	6	12	30
Malleable Iron	5	12	45
High Tensile Nickel Chrome Steel	3	6	45
Cast Steel	5	10	45
Light Metal	8	20	40

The factors to be borne in mind include the quantities in which the parts are to be milled, the type of work to be milled, the amount of power necessary, and the means of power transmission: by individual, group, or line-shaft drive. These factors govern the decision whether the machine shall be cone-driven or constant-speed driven. Choice or plain, universal, or vertical types of machine depends on whether or not it is the sole machine of milling type in the shop; by the amount of time it will be required to spend on spiral cutting; and by whether it will be employed for jobbing or for manufacturing. Other points in this connection are the need to mill plane surfaces, and to do die sinking or gang milling; finally, the decision as to automatic or non-automatic hinges on the number of pieces it is expected to produce.

Cone Drive

Some explanation of the terms cone drive and constant-speed drive may be found helpful. Cone drive is a method of driving a machine by means of a belt pulley used and formed into steps or sections of different diameters, the largest being at one end, the smallest at the other, thus roughly forming a cone. By this means different speeds are obtainable. This type of drive has certain limitations, but it is simple and relatively cheap and is still used for hand-milling and the smaller plain milling machines. It cannot, however, perform the heavy duty which is demanded by modern machine milling.

The constant-speed drive is more complex. The power is delivered to a pulley with a broad face running free on a sleeve on the main driving shaft through a belt from the counter-shaft,

or, if the direct drive is employed, through a silent chain from an electric motor. A friction clutch on the main shaft, lever-operated, transmits motion from pulley to shaft, and from the shaft through sliding gears to the machine spindle.

Gear Drive

The driving gears are of selective type and made of a suitable heat-treated alloy steel. They have integral keys—made in one piece with the gear—and are worked by levers or dials on the side of the machine. The main driving pulley runs at constant speed. When the clutch is in, the driving main-shaft of the miller runs at the same constant speed. The different speeds of spindle are governed wholly by the positions of the sliding gears and the engagement or otherwise of the back gears. The direction of spindle revolution is reversed by operating a lever, which slides a driving gear out of engagement with a driven gear and then introduces an intermediate gear between the two, thereby altering the direction of the driven gear.

This type of drive gives greater power at the cutter as a result of greater strength and increased rigidity of the milling machines. Identical power is delivered to the cutter at all spindle speeds, and the operator is therefore aware of what the machine will do under all circumstances.

Indexing

Indexing is carried out on milling machines provided with the necessary dividing head. Indexing means rotating the work on its axis to an exact indicated amount. There is a wide range of indexing operations involved in milling, fluting, and gear-cutting. Thus, if it is desired to cut a gear, each tooth must be an exact and identical distance from its neighbor. The same is true of the flutes of a reamer or a milling cutter. Calculations are necessary to produce the required setting of the machine to give the proper spacing, and index tables are usually provided. Indexing can be plain or universal. In plain indexing the index plate has three circles of holes 24, 30, and 26, and will index any number that divides evenly into any one of these. It is specially advantageous for indexing low numbers.

Universal indexing gives divisions of all types up to 400, which meets the needs of most shops. If larger and prime numbers have to be indexed, the Manufacturers of Milling Machines provide a high-number indexing attachment by means of which all indexing becomes plain indexing, and charts are needless, all possible divisions being indexed straight from the plates. This indexes all numbers up to and including 200, all even numbers, and those capable of being divided by five up to and including 400, and it will make many divisions above these thus being most versatile.

GRINDING

Grinding is recognized today as an essential and economical production process. While in many shops and industries it is employed primarily as a finishing operation, for bringing previously machined parts to the required accurate dimensions, it is also used extensively as a complete machining process in itself in which the rough pieces, as forged or cast, are ground to size without the use of any metal-cutting tool for preliminary shaping or metal-removal. The grinding operation comprises the application of an abrasive wheel rotating at high speed, to the external or internal surfaces of a metallic or other part hard enough to be ground, rather than indented, by the wheel.

caves, hammers, and the like, where the metal is first cast and then ground to final form and dimensions as a finishing process. An example of grinding as a complete machining process in the forming of tips of tungsten-carbide cutting alloy designed to be brazed on the mild-steel shanks to form lathe cutting tools. The tips are completely shaped by grinding alone. Another example is the shaping of parts made of Alnico—the iron-aluminum-nickel-cobalt magnetic alloy. Powder metallurgy has helped to solve this problem.

Main Types of Grinders

There are three main types of grinding machines in common use. The first are the cylindrical grinders, whose purpose is to true up and bring to dimensions such parts as shafts, spindles, rollers, etc. Then come the internal grinding machines, whose purpose is to grind the internal surfaces

Uses of Grinding

As an example of two different uses for the grinding process one may mention the grinding of manganese-steel castings, such as crusher jaws, con-

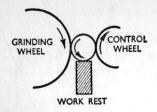

Fig. 28. The principle of centerless grinding. The control wheel makes the job rotate in the opposite direction to the grinding wheel.

of such parts as cylinders. Thirdly, there are the flat-surface grinding machines designed to grind every type of flat surface. These three types, as will be seen, are subdivided into a number of more specialized categories.

The cylindrical grinding machines are divisible into plain grinders, universal grinders, and centerless grinders. The plain grinder is designed for ordinary production grinding of such parts as shafts, sleeves, rollers, spindles, and numerous other parts, either cylindrical or tapered in form.

The universal grinder has a wider range of application and is particularly suitable for special jobs where its swiveling headstock enables it to grind work at any desired angle. It is a more complicated machine than the plain grinder, less massive in construction, and can, if desired, be adapted to internal grinding attachments. It is of great value in the production grinding of parts employed in small machines and special tools.

Centerless Grinders

The centerless grinder operates on a slightly different principle from the other machines. The part is passed between a grinding wheel revolving at high speed and a regulating or con-

trol wheel revolving at a slow speed over a work-rest. In addition, the work-rest comprises guides carrying the job to the wheels and taking it away again when the operation is finished. The pressure which the grinding wheel exerts as it turns, drives the job into contact with the control wheel and the work-rest. The control wheel compels the job to rotate in the opposite direction to that of the grinding wheel.

This means that a point on the surface of the job where it touches the grinding wheel revolves in the same direction as, but more slowly than, a corresponding point on the grinding wheel. The centerless grinder produces, as a result, a more accurately cylindrical surface. The reader interested can obtain the necessary theoretical calculations and explanations from the machine manufacturers.

Internal Grinders

We now come to the second class of grinding machines. These include a wide range of specialized machines devoted to the internal grinding of gears, gauges, bushings, and innumerable

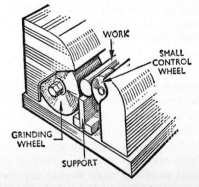

Fig. 29. How centerless grinding is performed, showing the position of the work in relation to the wheels.

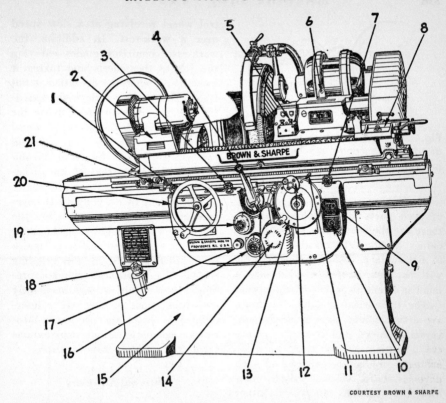

COURTESY BROWN & SHARPE

Fig. 30. Grinding machine: 1, knob which starts and stops headstock and coolant pump; 2, adjustable headstock; 3, start-stop knob for hydraulic table movement; 4, table reversing lever; 5, spindle box adjustment; 6, sight indicator for automatic lubricating system; 7, control knob for wheel truing; 8, adjustable footstock; 9, main start-stop push button switch; 10, selector switch for knob control or hand-wheel control of headstock and coolant; 11, lever disengaging cross feed positive stop; 12, index dial; 13, cross feed handwheel; 14, lever engaging automatic cross feed; 15, bed; 16, cross-feed control knob; 17, knob controlling period of table dwell; 18, bayonet gauge; 19, table throttle knob and dial; 20, table handwheel; 21, combined table reversing and positive-stop dog.

machine parts and articles of a specialized character. Included in these are chucking grinders for finishing bores and face-grinding at the same setting; traverse spindle grinders for highly-accurate internal grinding of small tools and other similar objects; and cutter and tool grinders for internal and external sharpening and grinding of small tools and other small parts—e.g., milling cutters, forming tools, dies, etc.

Finally, the flat surface grinders may be classified under five separate groups. There are first the horizontal machines, in which the work is carried on a table traveling backward and forward under the grinding wheel, which is fixed on a horizontal spindle. A variant on this type is the machine

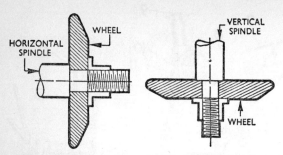

Fig. 31. How the wheel is mounted on its spindle (*left*) in a horizontal grinding machine where the work travels backward and forward below the wheel, and (*right*) in a vertical machine for work carried on either revolving or reciprocating tables.

other type of horizontal grinder in which the wheel spindle is mounted on a saddle somewhat after the fashion of a planing machine, the work passing on a carriage under the wheel.

The second group comprises the vertical spindle grinders. These are adapted for dealing with jobs carried on either revolving or reciprocating tables. Third, there are the face-grinders. In these, the grinding wheel is generally mounted horizontally, though there are exceptions to this rule, and the job is held for grinding on its edge or vertical face.

in which the table is circular in form and revolves, instead of traveling backward and forward. In these machines the wheel is still mounted on a horizontal spindle. There is also an-

Fig. 32. The general arrangement of a large file grinder.

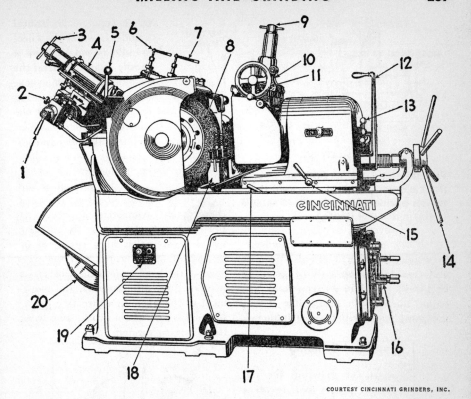

Fig. 33. Centerless grinding machine: 1, grinding wheel truing engaging lever; 2, truing rate adjustment; 3, micrometer adjustment; 4, grinding wheel profile truing attachment; 5, booster lever; 6, truing coolant; 7, grinding coolant; 8, grinding wheel; 9, micrometer adjustment; 10, regulating wheel truing attachment; 11, regulating wheel truing handwheel; 12, hand infeed lever; 13, micrometer hand adjustment for sizing; 14, quick hand adjustment of regulating wheel slide; 15, upper slide clamp; 16, regulating wheel speed change levers; 17, lower slide clamp; 18, work rest; 19, master start-stop buttons; 20, main motor drive.

Next come the disc-grinding machines which embody one disc or more of abrasive type mounted on a vertical spindle horizontally, the job lying on the surface of a flat revolving carrier or table. Finally, there are the belt-grinders, comprising bands or belts having abrasive surfaces and running continuously. It is against these that the part to be ground is held.

Fig. 33 shows a type of grinding machines used for the centerless grinding of stainless and other steel bars. Fig. 32 shows a machine for the grinding of files. These two illustrations indicate the wide constructional differences between grinding machines.

The reader may very well inquire the reason for this wide variety. The answer is essentially economic, and cannot be understood without a clearer indication than has been given thus

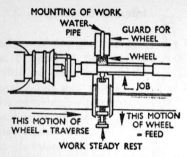

MOUNTING OF WORK
WATER PIPE
GUARD FOR WHEEL
WHEEL
JOB
THIS MOTION OF WHEEL = TRAVERSE
THIS MOTION OF WHEEL = FEED
WORK STEADY REST

Fig. 34. The essential parts of a cylindrical grinding machine. The work to be ground is held between two fixed centers and rotated.

far of the advantages and disadvantages of the various methods. We will therefore take each type of grinding in turn and explain its scope and economic justification in greater detail, beginning with cylindrical grinding.

Cylindrical Grinding

This consists of grinding the external surface of a part as it revolves on its axis between two fixed points or centers. Work, not held between two fixed points in this way, is done by the centerless method. Cylindrical grinding is not, despite its name, confined only to cylindrical objects. It can be applied to the grinding of tapered parts, cams, eccentrics, shoulders of shafts, and the like. Cylindrical grinding machines are not primarily metal removers on a large scale. For this the lathe is superior. These grinders are essentially precision tools which give an accuracy that lathe-machining cannot give, as well as a finer finish. In many drafting rooms parts are now so designed that they can be completely finished by cylindrical grinding, and the accuracy which is possible is within about one-thousandth of an inch (.001).

The Machine

The modern cylindrical grinding machine is heavy, rigid, powerful, highly specialized, and becomes every year more automatic in operation, so that less and less skill is called for on the part of the operator. These modifications and developments have mainly been brought about by mass production. The basic principles of cylindrical grinding are the holding of the work to be ground between two fixed centers; the controlled approach of the work (its *feed*) to an abrasive wheel revolving at high speed, or of the wheel to the work; and the passage of the work before the wheel (its *traverse*) or, alternatively, the movement of the wheel in a direction parallel to the axis of the work. The work itself is also rotated.

Fig. 36. The process of internal grinding designed to finish the surfaces of parallel-sided or tapered holes. A, Wheel; B, Spindle; C, Wheel sleeve; D, Work; E, Coolant; F, Wheel headstock; G, Table.

The abrasive wheel is mounted on a spindle free as far as possible from vibration, and normally driven by means of a belt from an electric motor. The work is traversed across the wheel by either mechanical or hydraulic means, the latter being more favored today on account of its greater speed; lower vibration; reduced wheel wear owing to the possibility, because of the higher speed, of using harder wheels; and greater output this latter being increasingly important.

Internal Grinding

Cylindrical grinding can be applied to the finishing and forming to accurate dimensions of parts as different in size as a tiny tool and a large cast-steel or iron roll weighing several tons. As stated, surface finish and accuracy are its main advantages, and its application is to cylindrical, tapered, and other parts or tools capable of being rotated between fixed centers.

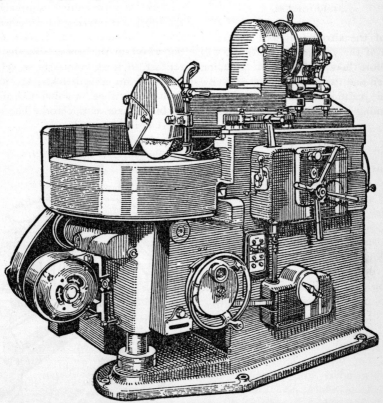

Fig. 35. This horizontal spindle, rotary type surface grinding machine is a precision machine designed for surface grinding piston rings and discs. It has a horizontal traversing wheel head with a peripheral grinding wheel, and the work table is mounted on an elevating knee. The head has a traverse of 14½ ins. The grinding wheel is 16 in. diameter by 1½ in. face, and 6½ in. bore. The reverse is actuated by dogs, and a withdrawable reverse pin allows for overrunning. All motors are push button controlled from the operator's working position.

Internal grinding is designed to finish the surface of holes, whether parallel-sided, tapered, or a combination of both; it can also be applied to holes of special form. It gives a high degree of accuracy, is economical, and produces a good surface finish. It is necessary, for example, in many instances to correct the slight deformation of internal diameters in long and slender hollow parts or tools caused by distortion under heat-treatment. Holes can be ground to an accuracy of .00025 in. and even as high as .0001 in., but the correct type of abrasive wheels must be employed, as will be indicated later.

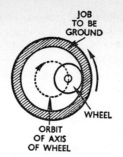

Fig. 37. Diagram showing how, in a planetary type of grinder, the wheel operates within the workpiece.

These internal grinders are grouped according to first, whether the work is held between fixed centers or is centerless—without fixed points of support; second, whether, if the job is centered, the work revolves or remains stationary; and third, whether the machine is manually operated or automatic. In machines of the centered type, the movement of the wheel down the hole is achieved by moving the work forward, or, in certain machines, backward and forward, which makes it possible for the wheel to hold rigid and without causing harmful vibration.

If, however, the work is heavy, the wheel may be moved instead of the work. Centerless grinding of internal type always necessitates the movement of the work, the wheel being fixed.

Parts so ground by making them rotate are bushings, cutters, gears, etc.

Their rotation causes the wheel to make contact with every part of their interior surface. Where the job is too heavy to be revolved, the method is adopted of not only making the grinding wheel revolve at high speed, but also causing it to describe an orbit about the axis of the job.

Surface grinding is a process designed to perform more cheaply and accurately work of metal removal and finishing that would otherwise have to be done by a milling, shaping, planing, or slotting machine, or else by hand filing. Whereas hard spots in an aluminum casting or in cast iron may cause a lathe tool or cutter to break, the grinding wheel overcomes such blemishes. Hard scale on the surface of castings may also seriously damage or reduce the cutting efficiency of a machine cutting tool, whereas the grinding wheel is undeterred by its presence. It will thus be

Fig. 38. Grinding with a magnetic chuck. A, Body of grinding machine; B, Magnetic chuck; C, Work; D, Grinding wheel; E, Guard; F, Clamp; G, Chuck control handle; H, Machine control handle.

seen why its use is often highly economical. If a suitable, well-designed grinder is used, the quality of finish obtained is often such as to enable the manufacturer to dispense with polishing operations, again saving expense. Flat surfaces are ground, therefore, whenever lower cost, higher accuracy, and superior finish can be obtained as compared with a machining operation. A magnetic chuck is often used to hold the work in position on the table. The electric current actuates powerful electro-magnets which retain the parts firmly in place.

The advantages of surface grinders can be summarized in this way. Horizontal spindle grinders employing the circumference of straight wheels will handle a wide variety of jobs requiring a very fine finish and accuracy to close limits. They give higher output and quicker metal removal than similar machines employing cup-shaped, segmental, or ring wheels. Machines of horizontal spindle type using a revolving work-table give a finish consisting of concentric circles which is often favored, and is, in fact, more suitable to certain parts.

The vertical spindle machines grind away metal more rapidly when using a cup, cylinder, or segmental wheel. They are accurate, and, as long as they are robust and rigid in construction, can be employed for grinding to close limits.

Disc Grinders

Disc grinders are used where rough and semi-precision surface grinding work is called for in which metal has to be removed quickly and efficiently to limits of accuracy of less than the severest type. For this work they are more economical. Characteristic jobs are sharpening tools, squaring the ends of die blanks, gear and crankcase covers, and other big and weighty parts. Surfaces having an area of as much as 300 sq. in. can be handled by these machines, as well as small surfaces not more than $\frac{1}{2}$ in. wide.

Centerless Grinding

Centerless grinding has been left to the last because of its importance. Its advantages are that it gives virtually continuous operation since the pieces do not have to be placed in position, and the machine is never standing while this is done. The bars are firmly supported, not only throughout their whole length, but right under the grinding cut. This means that they do not tend to be forced out of straight during the operation, and in consequence a heavier cut can be taken.

In grinding slender and delicate parts between centers, there is an axial thrust which is inclined to cause the work to become deformed, or, if the material is brittle, to fracture, unless careful steps are taken to prevent this. In centerless grinding this is not necessary, and slender rods can be ground without danger. Less stock has to be left on for removal by grinding owing to the mathematical accuracy of the process. Wheel life is thereby lenghtened. The machine has a low maintenance cost because of the small number of wearing parts. The operator need not be a skilled man, and can run more than one machine without difficulty. Hence there is a big saving in labor cost.

The work done by one make of centerless machine ranges from $\frac{1}{8}$ in. to $1\frac{1}{4}$ in. diameter bars up to 15 ft. in length. According to the amount of metal to be removed, the grinding is finished in three passes which remove about .010 in. at a time, except at the last pass, when the cut is lighter. The speed of pass is about 15 ft. a minute. Size can be guaranteed between plus and minus .0005 in. and a limit of .00025 in. can be obtained if desired. Higher speeds and accuracies can be reached.

Drive and Speed

The machine is driven by a 25 h.p. motor, and the grinding wheel is driven at a fixed speed of approximately 1,100 revs. per min. The speed of the control wheel is adjusted by means of a gearbox from 12 revs. per min. to as high as 300 revs. per min. The grinding wheel used (in the instance, for stainless steel bars) is 20 in. in diameter, the control wheel 12 in. in diameter, the maximum gap being $5\frac{1}{4}$ in. Forward adjustments allows these wheels to be used up until they measure no more than 15 in. and 9 in. diameter, respectively. The larger wheel has a 12 in. hole and the regulating wheel a recess measuring 8 in. in diameter. Consequently, as the radial thickness is worn down to $1\frac{1}{2}$ in. in the control wheel, it will be apparent that maximum wheel life can be obtained. For convenience of operation, both machine and bar fixture have sensitive close-adjusting means of clear index readings.

With the rod fixture employed, five blades cover the range from $\frac{1}{8}$ in. to $1\frac{1}{4}$ in. diameter. Change over from one rod diameter to another takes five minutes, unless the blade has to be altered, in which case ten minutes are needed. Before the last pass, the wheel is trimmed for wear to insure that it is perfectly cylindrical. Grease on the control wheel is also removed. Both these operations are carried out by means of a diamond tool.

A centrifugal pump provides 28 gallons of cutting lubricant a minute, with control of the quantity, the lubricant being taken from a 60 gallon container. The drives from motor to machine and from main shaft to spindle are by V belts, which provide for smooth and silent operation.

However modern and well constructed the grinding machine, it will achieve unsatisfactory results unless proper attention is paid to the choice of grinding wheels. Abrasive wheels for metal removal must be hard, tough, and possess a suitable surface condition when the crystals of which they are composed are broken. The abrasives of which they are formed are mainly artificial. Until the introduction of legislation concerning silicosis and its prevention, sandstone grinding wheels for file grinding, and emery wheels, were still used.

Material of Wheels

In all but a few unimportant instances of special type, the modern grinding wheel is made from either silicon carbide or aluminum oxide as a basis; both are artificial substances. Each of these materials has its special features and advantages. Briefly, it can be stated that silicon carbide grinding wheels are better for the brittle, hard materials, such as grey iron castings, chilled iron, tungsten carbide, hard steels, stone, procelain, and other ceramic substances, marble, etc. They are also to be recommended for soft and low-strength materials such as the non-ferrous metals, bronze, brass, copper, aluminum, rubber, and other plastic materials. The aluminum oxide grinding wheels are better for tough metals such as mild steels, alloy steels, high-speed steels, annealed malleable iron, tough bronze, wrought iron, and other metals.

Special Materials

There are, however, certain additional materials for which it is difficult to prescribe one or the other without a clear knowledge of operating conditions and output demands. Among these may be mentioned Monel metal (a high nickel-copper alloy), wood and glass. It should be borne in mind that by modifications in the processes of manufacture, it is possible to obtain intermediate types of abrasive wheels embodying some of the characteristics of silicon carbide in aluminum oxide compositions. Diamonds of commercial type can also be used as abrasives, and are generally employed for truing up the abrasive wheels themselves.

Variety of Wheels

The difficulty of choosing the right wheel for any particular job can be judged from the fact that more than 10,000 different combinations of abrasive materials, grain size, type of bond, hardness of bond, and structure, are obtainable in a single wheel. However, the problem can be reduced to simple elements. The choice of the right abrasive is, to some extent, determined by the type of material to be ground. This will govern whether the basis is to be silicon carbide, aluminum oxide, or a modified aluminum oxide. Other points are the quantity of metal or other substance to be ground, the degree of accuracy and surface finish desired, the extent of contact between

wheel and work, the character and condition of the grinding machine, the type of operation, the speed of the work, and the speed of the wheel.

The abrasive material of the wheel will not hold together while at work without some bonding agent.

Bonding Agents

Of these there are five main types —namely vitrified, silicate, shellac, synthetic resin, and rubber. The vitrified are the most commonly employed, and are suitable for both silicon carbide and aluminum oxide. They are strong enough for most heavy jobs, and can stand a speed of 6,500 surface ft. per min. They are employed when it is desired to grind away material at high speed and, in precision work where a good surface finish and close limits of size are the most important points. Silicate bond is for specially large wheels, but can also be used in small wheels where it is necessary to keep heat-generation to a minimum. An example is in grinding carbon-steel drills, where an excess of heat at the cutting point would draw the temper of the tools and lower their cutting efficiency.

Rubber-Bonded Wheels

Resin- or rubber-bonded wheels are employed where a thin wheel for parting off is desired or to lessen the risk of breakage as a result of lateral stresses parallel to the spindle. They are springier and less brittle than the other bonds, and can be run at higher speeds. Hence their use is economical wherever a large amount of material has to be removed as in grinding blooms, castings, etc. The synthetic-resin-bonded wheels can be safely used at speeds as high as 15,000 surface ft. per min. Rubber-bonded wheels will also give an excellent finish. Shellac-bonded wheels are designed for light work and thin cuts as in sharpening edge tools and finishing small steel-hardened rolls.

Each type of bond described can be obtained in varying grades—i.e. of different strengths of union with the crystals of the abrasive proper. The number of these grades varies according to the type of bond. There are a greater number of grades in the vitrified and silicate bonds. Usually, hard grades are employed for soft substances and soft grades for hard substances. The grade is also governed by the extent of contact between wheel and work. The greater the area of contact, the softer the grade, and *vice versa*. Heavy, rigid machines demand softer grades than light machines. If the condition of the grinding machines is such as to cause extensive vibration, a harder grade will be called for than where complete rigidity and freedom from vibration occur. The ratio of work-speed to wheel-speed is another factor governing grade, higher ratios requiring harder grades, and *vice versa*. This is because the greater the cut taken, the more severe the stresses created between bond and abrasive crystals embedded in it. Some operators endeavor to compensate for original unwise wheel choice by manipulating the speeds of wheel and work, but this practice is not to be recommended. It is a bad substitute for correct wheel choice.

Grain size of the abrasive is another factor to be studied. Hard, brittle substances are best cut with small-grained abrasive wheels. Coarse-grained wheels will, with most other materials, give a higher rate of material removal. Where a fine finish and a high degree of accuracy are required, however, small-grained wheels should be used.

Structure of the abrasive is important, and means the wider spacing of the grains in the bond. Widely spaced grains will cut soft and ductile substances more effectively. Closely spaced grains are better for hard and brittle materials, with the exception of tungsten-carbide. Close grains give superior finish. Where pressure is variable, wide spacing is to be preferred. Heavy pressures call for close grains. Medium-spaced grains are better for cylindrical, centerless, and cutter and tool grinding.

TABLE III

COARSEST.	COARSE.	MEDIUM.	FINE.	SUPERFINE.	
6	12	30	70	150	280
8	14	36	80	180	320
10	16	40	90	220	400
	20	50	100	240	500
	24	60	120		600
				1F	
				2F	
				3F	

Thus it will be seen that consideration of these various factors narrows down the problem of wheel selection to a large extent. When the operator has decided, as best he can, what type of wheel is best suited to the work, it will be a wise plan for him to ask abrasive wheel makers to submit samples for trial. He should then take careful records of performance and standardize on the wheel found most effective in use.

Table III gives a list of standard grain sizes of silicon carbide and aluminum oxide wheels.

We can best pursue the subject by considering certain typical kinds of grinding, but before we leave the subject of wheels, we must add a few notes on wheel diameters and speeds. For most ordinary cutting-off work, wheels 12 in. in diameter should be employed, unless the size of the job is so great that a bigger wheel must be used to give flange clearance. Otherwise larger wheels are to be avoided, as they involve a higher percentage of waste.

For high-speed cutting-off machines, 12 in. wheels should revolve at 5,200 r.p.m., 14 in. wheels at 4,400 r.p.m., and 16 in. wheels at 3,800 r.p.m. Low speed machines should have wheels running at from 9,000 to 12,000 s.f.p.m. These machines are chiefly used for dry cutting. Wet cutting-off is done at 4,000–6,750 s.f.p.m. For portable cutting-off machines, speeds should be 2,000–2,500 r.p.m. for wheels from 6 to 12 in. Polishing wheels should run at 7,000–7,500 s.f.p.m. for general work, but the higher limits should be used only in exceptional circumstances. For cylindrical grinding, 5,500–6,500 s.f.p.m. is advised with work-speeds ranging from 40–50 s.f.p.m. The maximum range is from 30 to 100, the lower figure for hardened steel, the upper for finishing grinding of soft material. Traverse speed should be in a ratio to work-speed such that the work-table will travel from two-thirds to three-quarters of the width of the wheel at each revolution.

The wheel-speed range for planetary-type internal grinders should be approximately from 2,300 to 4,500, and for the rotating type from 4,000 to 6,000 s.f.p.m. Table IV gives grinding-wheel speeds corresponding to surface ft. per minute, while Table V gives wheel speeds for disc grinding.

When beginning a job on the grinding machine, the first step is to see that the grinding wheel is sharp, properly guarded so as to prevent injury to the operator, and carefully mounted, neither too tight nor too loose on the machine spindle. If the wheel is loose, it may not be correctly centered, and will therefore be unbalanced. If considerable looseness is found when the wheel is mounted, some packing material should be wrapped around the spindle until the wheel is a nice fit. Force should not be used to compel a tight wheel to fit on to the spindle, as this may result in a fracture of the wheel. Instead, the surplus metal in the central hole of the wheel should be filed away, or removed with a knife if the hole has a bushing or inner lining of lead. The wheel should next be tested for soundness with a light blow. If it gives a clear ring, it is sound.

The first piece to be ground, if a cylindrical job, should then be measured and the machine adjusted to give the required setting, but as it is almost certain that the first set-up will not be exact, no piece should be ground absolutely to size until the setting has been thoroughly checked. Otherwise the job may be spoiled.

TABLE IV

WHEEL DIAMETER (INCHES).	SURFACE 4,000 FT. PER MIN. EXPRESSED IN R.P.M.	5,000 S.F.P.M. IN R.P.M.	5,500 S.F.P.M. IN R.P.M.	6,000 S.F.P.M. IN R.P.M.
1	15,279	19,099	21,000	22,918
2	7,639	9,549	10,500	11,459
3	5,093	6,366	7,350	7,639
4	3,820	4,775	5,250	5,730
5	3,056	3,820	4,200	4,584
6	2,546	3,183	3,500	3,820
7	2,183	2,728	3,000	3,274
8	1,910	2,387	2,600	2,865
10	1,528	1,910	2,100	2,292
12	1,273	1,592	1,750	1,910
14	1,091	1,364	1,500	1,637
16	955	1,194	1,300	1,432
18	849	1,061	1,150	1,273
20	764	955	1,050	1,146
22	694	868	950	1,042
24	637	796	875	955
26	586	733	800	879
28	546	683	750	819
30	509	637	700	764
32	477	591	650	716
34	449	561	620	674
36	424	531	580	637
38	402	503	550	603
40	382	478	525	573
42	364	455	500	546
44	347	434	475	521
46	332	415	455	498
48	318	397	440	477
50	306	383	420	459

Care should be taken to see that the grinding machine centers and the center holes in the work are smooth, thoroughly clean, and adequately lubricated. The job itself should also be clean, as well as the parts that hold it in position. When the work is fastened down, dirt may cause stresses that will lead to distortion and bad grinding. Care in clamping down is also essential to avoid excessive stresses. One end of the work should then be fastened to the driver plate and the tail-stock brought into such a position that the dead center is in correct pressure against the job.

Choosing Wheel Speed

The correct wheel speed must be selected. Surface speed must not be confused with revolutions of the wheel per minute. The larger the wheel diameter, the lower need be the spindle speed. A formula will help the operator to determine surface speed when the revolutions per minute is known.

R.p.m. $\times$ .25D = Surface speed, where D equals wheel diameter. To find the r.p.m. for a given surface speed, the formula is $\dfrac{SS}{.25D}$ = r.p.m., SS being the surface speed and D the wheel diameter.

Wheel speeds are dealt with in Table IV. After the setting for wheel speed has been made, table feed and traverse feed should be set, and if steady rests are used these should be adjusted.

Some hints may be of value in deciding if the settings are correct in practice. If excessive wheel wear is found to occur, the probability is that the wheel is running too slowly, or the work too quickly, in which case one or the other should be adjusted accordingly. Also it may be that the wheel-face is too narrow, while sometimes the work-speed may be too high.

If the wheel glazes and the job becomes too hot, the work is probably running too slowly, or the wheel too rapidly. It may be that the wheel chosen is too hard or of too fine a grain. Again it may be that grindings or chips have become embedded between the cutting points of the wheel. The operator can overcome this difficulty by various means—e.g. by using a softer or less dense wheel; by raising the work-speed; by reducing the amount of chips or by cutting down the table feed if belt is slipping.

A lighter cut is advisable in finishing than in roughing.

Using Dead Centers

It is good practice to use dead centers in grinding other than centerless, as this makes for greater accuracy. If the center rotates with the work, it may be thrown out of true by defects in the spindle bearings. Long slender jobs should be supported by steady rests. These are either plain or universal. If plain rests are used, the wheel should be fed in by hand until the diameter is two or three-thousandths of an inch above the required size. This will eliminate excessive vibrations and give longer life.

Machine Adjustment

The universal back-rest is very flexible for rough grinding and possesses

TABLE V

DISC DIAMETER (INCHES).	SPEED FOR STOCK REMOVAL R.P.M.	SPEED FOR BRASS WORK (FINISHING) R.P.M.
12	2,000	2,600
18	1,400	1,800
20	1,250	1,600
23	1,100	1,300
26	1,000	1,250

a positive series of stops that provides accuracy in finished work. In other words, they are adjustable so as to allow for jobs slightly distorted, out of round, or well oversize. They need careful adjustment, the detailed instructions for which can be obtained from the makers. If the machine is automatic in its operations, the reverse feed automatic stop should then be set.

In up-to-date grinders, work-speed, traverse-feed, and table-speed can be separately adjusted to provide a combination of these three factors which is suitable for rough grinding with maximum speed of metal removal, or for finish grinding with the best possible surface.

Whether or not the whole job, from start to finish, shall be done with one setting of the grinder, is governed by the dimensions of the pieces to be ground, the quantity, and the accuracy desired. If only one setting is used, however, finishing should be performed in a couple of light cuts, reducing the table feed to about three-quarters of the feed used for roughing.

In setting up the job, care should be taken to see that proper adjustment has been given to the table-feed reverse mechanism. If it is necessary to move the table by hand, the wheel should first be moved to a safe position so as to prevent injury to the operator. The table should not be moved lengthwise when the belt is idle, as this causes belt stretch and consequent slip. The belt should be kept moving, if necessary by hand. The head-stock should not be moved until the swiveling table has been thoroughly cleaned.

Grinding should not be performed if the belt slips, and if in finishing the job the machine is shut down for any reason, it should be allowed to run free so as to warm it up for a few minutes before work is resumed. Otherwise the piece may be spoiled.

Dressing the Wheel

Dressing and truing grinding wheels at proper and regular intervals greatly affects their efficiency and economical use. Dressing changes the cutting action of the wheel by sharpening it. Truing is a modification of the wheel itself in order to produce a particular form or to keep the form accurate. The words are, however, often interchanged. Tools for this work can be of steel, abrasive material in wheel form, or, in some cases, for special purposes, diamond.

Star dressers are pointed discs loosely mounted on a pin and separated by solid discs. They are designed for rapid dressing of snagging wheels and coarse segmental wheels. Corrugated-disc dressers are of special alloy steel and are used where a superior finish is desired with less abrasive removal. Disc dressers are steel discs with teeth, fastened together. They are used for medium-grade roughing wheels and for cam and crankshaft grinding wheels, and bar-grinding wheels of centerless grinders. Precision steel dressers, abrasive-stick dressers, abrasive-wheel dressers (small-diametered grinding wheels mounted at a slight angle), are employed for cast-iron grinding wheels, tool sharpening, and wheel profiling, and truing cylindrical grinding abrasive wheels, respectively. Diamonds are used for wheels employed in precision and superfine finish grinding, and for wheels employed in mass production, as well as for the forming of tungsten carbide tools.

Wheels should be trued whenever they have begun to lose their shape, and the work must be skilfully done. If, through constant use, a wheel has become out of balance to such an extent that it cannot be corrected by dressing, it must be taken out of the machine. Normal wheel running speed should be used for dressing and truing. For roughing, the traverse should be at 40 in. per minute with an in-feed of .002–.003 in. per pass. For standard finishing after a previous roughing, these figures should be lowered to 20 in. per min. with feed .001 in. for several passes across the face of the wheel. To obtain a medium-fine surface, the traverse should then be lowered to 10 in. feed. For the finest surfaces the same recommendation should be adopted, but water must be used and the tool operated at less of an angle. Wheel-glazing must be avoided by the use of feed, as otherwise this will spoil the wheel. Use a good grinding compound when dressing. The cut must not be too heavy or the work may be burned.

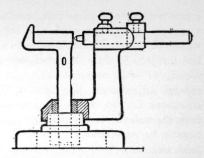

Fig. 39. Radial wheel-truing fixture, for truing a wheel to both male and female radii by means of a diamond-shaped fixture.

Precision Work

In making precision tools and dies, grinding to form has resulted in great accuracy with an excellent surface finish on hardened steel. To form-grind efficiently and at minimum cost, it is not essential nor even advantageous to complete the formed part with a wheel covering the whole piece. It is more satisfactory to grind suitable ribs and protrusions with thin wheels, making one diameter or height correspond to one ground earlier. Thus very wide forms can be accurately ground, for the reason that the desired wheel-forms are simply obtained.

For this work a radial truing fixture for both male and female radii is used. If the point of the diamond lies to the rear of the center of the fulcrum, a male radius is obtained. With this fixture radii can be obtained on a wheel with an accuracy of .0001 in.

It is essential that grinding wheels should be correctly mounted on properly-

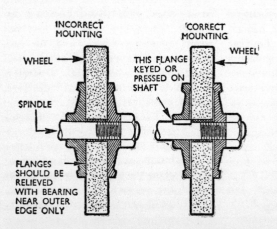

Fig. 40. Correct mounting of grinding wheels is of the highest importance. Above, incorrect (*left*) and correct (*right*) mounting of wheel in the grinder.

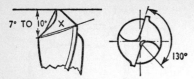

Fig. 41. Points to be watched in twist-drill grinding. *Left,* inadequate clearance; *right,* correct angle at the drill circumference.

proportioned spindles and between correctly-designed flanges with compressible washers between flanges and wheel, and a firm bearing around the external edge. The left-hand illustration (Fig. 40) shows the wrong procedure; straight flanges have been employed, without any washers between flanges and wheel.

Relieved flanges should be not less than half the wheel diameter and must have a true bearing at the outer edge. The inner flange must always be a firm fit on the spindle. Nuts should never be used to secure the wheel, as this is dangerous. The washers should be of rubber and a trifle larger than the flanges. They serve to proportion the pressure uniformly. Wheel bushings should be .005 in. larger in diameter than standard spindles, so as to insure easy fit of

the wheel on the spindle and against the internal flange. Flanges should not be tightened more than is essential to keep the wheel securely in place. Otherwise the strain may be too great.

Wherever feasible, a twist-drill grinder should be used for sharpening twist drills. When grinding drills, too much pressure must not be used, as this generates intense local heat, which causes uneven expansion of the steel, and consequent cracking. A free-cutting wheel should be used with a good water-supply. If the water-supply is small or inefficient and cannot

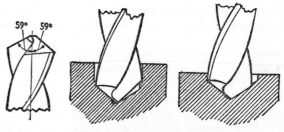

Fig. 42. Points to be watched in twist-drill grinding. *Left,* best lip angle for general use; *center,* too much, and *right,* too little lip clearance.

be improved, grind the drills dry with a light pressure only, so that the tool never becomes too hot. If in spite of precautions the drill does become hot, never cool it in cold water. It should be left to cool naturally, for otherwise a crack will probably result.

The methods adopted in hand grinding of twist-drills cannot be exhaustively explained here, but Figs. 41—48 will suffice to show the angles to be given and the points to be watched. Fig. 41 shows inadequate clearance, and also shows the correct angle at the drill's circumference. Fig. 42 shows the best lip angle for general use and also incor-

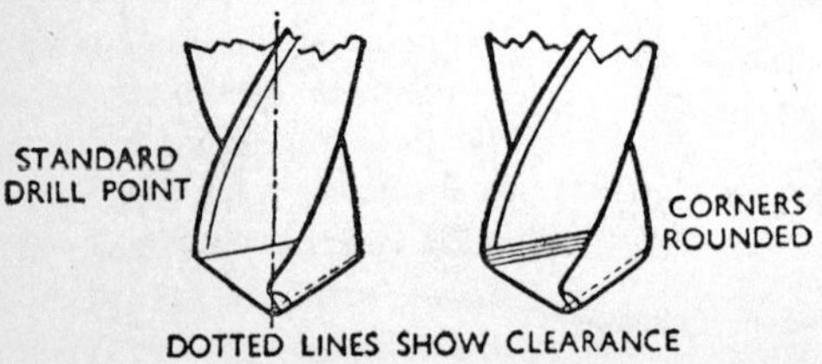

Fig. 43. In twist-drill grinding, rounding off the drill corners as indicated above is helpful in difficult jobs.

Fig. 44. Twist-drill grinding: point thinning.

rect practice. Fig. 43 shows the corner rounding of drills, useful when difficult jobs are attempted. Fig. 44 shows point thinning. Fig. 45 shows rake angle, and a reduced rake angle for drilling very hard materials. Fig. 46 shows operations in drill grinding. Fig. 48 makes these references easier to follow.

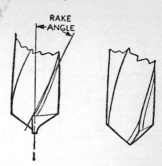

Fig. 45. Twist-drill grinding. *Left,* rake angle; *right,* reduced rake angle for drilling very hard materials.

Grinding Taps and Broaches

Taps usually need grinding on the tapered end only, and to give the necessary clearance behind the cutting edge. On occasion, however, it is desirable to grind the flutes though this is rarely necessary if taper and clearance are correctly ground. The relief length, which varies with the kind of tap, is of importance. Each flute must possess the same angle, or the tap will not start correctly.

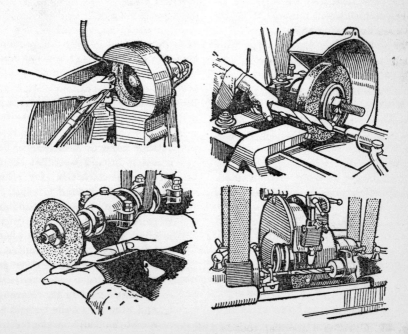

Fig. 46. The sequence of operations performed in drill grinding. A large drill is shown for the sake of clarity.

Fig. 47. Precision grinding for the points of large drills.

The correctness of the grinding may be determined by revolving the tap two-thirds of the way through a nut and looking at it from the other end to decide if all the flutes are functioning. A tool and cutter grinding machine should be used for these tools. Broken teeth should be completely removed, which will not greatly impair the performance of the tool.

When the relief becomes too long, particularly with bottom-in taps, the tool should be made shorter by paring off the unusable part with a suitable cutting-off wheel.

Broaches are usually backed off by means of a cup-shaped wheel. Rectangular and square broaches are ground with a dish-wheel. To back off those tools in which the teeth are cut on an angle, the swivel slide should be turned in a horizontal plane. The teeth are generally undercut 6–10 deg., so as to produce a curling chip. The top clearance is 30 deg. Round

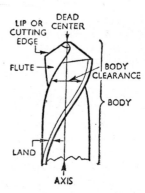

Fig. 48. Diagram showing the arrangement of drill adopted in hand or machine grinding of twist drills and also making clear Figs. 46 and 47.

broaches are sharpened between fixed centers. Light cuts should always be taken so as to prevent overheating and drawn temper in the teeth, and to maintain free cutting of the wheel.

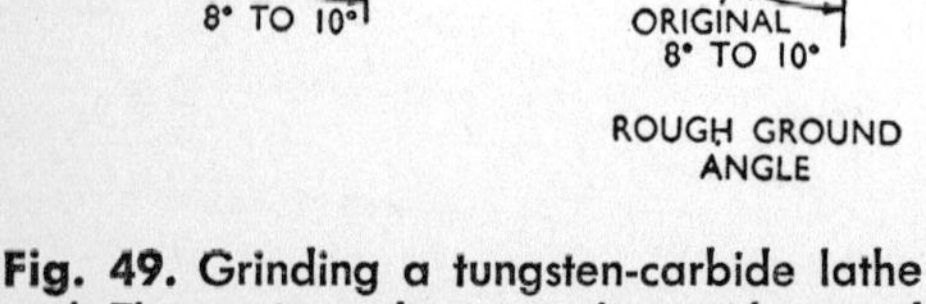

The grinding of tungsten-carbide cutting tools is becoming of increasing importance. The shank steel on to which tips of this cutting alloy are brazed is usually a good quality of carbon steel, and the tools themselves require grinding with extreme care. Wet grinding is advised, but if the requisite wet grinding machinery is not available, and dry grinding is the only course open to the operator, he should never let the tool tip become too hot, and he must on no account cool it quickly in water. This invariably cracks the tool

Fig. 49. Grinding a tungsten-carbide lathe tool. The cutting edges are diamond-ground after rough grinding on a coarse wheel.

and leads to breakdown and spoilage.

Pressure on the alloy material when grinding must not be too heavy, and if the proper grinding wheel is chosen, a light pressure will suffice. Tools should not be ground upside down. The cutting edge must always be presented to the wheel in such a way that the wheel rotates into and not away from the edge.

Diamond grinding wheels, which are being increasingly used for tungsten carbide grinding, are economical and give an excellent finish to the cutting edges. They are quick stock removers, but should not be employed for rough grinding. The tip and shank of the tools should first be rough ground on a coarse wheel of special grit and grade, free-cutting, and then the cutting edge of the tip should be diamond ground, as in Fig. 49. This technique gives flat cutting faces free from rounded edges; and smooth edges quickly and easily produced and free from danger of grinding cracks. If the operator tries to take off too much material with a fine wheel of normal type, the risk of cracking is considerable, but with a diamond wheel this risk becomes negligible, these wheels being so free in their cutting.

CHAPTER 7

SPECIAL MACHINE TOOLS

BROACHING. PUSH AND PULL MACHINES. CUTTING KEYWAYS. BURNISHING.
PLANING. SHAPING. PROFILING. MULTIPLE-TOOL LATHES. ROLL-TURNER'S
LATHES. AUTOMATIC TAPPING MACHINES. ENGRAVING MACHINES. MAG-
NETIC CHUCKS. MACHINE ATTACHMENTS.

THE best known of the machine tools used in machine shops is the lathe. It is still the most important, and can, in fact, be used for many of the processes which are dealt with in the following pages. But the present-day need for high-speed production of parts of great accuracy has led to the development of special equipment. Thus it is that we have, for example, broaching machines for making accurate holes, not only of circular, but of many other forms.

Planing machines, as the name suggests, are used for finishing flat surfaces; at least, that is their primary function, but it will be seen that there are other corresponding applications. In all cases the aim is to produce parts, large and small, which are accurate to a high degree, at a speed which is compatible with modern requirements.

Shaping and profiling machines are, in effect, modified forms of planing machines, and can be used to copy intricate shapes in a manner which meets the needs both of mass production and interchangeability.

Other machines dealt with in this section are in the nature of modifications of those already mentioned, but designed for high-speed tapping, turning large rollers, engraving, and so forth. Reference is also made to such fittings as magnetic chucks, which are of great assistance in increasing the efficiency and speed of modern engineering production.

BROACHING

BROACHING, reduced to its simplest terms, is a method of altering the size or finish of holes in metallic parts by pulling or pushing through them a tapered tool with a number of cutting teeth. These teeth become successively larger as they progress toward one end of the tool, which is termed a broach. The alteration of the holes may take the form of their enlarge-

ment, as when a round hole is increased in size by cutting away with the broach teeth a specific quantity of metal; or it may take the form of burnishing.

Two types of broaching are employed. The first consists of pushing a relatively short tool through the hole, using a form of press for the purpose, either hydraulically, mechanically, or

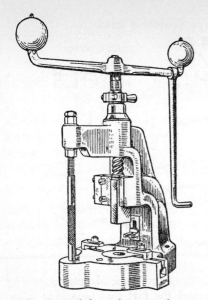

Fig. 1. Push-broaching machine.

manually operated (see Fig. 1). The second is to pull the broach through in a special broaching machine, shown in Fig. 2. For this latter work much longer tools are used. The reason for using a short tool in pushing is that otherwise the severe stress would probably cause the broach to bend to some extent, and thereby destroy the accuracy of the work. Hence, it may be necessary in this type of broaching to push more than one broach through the hole in order to attain the desired result.

It will also be seen in due course that broaching can be both internal and external, while the broaches themselves may have teeth either *solid*— that is, forming one whole with the body of the tool; or *inserted*—separate and fastened into position in the body.

In addition to enlarging or finishing square holes, round holes and keyways, broaching is also employed for making splines, which are parallel

keys partly sunk into a recess on a shaft; holes of irregular form; internal gears; etc. All these are internal broaching jobs. Fig. 4 gives a few examples of internal-broaching shapes. External broaching is used for bringing the external surface of a part or piece to the required shape, as when manufacturing shock absorber wings, toothed rolls for textile machines, etc. In external broaching, the broach is hollow. Sometimes the job is pulled through it, the tool remaining fixed; and sometimes the tool is pulled over the stationary job.

The advantages of broaching over other machining processes are speed, economy, high output, and simplicity. The time spent in clamping down an irregular job on the milling machine or the borer is saved, because the broaching action alone is often sufficient to maintain the work in position without additional holding appliances. The operation is thus quick and simple. Furthermore, it is economical, few pieces being spoiled, since there is no complicated set-up liable to er-

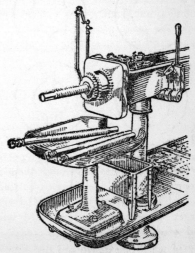

Fig. 2. Pull-broaching machine.

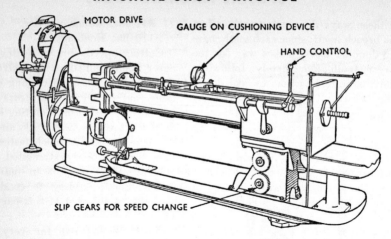

MOTOR DRIVE

GAUGE ON CUSHIONING DEVICE

HAND CONTROL

SLIP GEARS FOR SPEED CHANGE

Fig. 3. Illustration showing a good representative pull-type broaching machine.

ror. Finally, the tools themselves are not very costly to buy or to keep in good condition and accurate form.

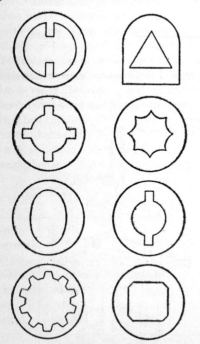

Fig. 4. Various shapes, regular or irregular, of which the above are but a few, can be produced by internal broaching.

As against these advantages must be placed the fact that broaching is not an operation capable of affording the highest degree of accuracy, though it is not therefore to be regarded as inaccurate. In general, limits of one- or two-thousandths of an inch can be worked to. For most broaching jobs this is quite adequate. The longest cut feasible with a broach is about 6 ft. 8 in.

Lubrication and Cooling

One of the most important factors in broaching is proper lubrication and cooling. All cutting tools generate heat at their cutting edges, and, in broaching, the amount of heat is governed by the power used in pulling or pushing the broach through the work. Another source of heat generation is chip friction and rubbing. Chip friction is caused by the chips thrown off from the work jamming against the teeth of the tool and the surface of the work, while rubbing is due to grinding of the sides of the broach teeth against the work. Such heat as is generated in these ways does not greatly affect the broach itself, since each tooth, having done its work, makes way for the larger tooth immediately following, and therefore has time to cool down. The injury, if any, is done to the work, especially if this is of thin section, because a permanent expansion due to heat may occur, throwing the dimensions completely out. While this can be remedied, where it is known to be inevitable, by making the broach slightly below size, it is much better to employ copious lubrication with a good quality of cutting oil, and keep the job cool enough to prevent distortion. The lubricant manufacturer should be consulted as to the best type of cutting compound for any given job, but the finer the surface finish required, the greater should be the amount of oil in the mixture.

The following compound is recommended by the Ford Motor Company for broaching hard or soft steel, or for burnishing hardened bushings by broaching:

15½ gals. clean oil
7¾ gals. denatured alcohol
79¼ gals. kerosine oil
3¾ gals. caustic soda
167.3 gals. water

441 lbs. laloum powder
110 lbs. Bentonite.

Cutting speeds for broaching have never been studied as intensively as the speeds of other machining operations, but during recent years there has been an increase in cutting speeds as a result of practical work, and jobs are now broached at much faster rates than were formerly attempted. As a general guide, subject to individual modification according to conditions, the table at the foot of this page may be found useful.

Speed is lowered for very hard metals in order to reduce the power consumption, which would otherwise be extremely high. Similarly, in cutting soft metals speed must be lessened, so as to prevent the teeth from seizing and tearing the metal.

Pull and Push Types

Broaching machines are of two kinds: those solely used and designed for broaching; those which serve other purposes as well as broaching. Among the latter are hydraulic and other types of presses. Detailed descriptions of the various machines can be obtained from the manufacturers'

MATERIAL.	TYPE OF WORK			
	ROUND HOLES.	SPLINES.	KEYWAYS.	BUR-NISHING.
	Cutting Speed in Ft. per Min.	Cutting Speed in Ft. per Min.	Cutting Speed in Ft. per Min.	Cutting Speed in Ft. per Min.
Soft Steel	7–10	10–12	12–16	..
Medium Hard Steel	10–15	15–18	18–20	..
Very Hard Steel	6–10	10–12	12–16	10

catalogues. Here we will confine ourselves to one or two of the simpler types.

The standard pull-type of broaching machine (see Fig. 3) comprises a large screw to which is attached an apparatus known as a draw-head (see Fig. 5), to which the broach itself is fixed. By rotating the nut that grips the screw, which is passed through it, the screw is moved forward or backward, according to the direction in which the nut is revolved. Thus, a pulling motion is given to the broach to draw it through or over the work. The extent of the pulling movement is controllable by means of adjustable tappets (pins or studs). A variant on this type of machine is the *duplex*, which enables two broaches to be employed together if necessary.

In another type of pulling machine the draw-head is operated by means, not of a screw and nut, but of a rack and pinion, which is an arrangement of gearing for converting rotary into straight line and reciprocating motion. The pinion wheel has a fixed center and actuates a movable rack, or straight length of toothed gearing.

The pushing machines, operate vertically, and often consist of simple presses. For example, an ordinary punch press can be employed for restricted types of push-broaching operations, while a manually-worked arbor press is often used for light broaching where the quantities required are not large.

In general, push machines are hydraulic in action, and comprise a pump mounted on top of the press, actuating pistons which thrust a ram or plunger downward. The motion is regulated by a valve operated by a lever. Vertical

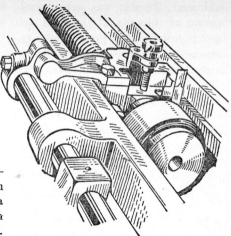

Fig. 5. The broach in a pull-type machine is fixed to a draw-head attached to a large screw, as shown above.

push-broaching machines can also be operated by a screw mechanism and by hand.

Selection of the proper machine for any particular operation is governed mainly by the characteristics of the specific piece to be broached, by the length of the pull or push (termed the stroke) and by the quantity of finished parts required in a given period. For jobbing work of intermittent character, an ordinary-sized horizontal pull-broaching machine is usually adequate. For short runs or single parts often repeated, a medium-sized machine should be used. Where big output is important, single or multiple vertical machines are recommended.

Choosing Steel for Broaches

The choice of the correct steel for the broaches is an important factor in the proper carrying out of the operation. In one instance, broaches made from a high-carbon tool steel had been used for broaching soft mild steel. Trouble was experienced because of chipping of the steel. In another instance, the problem was to broach plain round holes to fine limits in hard cast iron. Yet another difficulty was to find a proper steel for broaches for gun-metal castings, such as brake handles. In this last instance, 3 percent nickel case-hardening steel was tried, and was completely successful, the tools standing up to the work and being in every way more satisfactory than carbon-tool steel broaches. In this connection, while with broaches in which re-grinding is virtually impossible, cutting edges formed in nickel case-hardened steel would perhaps give a reasonable life, and the tough core would reduce risk of fracture, re-grinding to any extent would soon cut through the hardened case and render the teeth useless. Furthermore, uneven case hardening sometimes causes soft spots, while distortion may call for an uneven amount of grinding.

High-speed steel is probably the best all-round material, but is not always the most economical, because broaching speeds are often too low to give this steel full justification.

When Broaching Is Advisable

The following points are worthy of note. The broaching of plain round holes does not, on the whole, prove profitable, assuming that the work has first to go through the lathe. The broaching of holes other than plain holes is highly profitable. The material to be broached must be uniform and must have no gritty or hard places. The broach must be uniformly hard, and have no soft spots.

The heat-treatment of the material to be broached is another factor in broach performance. Some mild-steel broached in a certain shop proved unsatisfactory, being too soft, and tearing or leaving a rough surface. Sometimes the broach itself broke. The mild steel had been bought specially for the job, and to scrap it would have been costly. Instead, it was heat-treated by quenching it in water at 1625 deg. F., when it became quite suitable for the purpose. The carbon content was .1–.2 percent, and the treatment considerably raised the hardness of the steel. In another instance, 1.0 percent carbon steel tore badly, but by heating it to 1418 deg. F. and cooling it in air, it was normalized to such an extent that broaching proved entirely successful. Chrome-vanadium steel has also been heat-treated.

Cutting Keyways

The most common broaching operation is cutting keyways. All that is necessary in the way of set-up for this work is a bushing or sleeve (hollow cylinder) which holds and positions the job, while at the same time acting as a guide for the broach. When the broach is pulled through, it keeps the job firmly in place. When the tool has finished cutting, the job is merely pulled off. The broach is then run out to starting position and another part positioned on the push for the next cut. In broaching round holes, as for example, in steel castings, the job is positioned with the aid of a small plate screwed to the face-plate or face-chuck of the broaching machine. When the cut has been completed, the broach is run out and disconnected from the drawhead to allow the next piece to be positioned.

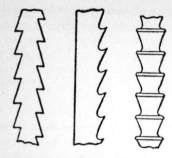

Fig. 6. *Left,* method of staggering teeth for rectangular broaches; *center,* teeth of keyway broach; *right,* teeth of round hole broach.

Broach Teeth

Teeth of broaches of round type are sometimes spirally cut, sometimes cut like a screw-thread and, more commonly, are circular with parallel edges. Rectangular broaches may have their teeth set straight across or in a diagonal pattern. Fig. 6 illustrates a few widely-used types. The pitch or spacing of the teeth may be uniform; or variable, when it is desired to reduce vibration at the cutting edges to a minimum.

There are also broaches for cutting spiral grooves of different types. This type of work is not especially difficult if the machine is adjusted correctly. Usually it is necessary to employ a rotating broach-holder together with a master broach-guide grooved in accordance with the groove to be broached. In other instances the broach is fixed and it is the work that is revolved by being fastened to a holder, which is then rotated in such a manner as to produce the desired spiral.

Broaches themselves are of such widely different and varied types that it is well-nigh impossible to split them into recognizable categories. Nevertheless, the reader should familiarize himself with their general characteristics. Keyway broaches, for example, are, for certain work, tipped with tungsten carbide, brazed on to the main body of the tooth. They will give excellent results when finishing previously tooled surfaces, but will not stand up to heavy roughing broach work. Holes of large diameter are often broached with assembled broaches, comprising a series of short rings or sections fixed on an arbor or shaft. This enables worn sections to be removed and replaced when necessary. Renewable finishing teeth are sometimes given to round broaches.

Burnishing broaches are employed when it is desired to improve the finish of a hole that has previously been bored in the lathe, drilled, or roughly broached. It can also be adopted for giving their correct dimensions and form to slightly warped hollow cylinders or bushings. The teeth of burnishing broaches have no cutting an-

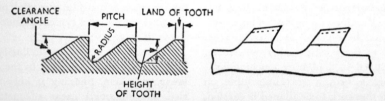

Fig. 7. *Left,* terms used for the various parts of broaches; *right,* the form of tooth used for a spline broach.

gles. The tool is pushed through the work and compresses the internal surface with its teeth, thereby smoothing out all surface irregularities and giving the entire surface a pleasing smooth finish.

Better results will be obtained in practice if broaches are given proper treatment. They should be stored in proper racks and oiled to prevent rust or corrosion. No broach should be put back into the rack in a blunted condition, and it is a good rule to see that the tools are sharpened after each job and before they go back into stock. After a certain period of service, the continual re-grinding will be found to have affected their height and diameter, and any such variation from the original dimensions should be carefully recorded, to obviate the issue of the broach for a job for which it is no longer suitable. The teeth of the broach are the most valuable and delicate part, and should not be allowed to clash against those of other broaches or against other hard, metallic objects. As with milling cutters, broaches should never be removed or placed in position by blows, and the cuttings should be cleared by stream lubrication or an air-blast. If neither of these is available, they can be brushed out with a wire brush.

In re-sharpening broaches, it will be found that the tooth-height eventually decreases. The operator should then grind down the first straight tooth until it has become the last on the taper of the broach, and go on doing this until in the end no more straight teeth are left, after which the tool can be scrapped. These straight teeth which are of uniform dimensions, are generally left at the end of the tapered part of the broach by the manufacturer or designer for this very purpose. The terms used in connection with broaches are clearly indicated in Fig. 7, while this figure also shows the form of the teeth for a spline broach.

PLANING, SHAPING, AND PROFILING

PLANING and shaping are akin in that they both comprise the machining of flat, metallic surfaces by means of tools with only one cutting edge, or what are technically termed single-point cutting tools. Profiling, on the other hand, is a form of milling, and is carried out on the milling machine. Planing can be more closely defined as the removal of material from plane surfaces with the help of cutting tools fixed in a planing machine comprising a bed, a traveling table on which the work to be planed is carried, standards, cross-slide, tool-box, and gearing. Fig. 10 shows, diagrammatically, the arrangement of a planing machine. The metal to be planed is carried under a fixed planing tool, the common forms of which can be seen in Fig. 9. The tool moves only at the end of each cut by a distance equal to the amount of feed. This movement is usually automatic. The essential parts and appearance of a typical planer are shown in Fig. 10.

Shaping has a certain similarity to planing, but differs from it in the following respects. Shaping is only carried out on small areas of metal—usually not above 1 ft. in length, and mostly much less. It is, in short, used

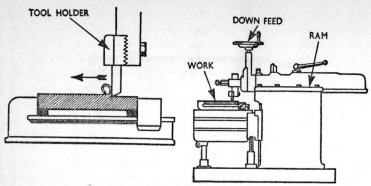

Fig. 8. *Right,* arrangement of a simple shaper shown diagrammatically. The planing tool is fixed and the metal carried beneath it, the tool moving at the end of each cut by a distance equal to the amount of the feed. The action of the tool is shown on the *left;* it is forced across the work in the direction of the arrow by means of a ram. See also Fig. 10.

for parts and pieces not bulky enough for the planing machine. Furthermore, shaping can be and is adapted quite readily to the cutting of convex or concave surfaces. In shaping convex parts, the work is threaded onto an arbor, which is caused to revolve at a low speed. Concave surfaces are shaped by using a tool-holder which has a worm or helical gear working in conjunction with a quadrant—a segment of worm-wheel teeth on the upper portion of the tool-box. By means of this arrangement, the tool is made to revolve slowly through the arc of a circle.

The shaping machine uses tools like those of the planing machine (see Fig. 9). These are carried on a rigid arm or *ram* moving in a horizontal direction (see Fig. 8). The length of the stroke, or distance covered in cutting, can be adjusted by means of a connecting rod movable in a slot in the arm. The larger machines usually have quick-reverse motion, the table being run back to the starting point of a new cut at a higher speed than when cutting, which enables a good deal of

time to be saved. The principle of the quick return motion is shown in Fig. 11. An angle plate is fixed to the front of the shaper, and can be moved either vertically or from side to side. A modern type of shaping machine is shown and its essential parts indicated in Fig. 12.

Profiling is a method of milling identical parts with an irregular form or contour, and is particularly designed for interchangeable parts of machines or appliances such as rifles, typewriters, sewing machines, and the like. In the profiling machine the spindle and milling cutter do not rotate in a fixed position, but are guided

 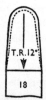 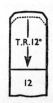

Fig. 9. Common forms of single-point tool used in planing or shaping machines: *left to right,* round-nosed tool, stub-nosed tool, finishing tool.

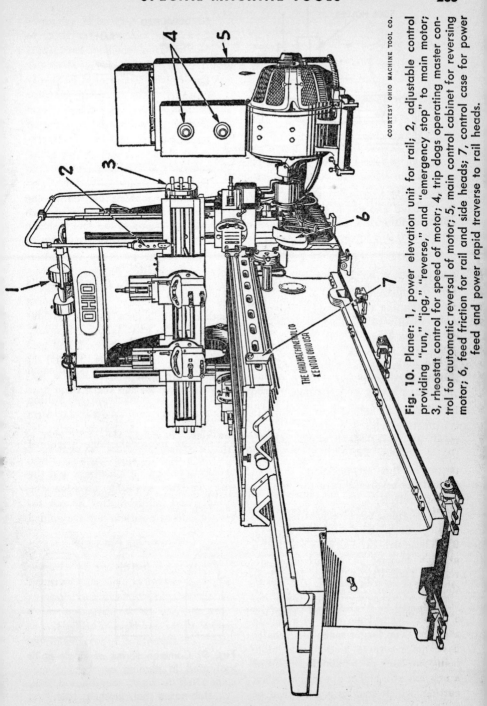

COURTESY OHIO MACHINE TOOL CO.

Fig. 10. Planer: 1, power elevation unit for rail; 2, adjustable control providing "run," "jog," "reverse," and "emergency stop" to main motor; 3, rheostat control for speed of motor; 4, trip dogs operating master control for automatic reversal of motor; 5, main control cabinet for reversing motor; 6, feed friction for rail and side heads; 7, control case for power feed and power rapid traverse to rail heads.

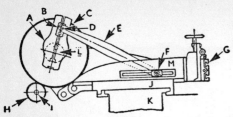

Fig. 11. This diagram shows the principle of the quick-return motion for large planing machines. *A*, crank-plate; *B*, crank-pin; *C*, geared spur-wheel disc; *D*, stroke adjustment; *E*, connecting rod; *F*, slot for ram adjustment; *G*, tool-holder; *H*, pinion; *I*, driving shaft; *J*, saddle; *K*, bed; *L*, fixed pin; *M*, ram. See text.

by a former pin which is held against and follows a template or guideblock whose contour is a precise copy of that required in the finished part. Profiling machines are sometimes manually fed, but semi-automatic or full automatic machines are also available. The spindle of these machines is vertical.

We may now consider the specific functions of these three types of machining. Planing and shaping overlap to some extent, but in general it can be said that planing is essential for large work, where the plane surfaces to be machined go the long way of the part. If the job is of small dimensions, whether to use planer or shaper will depend mainly on the quantity of parts required. Odd jobs are usually given to the shaper and machined one at a time, but if the quantity is larger, it is quite a common practice to place them one after the other in a long row or *string* as it is termed, and use the large planing machine, which machines one piece after the other with the one stroke.

Advantages of Shaping Machines

The milling machine can also be employed for very large quantities,

but if castings are to be machined it will be essential for them to be free from sand or hard spots if the miller is used, as otherwise the cutter teeth may be badly damaged. The shaping machine is more compact, simpler and cheaper to work, and speedier in operation on small work; is economical in tool outlay and maintenance; and is not expensive to buy. The planer and shaper are, in short, jobbing machines; the profiler is essentially a mass-production machine.

A few constructional details may help the reader to grasp the differences more easily. Planing machines are usually driven by helical or spiral gears which engage with a sloping toothed rack housed in the machine bed below the work-table. A diagrammatic illustration of the rack and gear principle is shown in Fig. 13. All the controls are grouped in such a way that the operator can reach them from the one side, thus saving the time that would be taken up if he had to keep walking around to the other side of the machine. Pressure lubrication is adopted for modern machines, and hydraulic feed is common. Electric drive is employed in most of the more modern machines.

Draw-Cut Machine

Shapers can be driven by means of a crank or by a hydraulic cylinder. A third type, termed the *draw-cut* cuts the job in the direction of the body of the machine. This is the reverse of the other types, which cut with the work moving away from the body. In other words, the job is drawn in rather than thrust out. This type is used chiefly for heavy work.

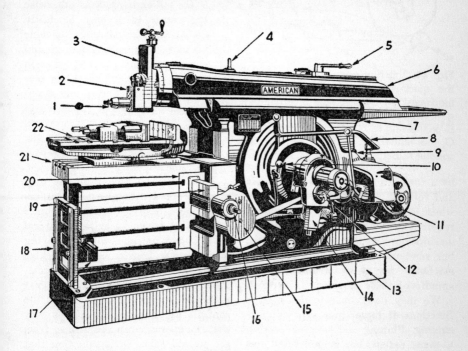

Fig. 12. A modern shaper. 1, tool post; 2, clapper box; 3, head; 4, ram adjuster; 5, ram clamp; 6, ram; 7, column; 8, clutch and brake lever; 9, gear shift lever; 10, back gear shift lever; 11, stroke adjuster; 12, feed adjuster; 13, base; 14, feed rocker arm; 15, feed box; 16, hand traverse for table; 17, automatic sag compensator; 18, table support; 19, rail; 20, saddle; 21, plain box table; 22, vise.

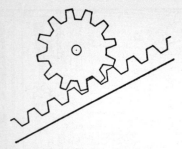

Fig. 13. Diagrammatic illustration showing rack and gear principles as applied to planing machines.

Profilers of the modern type have two spindles, each with a former-pin or guide-pin placed at a set distance from the cutter. This pin is guided about the template by feeding the cutter slide and pin sideways and the work-table longitudinally. The cutters are generally of small diameter and rotate at a high speed.

Holding Devices

Many forms and dimensions of jobs are planed, and holding devices are consequently numerous, some being of general type capable of holding down a wide range of work onto the work-table. Others are special fixtures made for particular jobs. The latter are, as a rule, employed only when there is a sufficient number of parts to be planed identically to warrant the cost of their special manufacture or purchase.

Planer vises of fixed or swiveling type are sometimes used, and the work can also be held between centers, though this is seldom done. Mostly, however, in the normal planing machine the work is secured to the planer work-table. Correct clamping-down of the job when setting up calls for the exercise of both skill and intelligence.

Bolts, blocks, clamps, and shims, which are metal plates, are all employed at different times, or in combination, according to the work. The essential thing in setting up for the planer is to prevent the job from *springing* as a result of too great a clamping pressure, or lack of adequate support at a particular point. This will almost certainly result in distortion of the piece and inaccurate work in consequence.

To insure absence of spring, every part of the job must be clamped down firmly. A tap with a small hammer—usually the type known as a babbitt hammer, or babbitt—if given in advance of actual clamping will generally enable the operator to detect by the kind of ringing tone he hears where the part is not firmly clamped down. At such points support must be afforded by packing blocks or shims inserted under the focal points of clamp pressure or elsewhere. The job must be held so firmly that it does not move when the tool begins its cut, or during the entire length of the cutting stroke.

In setting up jobs on the planer, damage to the work-table must also be avoided. Damage is always possible if a heavy casting or forging is dropped or clumsily handled. Solid

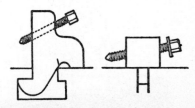

Fig. 14. *Left,* arrangement of a solid stop for the work-table of a planer for the purpose of reducing spring in heavy cutting. *Right,* the correct way of using a poppet in planing.

stops in the work-table (see Fig. 14) at the end of the work will likewise reduce spring in heavy cutting by taking the lateral tool-thrust. The correct method of using a poppet for planing is also shown in Fig. 14.

An interesting planing job is shown in Fig. 15. This is the machining of a large coupling shaft for the central drive of a tube-grinding mill for cement manufacture. Here the seatings are being planed. The shafts are of forged steel, 15 in. in diameter. The coupling ways are roughed out to shape by hand control of the tool in the machine, and are then finished as follows.

The shaft is supported at the ends on angle brackets in which a 2½-in. hole has been bored, a 2½-in. spigot or pin having been turned on each edge of the shaft. This allows the shaft to be rotated clear of the work-

Fig. 15. Machining a large coupling shaft in a planer for the central drive of a tube-grinding mill for cement manufacture.

table. A pair of clips is attached to the forging, and a loose link is fastened to the clips at one end, and at the other to a hand-operated screw, bolted to the planer table, and en-

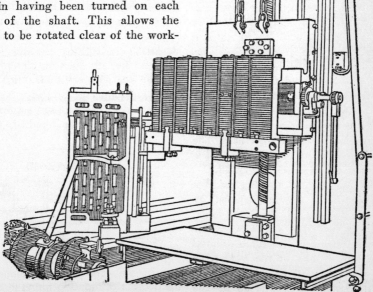

Fig. 16. Planing manganese steel lining plates which have been cast too wide. A corner of each has to be removed in the vertical planer.

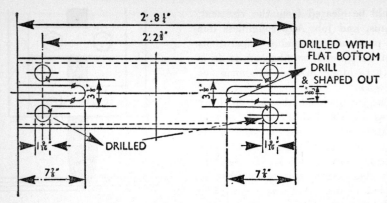

Fig. 17. This illustration shows a job in which it is necessary for hard steel scraper bars to be both planed and shaped. See also Fig. 17a.

abling the shaft to be rotated at a suitable speed.

Planing Lining Plates

Another typical job is the planing of manganese-steel lining plates which have been cast too wide, so that it is necessary to remove a corner on each plate in a vertical planer (see Fig. 16). These castings are machined at 11 ft. per minute with $\frac{1}{16}$ in. cut and $\frac{1}{32}$ in. feed. The lining plates themselves are 2 ft. 6 in. long and $1\frac{1}{2}$ in. thick. The tools used for this job are of superhigh-speed steel containing cobalt. Figs. 17 and 17a show a job in which it is necessary both to plane and to shape hard steel scraper bars. The correct position of the planing tool is important and is shown in Fig. 18.

Most jobs for the shaping machine are gripped in a vise fastened by bolts to the top of the work-table, though if too large or awkward for the vise, they are sometimes secured to the top or sides of the work-table or to an angle-plate or similar clamping attachment. In setting up for the shaper, the vise bottom should be tested to make sure that it is parallel,

and then the jaw, to make sure that it is square. Badly-grooved or battered vise-jaws must be replaced or restored. This trouble can be prevented by interposing a strip of soft metal or pasteboard between jaws and work. Lack of squareness in the vise-jaws means that the work will not fit squarely in the vise, and in consequence will not be squarely planed. If the jaw should prove to be out of square, it can be easily rectified by inserting or affixing packing pieces.

Tending the Shaping Machine

The machine itself should be kept clean and well-lubricated. Chips

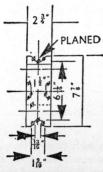

Fig. 17a. Sectional view of the job shown in Fig. 17.

should be cleared from the vise-seat, clamps, and job. Any roughness due to previous machining operations must be ground or filed off if it is likely to hinder correct alignment of the work.

The job should be bedded down by means of the babbitt (soft metal) hammer, and not with a wrench. It must never be hammered, but only tapped, into position. Excessively tight clamping of thin work must be avoided, or distortion may result. The work-table must be freed from chips and dirt before a vise is put back for resetting. If the tool is being set to a completed surface, precautions must be taken to insure that the tool-block, which holds the tool-post and tool, is firmly bedded down. A thin tissue paper should be inserted beneath the cutting point, and the tool gently lowered until it just nips the tissue.

Length of Stroke

If the work is irregular in form, it is essential that both top and bottom of the arm or *ram* should not touch the job, throughout either the full extent of the cutting stroke or the entire width of the cut. In setting for horizontal work, the length of the stroke should be regulated for about .75 in. longer than the job. The stroke should also be positioned so that .5 in.

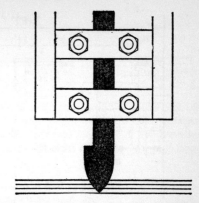

Fig. 18. In planing, the correct position of the tool is important. It should be arranged as here shown.

of this additional length is at the start of the cut, so as to let the tool-block bed correctly for the following cut. A long longitudinal stroke is more economical in time and power consumption than a short transverse stroke, because there is less wasted effort, the tool being idle, or non-cutting, over a much smaller area.

A typical shaping job is the surfacing of rectangular pieces. To carry out this operation, one of the longer sides of the rectangle should first be planed. This machined side is then utilized as a bed or seat against the fixed jaw of the vise, and the second side (see Fig. 19) machined.

Assuming that proper attention has been paid to the accuracy of the vise and the freedom of side 1 from roughness, and to the accurate bedding of the block or rectangle in the vise, these two sides should now be completely square with one another. The second finished surface is then bedded down on the vise-bottom with No. 1 once more against the fixed jaw, a rod or strip being now inserted between jaw and surface. The vise is then screwed up, and the block is lightly

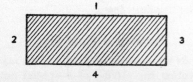

Fig. 19. In surfacing rectangular pieces the sides are planed in the order indicated above. See detailed description of these operations in the text.

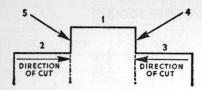

Fig. 20. When shaping a tongue, after roughing cuts have been taken, side 1 is machined first in finishing, and then sides 2 and 3, working inward from the outer edges.

tapped down in the vise to bed it down accurately on the vise-bottom. Side 3 is then planed, and should have edges parallel with those of side 2 and square with those of side 1. Side 1 is then bedded on suitable parallels. (Parallels are rectangular pieces of iron or steel much longer than wide and thick. Their adjacent sides are square and their opposite sides parallel. They are made in different sizes, and are used for the purpose of lifting the job to the desired height in the vise.)

The vise is again screwed up, but no rod is this time interposed between work and jaws, and the job is bedded down by light tapping as before. Side 4 is then planed.

For shaping a tongue, roughing cuts are first taken, bringing the cut reasonably near to the finished dimensions. A standard round-nosed shaping tool (see Fig. 9) should be used for this preliminary work. For finishing,

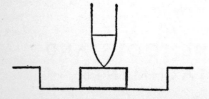

Fig. 21. If a size-gauge block is used in tongue-shaping, surfaces 2 and 3 (Fig. 21) are machined first, then surface 1.

a square-nosed tool (see Fig. 9) is employed. If the shoulder is less than .5 in. in height, the tool-block and clapper box—together commonly termed the *apron*—are held vertical, but if the shoulder is above this height, a right-hand or left-hand shoulder tool should be employed, with the apron turned in the correct direction; and the tool is then fed downward and side 1 (Fig. 20) is first machined. The tool is now lowered, and sides 2 and 3 are next shaped, working inward from the outer edges (Fig. 20). If downward graduated feed is not used, but a rec-

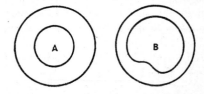

Fig. 22. In this example of profiling the plain ring A is machined to the shape shown at B; the final result is described as a formed ring.

tangular block of the right height is interposed to serve as a guide or gauge (see Fig. 21) in adjusting the feed of the tool, surfaces 2 and 3 are first machined, and the tool is then adjusted to the gauge block and put to work on surface 1. The vertical surfaces 4 and 5 are cut by setting the head at 0 precisely, making sure that the tool will not come in contact with the work on the return stroke, and then feeding down.

Profiling a Plain Ring

As an example of profiling, we may mention the cutting of a special outline or form on the internal surface of a plain ring. The ring (Fig. 22) is gripped under a clamp with a forked extremity, and is positioned by pins

PLANING SPEEDS FOR STEEL TOOLS

MATERIAL.	TYPE OF WORK	SPEED IN FT. PER MIN.	FEED IN IN.
Aluminum	General	60–100	$\frac{1}{32}$–$\frac{1}{20}$
Brass	"	50–90	$\frac{1}{20}$–$\frac{1}{16}$
Bronze	"	50–90	$\frac{1}{20}$–$\frac{1}{16}$
Cast Iron	Roughing	40–60	$\frac{1}{8}$–$\frac{1}{4}$
	Finishing	20–40	$\frac{1}{4}$–$\frac{1}{2}$
Gun-metal	General	50–90	$\frac{1}{20}$–$\frac{1}{16}$
Mild Steel	Roughing	30–65	$\frac{1}{16}$–$\frac{3}{16}$
	Finishing	20–40	$\frac{1}{4}$–1
Steel Castings	Roughing	30–45	$\frac{1}{16}$
	Finishing	20–40	$\frac{1}{32}$–$\frac{3}{16}$
Wrought Iron	Roughing	30–50	$\frac{1}{16}$–$\frac{3}{16}$
	Finishing	20–40	$\frac{1}{4}$–1

inserted in three holes. The guide-pin held in the head to which the cutter is secured has the former guide below it. The transverse movement of the head combined with the reciprocating motion of the work-table enables the guide-pin to trace the required form in the former, and so cause the cutter operating at an unchangeable distance from the pin to trace the required form on the inner side of the ring.

The principle will easily be grasped if one images two pencils connected together by a short rod, one of which is set to trace the interior shape of a ring, while the other automatically traces an identical shape on a piece of paper.

General instructions on setting up and using the profiling machine can be learned from the Milling section (Chapter 6) where other milling machines are discussed.

Speeds and feeds are, of course, important for all these operations, and while conditions vary from shop to shop, making specific recommendations difficult, some figures may serve as a rough guide. For planing with high-speed steel tools the Table is a guide.

The speeds and feeds for profiling are very much akin to those for milling, and a Table that may be used as a rough guide is given on page 215. At the same time it must be repeated that these speeds and feeds are merely working averages, and are inevitably modified by actual conditions in the workshop.

SPECIAL MACHINE TOOLS AND MACHINE ATTACHMENTS

IN ADDITION to the various types of machine tools and machining operations described in previous sections, there are a large number of special machines designed for special purposes. It is, of course, impossible

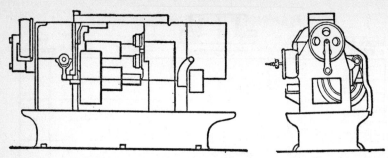

Fig. 23. View of a multiple-tool lathe. Machines such as these may be of *chucking* or of *bar* type, and have usually four spindles.

within the limits of this book to describe in detail every single tool of this type. An attempt will, however, be made to deal with a number of the more important machines, many of which incorporate features of one or other of the machines already discussed.

Multiple-tool lathes may be taken as one example. These are of two types: the *chucking* and the *bar* type. These lathes usually have four spindles, and were originally developed for the rapid production of parts from bars fed through spindles. The need for higher output of separate parts such as castings, stampings, etc., led to a modification of this type of machine for the work in which there is a saving of floor-space, as compared

with that required by machines having a single spindle only.

In principle, these machines have rotating spindles, opposite to which is a main tool-slide, upon which are mounted tool-boxes or holders for end-cutting tools, such as drills, reamers, recessing tools, and boring bars. In simultaneous operation with the end-cutting tools are two cross-slides, one at the front and one at the back of the machine, for forming and facing.

In one type, the four work-spindles are mounted in a carrier, which revolves and is located at 90 deg. in synchronism with the timing of the tool-slides. As, therefore, all tools operate simultaneously on four components, a completely machined part is produced at each quarter revolution of

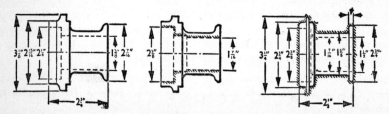

Fig. 24. Producing hub shells from steel forgings on a multiple-tool lathe. In the first operation, the register is turned on a standard lathe for locating in the special chucks for the second operation, which is boring the three diameters on a special boring and facing machine. In the third operation, on a four-spindle automatic chucking machine, the outside of the hub shell is completely machined and the bore recess at the small end finished.

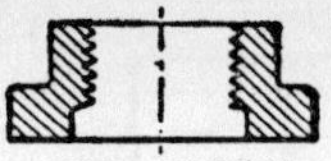

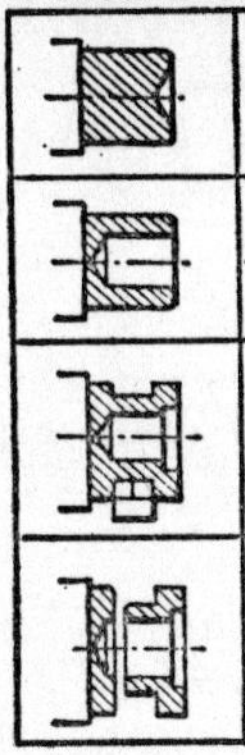

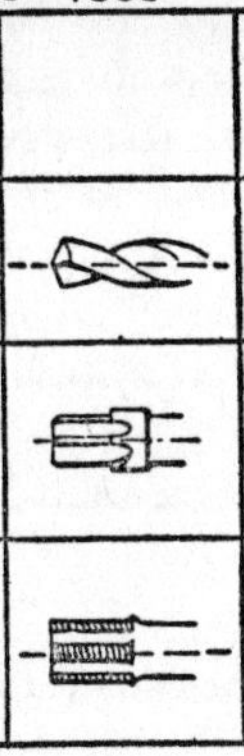

WORK SPINDLE & CROSS SLIDE	END TOOL	TOOL STATION	CROSS SLIDE	END TOOL	TOOL STATION
		4	(FEED STOCK)		4
		1		DRILL	1
		2	FORM	RECESS & BORE COMBINED TOOL	12
		3	PART OFF	TAP	3

Fig. 25. This shows the sequence of operations for producing the component illustrated above. The work is done on a four-spindle bar-type automatic lathe.

the spindle carrier. This method of machining undoubtedly minimizes idle time, that is, time during which the machine is not at work. The expression "4½ in." applied to a machine of this type signifies that it will turn bars up to 4½ in. in diameter. The principal function is to produce automatically components from forgings, steel blanks, or castings.

According to the character of the blank or casting, the work spindles can be equipped with mechanically-operated chucks, scroll chucks (a type of universal chuck whose jaws are actuated by a scroll-type gear), or expanding collets (discs or rings by which the tool is held fast). When provided with efficient chucking arrangements and proper tools, these machines are capable of highly accurate production, as well as high output.

Fig. 23 shows one view of the machine, while Fig. 24 shows the operations in the production of hub shells from steel forgings on this type of lathe.

It should be borne in mind that, unlike a turret lathe, where the tools operate in single progression—one after the other, successively—in these lathes and those of *bar* type it is the work-spindles that are successively applied to the fixed tool stations. For those not familiar with this class of machine, its principle may be broadly explained by reference to Fig. 25, which shows the sequence of operations for the production of the component illustrated. In this diagram, the four work-spindles (which by the rotation of their carrier are applied successively to each tool station) are shown as if located in a vertical plane. The first station is the bottom rear spindle seen in the illustration.

The machine in which this operation is carried out is a four-spindle bar-type automatic machine.

Roll Turning

Another interesting type of tool is the roll-turner's lathe. During the last few years rapid developments have taken place in the design and construction of roll-turning lathes, for turning rolls used in rolling steel, etc., and these have been brought about principally by the use of tungsten-carbide cutting tools. The old type of lathe for roll turning had a piano-board tool-rest. This was not entirely suitable for tungsten-carbide tools, owing to the manner in which the tools are fed into the work by means of wedges driven by hammers. The sudden shock of a cut being put on by this method would break many tungsten-carbide tools, which are expensive. Lathes designed for these tools differ considerably, therefore, from the older type. The first development has been to apply saddles with compound slides to the lathe-bed, so that the tool can be fed in gradually when dealing with rolls for rolling sections, known as section rolls. Automatic longitudinal traverse is applied to the tool for turning plain rolls—those with no special

form, and mainly cylindrical. A characteristic lathe of this type is shown in Fig. 26, which shows a lathe with a three-shear bed, shears being the parts that take the saddles. A modern roll-lathe is virtually a heavy-duty roughing lathe. It is not possible to standardize any one type of machine for roll turning, as conditions vary in each individual instance. Fig. 27 shows the type of plain roll dealt with by these machines, and also shows a more complicated roll.

Operations Involved

With the first type, the operation comprises rough turning the wobbler diameter, the wobbler being the driving end of the roll. The necks of the roll are then turned, these being the ends that revolve on the bearings. The roll is then radiused, finished, and undercut for grinding-wheel clearance. The body is next finished for grinding. A chamfered or beveled finish is then

Fig. 26. The roll-turner's lathe is specially designed for tungsten-carbide tools. Saddles with compound slides are applied to the lathe-bed so that the tool can be fed in gradually when dealing with section rolls.

given where required, and the wobbler at the right-hand end is faced. As an example of the time saved by the modern type of lathe, this operation formerly took 170 hours, as against 22.25 hours with the new lathes, for a roll weighing about 26 tons.

In turning the more complicated rolls shown in Fig. 27 the first operation comprises finishing the machining of wobbler and necks, which is followed by finish machining the radius and the lengths. This type of roll is usually made as a steel casting. Whereas a 43-in. and 20-in. diameter roll dealt with on the old lathe took 257 hours of machining time, with the new type lathe, this same job was carried out in the short space of 40 hours of machining time.

Automatic Tappers

Reference has been made earlier to the multiple-spindle lathes. Equally interesting are the automatic tapping

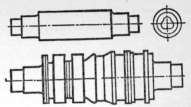

Fig. 27. Samples of work dealt with by roll-turning lathes: *above*, a plain roll; *below*, a more complicated type.

machines. These are of various types. In one, for example the container of the feeding magazine and feeding channel are filled with nuts to be tapped (to be given their screw-threads), a number of blanks of tapped nuts being placed on the shank of the tap so as to guide the tap in the holder. When the machine is in motion, a feeding device conveys the nuts into position for tapping.

The finished nuts travel along the shank of the tap until they are ejected. The spindles of this type of machine are double, but operate independently of each other, so that it is possible for

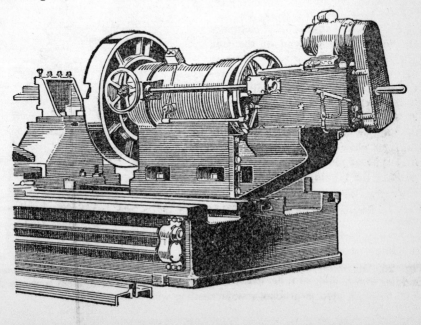

Fig. 28. Typical tap for screw-threading nuts as used in an automatic tapping or threading machine.

work to proceed on one spindle while any necessary adjustments are being made on the other; alternatively, the machine can be used for tapping two different jobs at the same time, one on each spindle. A change over from one size to another is quickly carried out.

Another form of nut-tapping machine has four to six spindles, sloping at an angle of 30 deg. from the vertical, and operating simultaneously. There are twice as many fixtures as spindles, which means that while the nuts in one lot of fixtures are being tapped, the remainder can be charged with fresh work. As soon as one batch is completed, the alternate carriages are moved into line with the spindles and fed by foot-treadle into the taps. As the taps enter the work, the lead of the thread automatically continues the feed. When the end of the hole is attained, the tap is reversed so as to remove it from the hole, but reversed at double the speed with which it did its cutting, thus saving time. Fig. 28 shows a typical tap for use in a tapping or threading machine, while Fig. 29 shows the magazine of the first type of machine with the nut in position for tapping.

Engraving Machines

The engraving machine is employed in many modern workshops for engraving, either sunk or in relief, in any material that can be cut, from soft wood to cast steel. Flat or cylin-drical work can be engraved, and by means of a forming attachment, work with irregular surfaces may be dealt with. The copy is clamped to a copy-holder, and is followed by hand with a tracer held in a lever which controls the movement of the cutter. The size of the engraving may be from one-third to one-sixteenth that of the copy. The machines are usually driven electrically, and many of them embody a cutter-grinding attachment, although a separate cutter grinding machine can be purchased if the amount of work justifies it. The machine consists essentially of a work-table, a *fence* for squaring the work on the table, a pair of work-holding dogs and bolts, which are clamping devices, a circular copy-holder, and the driving band. Other attachments, such as a direct-copying attachment, a circular table, a machine vise, etc., can also be obtained. Such a machine is illustrated on page 279.

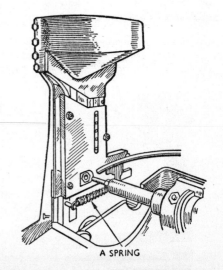

A SPRING

Fig. 29. Magazine of a nut-tapping machine of the type described in the text. The nut is shown in position ready for tapping.

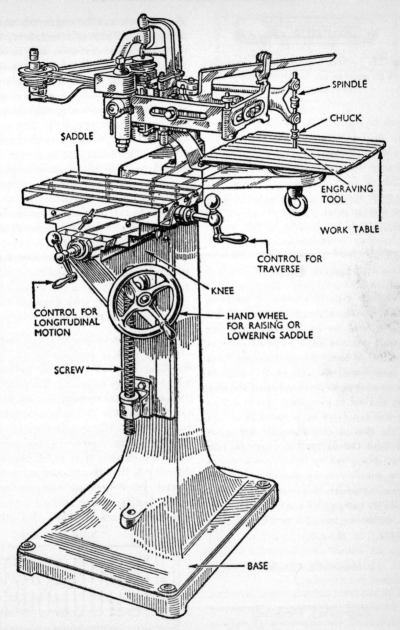

SPINDLE

CHUCK

SADDLE

ENGRAVING
TOOL

WORK TABLE

CONTROL FOR
TRAVERSE

KNEE

CONTROL FOR
LONGITUDINAL
MOTION

HAND WHEEL
FOR RAISING OR
LOWERING SADDLE

SCREW

BASE

Fig. 30. Engraving machines of this kind can be used for engraving any material that can be cut, from wood to cast steel. They can be used for flat, cylindrical, or irregularly-surfaced work.

Fig. 31. Samples of the type of work that can be produced by the engraving machine (*above*) and the electric etcher (*below*).

Electric Etcher

Another type of engraving machine is the electric etcher, which is used for etching trademarks, lettering, and figures. It adjusts itself automatically to the level of the surface being marked, so that round as well as flat objects can be etched without the need for any special skill in operation. Even marking without burr or roughness at the edges, and uniform depth are provided by the better machines of this class. The machine itself has a work-table which can be moved longitudinally, vertically or transversely. Fig. 31 shows samples of work produced by the engraving machine and the electric etcher.

Magnetic Chucks

The modern machine tool has had its uses and advantages enormously amplified by the invention of various attachments enabling it to carry out its work with greater ease and efficiency, or to undertake operations otherwise impossible. The industrial historian of the future, in his analysis of the various relations between new sources of power and new inventions to utilize these sources, may have a paragraph or two on the magnetic chuck. This relatively small feature of the modern machine shop is not much more than 25 years old, any magnetic chucks used before that date being employed only for small surface grinders in tool-rooms. Little power was needed to drive these, and dry grinding was often the rule, so that the primitive magnetic chucks were not faced with the problem of maintaining the work in position during heavy cuts, nor of withstanding the heavy volumes of water which are encountered today in grinding operations.

Contending with Some of the Difficulties

The modern magnetic chuck has to maintain work in position on machines weighing over 50 tons and having a wheel-drive up to 60 h.p. Forty to 50 gallons of water or cutting compounds are common. The chuck has, therefore, not only to withstand this water, but also to resist effectively the power machines of this type exert. Another difficulty is that the discontinuous segmental grinding ring has not only made possible wider cutting surfaces and heavier cuts, but has also intro-

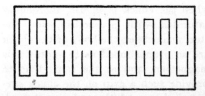

Fig. 32. Working face of a heavy-duty magnetic chuck of one-piece construction. The chuck-face plate is in one piece and is slotted to form the poles. The pole-faces are not separated.

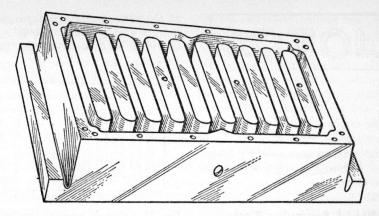

Fig. 33. Magnetic chucks are built of high-permeability steel castings and forgings. In this casting the heavy magnetic cores can be seen.

duced by its intermittent cutting action great vibratory stresses on the chuck face that tend to cause its disintegration.

One-Piece Construction

The most modern magnetic chucks for heavy duty have *one-piece* construction of the working face (see Fig. 32). The essence of this one-piece construction is that the chuck-face plate is in one piece, slotted to form the poles. The pole-faces are not separated, and are not held together by non-magnetic metal. The small bridges of steel connecting any individual pole with the rest of the pole-face are, when the chuck is in use, thoroughly saturated with magnetism, and the steel magnets on the body of the chuck are so proportioned as to supply this magnetism, and at the same time to provide such a grip on the chuck surface as has not hitherto been attained. The pole-face is carefully jointed to the chuck body, and the whole is impervious to moisture, which would destroy the windings.

Construction of Chuck

Apart from cover and windings, the chucks are built of high-permeability steel castings and steel forgings. Fig. 33 shows a typical magnet-steel chuck casting showing the heavy magnetic cores.

The holding power of a magnetic chuck in lb. per sq. in. depends on both the shape of the piece and its section and on the type of chuck. Small sections will have only a light hold.

Planing and Milling

Planing and milling can be effectively carried out with magnetic chucks wherever the pieces to be operated upon are thick enough and have a big enough area to carry the necessary magnetism. On a mild steel bar 4 in. by $1\frac{1}{4}$ in. by 48 in. long, a cut $\frac{5}{8}$ in. deep by $\frac{3}{16}$ in. feed was taken on a planing machine, setting-up time being almost entirely eliminated. Chucks for the largest sizes of machines are made to embody great holding power, perfect rigidity, absence of residual magnetism, and perfect protection for the windings. Water and cutting compounds can be used in any quantity. For the small and medium-sized machines, the chucks are lighter in construction, lower in height, and are not fitted with projections by which they may be mechanically lifted. For dealing with taper work, a chuck can be obtained carried on a sub-base hinged at one end with a screw adjustment at the other.

Use of Supporting Blocks

For pieces presenting great difficulty on ordinary magnetic chucks, such as those requiring the vertical support of parallels (thin and narrow strips and parts that offer a small area of contact against the chuck face), another type of chuck is manufactured. By the use of supporting blocks of parallel or angular section, a large variety of work can be securely held and machined to a minute degree of accuracy. For grinding angular or taper pieces, as in flat siding, edging and beveling

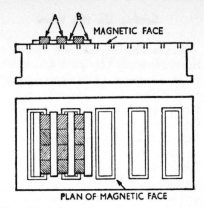

Fig. 35. Soft steel supports may be used, as here, to carry the magnetism up to the work and thus support the variously shaped articles.

the work, for flat-facing an angle block, grinding the V of an angle block, etc., a swiveled magnetic steel chuck is also obtainable. Circular magnetic chucks for holding a large number of small pieces are supplied, and used for holding slender rings, discs, and work usually ground concentrically. Special chucks for piston rings are also made, as well as chucks for the small surface-grinding machines.

Magnetic Holding

When setting up work on a magnetic chuck, it is useful to understand the principles of magnetic holding. A magnet will only attract metals that can be magnetized, such as iron, steel, and some of the alloy steels. Non-ferrous metals cannot be used on a magnetic chuck. The working face of a magnetic chuck is made up of north and south poles, separated by strips of white metal or brass, and the work, when placed upon it, connects the poles together and acts as a *keeper* or retainer of the magnetism. There is no electricity on the chuck face.

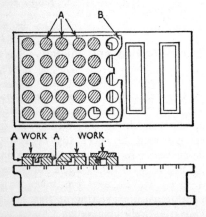

Fig. 34. Small pieces, such as the discs here shown, can be held by using a thin perforated plate of brass or iron which will locate them on the pole edges.

Setting Up the Work

The surface of the work resting on the chuck should be quite flat, with as large an area in actual contact as possible. Large, thick pieces hold much more firmly than small thin ones, as they can carry much more magnetism from one pole to the other. This should be kept in mind when dealing with light work. Convex surfaces, or castings whose work-face has a slight projection in the middle so that it rocks, cannot be safely ground on a magnetic chuck. Small strips will hold better if placed along the pole edges (over the white metal), instead of across, thereby carrying more magnetism from pole to pole. Packing strips of soft iron or mild steel may be placed between the pieces, and will be found very useful when the work has poor magnetic qualities. Very small pieces may be successfully held by using a thin perforated plate, which will locate them on the pole edges. This may be of brass or iron, but not thicker than about $\frac{3}{32}$ in. if the latter. Fig. 34 shows small discs supported in this way.

Many articles of diverse shape can be secured by using soft steel supports to carry the magnetism up to the work. The supports must not cross the white-metal lines—this is important. Several instances are shown in Fig. 35.

Testing a Chuck

If the work does not hold securely, clear the surface of the chuck, turn the switch on and test the pull by placing a small piece of soft steel across the white-metal lines. The steel can be held in the hand, and moved from pole to pole, so that every one is tested. This will indicate whether the chuck

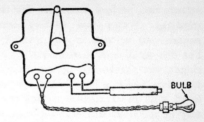

Fig. 36. Showing how a lamp may be connected to the switch terminals for testing the wiring of a magnetic chuck.

is fully magnetized. The piece should hold firmly across all the white-metal lines. If it does, the trouble is not with the chuck. Except in extreme cases of wear on the top face, magnetic chucks do not weaken if the current supply is maintained at the proper voltage. If the current is taken from a small dynamo, the voltage should be checked. A variation of 10 percent from the normal will make little difference. All being well, the cause, should the work continue to slip, is due to different grinding conditions. The surface must not be flat, or glazing grinding wheels may heat the work and cause distortion, which would involve consequent instability of the work.

If there is no magnetism in the chuck face when the switch is first turned on, test the outside wiring to see if the current is reaching it. This needs only an electric lamp, a lamp-holder and a short piece of thin flexible wire. Connect the lamp, of the same voltage as the chuck, to the switch terminals (marked *chuck*), as shown in Fig. 36. If the lamp lights, the trailing cable must be at fault. Remove the terminal-box cover and connect the lamp to the chuck terminals. Plug the trailing cable into the switch and turn on. If there is no light, the cable is broken. If lamp lights and there is still no magnetism, the chuck is wrong and should be returned for investigation. If only part of the chuck is magnetized and there are *dead* poles, do not use it, as dangerous overheating may occur.

Make sure that the current is switched off when you are making the connections for these tests.

In setting up rectangular chucks, make sure that table and underside of the chuck are clean and free from dents and bruises, so that the chuck will be perfectly flat. Large chucks sometimes do not lie quite flat at once, having been slightly distorted in transit, but if left for a few hours they will *lie down* if the machine table is perfectly flat. The chucks need clamping down only at the ends, and suitable clamps are usually provided. The bolts should not be tightened too severely, or the machine table will be distorted and the chuck unable to expand as it warms up. A good plan is to make it firm at one end, and have less pressure at the other.

Circular Magnetic Chucks

Circular chucks are secured to the machine spindle as are mechanical chucks, and if properly mounted will run perfectly true. Some chucks, particularly those for vertical spindles, have a rubber gasket on the underside to prevent water passing to the spindle hole. When fitting these to their face-plates, do not turn the chuck while there is any pressure on the rubber ring, or it may be destroyed. If the hold-down bolts and their respective holes do not coincide, lift the chuck until the rubber is free, and then turn to the right position. If the chuck has its current collecting rings on its underface, the carbon brush-gear should be adjusted so that the carbons fit centrally, one on each ring. The carbon holders should be close to the chuck rings and not more than $\frac{1}{16}$ in. away. This will give the maximum of life to the carbon.

Adjusting Carbons

When the collector rings are separate from the chuck, they should be fitted into the opposite end of the spindle to the chuck and made to run absolutely true. The carbons should then be adjusted to the rings as indicated in Fig. 37. A two-pin plug and a twin wire

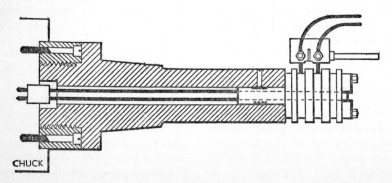

CHUCK

Fig. 37. Fitting the collector rings to a chuck. The rings are fitted into the end of the spindle opposite to the chuck and the carbons adjusted to the rings as here indicated. The two-pin plug must be pushed firmly into the socket on the chuck.

cable are provided, and the former must be pushed firmly into the socket on the rear of the chuck and the ends of the cables connected to the terminals on the slip-rings. This is clearly shown in Fig. 37.

Taper Attachments

Other attachments include the taper attachment for the turning of accurate tapers on parts. These attachments are usually firmly bolted to the rear of the lathe-bed or to the rear of the carriage. A relieving attachment is an apparatus attached to lathes for the purpose of regulating the movement of the cutting tool so as to give the necessary clearance or relief to the cutting edges of tools, such as dies, taps, hobs, etc. Relieving is performed at a lower speed than ordinary turn-

ing, and for this reason some lathes are provided with a sub-headstock to enable the speed to be reduced.

Automatic Turning Forms

Automatic feeding devices for turning forms in accordance with prepared templates constitute a further type of tool attachment. Lathe centers for supporting the work to be machined are normally made of solid hard-cast tool steel. The center in the headstock revolves with the job. The center in the tailstock, on the other hand, remains stationary as the job revolves, and needs lubrication. The latest practice to prevent any possibility of friction due to the high speeds causing the center to burn is to use a live or anti-friction bearing center running on ball bearings or tapered roller bearings.

CHAPTER 8

GEARS AND GEAR-CUTTING

TYPES OF GEARS, THEIR USES. GEAR-TRAIN RATIOS. DEFINITIONS OF TERMS. PITCHES. FORMULA. GEAR-CUTTING MACHINES. THE GENERATING PRINCIPLE. CROSSED-AXIS SHAVING. WORM MANUFACTURE. ACCURACY TESTS. MATERIALS. LUBRICATION.

T HE term *gear* may be used in engineering for almost any kind of mechanism, but it refers especially to a toothed wheel. A pair of toothed wheels carried on separate shafts and having the teeth meshing together form a convenient means of causing one shaft to drive the other at an exact speed ratio. There are many types of toothed gear, but the relation between the speeds of two shafts carrying meshing gears is found in the same manner in every case.

Let Rd = Speed of the driving gear in revolutions per minute

Rn = Speed of the driven gear in revolutions per minute

Nd = Number of teeth in the driving gear

Nn = Number of teeth in the driven gear

Then $Rn = Rd \dfrac{Nd}{Nn}$

The speed of the driven gear is that of the driving gear multiplied by the ratio of the number of teeth in each. Examples. A gear having eight teeth and turning at 100 revolutions a minute is meshed with a gear having 40 teeth. Then the speed of the driven gear is 100 multiplied by $\frac{8}{40}$, or 20 revolutions per minute.

Types of gear which are used for transmitting motion between parallel shafts are shown in Figs. 1, 2, and 3. The differences between them lie in the arrangement of the teeth.

Types of Gears

In the *straight-tooth spur gear* (Fig. 1) the teeth are parallel to the center line of the gear; this is the simplest possible formation.

The *helical gear* (Fig. 2) is used when smoother operation is required than the spur gear can give. In this case each tooth forms part of a spiral or helix. The helical gear is more difficult to make than the spur gear, but it is nearly always used for high speeds, as spur gears would be too noisy.

Helical Gears

A disadvantage of helical gears is that when transmitting a load they tend to push each other sideways out of mesh, and special thrust bearings have to be provided to prevent this. Another way of avoiding this difficulty is to use the *double-helical* or *herringbone gear* (Fig. 3), which is made up of two helical gears with the spirals

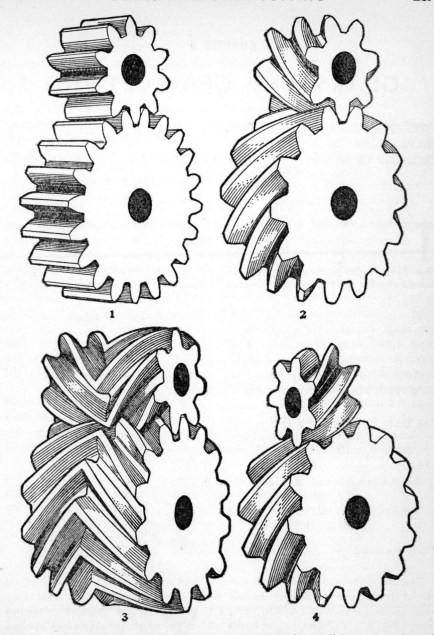

Figs. 1–4. *Top left*, straight-tooth spur gears, with teeth parallel to center line of gear; *top right*, helical gears, in which each tooth forms part of a spiral; *bottom left*, herringbone gears; *bottom right*, spiral gear.

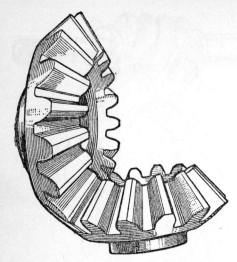

Fig. 5. Straight bevel gears used for connecting shafts which are not parallel to each other.

opposing each other. When this type of gear is running, the end thrust on one half of each gear balances the end thrust on the other half, and thrust bearings are not necessary.

Fig. 4 shows a pair of *spiral gears*. It will be noted that the center lines of these gears are not parallel but at an angle—usually a right angle—to each other. As the contact between the spiral gears is limited to a single point instead of a line the width of the gears, their load carrying capacity is less and the wear greater.

Bevel Gears

A commonly used type of connection between shafts, which are not parallel to each other, is the *bevel gear* (Fig. 5). The illustration shows a pair of gears for shafts whose center lines meet each other at right angles. Bevel gears may easily be made, however, for shafts whose center lines meet, but are not at right angles to

each other; in this case the gears are sometimes called *angular gears*. Occasionally the shaft center lines do not intersect each other, and in that case *hypoid* (offset bevel gears) may be used.

For smooth running and to avoid noise at high speeds, the straight bevel gear (Fig. 5) tends to be unsuitable, and the spiral bevel gear (Fig. 6) may be used instead.

Another form of gear used to connect shafts whose center lines do not meet is the *worm gear* (Fig. 7). This is especially useful when a big ratio of speed reduction is required, for it can be made to give a ratio of 70 to 1, whereas the other types of gear cannot easily give more than about 6 to 1 in one pair. Nearly all worm gears work with shafts at 90 deg., although they are sometimes made for shaft angles of about 70 deg.

Ratios of Gear Trains

Fig. 8 shows an arrangement in which gear 2 is carried on the same

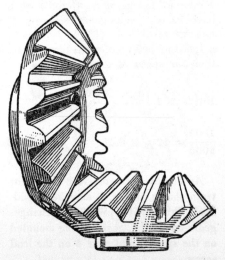

Fig. 6. Spiral bevel gears.

shaft as gear 3, and gear 4 is carried on the same shaft as gear 5. Thus, rotation of gear 1 causes rotation of the whole "train" of gears. In this case gears 1, 3, and 5 are driving gears, and gears 2, 4, and 6 are driven gears. The ratio of the complete train is:

Number of revolutions of first driving gear

Number of revolutions of last driven gear

Let R = Revolutions per minute ($R1$ for gear 1; $R2$ for gear 2; etc.)

T = Number of Teeth in gear ($T1$, for gear 1; $T2$ for gear 2; etc.)

Then $\dfrac{R6}{R1} = \dfrac{T1}{T2} \times \dfrac{T3}{T4} \times \dfrac{T5}{T6}$

or $R6 = R1 \dfrac{T1 \times T3 \times T5}{T2 \times T4 \times T6}$

Example: Let gears 1, 3, and 5 each have 10 teeth and gears 2, 4, and 6 have 20 teeth each. If gear 1 turns at a speed of 100 revolutions per minute, then the speed of gear 6 will be:

$R6 = 100 \dfrac{10 \times 10 \times 10}{20 \times 20 \times 20} = 100 \times$

$\dfrac{1000}{8000} = 12\frac{1}{2}$ R.P.M.

As further example, the four-gear train shown in Fig. 9 may be considered. This might represent the change-gears on a lathe, gear 1 being mounted on the spindle and gear 4 on the lead screw.

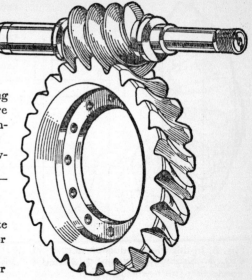

Fig. 7. Worm gears, of which this is an example, can be made to give a ratio of 70 to 1 for speed reduction.

Let $R1$ = R.P.M. of lead screw

Rs = R.P.M. of spindle

Then: $R1 = Rs \dfrac{16 \times 25}{40 \times 50}$

$= Rs \dfrac{1}{5}$

Thus, if the pitch of the lead-screw is $\frac{1}{4}$-in., the saddle would move through $\frac{1}{4} \times \frac{1}{5} = \frac{1}{20}$ in. while the work-spindle makes one revolution; in other words, the lathe would cut 20 threads per inch.

Selecting Change-Gears

The gears which drive the lead-screw of a lathe are known as *change-gears*, and the problem of selecting gears to give a required ratio may be easy or difficult according to the ratio. Such a ratio as $\frac{1}{5}$ (as mentioned above) is easy because all that is nec-

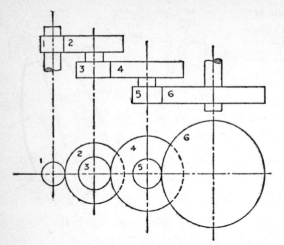

Fig. 8. In this triple reduction gear train, gears 1, 3, and 5 are "driving" and 2, 4, and 6 "driven" gears.

$$\frac{1000}{4160} = \frac{100}{416} = \frac{2 \times 50}{2 \times 4 \times 52} =$$

$$\frac{1 \times 50}{4 \times 52}$$

Multiplying $\frac{1}{4}$ by 20 gives $\frac{20 \times 50}{80 \times 52}$ as the gear combination to use.

The logarithmic method is another way of obtaining fractional gear ratios. This is more accurate but requires a table of the logarithms of gear ratios.

essary is to use one pair of gears with a ratio of $\frac{1}{2}$ and the other with a ratio of $\frac{2}{5} = \frac{1}{2.5}$; for example $\frac{18}{36}$ and $\frac{20}{50}$ or $\frac{21}{42}$ and $\frac{22}{55}$. Or, again, a combination of $\frac{1}{3}$ and $\frac{3}{5}$ would work equally well; for example, $\frac{15}{45}$ and $\frac{30}{50}$ or $\frac{17}{51}$ and $\frac{18}{30}$. Even with the limited numbers of gears in standard lathe equipment, several combinations can usually be found to give a ratio such as $\frac{1}{5}$.

Sometimes it is necessary to have a ratio such as $\frac{1}{4.161}$. Now, it may be impossible to produce such a ratio exactly with four gears, but it is usually possible to find a combination which gives a ratio very close to the required figure.

The first step is to find a series of approximating fractions by the method of *cancellation*. First clear the fraction $\frac{1}{4.161}$ of decimals by multiplying numerator and denominator by 1000, giving $\frac{1,000}{4,171}$. In order to secure a fraction that can be reduced, change 4161 to 4160 and obtain

Definitions

Of two gears which mesh together, the one with the smaller number of teeth is called the *pinion,* and the other is the *gear.* An exception occurs in worm gearing, where the gear with the smaller number of teeth is the worm and the other is the worm wheel. A gear whose teeth lie in a straight line instead of on a circle is called a *rack.* It is really part of a gear of infinite size.

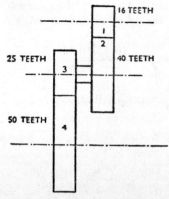

Fig. 9. Double reduction gear train, as used for change-gears on a lathe.

The pitch *cylinders* of a pair of gears are the cylinders which, when running on the same center lines as the gears, would roll together with the same speeds as the gears, without slipping. The pitch *circle* is the end view of the pitch cylinder. In bevel gearing, the corresponding figures are pitch cones, and the pitch circle is the large end of the cone. A worm has a pitch plane lying parallel to the center lines of worm and gear and touching the pitch cylinder of the worm wheel. (See Fig. 10.)

The *circular pitch* of gear teeth is the distance between similar flanks of adjacent teeth, measured along the pitch circle. In helical gearing this is called the *transverse pitch*. The distance between adjacent teeth measured on the pitch cylinder at right angles to the tooth spirals is the *normal pitch*. The distance measured parallel to the center line of the gear is the *axial pitch*.

The *addendum* of a tooth is the distance from its tip to the pitch circle. The *dedendum* is the distance from the pitch circle to the root circle.

Pressure Angles

The *pressure angle* is the angle between the tooth profile where it cuts the pitch circle and the line joining that point to the center of the pitch circle. In helical gearing this is called the *transverse pressure angle*. If a helical gear-tooth is cut on a plane at right angles to the tooth spirals, a different tooth profile is seen. This is called the normal section of the tooth, and its pressure angle is the *normal pressure angle;* it is always less than the transverse pressure angle.

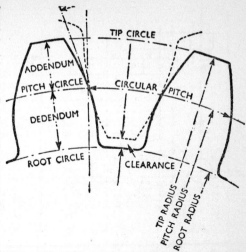

Fig. 10. Elements of spur and helical gears, illustrating the terms used in gear-cutting. These terms are fully explained in the text.

Systems of Pitch Measurements

If the number 3.1416 is divided by the circular pitch of a gear, the result is the *diametral pitch* of the teeth. If the pitch is divided by 3.1416, the result is the *module* of the teeth.

In American and British practice both circular pitch and diametral pitch are used on the basis of the inch. In Continental practice pitches are standardized on the module system in millimeters. The table on the next page gives a list of standard pitches in all three systems, and shows also its equivalent in each of the other systems.

With worms and worm wheels, the distance which a tooth of the wheel advances in one revolution of the worm, is called the *lead*.

The angle between the tooth-surface at the pitch-cylinder and a line parallel to the center line is the *helix*

TABLE I—STANDARD PITCHES

CIRCULAR PITCH IN.	D.P. IN.	MODULE MM.	CIRCULAR PITCH IN.	D.P. IN.	MODULE MM.	CIRCULAR PITCH IN.	D.P. IN.	MODULE MM.
.1855	16.933	1.5	.618	5.080	5	1.396	2.25	11.286
.1875	16.755	1.516	.625	5.026	5.053	1.484	2.117	12
.1963	16	1.587	.628	5	5.077	1.5	2.094	12.127
.2164	14.514	1.75	.680	4.618	5.5	1.571	2	12.701
.2244	14	1.814	.6875	4.569	5.558	1.608	1.954	13
.247	12.700	2	.742	4.233	6	1.625	1.933	13.138
.250	12.566	2.021	.75	4.189	6.064	1.732	1.814	14
.262	12	2.118	.7854	4	6.350	1.75	1.795	14.148
.278	11.288	2.25	.8125	3.867	6.569	1.795	1.75	14.512
.309	10.160	2.5	.866	3.628	7	1.855	1.693	15
.3125	10.053	2.527	.875	3.590	7.074	1.875	1.676	15.159
.314	10	2.540	.898	3.5	7.260	1.978	1.587	16
.340	9.236	2.75	.9375	3.351	7.580	2	1.571	16.170
.371	8.466	3.	.990	3.175	8	2.094	1.5	16.930
.375	8.377	3.032	1.000	3.142	8.085	2.226	1.412	18
.393	8	3.177	1.047	3	8.465	2.25	1.396	18.191
.433	7.257	3.5	1.113	2.822	9	2.474	1.270	20
.4375	7.181	3.537	1.125	2.792	9.095	2.5	1.257	20.212
.449	7	3.630	1.142	2.75	9.233	2.513	1.25	20.317
.495	6.350	4	1.237	2.54	10	2.75	1.142	22.233
.5	6.283	4.042	1.25	2.513	10.106	3	1.047	24.254
.524	6	4.236	1.257	2.5	10.163	3.142	1	25.400
.557	5.644	4.5	1.361	2.309	11			
.5625	5.585	4.547	1.375	2.285	11.117			

angle. The *lead angle* or *worm angle* is found by subtracting the helix angle from 90 deg. If the remote end of a tooth (or thread) is seen to be twisted in the clock-wise direction from the near end, the helix is right-hand; if it is twisted in the opposite direction, it is left-hand. (See Fig. 11.)

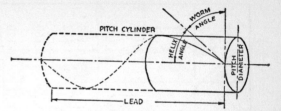

Fig. 11. This illustration makes clear the basic formation of a helical gear-tooth.

A gear made by cutting a number of equally-spaced notches in a circular blank could be meshed with a similar gear, and one would drive the other, perhaps in a jerky fashion, at low speeds. If the gears are to work smoothly at high speeds, however, the teeth must be accurately shaped to some particular form.

The tooth form which is now nearly always used is the *involute.* The involute cannot be drawn in any such simple way as the circle and it is usually produced in practice by a *generating* process. In such a process the cutting tool and the gear blank have regular motions, and the shape of the teeth produced in the blank depends upon these motions and upon the shape of the cutter.

In the involute system, the shape of a tooth of any given pitch depends upon the number of teeth in the gear. In the case of a rack the tooth is

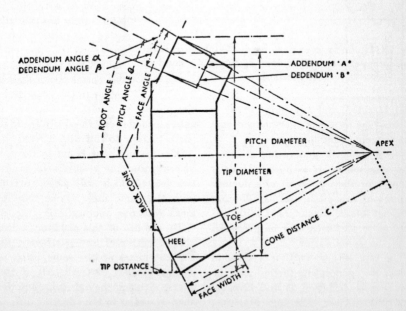

Fig. 12. Elements of bevel gears, illustrating the terms used in connection with them, and fully explained in the text. (See also Figs. 10 and 11.)

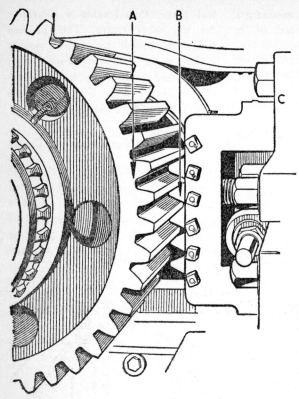

Fig. 13. Planing a spur gear by the Sunderland rack-generating process. A, blank; B, cutter; C, head of machine.

action it is moved backward and forward, parallel to the center line of the blank, A. (See Fig. 13.)

If the head, C, of the machine were gradually moved toward the blank while the cutter is moving backward and forward, the effect would be to cut grooves of the same shape as the teeth of the cutter.

In practice the head is moved toward the blank until the cutter teeth are sunk into it to about half the total depth of tooth required, when the generating motion is started. This consists of a vertical movement of the cutter slide, while at the same time, the blank is rotated at such a rate that its pitch circle has the same speed as the vertical movement of the cutter head. Thus the blank and the cutter are *rolled* together in the same way as the pinion rolls with a rack, and the cutter produces teeth which are of the correct shape to roll with a rack.

straight-sided, and advantage is taken of this fact by using rack-shaped cutters in generating processes.

When using a generating process, only one cutter is required of each pitch to produce gears of any number of teeth of this pitch, and by adopting different blank diameters a wide variety of tooth-forms may be produced from the same cutter.

The type of gear-cutting machine in which the generating action can be most easily followed is the *Sunderland* Spur Gear Planing Machine.

Here the cutter, B, is in the form of a rack, and so as to give a cutting

The mating gear is cut in the same manner, and the result is to produce two gears which will mesh correctly with the same rack, hence they will mesh with one another.

By the use of this machine, a rack-shaped cutter of any particular pitch can cut gears of the same pitch and of any number of teeth. All of these gears, although having different tooth shapes, owing to the effect of different blank size on generation, will mesh.

The mechanism of the machine has

to provide for additional movements, because of the limited length of the cutter. When the cutter slide has been moved so far downward that the upper end of the cutter begins to mesh with the blank, the generating action ceases. The cutter is stopped clear of the blank, and the cutter slide is then moved vertically through an exact number of pitches without rotation of the blank. The generating action is then resumed and the cycle is repeated. By repeating this process a sufficient number of times, all the teeth can be generated in a blank of any size that the machine can take. All of the machine motions are fully automatic.

It is not usual to cut the full depth of tooth at once, a second or third revolution of the blank being made with increased depth of cut to bring the teeth to the correct thickness and depth.

By setting the cutter slide at an angle to the center line of the blank, the Sunderland machine can be arranged to cut single helical gears.

Another form of Sunderland machine is that designed to cut double helical gears (Fig. 14). This has two cutter slides, set at the angles required for the right- and left-hand teeth, and with cutters facing each other, one for each slide. The mechanism is arranged so that as one cutter approaches the center of the width of the gear the other moves away from it. Actually, each cutter very slightly overruns the central plane, thus leaving a clearance for the other cutter. This process makes it possible to produce double helical gears with continuous teeth; some other processes make it necessary to provide a gap between the two helices for cutting clearance.

Generation by Pinion-Shaped Cutter

Since all involute gears of the same pitch and pressure angle will mesh with each other and with a rack, it is possible to generate gears by use of a cutter in the form of a pinion, just as easily as can be done with a rack-shaped cutter.

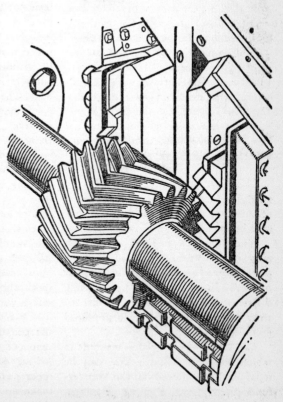

Fig. 14. Planing a double-helical gear by means of the Sunderland rack-generating process.

The first machines to use this method of generation were those made by the Fellows Company and an example is shown in Fig. 15. The cutter is moved up and down parallel to the center line of the blank, in order to give the cutting action, and at the same time the cutter and the blank are rotated at the speeds which gears of the same diameter would need to have to mesh correctly together. The actual speed of rotation is chosen so that the cutter removes a chip of suitable thickness at each stroke. On the up stroke, the cutter is moved slightly away from the rack, so that the teeth do not rub against each other.

An advantage of the Fellows process is that a gear of any diameter can be cut without stopping the motions, as is necessary in the case of the Sunderland process when the end of the cutter approaches the blank.

Pinion-shaped cutters with helical teeth may be used for generating helical gears. In that case the cutter spindle works in a spiral guide, so that as the cutter moves downward it also rotates through an angle which gives the

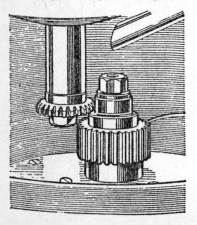

Fig. 15. Generating the teeth of a spur gear by the Fellows process, which uses a cutter in the form of a pinion.

required spiral form to the teeth which are cut in the blank.

In the Sykes process, spiral pinion-shaped cutters are used to generate double helical gears.

Generation by Hobbing

The most accurate way of cutting gears is by the *hobbing* process (Figs. 16, 16a, and 16b). The hob is a cutting tool in the form of a worm. Very often, as in Fig. 16, it is a single-thread worm, which is the same thing as a spiral gear having one tooth and a spiral angle nearly equal to 90 deg. The hob is provided with *gashes* or *flutes* forming edges wherever they meet the thread, which is cut away behind each edge. This cutting-away or *relieving* is done in such a way that the cutting edges may be sharpened by grinding on the radial faces without altering the shape of the cutting edge. The hob may therefore be sharpened many times without losing its accuracy, even though its diameter is reduced.

The hob may be used to generate spur or helical gears by setting up the hobbing machine in the correct manner.

The hob is rotated at a rate which gives the cutting edges a suitable cutting speed, and the blank is rotated at the rate that the finished gear would have, to mesh correctly with a single-tooth spiral gear similar to the hob, and running at the speed of the hob. The hob is also fed slowly parallel to the center line of the blank in order to cover the whole face width. If a helical gear is being cut, the blank must have an additional rotation to make up for this sliding of the hob across the face. A hobbing machine has no change in speed of **any part**

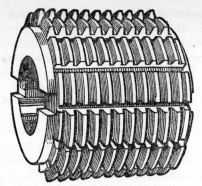

Fig. 16. Spur or helical gears are most accurately cut by the use of the hob (above), a worm-shaped tool.

from the start of the cut to the end of it, and that is why hobbing gives more accurate work than does any other gear-cutting process.

Form-Cutting of Gears

A spur gear may be formed by using a milling cutter to make a number of grooves of the correct shape in the blank. This means that the cutter itself must first be formed, and even when this has been done—and it is not easy if accuracy is to be insured—the cutter is correct only for the number of teeth for which it was made. In the Brown and Sharpe system of gearing one milling cutter is required to cut any number of teeth within a certain range, so that a high degree of accuracy is impossible. This process has been widely used in the past, and is still used occasionally because it can be carried out on a standard milling machine with a dividing head.

By setting the milling-machine table to the proper angle and by connecting the driving spindle on the dividing head to the feed screw of the table by suitable gears, the form-milling process can be used for cutting helical gears. The cutter used is that which would be used for a spur gear having the actual number of teeth required in the helical gear, divided by the cube of the cosine of the spiral angle.

Another form-milling process which is still used is *end-milling* (Fig. 17). It can be used to make gears of very large pitch, beyond the range of standard generating machines. The end-milling cutters are much less expensive than generating cutters would be, but they are weak, and more than one cutter may be needed to cut a single large gear. The end-milling process is the only one that can produce triple-helical gears with continuous teeth, but that type of gear is now rarely used.

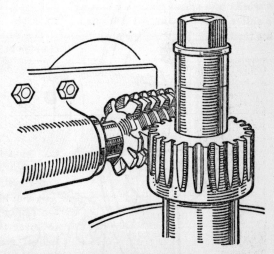

Fig. 16a. Hobbing a spur gear. The gashes or flutes of the hob form edges wherever they meet the thread, which is cut away behind each edge. (See also Fig. 16b.)

Cutting Bevel Gears

The types of gear already considered are similar, in that the size and shape of the tooth are the same at all points in its length. In bevel gears, however, each tooth is smaller at one end than at the other, a gradual change in size taking place across the width of the face. The tooth-shape is similar at all points, depth and thickness being altered in proportion.

By referring to Fig. 12 it will be seen that the important point in a pair of bevel gears is the apex where the shaft center lines meet. A straight line joining the apex to any point on the profile of a bevel gear tooth at the large end lies along the surface of the tooth. The planing process for straight bevel gears makes use of this fact. A planing tool is moved backward and forward along a line which, if extended, would always pass through the apex of the gear. This is done by

mounting the tool in a box which moves on a guide able to swing about two lines—one horizontal and one vertical passing through the apex of the gear.

The movements of the slide are also controlled by a roller pressing on a former-plate, so that as the head of the machine rotates about the vertical line through the apex of the gear, the cutter slide is compelled to rotate about the horizontal line in such a way that the path of the cutter always lies in the required surface of the gear-tooth. The arrangement of the essential parts of the machine is indicated in Fig. 18.

Generation of Bevel Gears

A bevel gear of 90 deg. pitch angle is known as a *crown* gear, and it bears the same relation to bevel gears as the rack does to spur gears. The teeth of the crown gear are straight-sided, and this enables it to form the basis of a

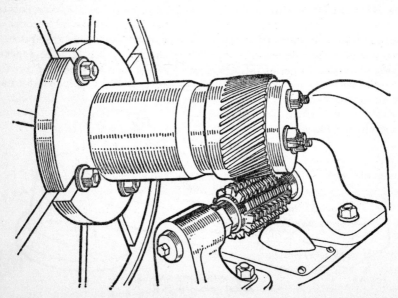

Fig. 16b. Hobbing a helical gear by the use of a worm-shaped hobbing tool. (See Fig. 16.)

generation system using straight-sided cutters.

This is important, not only because a straight-sided cutter is fairly easy to make, but also because the same cutter can represent both the large end and the small end of the crown-gear tooth. As the tooth profile is straight at both ends, the profile at the small end is simply a part of the profile at the large end.

In the bevel-gear generating machine, the crown gear is imaginary, but two straight cutter blades move backward and forward in positions which cause them to sweep out the surfaces of two imaginary crown-gear teeth.

At the same time, the whole cutter head is rotated about the center line of the imaginary crown gear and the gear blank is given the rotation that the finished gear would have if meshed with the crown gear. Thus the cutter blades cut out tooth forms which would mesh correctly with the crown gear. The mating gear is made in the same way, and the two gears will mesh correctly together because each would mesh with the same crown gear.

After one pair of tooth profiles have been generated, the cutter blades are

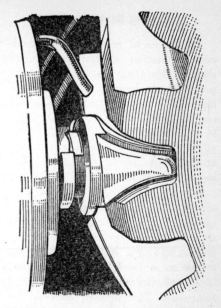

Fig. 17. Gears of a very large pitch can be cut by the use of the end-mill process, as illustrated above.

drawn away from the blank, the generating mechanism is disconnected, and the blank is rotated through an angle corresponding to one pitch, so that the cycle may then be repeated to produce the next pair of profiles. Operation of the machine is automatic until all the teeth have been cut.

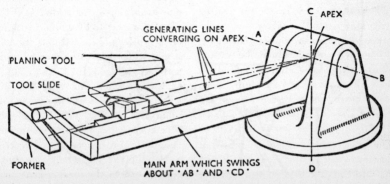

Fig. 18. General principles and arrangement of the essential parts of a bevel gear planing machine. Its operation is explained in the text.

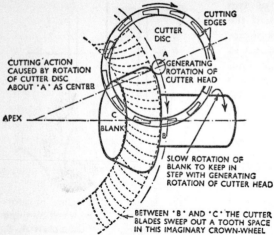

Fig. 19. In the Gleason process for producing spiral bevel gear teeth the cutter blades are mounted near the edge of a disc and follow c. circular path.

Generation of Spiral Bevel Gears

A widely used type of spiral bevel gear is that produced by the Gleason process (see Fig. 19), in which the cutter blades are mounted near the edge of a disc and follow a circular path.

The cutter disc rotates about a spindle which is carried in the cutter head, and this turns slowly about a center line which is also that of the imaginary crown gear. In one small portion of the circular path, the cutter blades are sweeping out a tooth-space in the imaginary crown gear. When the cutter head and the gear-blank are rolled together, the moving cutter blades generate a tooth-space whose flanks are correctly shaped to mesh with a tooth of the imaginary crown gear.

The generating action is repeated for every tooth in the gear, the blank being additionally rotated through one pitch, after each generating motion is finished.

When gears have to withstand heavy loading conditions, they are usually made from case-hardened steel. The disadvantage of this process is that distortion occurs in the hardening operation, and as the material is then too hard to cut, accuracy can be restored only by grinding.

Grinding Spur Gears

Spur gears and single helical gears can be ground on the tooth profiles to a higher degree of accuracy than is possible in cutting. Some gear-grinding machines work on the forming principle, the tooth-shape, in the case of spur gears, being that of the grinding wheel which is trimmed by diamonds, whose movements are controlled by former-plates. The principle of this process is shown in Fig. 20, although the arrangement of the mechanism which controls the movement of the diamond is not necessarily the same in all types of machines.

Other types of gear-grinding machine use the generating principle, and one example is illustrated in Fig. 21. Here the gear to be ground is mounted on a work-spindle carried in a headstock, which moves backward and forward at right angles to the center line of the spindle. The rear end of the spindle carries a master gear of the same size as the gear to be ground. The master gear meshes with a fixed rack set parallel to the direction of motion of the headstock, so that this motion causes the master gear and the work-spindle to rotate. Two flat grinding wheels are used, set in positions which correspond to flanks of two rack-teeth. The rolling action of the master gear on the fixed rack therefore causes the gear being ground to roll in contact with the grinding wheels, with the result that the teeth are ground to an accurate involute form.

The work is moved slowly parallel to the center lines in order that the grinding wheels may cover the whole face width. When this has been done, the work is rotated through a distance equal to one pitch without moving the master gear, and on the return motion two other tooth profiles are ground.

Lapping of Gear Teeth

In dealing with large quantities of fairly small case-hardened steel gears, it is possible to control the distortion which takes place during hardening closely enough to keep the errors reasonably small. If so, it may be possible to correct the errors by *lapping*, which is a much less expensive process than profile grinding.

The lap is a cast-iron gear of the same normal pitch and pressure angle as the gear to be lapped, but with a

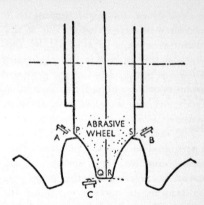

Fig. 20. The forming principle of gear-grinding. Profile *PQRS* trimmed by three mechanically-controlled diamonds *A, B, C.*

different spiral angle, so that when the two are meshed together their center lines are not parallel. This means that when gear and lap are rotated, a sliding action occurs at all points in the area of contact. The lap is coated with grinding paste, and when it is rotated in mesh with the gear to be lapped, the sliding action causes the grinding paste to smooth away the high spots on the teeth of the gear. As always occurs in lapping, the harder member (the gear) is lapped, while the softer one (the lap) is only very slightly affected, and may be used many times without serious loss of accuracy. To cover the face width of the gear, it is moved backward and forward parallel to its center line while rotating in mesh with the lap.

Spiral-bevel gears for automobile rear axles are nearly always made from case-hardened steel, and as there is no process for grinding the profiles of the teeth

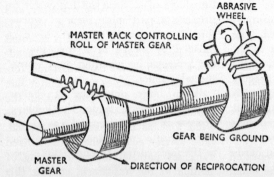

Fig. 21. Principle of a machine for gear-grinding which uses the generating method. See description on page 300.

of such gears, the correction which is necessary to remove errors due to distortion is always carried out by lapping. In this case it is not customary to use a separate lap, but the gear and pinion which are actually to be used as a pair, are run together with grinding paste.

The machine in which this is done is arranged so that the position of the pinion can be very accurately adjusted in relation to the gear, and the lapping is carried out until the tooth surfaces have become polished and the positions of the contact areas on gear and pinion are such as will give satisfactory operation in service.

Shaving the Gear Teeth

A process which is used for improving the accuracy of spur or helical gears is that known as *crossed-axis shaving*.

In this process the gear to be treated is meshed with a shaving cutter in the form of a spiral gear of the same normal pitch and pressure angle as the gear. This cutter is made with grooves running down the teeth, the edges of the grooves acting as cutting edges when the shaving tool is rotated in mesh with the gear to be treated. The shaving tool is made very accurately, the tooth profiles being ground. The result of the shaving process is to improve the accuracy of pitch and tooth-form of the gear treated. This process is extensively used in dealing with large quantities of the relatively small gears used in automobile transmissions. Gears treated in this way and subjected to carefully-controlled hardening operations can be finally corrected by lapping, the total cost of manufacture being lower than would be the case if the teeth were ground

on the profiles. The accuracy is about the same in both cases.

Worm Gearing

In most types of gear the pinion is manufactured in the same way as the gear, apart from differences due to variations in size.

On the other hand, in worm gearing, the processes in the manufacture of the worm are quite different from those used in manufacturing the wheel. The worm may be looked upon as being similar to a screw with one or more *threads* or as a single helical gear with one or more teeth. The former is more natural when the worm has a small lead angle, and the latter if the lead angle is large.

Usually the worm-thread is cut on a worm milling machine in which the blank is moved parallel to its center line and at the same time slowly rotated so that the milling cutter produces a spiral groove. If the worm has more than one thread, it is then rotated through a distance corresponding to the transverse pitch, and a second similar groove is cut; the process is repeated until all the threads are completed. It is not easy to determine the shape of a worm milling cutter to produce a particular form of worm-thread, and very often the thread is finished by means of a form-tool in the lathe, or by grinding on a worm-thread grinder.

When large quantities of similar worms are being made, the hobbing process is sometimes used (as if the worm were a spiral gear), but, owing to the high cost of the hob, this process is too expensive in the case of cutting small numbers of worms.

Usually the worm is made from case-hardened steel and the thread surfaces are finished by grinding after the hardening operation. The thread grinding is carried out on a machine of the same general type as the thread-milling machine, but the traverse of the worm is more rapid, and several cuts are usually necessary to bring the worm-thread thickness down to the required amount. The grinding wheel is trimmed to the correct shape by means of a diamond whose movements are controlled by a former-plate.

Cutting Worm-Wheel Teeth

The teeth of the worm-wheel can be cut correctly only by a generating process, using a hob of the same general dimensions as the worm. The hob is rotated at a rate which gives its cutting edges a suitable cutting speed, and the worm-wheel blank is rotated at the rate which the finished wheel would have in order to mesh with a worm running at the speed of the hob. As the hob is sunk more deeply into the worm-wheel blank, it generates teeth which are of the correct shape to mesh exactly with the worm.

Preferably, the hob is first offset from the worm-wheel blank in the direction of its center line, which is placed at the correct center distance from the blank. To compensate for this movement of the hob, the blank is given an additional rotation so that hob and blank continue to mesh correctly.

Tangential Feed

This *tangential feed* gives a smoother finish to the worm-wheel teeth than does the direct infeed, and a machine which works on the tangential-feed principle is specially valua-ble because it can use a *fly cutter*, which is actually one tooth of the full hob corresponding to the worm. Such a fly cutter is very much less expensive to make than is a full hob, and it is used when only one or two worm wheels are to be cut, even though this cutter is comparatively slow in operation.

Worm-wheel teeth are sometimes finished by running the worm-wheel in mesh with a finely-serrated worm which shaves the teeth to a high degree of finish and accuracy.

Worm-threads are polished to a mirror finish by running the worm in mesh with a lap in the form of a wooden worm-wheel smeared with grinding paste.

Test of Accuracy

Gears have to be made accurately, first so that the load is properly distributed over the width of the teeth, and second in order that they will have smooth action. If the gears do not work smoothly, they suffer heavy wear, and unless the speeds are very low they run noisily. Quiet running is, in fact, a test of accuracy.

If a pair of gears runs quietly at full speed, it is not likely that there are any errors which would have serious effect on life or load capacity. There are instruments for directly measuring the accuracy of tooth pitch and tooth shape, but the final test of quiet running is usually simpler. If the gears are noisy, testing instruments may then be applied to them to show where the errors lie, but otherwise the gears may be accepted.

To obtain quiet running, the gears must be mounted accurately in relation to each other, the angle between the shafts being especially important, and,

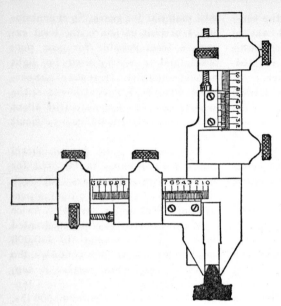

A high-pitched note is an indication of an error in tooth shape. A noise which shows a beat in every revolution of one of the gears indicates a pitch error in that gear.

On the other hand, each gear may contain pitch errors, and the noise produced may show a beat every time the two worst places come together. If the numbers of teeth have no common factor, this fault occurs every time the pinion has made a number of revolutions equal to the number of teeth in the gear.

Fig. 22. Gear-tooth caliper. Used to measure the chordal thickness of teeth at the pitch circle.

except in the case of spur or helical gears, where a small error does not matter, center distance or apex distance of the gears must be accurate.

Testing Mounting

A simple method of testing accuracy of mounting is to smear the teeth of one gear very lightly with red lead, or other marking substance, and to rotate the gears slowly together under light load. The position of the marking which spreads on to the teeth of the other gear shows whether a uniform tooth contact is being obtained, and if not, how the gear positions should be altered in order to improve matters. When the gears have been adjusted to give the best possible contact positions, they are run at full speed under different loads, and if they are reasonably quiet their accuracy is thereby proved.

Contact Marking

In many cases the contact marking shown by a pair of gears varies according to the load upon them. This difference is caused by slight yielding of gears, shafts, bearings, and mountings, when the load is applied. For example, if a double-helical pinion is of small diameter compared with its width, the tooth load tends to be heavier at the outer ends of the teeth than at the middle of the face width. In the case of bevel gears, heavy loading tends to fall on the large ends of the teeth. In the case of worm gears, the greater the load the more it tends to be concentrated in that part of the worm-wheel teeth at which the approaching surfaces of the threads first make contact.

First Setting

In the first setting of the gears it is usually convenient to apply only light loading, and therefore the adjustment must be made so as to place the contact marking, not where it will have to be under load, but in some other position which makes allowance for the probable movement of contact area when the load is applied. The amount of this movement depends on the rigidity of gears and mounting, and has to be estimated from experience on similar work.

As a general rule, the contact areas on a loaded gear tooth should never extend quite to the edge which the mating tooth approaches. The reason is that if such an edge makes contact, it tends to scrape away the oil film. This must surely result in heavy wear and short life.

Materials of Gears

The load on a gear tooth may cause it to fail in two entirely different ways. In most cases failure of the tooth surface is more likely, and this may take the form of rapid wear, seizing, or heavy pitting. The other type of failure is by breakage of the tooth under the bending effect of the load. Tooth breakage does not often occur, and when it does it is usually the result of applying a shock load to a gear made of brittle material.

In some cases the thickness of the tooth is so much reduced by wear that its bending strength becomes very small and it fails by breakage or bending over. This kind of failure is rare.

Steels in Use

It is important, therefore, that a gear material should first of all be capable of withstanding rubbing action under load, and secondly should be able to resist bending. Steel in one form or another is the most commonly used material for gears. Steel containing .4 percent carbon is the least expensive form suitable for gear purposes, and is widely used for light loading conditions Increase of the carbon content to .5 percent increases the wear resistance of the steel by about 40 percent, but makes it more difficult to cut accurately.

Steel containing 3.5 percent nickel and 1 percent chromium is used for more heavily-loaded gears. Although it is much more expensive than .4 percent carbon steel, it has about twice the load capacity when heat-treated to give a tensile strength of 120,000 lbs., per sq. in. In this condition the steel can be cut accurately; it can, however, be heat-treated to give a tensile strength of 180,000 to 200,000 lbs. per sq. in., but this has to be done after the teeth have been cut, because the material cannot be machined when in that condition. The distortion which occurs in the heat-treatment introduces errors, and so a high degree of accuracy is not possible in this steel unless the teeth are finished by grinding or lapping.

Case-Hardened Steel

To obtain the greatest load capacity in gears of a given size, it is necessary to use case-hardened steel. The most commonly-used type of steel for this purpose contains 3.5 percent nickel, and other varieties contain both nickel and chromium. The wear-resistance of any case-hardened steel is more than three times that of 130,000 pound nickel-chrome steel and over seven times that of .4 percent carbon steel. The bending strength is also higher than that of nickel-chrome steel and more than twice that of .4 percent carbon steel.

CHAPTER 9

JIGS AND FIXTURES

WHY JIGS AND FIXTURES ARE USED. ANGLE PLATES. BOX-JIGS. CLAMPING
DEVICES. DRILLING JIGS AND BUSHINGS. STANDARD FOR JIGS. TEMPLATES.
LATHE FIXTURES. JIG-BORING MACHINES. MAGNETIC CHUCKS. INDEXING FIX-
TURES. SLOT MILLING. IRREGULAR PROFILES.

THE present-day demand for production of articles in large quantities has rendered obsolete the old
method of making component parts by
hand. In the first place, hand-work is
far too slow for large-scale production, and in the second place the skill
required to produce parts by hand
makes the cost prohibitive. Some
means, therefore, had to be found to
make use of unskilled or semi-skilled
labor, and also to make production
work as automatic and rapid as possible, by splitting the work up into a
number of simple operations in which
the machines could be relied upon to
provide accuracy without the need for
skill on the part of the operator.

Interchanging Parts

In the old days of hand-work it was
sufficient for component parts to fit
each other, whereas with mass production a certain part has to fit not only
one but any one of thousands of other
parts with which it may have to be assembled. The need for this interchangeability calls for much greater
accuracy than would otherwise be necessary. This is achieved by means of
attachments or appliances used in conjunction with the machines to control

the operation. The appliances are
known as *jigs* or *fixtures,* and as a general rule the term jig is used if the appliance actually guides the cutting
tool, and the term fixture where it is
concerned with holding the work.

What Is a Jig?

A definition of a jig is, a frame or
body to which the work may be fastened, and which contains a device for
guiding the tool so that both the work
and the tool are located in the true
position relative to each other. Figure
1 shows three common ways to make
up jigs. The *built-up* jig is usually applied only to small parts such as cash
register and typewriter parts. The *cast*
type is most common today. *Welded*
jigs are often preferred because they
can be quickly made, are lower in cost
because no pattern is required, and are
adaptable to later changes of design.
Jigs and fixtures are used in connection with almost every machine operation, and are sometimes very simple,
sometimes complicated; but generally
the more simple the appliance, the better, as long as it will perform the function for which it is intended.

The first requirement is that of accuracy; the second, ease of handling

to facilitate rapid operation and high output; and the third, convenience for cleaning and maintenance to reduce waste time to a minimum. On small-scale production, jigs, etc., must be simple and cheap to make, for otherwise they would not pay for themselves.

On the other hand, where parts are to be produced in enormous quantities, the initial cost of jigs is of secondary importance, and it may well be that the expenditure of an extra $100 or so on a jig to save a few seconds of the operator's time pays a handsome dividend.

The simplest and probably the oldest forms of fixture in use are the angle plate, V blocks, and parallels shown in Fig. 2. Many of the more elaborate appliances designed for special purposes

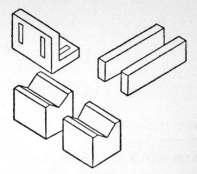

Fig. 2. Simple fixtures in common use: (*left, above*) angle plate; (*right, above*) parallel blocks; (*below*), V blocks.

are constructed with one or the other of the above as the basic principle. Fig. 4 shows how the work is fixed in position. Each of these fixtures can be used on the bench or with any machine tool. For example, the job

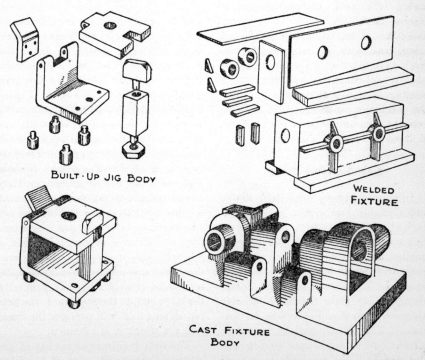

BUILT·UP JIG BODY

WELDED FIXTURE

CAST FIXTURE BODY

Fig. 1. Three common ways to build jigs.

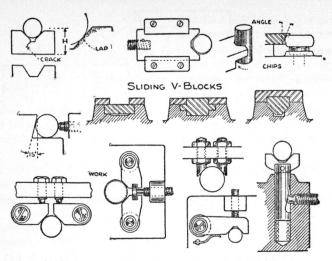

Fig. 3. Design and application of V blocks.

clamped on the parallels could be set up that way for drilling holes, or on a milling-machine table for milling the top face, or on a grinding, planing, or any other machine.

Such parallel strips or blocks are sometimes made in cast iron for the larger sizes, or mild steel for smaller ones, or may be of tool steel, hardened and ground very accurately for high-class work. They are made exactly the same thickness either way by being machined together and the finishing cut taken over both at once. When in use, they are kept in pairs, preferably marked for identification to avoid the possibility of being mixed with other similar ones.

Angle plates are made in various sizes, sometimes in cast iron, sometimes tool steel, hardened and ground, the chief essential being that the working faces should be perfectly square with each other. The V blocks, like the parallel blocks, should be finished in pairs to insure that they are the same height, and the grooves must be central and parallel with the bottom and sides. Sharp angles should be avoided. It is preferable to lap the last 0.002 in. with a bar of the same diameter as the work piece in order to get extreme accuracy in height. These principles as well as several other methods of applying the V design to holding round work are all shown in Fig. 3.

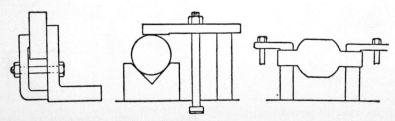

Fig. 4. Methods of holding work by means of the simple fixtures shown separately in Fig. 2. They may be used on the bench or with any machine tool.

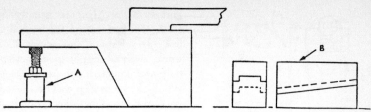

Fig. 5. These two devices, the screw jack (A) and the adjustable parallel block (B) are invaluable aids in setting up irregular work, and they avoid waste of time.

Setting up Devices

In Fig. 5 two devices are shown which are invaluable in setting up irregular work, the screw jack, A, or the adjustable parallel block, B.

When work is being set up on a machine table much time is wasted in searching round the shop for suitable clamps, bolts, and bits of steel, etc., for packing, to suit the height of work. This trouble can be avoided by use of the form of clamp and block shown in Fig. 6, the nearest suitable step on the packing block being chosen, and the adjusting screw on the clamp used for the final setting of the height.

A simple form of jig which is very satisfactory for some jobs is as follows. The work-piece is a flat plate and two holes are to be drilled in the plate. The jig consists of a plate which can be made in mild steel, with the pins a tight fit in the plate, and arranged so that the contour of the work-piece just fits between them. Where the holes are to be drilled, bushings are fitted in the jig-plate, the hole bored in the bushing being a running fit for the drill to be used.

The work is placed on the drilling-machine table with the jig held or clamped on top, and as the pins locate the work in position relative to the bushings, the drill can be fed through the bushings and the holes drilled in the work in the true position. However many parts are drilled with the jig, they will all be absolutely correct and exactly alike.

An example of how an angle plate may be used for the construction of a drilling jig is shown in Fig. 7; the work-piece, A, to be drilled is shown by the dotted line, B. The stud, C, is fastened to the angle plate, and the work held in place on the stud by the slotted washer and nut, D; if a plain washer were to be used, the nut would have to be unscrewed right off the stud to remove the finished job and insert the next one.

Use of Slotted Washer

With the slotted washer the nut has only to be backed off sufficiently to enable the washer to be slipped off. Then, the center hole in the work-piece being larger than the nut, the work can be removed over the nut. The drill is guided by the bushing, E, in the plate, F, which is screwed and

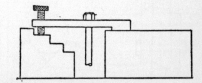

Fig. 6. Thumb screw-adjusted clamp and stepped packing block adaptable to height of work.

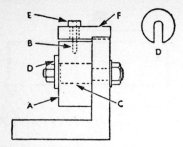

Fig. 7. How an angle plate may be used as a drilling jig. The reference letters are explained in the text.

doweled in the true position in the angle plate.

With a jig of this type the stud, C, and the drill bushing, E, would be made of tool steel hardened and ground, while the rest of the jig would be left soft.

When holes are to be drilled from different angles a type of jig known as the box-jig is used, and may be constructed either as a casting or built up of steel plates screwed or welded to-gether. These jigs are usually in the form of a box with a lid hinged to allow for insertion and removal of the work, with a simple quick-action eye bolt and knurled nut for locking the lid, as shown in Fig. 8. The slotted lug, A, in the lid allows the eye-bolt, B, to swing aside when the knurled nut is unscrewed a few turns, and when the work-piece is inserted and the lid closed the work is held in position by the thumb-screw, C.

The holes to be drilled may be seen at X, the large holes drilled through the bushings, D, on one face of the box and the small holes through the bushings, E, on the other face. On the opposite faces of the jig the feet, F, are provided for the jig to stand on, so that there is less risk of dirt or chips under the jig throwing it out of alignment.

Although the box-type of jig is often the only way in which a job can be done, it is inclined to be somewhat

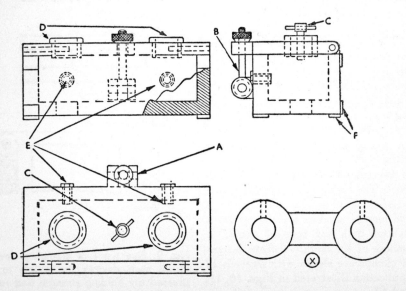

Fig. 8. A box-type drilling jig with hinged lid and quick-action eye-bolt.

slow to handle and troublesome to keep clean. Consequently, as a general rule, it should be avoided whenever possible.

There are certain details which are required on all types of jigs and fixtures, the choice of the most suitable for any particular job being governed by circumstances. In Fig. 9 several clamping devices are shown, the important point of any such device being quick operation for tightening and releasing the work, coupled of course with strength for positively holding the work or jig to be clamped with no chance of movement.

The type A is useful where the job can be slid under the clamp and slid out again sideways on being released, the spring serving to hold up the clamp when the work is removed. Types B and C are extremely useful under certain conditions, one turn of the nut or screw being sufficient to allow the clamp to be swung aside. A distinct advantage lies in the fact that the clamp remains attached to the fixture, thus reducing handling.

The slotted clamp, D, is adjustable for position lengthways, the most useful feature being that it can be slid aside for releasing work, or slipped right off the bolt as required, according to circumstances. It will be noticed that with all these clamping devices the clamp may be used continually without the nuts or bolts ever having to be removed, loosening being sufficient. The clamp, E, is similar to the lid of the box-jig illustrated in Fig. 8 and may be used as a clamp or for a location with any type of fixture. A number of the more elaborate designs of clamps are shown with methods of application illustrated in Figs. 10, 11, and 12.

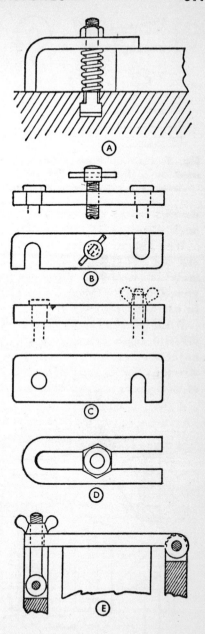

Fig. 9. Five types of clamping device. In all such devices the points to be stressed are holding strength and **rapid tightening and releasing action.**

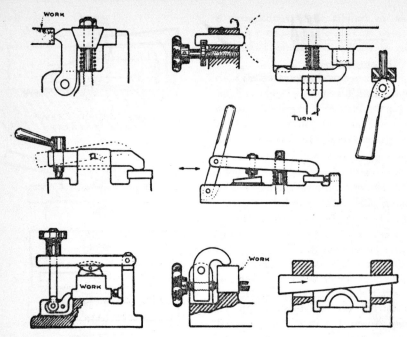

Fig. 10. Varieties of fixture clamps.

Use of Location Points

A clamp should not be used in such a manner as to take the pressure of the cutting tool if this can be avoided. Such pressure should, whenever possible, be taken on fixed location points, and the work-piece should not be located on the flat base of a jig or fixture, but on some form of insert such as is shown in Fig. 13. Detail A would be suitable for taking the thrust of a drill for a drilling jig, the hole in the bushing being a clearance size to allow the drill to pass right through. Detail B could be used as a location or support for the work for any type of jig or fixture; being adjustable, it can easily be set to the required position, and on

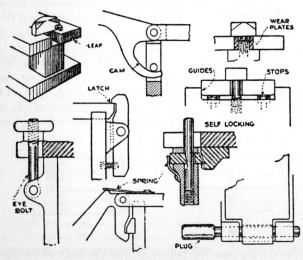

Fig. 11. Jig leaf clamps.

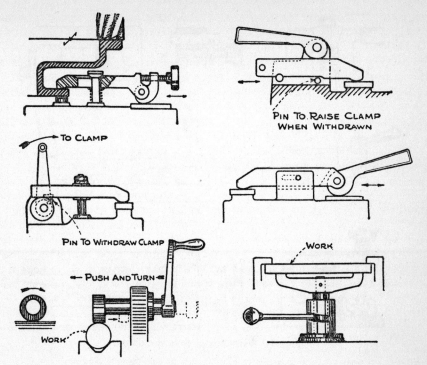

Fig. 12. Cam type fixture clamps.

a small locating point there is less danger of dirt lodging to cause inaccuracy. Such locating points may be in the form of shaped pads to conform to irregular or curved surfaces as at C, and by means of a number of points any shape of work-piece may be conveniently held in position.

With drilling jigs, the drill should always be guided by a hardened-steel bushing let into the body of the jig.

For a single drilling operation the type of bushing shown at A, Fig. 13 is very suitable, the hole in the bushing being a good running fit for the drill and the bushing a tight press fit in the jig. It often happens, however, that a hole is to be drilled slightly small, to be followed by a reamer, in which case the arrangement shown at A, Fig. 14 should be adopted. The bushing, X, is fixed in the jig, and two bushings, one

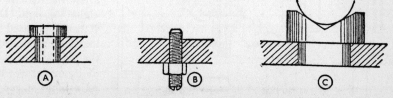

Fig. 13. Location inserts for drilling jigs. The bushes let into the body of the jigs are of hardened steel. The type at A is excellent for a single drilling operation.

of which is shown at Y, are inserted one at a time in the bushing X. One of the bushings, Y, will have a center hole to suit the drill, and the other to suit the reamer. As the bushing Y will be a push fit in X, the pin, Z, is provided to prevent them from running round with the drill or reamer.

In use, the bushing to suit the drill would be inserted while the hole in the work is drilled, and then changed for the one to suit the reamer while the hole is reamed. All bushings for guiding drills should extend downward as far as possible, to provide a support for the drill right up to the point where it meets the work.

A bushing is sometimes required to serve as a location for the work-piece as well as to guide the drill, and such a bushing is shown at B, Fig. 14. The body for the bushing is threaded, and the under-face shaped to the contour of the work-piece, so that the bushing may be screwed down on to the work to hold it. The thread should not be relied on to hold the bushing central, but a plain portion should be left on the bottom of the bushing for the purpose. The head of the bushing may be knurled for a finer grip and holes provided in convenient places for a tommy bar to screw it up tight.

In manufacturing concerns where jigs, etc., are made and used to a large extent, the usual practice is to adopt a range of standard sizes for bushings, locating pads and stops, bolts, wing and knurled nuts, etc. These detail parts may then be made in quantities and kept in stock, thus making them less costly to produce than if they were made singly. And as all such parts would be listed and numbered

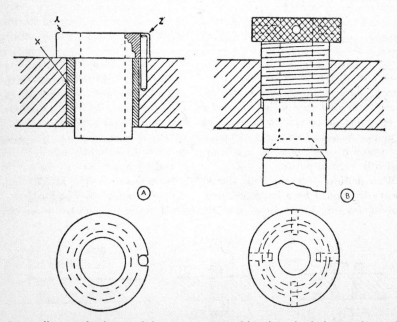

Fig. 14. Drilling jig-bushings of this type are suitable when the hole is to be drilled slightly small and completed by reaming. One bushing Y is holed to suit the drill, the other to suit the reamer. See text for detailed description.

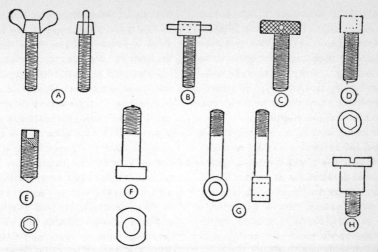

Fig. 15. Standard screws, bolts, and nuts for jigs and fixtures. Each type illustrated has its own advantages for particular jobs, as explained in the text.

in sizes, the tool designer need only specify the parts required by the part numbers, without having to make a detail drawing each time, and the toolmaker can draw the parts from the stockroom at once, without waiting for them to be made.

System of Standards

The system of standards can be applied to all details such as special bolts and nuts, examples being shown in Figs. 15 and 16. Referring to Fig. 15 the thumb-screw, A, gives a very good grip for the fingers and thumb, and, being made solid, is very strong, and will stand a lot of hard use. As this type of screw is made from a drop forging, it can be bought from firms that specialize in making screws much more cheaply than they could be made in the ordinary shop.

The screw, B, is a plain cheese-head

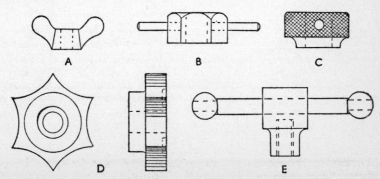

Fig. 16. Nuts such as these, needing no wrench, are suitable for jig work.

screw, drilled and fitted with a pin, and can be made up easily and quickly for a temporary job, but does not give a very good grip for the fingers. The knurled-head screw, C, is very convenient, giving a good grip for screwing up quickly, and a small pin can be used in the hole for the final tightening. The screw, D, is the well-known socket-head type, a special key being used which fits the hexagonal recess in the head. This screw is invaluable in cases where the head must be sunk flush with a face, the key giving a much more powerful locking effect than the old cheese-head screw locked with a screw-driver. E shows the same idea applied to a grub screw.

At F is shown the kind of bolt used in a T slot in a machine table. The head of the bolt, being a fit in the slot, prevents the bolt from turning while the nut is tightened for clamping the work on the machine. The bolt, G, is known as an eye-bolt, and is used in cases where the bolt must be swung aside to release a clamp or the work itself, as the case may be. A shoulder screw as used for clamps, latches, or parts which must be allowed to swing or pivot about a point while still remaining attached to the jig is shown at H.

Special Nuts

In Fig. 16 several types of nut are shown which are suitable for quick handling on jig and fixture work. The main feature of these nuts is that they can be turned without the need for a spanner. The nut, A, is the common wing nut, and is very useful in a confined space, while the nut, B, is a plain hexagonal nut fitted with two pins, a rather weak arrangement, but one which may have its uses occasionally. The knurled nut, C, may be tightened sufficiently with the fingers for light work, and holes may be provided for a small pin for locking more firmly. The hand nut, D, is used chiefly in the larger sizes, and the blanks may be castings kept in stock and the hole drilled and tapped any size needed.

The nut, E, provides the strongest grip of all, and the small pin may be a loose fit in the nut to allow it to be moved to one side to avoid projections on the fixture.

Use of Templates

Simple forms of jigs, sometimes known as templates, are used in the bench-vise when parts with irregular profiles have to be made by hand. Such a template is shown in Fig. 17, and is used as a guide for the file just as a drilling jig is a guide for the drill. The template is very useful when several parts such as flat plates have to be filed to a certain shape.

The plate, A, can first be filed roughly to shape, and then placed on the template, B, using the pins, C, to

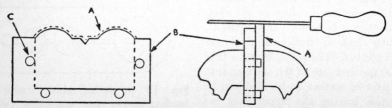

Fig. 17. Template for use as a file guide in hand-work with irregular profile.

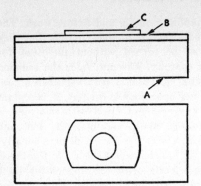

Fig. 18. Vise-holding block for filing washers or thin flat work-pieces.

locate the work correctly with the profile formed on the template, both being then placed in the vise. The work can now be filed away with the file kept straight and level until the edge of the work is down even with the edge of the template. The pins, C, should protrude from the template slightly less than the thickness of the work so that the job will be firmly gripped in the vise; with very thin plates, several may be placed together in the template and filed at the same time.

The template should be made of tool steel and hardened to prevent it from being damaged by the file when the work is finally down to size and shape.

Sometimes washers or thin flat parts have to be filed on the faces to reduce the thickness. These are very difficult to hold in the vise, but with a holding block such as that shown in Fig. 18 this is much simplified. The body, A, is a plain block of steel of suitable size for holding in the vise. On the top is fastened a thin plate, B, slightly less in thickness than the work-piece, C. The plate, B, has a hole the shape and size of the work so that the part or washer to be filed can be inserted, leaving the upper face exposed.

Another convenient type of holding plate is the one shown in Fig. 19 for holding screws. When a screw has to be held for work to be done on the head or the screw cut to length, it is difficult to hold in the vise without doing damage to the thread. The plate in Fig. 19 is of mild steel plate, and is drilled and tapped for different-size screws, and then sawed down the middle.

The screw to be held can be placed in the appropriate hole in the plate, and the plate then held in the vise, leaving the ends of the screw free for whatever work may have to be carried out.

The vise-clamp shown in Fig. 20 is convenient for holding a small work, the work being held in the vise-clamp and the vise clamp itself held in the bench-vise. The work may be held in that way for filing, or the vise-clamp used on the surface plate for marking out, or on the drilling table for drilling fine holes in small work. These vise-clamps are usually made in pairs, so that long, slender work may be held in the two vises, one at each end, thereby being kept exactly level.

Although fixtures are not used on lathes to the same extent as they are on other machines, there are certain devices which have proved of value on repetitive work where the quantity

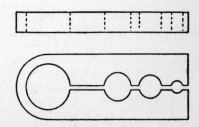

Fig. 19. A drilled plate, useful for holding screws that are being cut or worked on at the head.

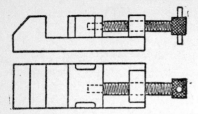

Fig. 20. Vise-clamp for holding small work; the clamp itself is held in the bench-vise. Vise-clamps are usually made in pairs, to keep long work level.

justifies the cost of making a fixture.

The reason why fixtures are not found very much in use on lathe work is that repetitive work is nearly always performed on capstan, turret, or automatic machines, and these machines, together with the wide range of tools and tool-holders, are so universal in themselves as to be capable of almost any job without accessories.

A very useful fixture is shown in Fig. 22 for guiding a lathe tool for forming the radius in the work-piece, A. This should perhaps be termed a special tool-holder rather than a fixture, and consists of a worm wheel, B, to which is fastened the tool-bit, C, the whole rotating on the stud, D. The tool is fed into the work to the required depth of cut with the lathe slide-rest, and then rotated by the handle, E, and the worm, F, the whole attachment being bolted to the tool-holder slide through the base-plate, G.

Such an attachment would have to be specially designed to suit the particular size of lathe on which it would be used, as the thickness of the various parts would have to be such as to maintain the correct center height of the tool. The actual radius formed on the work is governed by the distance

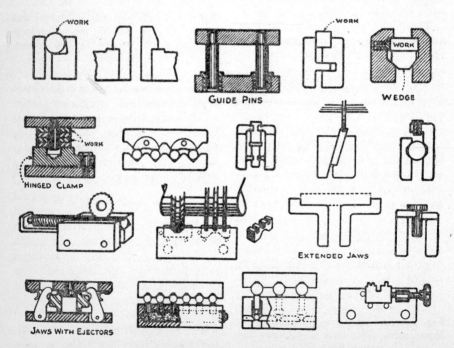

Fig. 21. Varieties of vise jaws.

by which the tool bit stands out from the center of the pivot.

In Fig. 23 is shown a simple fixture built up with the aid of an angle plate, A, mounted on the face-plate, B, of the lathe, the work being held on a special stud, C, made to suit the hole in the work. The flat face of the work-piece would first be machined to provide a clean surface suitable for bolting to the angle plate, and then set up in the lathe to run true, or on a center line the correct distance from the machined face as required, extra support being provided by the tailstock center if necessary. In this case, a simple example has been chosen for the sake of a clear illustration of the principle of this type of fixture, but it will be evident that the idea may be enlarged upon and more elaborate fixtures designed on the same lines to cope with more complicated jobs.

The device shown in Fig. 24 is an attachment for an ordinary center lathe for cutting an oil groove in solid bearing bushings. This is a job usually done by hand in small shops. It is done by special-purpose machines in shops equipped for specialized production on a large scale, but where such machinery is not justified by reason of the smaller quantities in which parts are produced, the arrangement shown will prove a very useful and advantageous one.

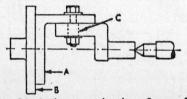

Fig. 23. Built-up angle-plate fixture for lathe work. The stud C matches the hole in the work.

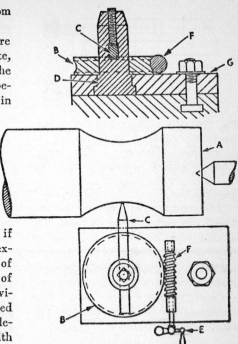

Fig. 22. A fixture or tool-holder of this type is useful for forming the radius in a work-piece such as A in the above diagram.

The work is held in the lathe-chuck in the usual manner, and the oil-groove cut by a suitably-shaped boring tool held in the tool-post. The cam, A, is fastened to the end of the lathe spindle, and draws the lathe saddle to and fro during the revolution of the lathe spindle by the guide roller and stud at B and the links, C. The cam will have to be designed to provide a length of stroke slightly less than the length of the bushing, and may be arranged to move the tool one stroke each way or twice during one revolution of the work, in accordance with the style of oil groove required.

The lathe must be run very slowly, and a very light cut taken at each

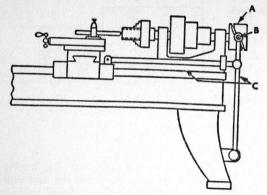

Fig. 24. Center lathe attachment for cutting oil grooves in solid bearing bushings, a job which is usually done by hand in small shops.

revolution until the desired depth of groove is obtained.

Toolmakers' Buttons

A job often required to be done on the lathe is that of boring holes in a jig-plate or press-tool die, where the holes are to be spaced out correctly. The usual method adopted is to drill small holes in the positions as required and tap them for a small screw.

A small bushing, known as a button, which is ground true on the outside to a certain known diameter, usually about .500 in., is then fixed with a screw at each place where a hole is to be bored, and by means of slip-gauges or some other measuring device the buttons are spaced out in the exact position. The die or jig-plate is then mounted on the face-plate of the lathe, clamped in position for boring the first hole, and with the aid of an indicator on the outside of the bushing the work is adjusted on the face-plate until the bushing is running true, when the bushing or button may be removed and the hole bored. Each hole is dealt with in the same manner in turn, and although the method insures accuracy, it is generally a rather slow and laborious way of doing the job.

A Better Method

A much quicker method is shown in Fig. 25, and with the same amount of care taken will prove quite as accurate as using buttons. The jig-plate, A, is to be bored at points 1, 2, 3, and 4, and for simplicity we may assume that the centers of the holes are 2 inches apart as shown. The job is shown set up on the face-plate of the lathe, ready for boring hole number 1, and the guide-strips, B and C, are set against the sides of the work, and clamped securely to the face-plate.

Having bored hole number 1, the work is moved, leaving B and C still clamped in place, and blocks or slip-gages placed between strip, B, and the work, A, equal to the distance between holes 1 and 2. The work is next

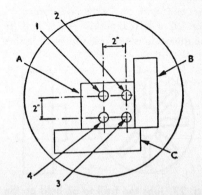

Fig. 25. A jig-plate can be bored by this method (see text) more quickly and as accurately as by using buttons.

clamped to the face-plate in the position for boring hole number 2, after which slip-gages can be placed between the work and the strip, C, for boring hole 3, and the first slip-gauges taken away for boring hole 4.

The four holes to be bored being in the form of a square makes the example a simple one to explain, and if the holes were spaced unequally or in any other pattern, a certain amount of calculation would be necessary to determine the distance the work would have to be moved for each successive hole. Such calculations would also be required and, in fact, would be exactly the same if the job were to be done in a special jig boring machine, and would be very simple, an elementary knowledge of the first principles of trigonometry being all that would be required.

Designing Holed Jigs

When designing jig and tool parts having holes which will be bored on a jig boring machine, the dimensions on the drawing for the positions of the holes will be of most assistance to the operator if they are all given from one end and one side. Reference to Fig. 26 will make this clear, and as the dimensions are laid out in the same

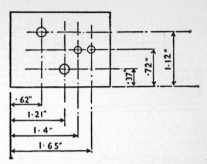

Fig. 26. Dimensions for jig boring should all be given from one end and one side, as here shown.

manner as the operator will work in setting the job for each hole, the figures will be the actual figures required for the various movements of the machine table.

The majority of work done in the lathe is held between centers, bolted to the face-plate, or held in a three- or four-jaw chuck, according to the nature of the job and the work to be performed.

Some jobs, however, are too frail to be held in any of these ways, and to overcome this difficulty a magnetic chuck is used. Referring to Fig. 27 the chuck consists of a plain cylindrical body in which are set several pole-pieces, separated from the chuck and each other by a surrounding of lead. Behind these pole-pieces inside the chuck are the magnets, which may be switched on or off with a key on the stud.

Magnetic Chucks

The work is simply placed on the chuck-face in the desired position, and when the magnets are switched on, the work is held firmly against the chuck without any distortion. The grip is not as powerful as an ordinary jaw-chuck, therefore much lighter cuts

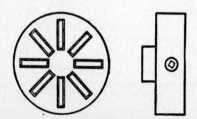

Fig. 27. Jobs too frail to be held on the lathe in the ordinary way may be secured by a chuck by means of permanent magnets.

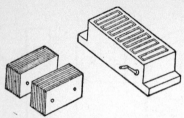

Fig. 28. *Right,* chuck for surface grinding, with permanent magnets; *left,* magnetic parallel blocks for holding small work.

must be taken, but this condition would apply to frail jobs in any case.

Some of these magnetic chucks are actuated by electro-magnets, and some by permanent magnets. The latter are more convenient, as the chuck is self-contained, and is switched on or off by moving the magnets into or out of contact with the pole-pieces. With electro-magnets an outside source of electric current is required, and this entails the use of slip-rings on the chuck and a separate switch.

The rotary magnetic chuck just described for use on the lathe is also used on the cylindrical and universal grinding machines; in fact, it can be used to a larger extent for grind work, as the pressure of the cut is comparatively lighter than with any other machine. On the surface grinder the type of chuck shown in Fig. 28 is used.

The method of operation is the same as for the rotary chuck, and in this case electro-magnets are not much of an inconvenience, for since the chuck is stationary on the machine table no slip-rings are required, the feed wires being connected directly to the chuck.

When very small work has to be held on a magnetic chuck the pieces may be too small to bridge across the pole-pieces, and the magnetic blocks shown in Fig. 28 have to be used. These blocks are made up of lamina-

tions of soft iron plates and brass or aluminum plates riveted together, and are usually made in pairs the same length, width, and thickness. When in use, the blocks are laid on the chuck with the edges of the laminations upward, and the work laid on the blocks. As small pieces of work have not sufficient mass to allow them to be held very firmly, only very light cuts should be attempted.

Grinding of Curves

The grinding of curves and radii often involves the dressing of the grinding wheel to the radius required, and a diamond holder designed for this purpose is shown in Fig. 29.

The base-plate, A, is placed on the table or chuck of the machine, and the arm and pillar, B, rotates about the center of the stud. The pillar is made a certain distance from the center of the stud, usually 1 in., and the diamond pencil, C, is set either in front of or behind the center, according to whether an inside or outside radius is required. For instance, if the point of the diamond is set $1\frac{1}{2}$ in. from the center line of the stud a $\frac{1}{2}$-in. concave

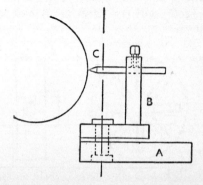

Fig. 29. Grinding wheel dressing fixture with diamond-holder for grinding curved surfaces and radii.

radius will be formed in the wheel. Similarly, if the diamond is set ½ in. from the pillar it will be ½ in. from the center line of the stud and a ½-in. convex radius would be formed on the wheel. Thus it will be seen that by carefully setting the diamond point the required distance from the pillar any desired radius within the capacity of the fixture, either convex or concave, may be formed.

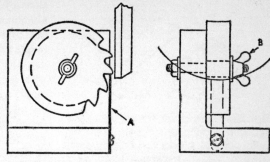

Fig. 30. Milling cutters may be sharpened on a surface grinder with the aid of such a fixture as this.

An important point which must be carefully observed is that the height of the diamond point must be the same as the height of the center of the grinding wheel which is to be dressed.

In Fig. 30 is shown a simple device for sharpening milling cutters on a surface grinder when a special cutter grinding machine is not available. The cutter is mounted on a stud on an angle plate, and a stop, A, provided to set the cutter in position for grinding each successive tooth. When set, the cutter is traversed past the grinding wheel, and after each tooth is ground the wing-nut, B, is loosened, stop, A, swung aside and the cutter turned and re-set ready for grinding the next tooth.

A job sometimes called for on the surface grinder is the grinding of longitudinal grooves or splines, which have to be spaced equally around the circumference of a shaft or plug. After each groove is ground, the shaft has to be turned round through a certain angle to bring it into position for the next one. This is known as indexing.

The fixture shown in Fig. 31 is a simple indexing fixture, and consists of the centers for supporting the work and the index plate, A. This index plate or dividing plate has notches carefully spaced round the edge, and a locating stop, B, is made a good fit in the notch. A separate index plate is required for each different job with the notches spaced the same as the spaces on the work, and the larger the plate can be made the better, as any errors in spacing are thereby more easily minimized.

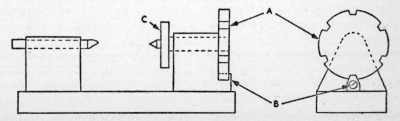

Fig. 31. Simple indexing fixture. A, Index plate; B, locating stop fitting securely into notch; C, driving plate, with slot into which fits the tool of a carrier.

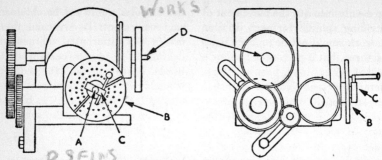

Fig. 32. Universal dividing head set for differential indexing. The work-spindle may be used horizontal, as shown, or at any angle up to the vertical.

The work is set between the centers and fitted with a carrier, the tail of which fits in a slot in the driving plate, C, as in ordinary lathe work. When once set the carrier must not be moved until the job is finished. As each groove is ground in the work the stop, B, is moved aside, the index plate turned through one division, and the stop replaced ready for the next groove.

Indexing Fixtures

Instead of notches, the index plates are sometimes made with a circle of holes with a peg for a stop, but as a peg needs a certain amount of clearance, however small, to be able to enter all the holes, the wedge action of the stop as shown in the slightly tapered notches will be found to be more accurate and positive.

This type of dividing fixture is also used in the same way on the milling machine for milling splined shafts, the flutes in reamers, and jobs of a similar nature.

The simple indexing fixture described above is quite satisfactory for dividing work into a convenient number of divisions which will allow room in the index plate for the holes or notches, up to about 24 divisions, but if a larger number of divisions is re-

quired, or the spacing is uneven, it would be very difficult to make a plate with the holes in exactly the right positions. In such cases, therefore, the attachment known as the universal dividing head is used, and the dividing termed indirect indexing.

The work is held between centers of a face-plate which may be fitted to the dividing head, as in Fig. 32, and the head may be used with the work-spindle in the horizontal position shown or at any angle up to the vertical. The actual indexing is done on a separate spindle which is connected to the work-spindle by a worm and wheel reduction gear with a ratio of 40 to 1, so that the dividing spindle, A, has to be moved 40 turns to produce 1 turn on the work spindle, D.

Indirect Indexing

Therefore, if the work is to be divided into 40 divisions, the dividing spindle would have to be turned one complete revolution to provide each division, or $\frac{1}{40}$ of a turn of the work-spindle. Similarly, if 10 divisions are required, then the dividing spindle would be turned 4 turns for each division.

For a number of divisions greater than 40, or a number which will not divide evenly into 40, the movement of the dividing spindle for each division of the work would not be an even number of turns, but a part of a turn or a number of turns plus a part of a turn. To determine such part of a turn a certain amount of simple arithmetic is required. To understand the method of working as clearly as possible, suppose for example that it is desired to divide a job into 100 divisions. Forty must be divided by the number of divisions required, which is $^{40}/_{100}$ or $^4/_{10}$, and that is the amount the dividing spindle must be turned for each division.

The Index Plate

An index plate, B, Fig. 32, is used with several circles of holes, each circle having a different number of holes, and a crank-arm, C, is fitted on the dividing spindle and provided with a peg which can be pushed into any hole. The peg is made to be moved along the arm so that any circle of holes can be used, and if the dividing spindle has to be moved $^4/_{10}$ of a turn, a plate is selected having a circle of 20 holes and the movement will be 8 holes each time.

To save the trouble of counting the holes each time, and also to avoid any possibility of error, the sector arms can be set nine holes apart. Then, when each movement is made, the crank is moved forward until it meets the next sector arm, and the peg placed in the adjacent hole. After that, the two arms are moved forward together until the first arm meets the peg and in this manner is left ready for the next movement. There are certain numbers which cannot be divided in this way, for whatever the number of holes in the index plate, a whole num-

ber of holes would not be obtained for each movement. To overcome this difficulty the differential method of indexing is used on certain dividing heads. By this method the index plate is made to turn by gears from the spindle, so that as the crank is turned the plate turns, either in the same or opposite direction.

Finding the Gear Ratio

A full set of gears and index plates are provided with these dividing heads; to find the ratio of gears required, select the nearest number, either above or below the number of divisions required, which is easy to factor. Then if X is the number of divisions required, and Y the nearest number selected, the gear ratio is equal to the difference between X and Y multiplied by 40 and divided by Y.

To find the indexing movement, divide 40 by Y, and this is the amount the crank must be turned each time. For instance, if Y is 90, the movement of the crank would be $^4/_9$ of a turn, and an index circle of 27 holes could be used, and 12 holes moved each time. One or two idler gears will be required to connect the driver and driven gears, according to whether the plate and crank must move in the same or the opposite directions.

Idler Gears

If the number Y is more than the number X, the plate and crank move in the same direction and one idler gear is used. But if Y is smaller than the number X, the plate and crank move in opposite directions and two idler gears are required to reverse the motion. A certain amount of trial may be required to find a gear ratio which may be convenient for the gears available and in some cases compound gears may have to be used. In any case the principle is the same.

For cutting a helix or spiral, the worm spindle of the dividing head is geared to the lead screw of the machine table. To find the gears required to cut a spiral of any given lead, the lead of the machine must be known; that is, the distance the machine table would travel during one revolution of the dividing spindle if gears with equal numbers of teeth were used, giving a ratio of one to one.

Cutting Spirals

As the common practice is to make the gearing of the dividing head with a ratio of 40 to 1 and the lead of the machine table feed screw ¼ in., the lead of the machine is usually 10 in. To find the gear ratio required, divide the lead of the spiral to be cut by the lead of the machine or, in other words, the ratio may be expressed as a frac-

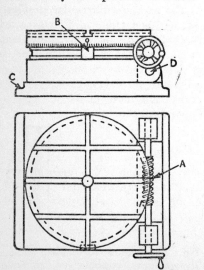

Fig. 33. Dividing table with calibrated rim for vertical milling machine.

tion in which the lead of the spiral is the numerator and the lead of the machine is the denominator.

When using the dividing head geared to the machine lead screw for cutting spirals, the work spindle may be used either horizontal, vertical, or at any angle between, but when differential indexing is used the spindle must be horizontal. The spindle can be used only at an angle other than horizontal when the work is to be held in a chuck or on the face-plate, either a three-jaw self-centering chuck screwed on the spindle or a collett chuck in the taper hollow spindle being used, according to the size of the job.

Dividing Turn-Tables

On some vertical milling machines a dividing table (Fig. 33) is used which has the rim of the table calibrated in degrees, and a block or plate fixed to the base which carries a zero line. The table turns on a stud in the center, and can be moved around through any angle required, a worm, A, being provided meshing with teeth cut in the rim of the turn-table.

For fine work, where angles must be accurate, a vernier is sometimes provided on the plate, B, carrying the zero line, but the most accurate arrangement consists of the use of reduction gears between the handle and the worm, with the rim of the hand-wheel marked off in suitable divisions. By this means it is possible to set the table to any angle accurate to one second.

These turn-tables are sometimes also made to be used horizontal, vertical, or at any angle, the table and its base being mounted on another base, C, hinged at the point, D, and locked in

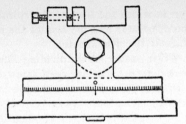

Fig. 34. Adjustable vise for setting up work at an angle, for use with a dividing table which cannot be elevated.

any desired position. They are extremely useful for milling work or boring holes at any combination of angles.

Adjustable Vise

For use in connection with a dividing table which cannot be elevated, or on a plain machine table, the adjustable vise shown in Fig. 34 can be used for setting up work at an angle. The base of the vise has keys which fit the bolt-slots in the machine table, and the vise can be turned on the base to any angle as well as being set at any angle from horizontal to vertical. Division scales are provided for setting the angles, and are usually graduated in degrees or half degrees, which is sufficiently accurate for most jobs for which such a fixture would be used.

In Fig. 35 is shown an arrangement for milling the slots in screw-heads, a good feature of the device being that the production is continuous, as the machine does not have to be stopped for loading and unloading.

Two circular discs are mounted face to face on spindles, with the spindles set at a slight angle so that the faces of the discs are closer at the top than at the bottom. Holes to receive the screws are drilled half in each disc, all around the edges, and the discs are rotated by a worm-gear, the two discs being kept together by dowels which are tight fit in one disc and a loose fit in the other, to allow a certain amount of movement. The screws to be milled are placed in the holes at one side, and as they are carried round as the discs rotate, they are gripped tight when reaching the opposition, owing to the disc being set closer together at the top. The slots are milled as the screws are carried past the slitting saw or cutter A, and when they reach the other side the discs become farther apart and the screws fall out into a chute. The cutter and the fixture run in opposite directions, and all the operator has to do is to keep feeding screws into the holes, and the rest is done automatically.

An efficient guard must be provided to protect the operator's fingers from being injured by the cutter, an important point which applies to all milling and most other machine work.

A Profile-Milling Feature

The milling of irregular profiles is another job with which fixtures may be used to advantage, much time being saved and also production costs re-

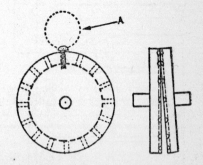

Fig. 35. Fixture for milling slots in screw-heads, capable of continuous production without stopping the machine for loading and unloading.

duced by employing a semi-skilled operator.

In Fig. 36 two arrangements are shown, in both of which a hardened-steel former or master copy, A, is used with a profile the exact replica of the work-piece to be milled. In the first case, shown at X, the copy and work-piece, B, are mounted together, and the cutter, C, has a roller, D, on the shank the same size as the cutter. The job is clamped on the table of a vertical milling machine of the type in which the table-slides are operated by long levers and a rack and pinion. By means of one lever the operator keeps the work and former pressed against the cutter and roller, and with the other lever feeds the work past the cutter. The roller following the profile of the master copy guides the work past the cutter, and the required shape is reproduced automatically.

A disadvantage of this method is that too much pressure is likely to force the cutter out of line, and also it is difficult to provide compensation for the effect of the wear of the cutter.

With the arrangement shown at Y, the cutter is relieved of the pressure on the copy, the follower, E, being mounted independently on a bracket; and as the end of the follower and the edge of the copy are made at an angle of about 5 deg., by slightly raising or lowering the follower a fine adjustment is possible to control the finished size of the work.

In any case, it is important that where the master copy and the work are the same size, the follower and the cutter must also be the same size.

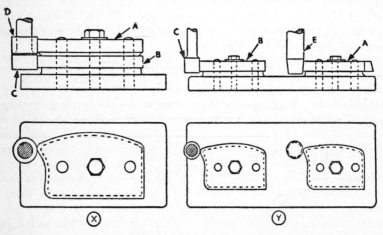

Fig. 36. Two fixtures for milling irregular profiles. A master-copy (A) is used, the profile of which is a replica of that to be given to the work-piece (B).

CHAPTER 10

PRESSING, STAMPING, AND PUNCHING

TYPES OF PRESS, OPERATIONS THEY PERFORM. FLY, POWER, AND INCLINABLE PRESSES. FEEDING DEVICES. MOTORS. DOUBLE-ACTION PRESSES. PRESS TOOLS. DIES. DRAWING CUP-SHAPED ARTICLES. CURLING EDGES. MEDAL PRESSING. PUNCHES AND PUNCHING. DRIFTS. DINKING PUNCHES.

THERE is a wide variety of things produced by means of presses of various types, and this section deals first with the presses used for different purposes, with a description of each type. This will be followed by a description of the tools used in the presses, with hints on their design, construction, and operation.

The type of press most commonly used is the single-action crank press, this being a more or less standard machine and adaptable to many special purposes. It is in general use for the majority of press jobs.

Variety of Machines

When one considers, however, the number of different industries in which presses are employed—in the manufacture of telephones, electrical goods, sewing-machines, radio, automobile, and aircraft parts, and the large quantities in which such articles are produced, the modern tendency towards the use of special machines will be easily understood.

A power-press, or any other machine which is specially built for a certain class of work, is far more efficient than a machine which is adapted as a makeshift, and where a large volume of work of a certain class has to be handled, the use of a machine designed for the purpose is well worth while. On the other hand, if the demand for an article is small, and the cost of a special machine is not justified, the adaptation of the standard type of press offers some interesting possibilities.

Aids to Speedy Work

As economy means everything in press work, full use should be made of all possible aids to rapid production, such as roll feeds, magazine feeds, automatic ejectors, etc., and where dies can be designed to produce two or more pieces at a time, this should, of course, be done.

The usual operations called for in press work are hot pressing or stamping, cold pressing, embossing, coining, blanking, punching, drawing, bending, forming, and swaging, many of these processes being sometimes combined in one operation.

Presses vary in size and capacity from small bench presses, of a few tons pressure, to massive machines 20 ft. in height, capable of exerting a

329

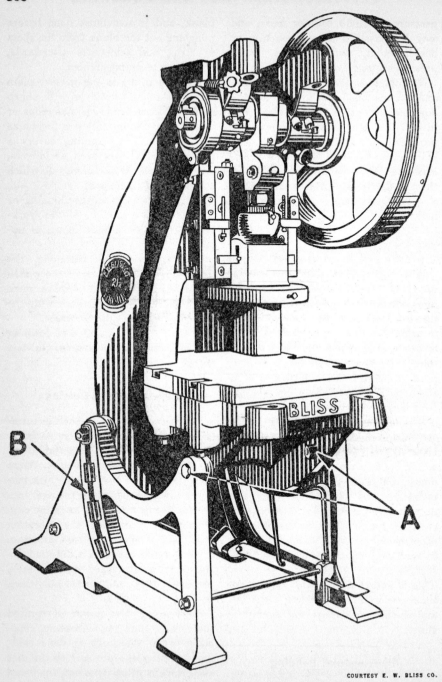

Fig. 1. An inclinable open-back power press: *A,* Press frame pivots; *B,* Quadrant for locking the frame in any of four positions.

pressure of 1,000 tons or more, and may be classified as single-action or double-action, and also as crank presses or toggle presses.

The single-action press has one ram, and carries one punch, whereas the double-action press has two rams, one inside the other, and carries two punches working independently. The crank-press provides what may be described as a heavy blow compared with that of the toggle press, which gives a steady squeeze; a description of both will be given later.

Terms in Common Use

Although terms and expressions used to describe operations vary to some extent, the following explanation of common terms will be found to comply with general practice. The terms *pressing* and *stamping* sometimes refer to the whole job, a finished piece of work being referred to as a stamping if flat, or as a pressing if formed or shaped.

The operation of *blanking* means the cutting or punching out of the flat material the shape required, from which the finished article is to be produced. This is nearly always the first operation, and may be the only one necessary, or it may be followed successively by many others. Blanking is often combined with other operations in one tool, all the work being performed at one stroke of the press. This is an aid to economy, and sometimes assists in maintaining accuracy, and should be adopted whenever possible.

Piercing and Bending

Piercing or *punching* means the punching of holes of any shape in the blank, and is sometimes done before punching out the blank from the sheet or strip, and sometimes afterwards, according to circumstances.

Bending refers to one or more plain bends, whether curved or with sharp corners. When bends are numerous or complicated the operation is known as *forming;* in fact, forming covers a multitude of shapes such as indents, recesses, channels, or curves into which the work may be bent.

Swaging usually means thinning or squashing of a portion of the workpiece, and is sometimes known as upsetting.

Planishing means flattening the work between flat faces of the punch and die, usually done to remove burrs and wrinkles, but sometimes with the object of reducing the thickness.

Drawing is the process of forming cup or dish-shaped articles in one piece.

Embossing and Coining

Embossing usually means the forming of shapes such as letters or fancy designs on fairly thin material where the design shows on both sides. When such designs are formed on thick material and the shape is pressed into the surface of the metal, as in the case of coins or medallions, the operation is known as *coining* or *cold pressing.* With this class of work a different design may be produced on each side, provided that the metal is thick enough.

Very much more power is required for coining than for embossing, especially when the work is done cold; and to relieve the pressure on the dies such work is often done hot, the metal being heated sufficiently to cause it to flow easily. This is known as *hot press-*

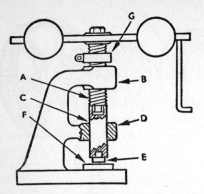

Fig. 2. The simplest of all presses is the fly-press, as here shown. A, screw; B, nut; C, ram; D, guide; E, punch; F, die; G, stop collar for setting the punch to the correct depth.

ing and is, in fact, very similar to forging as far as the mechanical action of the dies on the work is concerned.

The fly-press is the simplest of all presses, and was the forerunner of the efficient machines in use at the present time. It is an early example of the use of energy in a moving body, the rotary motion of heavy iron balls being transformed into the vertical motion of a ram by a screw.

Although it is a machine used chiefly for rough work such as bending bars and punching holes in plates, a well-made press of this type can be used, on a small scale, for all work usually done in a power-press. In fact, small press-tools intended for use in a power-press are sometimes *tried out* in a fly-press, but care must be taken to see that the ram is a good fit in the guide and square with the base. See Fig. 2.

As far as the action of the punch and die is concerned, the fly-press is the same as the power-press, the only difference being that with the fly-press the ram is moved up and down by the

screw, whereas with the power-press the ram is driven by the crankshaft and connecting rod. The punch is fastened to the ram in a similar manner, and the die is bolted to the bed of the press.

The power-press, illustrated in Fig. 3, is a type of press in very common use for all kinds of press-work, and, being a standard type, those built by different makers vary very little in construction, except in details, such as the manner of locking adjustments.

In the press illustrated, for instance, the adjustment for setting the ram is locked by means of the lock-nuts shown at A, and the punch is held in the ram by means of the clamp-nuts shown at B. This machine is driven directly by a belt running on the flywheel, the clutch inside the fly-

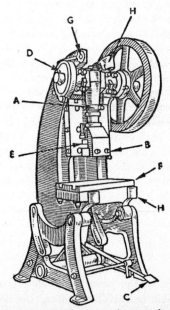

Fig. 3. Principal parts of an inclinable power-press. A, lock nuts; B, clamp nut for punch; C, clutch pedal; D, brake; E, knock-out bar; F, bolster-plate; G, brake adjustment; H, tie-bar lugs.

wheel, operated by the pedal, C, transmitting the drive to the crankshaft. The clutch is automatically disengaged just before the ram reaches the top of the stroke, and the crankshaft is held in that position by the brake, D.

When the pedal is kept pressed down and the press runs continuously for blanking from strip stock, the brake should be released to prevent it becoming overheated, except on the better-class of machine, where the brake is coupled to the clutch-pedal and only comes into operation when the pedal is released.

The brake is adjusted by the hand-wheel, G, and should normally be set just tight enough to hold the crankshaft, and prevent it from turning under the weight of the ram.

When certain types of tool are used for operations such as forming and drawing (to be described later), the work has a tendency to remain held in the punch, and means must be provided for ejection. This is done by the knock-out bar shown at E, which is so arranged as to bear on an ejector rod placed at the center of the punch, ejecting the work from the punch on the upward stroke of the ram.

Setting the Dies

The bolster plate shown at F is adjustable to facilitate setting the dies, and most shops keep a few spare bolsters with different sizes and shapes of hole in the middle to accommodate various sizes of dies. The dies are bolted by their bases directly on the

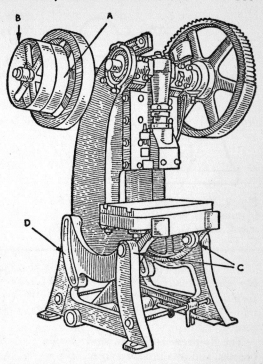

Fig. 4. A gear-driven press. A and B are loose pulleys; C, press-frame pivots; D, quadrant for locking the frame in any of four positions.

bolster, and when the work is delivered through the die into a chute or tray, as in the case of blanking or drawing dies, the hole in the bolster plate must be slightly larger than the work, to allow for delivery.

Presses of this type are built in capacities of from 10 tons to about 100 tons, and for ordinary purpose have a stroke of about 1 in. for the 10-ton size to 3 in. for the 100-ton size.

For special purposes, however, presses are built with an extra long stroke for deep drawing, or with an extra short stroke for high-speed blanking.

In small shops where a large variety of work has to be handled, use is sometimes made of presses with adjustable

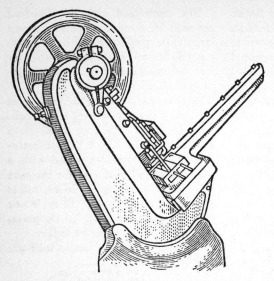

Fig. 5. Press in inclined position, with chute-feed instead of hand-feeding for placing work in the die.

stroke, adjustment being made by an eccentric bushing on the crank-pin.

When presses of this type are used up to or near their maximum capacity, tie-bars are fitted in the lugs shown at H, thereby increasing the rigidity of the frame.

In Fig. 4 is shown the same press arranged with a gear-drive instead of the direct drive on the flywheel. The fast and loose pulleys, A and B, are mounted with the flywheel on the shaft at the near end of the press, and the drive transmitted by pinion and gear to the crankshaft. This arrangement not only reduces the load on the line-shaft, but provides a low speed for the press, which is often essential for certain forming and drawing operations. Another valuable feature of this press is that it can be used either in a vertical position or inclined backward in one of several positions.

The press-frame is pivoted in the stand at point C, and is locked in the desired position in the quadrant at D, four alternative positions being provided in this particular case. For this reason the type of press shown is sometimes referred to as the inclinable press, and is used in the inclined position when the work is to be ejected on top of the die, allowing the work to slide down a chute into a tray at the back of the machine. A considerable saving on production time is thereby effected, the automatic removal of the finished work by gravity leaving the operator free to insert the next piece.

A press in use in the inclined position is shown in Fig. 5, with a chute-feed to replace hand-feeding for placing the work in the die. This arrangement enables a very high production rate to be maintained for those secondary operations to which it may be applied, as the operator does not have to put the work in the die nor does he have to remove it.

This method of feeding can be applied only to work-pieces which will slide down the chute without turning over or getting on top of each other, and a latch or other releasing device is usually required, operated from the ram, to allow the pieces to drop one at a time on to the die.

An important advantage in using an automatic feed of any kind lies in the fact that the operator is relieved from the necessity of placing his fingers anywhere near the die, the danger of injury to fingers which is sometimes present with hand-feeding, being eliminated.

Another type of feeding device known as the index or dial-feed is shown in Fig. 6. The mechanism is arranged on a special bolster mounted on the press-bed, and the work-pieces are placed by the operator in the recesses provided on the disc, A.

This disc is turned one division after each stroke of the ram by the rod-and-lever mechanism, B, operated from the crankshaft. As the finished work is either ejected from the top of the die or pushed out below, according to the particular operation, the operator is required to attend only to the feeding, and the press may be run continuously.

This type of feeding device may be arranged with one die on the bolster at the back of the dial, in which case the dial is merely a feeding plate; or separate dies may be mounted on the dial, each one coming in turn under the punch. Although it is a matter which must depend on the particular job in hand, the former arrangement is usually more satisfactory, and should be adopted whenever it is found possible.

The disadvantage of the latter arrangement is that when the dies are carried round on the dial and each one is brought in turn under the punch, the indexing must be very accurate to insure perfect alignment of the punch and dies. The spacing of the dies on the dial must be perfectly accurate, and a safety device is required to insure that the ram cannot descend until the die is in the exact position under the punch.

The chute-feed and the dial-feed are used for secondary operations on a large variety of work, and may be arranged to suit a standard press, or may be incorporated in a special-purpose machine.

The type of automatic feed most commonly used, however, is the roll-feed used for blanking from strip stock, shown in Fig. 7. The illustration shows a press equipped with a single roll, and is chosen for the sake of simplicity, although a double roll is sometimes used. In this there is one pair of rolls at each side of the press, both rolls being coupled together.

Whether double or single rolls are

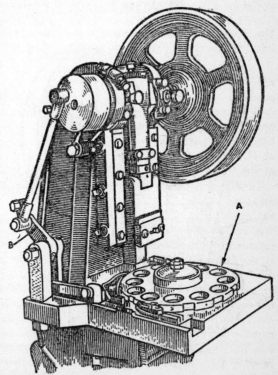

Fig. 6. Press fed by index or dial-feeding device. A is one of the recesses in the disc in which the work-pieces are placed; B, is the rod-and-lever mechanism, operated from the crankshaft, for turning the disc.

used, the method of operation is the same, the motion being taken from the crankshaft through rod, A, to the ratchet, B, the roll, C, and another roll below (not shown) rotating together and drawing the strip-stock along a predetermined distance while the ram is on the upward stroke.

The distance the strip is moved is set as required by the adjustable crank, D, on the end of the crankshaft, and when the rolls have to lift for a moment at the bottom of the stroke, as is the case when certain types of combination tools are used, this is set by means of the adjustable lever, E.

As the height of different tools varies to some extent, and the roll-feed, being part of the press, must accommodate all sizes of tools, the whole of the feed mechanism is adjustable for height and must be set to the same height as the level on the die, in this case by means of the set-screws shown at F.

Roll-feeds are sometimes arranged from side to side across the machine, or from front to back, but the general lay-out is the same.

The increase in production due to the use of a mechanical feed varies with different classes of work, but usually the output is about double that of hand-feeding. In recent years much higher speeds have been built into some presses. This is due to two things; in the first place a mechanical feed allows the press to be run at a higher speed, 200 strokes per minute being quite common—a speed which an operator could hardly be expected to maintain constantly with hand-feeding; secondly, every stroke of the press is productive, whereas with hand-feeding certain strokes are missed occasionally as the operator moves his hands to get a fresh grip of the strip.

In common with other machine tools, the modern tendency is to equip each press with its own motor, the old-fashioned line-shaft being rarely used in the up-to-date shop. Although the first cost of a separate motor for each press is greater, this is offset by the saving in operating costs.

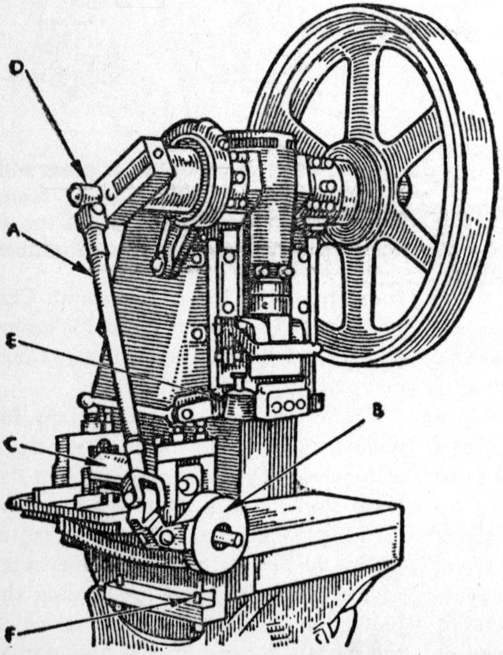

Fig. 7. The commonest automatic feed for presses is the roll-feed used for blanking from strip-stock. There may be a single roll, as above, or a pair of rolls on each side of the press. For references see text.

Driving Motors

With a line-shaft the main driving motor, shaft, and numerous belts, all contributing frictional losses, have to be sufficiently powerful to allow for all the presses being run together. In practice, however, a certain number of presses are usually stopped for adjustments or setting up, and when each press has its own motor any unnecessary waste of power is eliminated. A machine so equipped is shown in Fig. 8, the view from the back of the press showing clearly the motor mounted on a bracket on the top of the press, and the V-belt to the flywheel, the bracket being adjustable to provide the correct tension on the belts.

Although the standard type of press so far described is capable of a very wide range of work, a considerable departure from this design is often necessary for certain kinds of work.

The machine shown in Fig. 9 is a typical example of a press designed for handling work of considerable length, such as sections of cupboards and drawers for office furniture, automobile, and aircraft parts. The operations performed on this type of press are usually cutting, piercing, bending, and forming, and many intricate shapes may be produced in long sections by successive operations.

In the larger sizes, these presses are built up to 15 ft. in length, with a stroke of about 6 in., and are run at a speed of approximately 30 strokes per minute. Some machines also have a second speed available of about 10 strokes per minute.

When the full length of the press is utilized for long work the usual practice is to have two or more operators to handle the large sheets of metal, the operating pedals, shown at A, being adjusted to the most convenient position. The adjustment for the ram is shown at B, both adjusters being coupled together to insure that

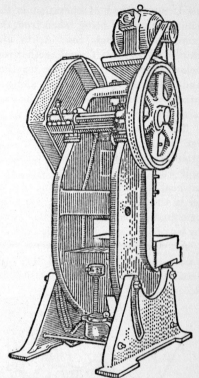

Fig. 8. View from back of a press with direct motor drive. The electric motor is mounted on a bracket on the top of the press, the bracket being adjustable.

they are moved the same amount. Certain machines, known as double-action presses, are constructed with two rams, one working inside the other.

These machines are used chiefly for deep drawing, or forming cup- or dish-shaped articles in one piece from flat sheet-stock, and in the larger sizes for forming panels and sections for automobile bodies. In operation the outer ram is generally used for holding the blank, or sheet of metal from which the part is formed, and in the case of medium or small work the outer punch also cuts the blank from the sheet, the inner punch doing the forming. On very large work, where the sheet of metal would be too cumbersome to handle in strip, the blanks are cut to approximate size first, then formed, and finally trimmed to size and shape after forming.

Action of the Rams

The two rams carrying the outer and inner punches act independently of each other, the outer ram descending first to cut the blank from the sheet and then to dwell, holding the blank against the die-face, while the inner punch descends farther into the die forming the blank to the required shape. This will be dealt with in further detail in the section devoted to press tools.

In Fig. 11 is shown a typical double-action drawing press of the type used in the manufacture of automobile bodies. The actual machine illustrated represents the largest type of machine in use for this class of work, and is approximately 20 ft. in height, with a total weight of 80 tons.

A Monster Press

This machine is capable of drawing or forming to a depth of 15 in., and with a crankshaft of 12 in. diameter may exert a total pressure of about

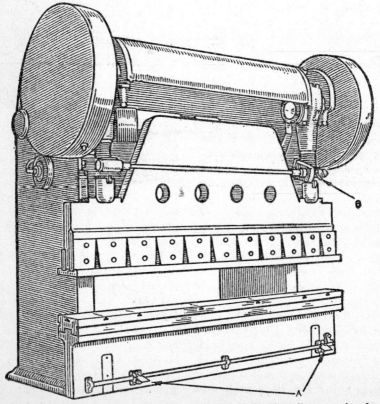

Fig. 9. Special presses such as this are designed for handling work of great length, such as office furniture, and automobile and aircraft parts. Operating pedals are shown at A, ram adjusters at B, which are coupled together.

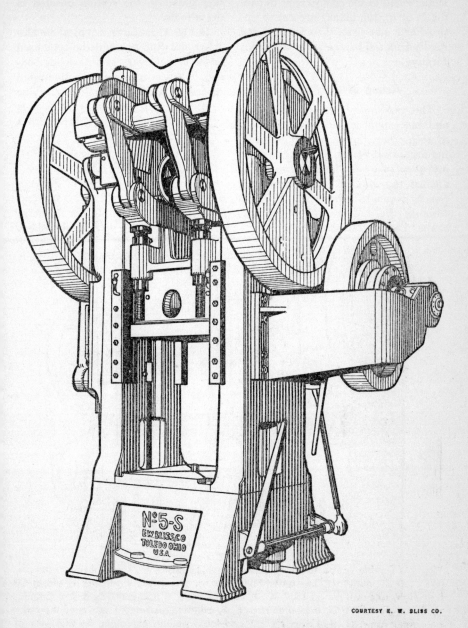

Fig. 10. A single-crank toggle drawing press.

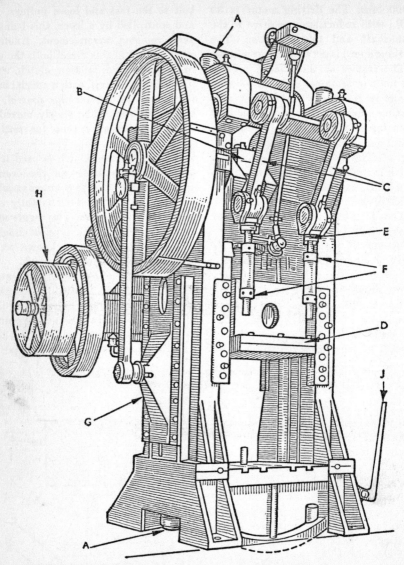

Fig. 11. Double-action toggle presses, of which this is a representative example, are used in manufacturing automobile bodies. The press illustrated is about 20 feet high, and weighs 80 tons. *A, A,* are the rods; *B,* the crankshaft and pitman; *C, C,* toggle levers; *D,* the outer ram; *E, F,* adjustments for the stroke of the inner and outer rams; *G,* side ram; *H,* fast and loose pulleys controlled by the lever at *J.* See page 341 for detailed description of working.

1,000 tons. The driving motor is 80 H.P., with reduction-gear drive to the crankshaft and toggle motion. The working speed is six strokes per minute.

The frames of these large presses are built in sections, and the working strain is taken by massive tie-rods passing through the side members from top to bottom, and shrunk into place, one being seen in position at A, Fig. 11. The crankshaft and pitman, to which is coupled the inner ram, can be seen at B, and at C the toggle levers which operate the outer ram, D.

The adjustments for the depth of stroke of the inner and outer rams are at E and F respectively, being entirely independent. The side-ram shown at G is used for cutting the waste metal into short lengths to facilitate handling, and is known as the scrap-cutter, and is only required when the metal is fed to the dies in strip form. The drive from the motor is by belt to the fast and loose pulleys, H, and controlled by a lever, this being a very common arrangement. Another development in this direction is the use of a pneumatic friction clutch with push-button control, with a special button known as the *inching control*, to enable the ram to be slowly moved a small distance at a time for setting purposes.

When a friction clutch is used it is coupled to the brake on the crankshaft so that the brake is automatically released when the clutch is fully engaged, and vice versa. The toggle motion is also used in a type of single-action press, sometimes known as a knuckle-press, for coining work.

These presses are usually run at a low speed and as the toggle or knuckle action imparts great pressure to the ram, a slow, steady squeeze is applied to the work, allowing time for the metal to flow to the required shape.

PRESS-TOOLS

To illustrate the general arrangement of a simple press-tool, the example in Fig. 12 shows a punch and die which would be used for punching bolt-holes in steel plates. The punch, A, is made in one solid piece, and, being a plain turning job, is very easily made in the lathe. It is held in the press-ram, B, by a set-screw or by a clamp, according to the type of press. The die, C, is held in the die-base, D, by taper gib, E, and the die has a hole in the center slightly larger than the diameter of the punch, and slightly tapered.

The punch is made the same diameter as the hole required in the plate, and, as the punch, after passing through the plate, is set to enter the

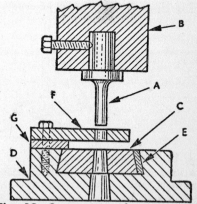

Fig. 12. Construction of a punch and die for punching bolt-holes in steel plates. A, punch, held in press-ram B by a clamp or set-screw; C, die, held in die-base D by taper-gib E; F, stripper plate; G, packing piece.

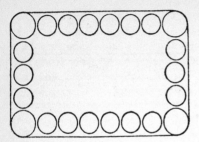

Fig. 13. To cut a hole in a solid die, a series of holes of suitable size is drilled within its boundaries, and the waste piece knocked or cut out.

die a short distance, a certain amount of working clearance is necessary between the punch and the hole in the die. This clearance depends on the thickness of the material to be punched, and should be about 5 percent of the thickness, allowed all around the punch. This is a fairly constant figure, regardless of the punch diameter.

Parts of Press-Tools

The taper in the die-hole is to allow the slugs or punchings to press easily through the die, and is usually ½ deg. all round the hole. Although the figure of ½ deg. may be departed from in certain circumstances for special work, it may be taken as being suitable for the majority of jobs of this class. Round holes up to about ⅜ in. diameter are drilled and reamed with a taper reamer, larger holes being bored in the lathe.

The stripper plate, F, has a hole which is a good fit for the punch, and serves to steady the punch on the down-stroke as well as to hold the work down while the punch is withdrawn on the up-stroke.

The packing piece, G, is made slightly thicker than the work, and is usually set a certain distance from

the punch and used as a guide-plate; the work is pushed up to it.

Instead of the taper gib being used for holding the die, a plain parallel groove is sometimes provided in the bolster, or the die may be merely screwed and doweled, according to the nature of the work.

Plain Blanking Tools

The principles of punches and dies as outlined above can be applied to the punching of any shape, and the general arrangement is the same whether the hole is round or some irregular shape.

We must now make a distinction between piercing and blanking. If we have a plate in which we have to make holes, we make the punch and the hole in the die the shape and size of the hole required, and the piece removed from the hole is waste. This operation is known as *punching*.

If, however, we have a strip or a sheet of metal from which we have to

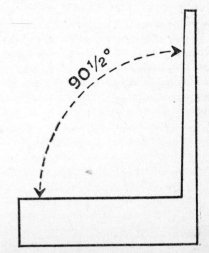

Fig. 14. Die-maker's gages, of thin plate, to check the angle of relief, can be made to any required size.

cut pieces of a certain shape, we make a punch and die the shape and size of the piece required, punch them out of the strip or sheet as close together as possible, and the remainder of the strip is waste. This operation is known as *blanking*.

The chief difference between blanking and punching lies in the allowance for working clearance between the punch and die. In the case of punching, the size of the hole is governed by the size of the punch, and the clearance must be allowed in the die, whereas in the case of blanking the size of the blank is governed by the die, and the clearance must be allowed for on the punch.

The construction of punches and dies for producing irregular shapes calls for much care and skill, as they usually have to be finished by hand or machine filing. With solid dies the shape of the hole is usually marked out on the top face of the die, and a series of holes of a suitable size drilled just inside the line, as in Fig. 13, and the waste piece knocked out or cut out on a band-saw.

Some die-makers drill the holes touching each other so that the piece in the middle falls out easily, but owing to the possibility of trouble being caused through the drill running out of position, others prefer to drill

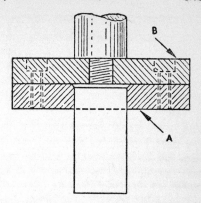

Fig. 16. How a punch may be arranged to allow of the form being ground. The punch fits tightly into plate A, screwed and doweled to plate B.

the holes slightly apart and chip out the narrow portion left between the holes with a drift or hand-punch.

When a radius is required in the corner of a die, a hole is drilled in the true position, and reamed to size with a taper reamer before any of the other holes are drilled.

After the waste piece is removed, the hole can be finished by hand, being carefully filed to size and shape at the top with the required angle of relief. Here, again, opinion is divided to some extent among experienced die-makers, as some make the die taper right to the top, while others consider that the first $\frac{1}{8}$ in. or so should be made parallel.

A very useful tool for checking the angle of relief is the die-maker's gage shown in Fig. 14. These gages are made from thin plate, and can be made to any angle desired. They are most convenient if made with a knife-edge on the working faces. Adjustable gages, known as die-maker's squares, are made for this purpose by the leading small-tool manufacturers, and these are found to be very useful.

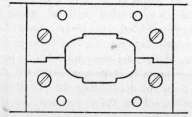

Fig. 15. Absolute accuracy in die-making is sometimes secured by making the die in sections, ground to fit each other.

Sectional Dies

When the form of a die is very intricate or accuracy is absolutely essential, dies are sometimes made in sections and ground to fit each other after being hardened. Fig. 15 shows a die arranged in two halves and set in a groove in the bolster so that the sections are held firmly together. To locate the sections, and to prevent any movement endways, steps are made along the dividing line, and the sections are fastened down in the die-base by screws and dowels.

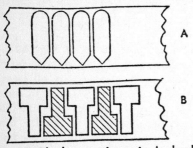

A

B

Fig. 17. Blanks on strip, as in A, should be as close together as possible. In B the position of the blank in the strip is chosen to save metal.

Punches are usually rough-machined and finished by hand, the best method being to file almost to size and then to press the punch into the die, the die having been finished and hardened first, so that the die shears the punch to shape. Further filing is then necessary to provide the correct clearance. When extreme accuracy is required, the punch should be hardened while still oversize and finished by grinding, such work being done by a highly-skilled grinding specialist.

Fig. 16 shows a punch arranged in such a manner as to allow of the form being ground, as the whole length of the punch may be finished to shape, and the top end softened so that the edges may be peened over. The punch will, of course, be made a good tight fit in the plate, A, and the plates, A and B, screwed and doweled together. This method of holding a punch is very satisfactory for light work, but for heavy work, where considerable force is necessary to strip the work from the punch, the method of Fig. 12 is preferable.

When laying out the position of a blank on the die, when blanks are to be punched from strip material, the direction in which the strip will run across the die should be carefully considered. In Fig. 17, A shows a narrow blank arranged across the strip, the short distance the strip needs to be moved between each blank being convenient for quick operation. The blank shown at B illustrates a case where economy can be effected by choosing the best position for the blank in the strip.

The blanks should be as close together as possible, and the T-shaped piece shown would have to be punched in each alternate position, and the strip then turned over and run through the press again, punching out the spaces left.

Producing Large Quantities

Another way of achieving the same result would be to have a double die and two punches in the positions shown shaded, to leave space for strength between the two holes in the die. If the tool were intended to produce parts in large quantities, the extra cost of duplicating the punch and die would be fully justified, as the output per stroke would then be doubled.

Parts which require holes punched in them can usually be blanked and punched in the same tool, both operations being performed at one stroke of the press. The plan view in Fig. 18 shows the lay-out of a die for producing such a part, the strip of material being moved from right to left as indicated by the arrow. The end of the strip is placed between the guide-plates, A, and pushed in as far as the sliding stop, B, which works in a groove in the guide. The holes are then punched at the position, C, the stop, B, is withdrawn, and the strip moved forward until the end meets stop, D, which is a peg protruding slightly above the face of the die.

The holes are now brought into position above the blanking hole in the die, and when the press is operated the second time the blank is punched out with the holes in position, and at the same time the holes are punched for the next piece. By continuing the sequence of moving the strip after each stroke of the punches, and allowing the peg-stop, D, to stop against the edge of the last blank hole in the strip, the operations of punching and blanking follow each other throughout the length of strip.

As all the five punches have to work together, they must all be in perfect alignment, so as to enter the die without fouling, and the arrangement for

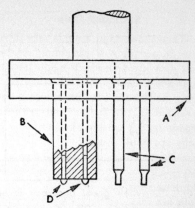

Fig. 19. Arrangement of punches and pilots for combined blanking piercing as in Fig. 18. For references see text.

holding them shown in Fig. 19 has been found to be very suitable for the purpose. The punches are all located in one solid plate, A, and to insure each being in the right position, the blanking punch, B, is usually fitted first, inserted in the die, and the holes for the piercing punches, C, transferred by drilling through the piercing holes in the die.

The Blanking Punch

When the strip of material is moved along from the punching to the blanking position, the punched holes must be brought into the right position under the blanking punch, so that the holes will be accurately spaced in the finished blank. For this purpose the pilots, D, are provided in the blanking punch, the holes being drilled right through the punch so as to enable the pilots to be removed without difficulty when the punch is re-ground for sharpening.

When extra thick material is being worked a very heavy load is imposed on the tool, and to relieve some of the

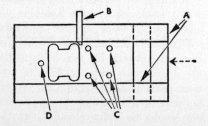

Fig. 18. Lay-out of a die for blanking and punching in one operation. A, guide-plates; B, sliding stop; C, position of holes; D, end stop.

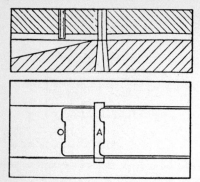

Fig. 20. When great accuracy is not essential, blanks can be produced simply and cheaply by using a cropping tool of the type shown above.

load the die may be chamfered to give a shearing effect. The chamfer should be made on the die for blanking and on the punch for piercing, to avoid distortion of the work, and, where several punches are used in one tool, a similar effect can be obtained by making the punches slightly different in length.

Guide-Pillars

When very thin material is being worked, the clearance between punch and die is very small, and to be sure that the punch enters the die without fouling, some form of guide is necessary. The use of guide-pillars is almost universal, two pillars being fitted at the back of the die-base, working in bushings fitted in the punch-holder, so that the punch and die are maintained in true alignment without having to rely on the slide-ways of the press ram.

A simple and very economical method of producing a blank when the dimensions are not required to be very accurate is shown in Fig. 20. The strip of material is used with the width already correct for the width of the

blank, and the punch and die cut out the waste strip, A, between the blanks.

The advantage of this arrangement lies in the fact that there is no waste material at the edges of the strip, but it should be noted that owing to the slight clearance required between the guides and the material, and also the difficulty of maintaining the width of the material to a fixed size over any considerable length, the size of the blank cannot be held within close limits.

Referring to the upper view in Fig. 20, the stop-pin is shown fixed in the stripper plate, and the die cut away, so that after the piece is cut off it will fall clear.

Drawing Tools

Tools used for drawing cup or dish shaped articles from flat sheet are of

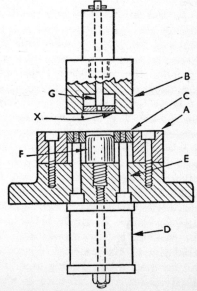

Fig. 21. Section through a blanking and drawing tool designed for use in a single-action press. The pressure pad C prevents wrinkles in the material.

many different types, but the principle
is the same. They may be divided into
two classes: those used in single-action
and those used in double-action
presses. In Fig. 21 is shown a tool for
use in a single-action press, designed
for cutting out the blank and drawing
it into a shallow cup at one stroke; it
is of the type known as the compound
tool. The strip of material is placed
across the die, A, and, as the punch
descends, the blank is cut with the die
and the outside of the punch, B. As
the punch descends farther, the blank
is carried down into the die, gripped
between the lower face of the punch
and the pressure pad, C, pressure being applied by the rubber block, D,
through the studs, E. The object of
the pressure pad is to prevent wrinkles
forming in the material as the blank is
being drawn into shape between the
block, F, and the inside of the punch
itself.

As the punch ascends after completing the stroke, the pressure pad
acts as a stripper and removes the finished cup from the die, and when the
up-stroke is completed the knock-out
rod, G, strikes the knock-out bar in the
press-ram and the cup is ejected from
the punch. The compression on the
rubber block, D, should be set so that
just enough pressure is applied to prevent wrinkles from forming. The space
allowed between the block, F, and the
inside of the punch should be equal to
the original thickness of the material,
and the radius, X, should be as small
as possible, usually about twice the
thickness of the material, depending
on the kind of metal being used. The
ideal condition for drawing is when
the pressure on the pad, C, is constant
throughout the stroke, and as with a
rubber block the pressure increases the
more the rubber is compressed, this

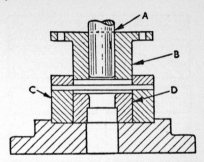

Fig. 22. With a double-action press
tool such as this cups can be drawn
more deeply at one stroke than in the
case of the single-action variety.

arrangement can only be used for shal-
low-cup work since in forming a deep
cup too much pressure results.

The Double-Action Press

As a general rule, the maximum
depth which can be drawn on a single-
action press is about one-half of the
diameter of the cup, although much
depends on the material used. A deeper
cup can be drawn at one stroke in a
double-action press, a tool for which
is shown in Fig. 22. This type of tool
is simpler to construct, the two
punches, A and B, being separate
parts, each fixed to its own ram in the
press.

In operation, the outer punch, B,
descends first, cutting the blank, into
the die, C, where it remains holding
the blank with the required pressure
against the upper face of the drawing
die, D. The punch, A, now descends
and draws the blank into the die, D,
forming the cup and passing it right
through the die. On the up-stroke the
finished cup is caught by the lower
edge of the die and drawn off the
punch.

The deepest cup which can be drawn
at one stroke is of a depth equal to the

diameter, and any depth greater than that requires further drawing operations. The amount by which a cup or shell can be reduced in diameter becomes less with each successive operation.

Reducing the Diameter

Suppose, for instance, that we have to produce a shell 2.3 in. diameter and 3.3 in. in height, and we use a blank diameter of 6 in. Three drawing operations would be required; in the first operation the diameter would be reduced by 40 percent to 3.6 in.; in the second by 25 percent to 2.7 in., and in the third by 15 percent to 2.3 in. Although no hard and fast rules can be laid down in this respect the above figures can be taken as a safe guide to cover general conditions.

Developing the Blank

Another detail which cannot be determined with accuracy is the size of blank required to produce a certain size of shell. For this reason the best practice is to make the drawing die

or dies first, and by repeated trial and correction of error to discover the size of blank required. This method is known as developing the blank. For the first trial, however, the size of blank required can be calculated fairly closely. Though there are several methods of doing this, the quickest and most satisfactory is that known as the area method—that is, by calculating the surface area of the shell required and making the blank the same. A simple formula for calculating the diameter of the blank for a circular shell is as follows:

D = the diameter of the blank,
d = the diameter of the shell,
h = the height of the shell,
r = the radius at the bottom corner.

$$D = \sqrt{d + 4dh} - r.$$

Where there is no radius at the bottom corner of the shell, omit the $(-r)$.

For deep drawing, whether in brass or steel, special materials must be used, known as drawing brass or drawing steel. A good drawing brass is an alloy of 70 percent copper, 30 percent zinc; and drawing steels, although varying to some extent in their manganese, chromium, and nickel content, have a maximum of .1 percent carbon, .75 percent silicon, and .03 percent sulphur and phosphorus.

When several successive drawing operations are necessary, the shells usually require annealing either after each operation or, sometimes, every other one. The annealing is done in a muffle furnace at the normalizing temperature for the particular material which is being used.

An interesting operation which sometimes follows drawing is curling the edges of products such as saucepans, buckets, etc., sometimes known as beading. The method of performing

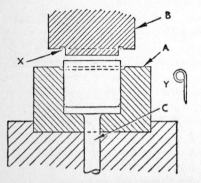

Fig. 23. This tool is used for curling the edges of buckets, saucepans, etc. The work is placed on the die A with sufficient of the edge protruding above to form the curl at the edge.

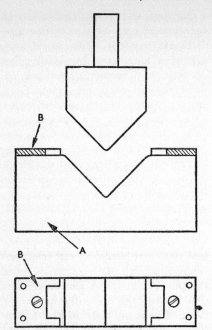

Fig. 24. V bending tool for curling thin sheet metals. The work is placed on die A and located in gage-plates B.

tool for this operation, known as the V bending tool, is shown in Fig. 24. The work is laid across the die, A, and located in the gauge-plates, B.

As most metals have a certain amount of natural spring, the work will have a tendency to open after being bent, and to counteract this tendency a bending allowance is made on the angle of the punch and die. As a general rule, soft brass and steel do not spring to any large extent, and an angle of 85 deg. on the punch and die will probably be suitable to produce an angle of 90 deg. on the work. For great accuracy a certain amount of trial and error will be necessary, and, because of this, bending and forming tools are often tried out while soft, and then hardened after finally being passed as correct.

this operation is shown in Fig. 23, the work being placed in the die, A, with sufficient of the edge protruding above the die to form the curl. As the punch, B, descends, the edge of the shell meets the form, X, and is made to curl outward; and as the punch continues to the full depth the curl flows round until fully formed as shown at Y. As there is usually a tendency for the work to stick in the die, an ejector, C, is used to free the shell, after which it can be lifted out by hand.

Curling Metals

Thin sheet-metals up to about 20-gauge can be curled quite well by this method, and the bead should be kept small in diameter to prevent cracks.

A plain, single bend on flat stock is usually a straightforward job, and a

Double Bending

A double bend is not as simple as a single bend, especially for accurate work, as the amount of stretch which occurs in bending must be taken into account. In bending the material is

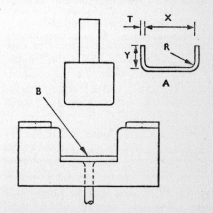

Fig. 25. A plain bending tool with an ejector B operated by springs or a rubber pad to remove the work.

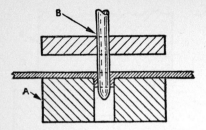

Fig. 26. Forming a boss to provide the metal for tapping a hole is done by a punch and die like those here illustrated and described in the text.

compressed on the inside of the bend and stretched on the outside, and as the tensile and compression strengths of materials vary considerably, no positive rule can be laid down for calculating the amount of metal to allow for bending. An approximate figure can be obtained, however, which will probably be close enough for many jobs, and as an example we will consider the length required to form the piece, A, Fig. 25.

For the straight portions the inside measurements can be taken direct as X and Y. For the corners we take the inside radius, R, the thickness of the material, T, and from the formula

$$\frac{3.14(R + \frac{1}{3}T)}{2}$$

we find the length required for each corner. If we now add in the lengths, X and Y, we have the approximate length required, and a few experiments with the tool will be sufficient to find the exact length.

With the tool shown in Fig. 25 for performing this bend, the work will stick in the die, therefore the ejector, B, operated by springs or a rubber pad, will be required to remove the work. The gap in the die will be equal to the width of the punch, plus twice the thickness of the material or slightly less, so that the punch and the work

together will be a tight fit in the die to give an ironing effect.

A very important point regarding the bending of strip or sheet-metal is the direction of the grain in the metal. Owing to the rolling process by which sheet-metal is produced there is a grain in the metal running lengthways in the sheet or strip, not unlike the grain in a piece of timber. A bend should, whenever possible, be across this grain rather than along it, as there will then be less tendency for the metal to crack.

On small press tools the working parts are made solid of good quality tool steel and hardened and tempered throughout, but on very large work the punches and dies are so massive that it would be impossible to harden them. The main body of the tool is then made as a casting, and hardened tool steel blocks are inserted at the highly stressed points where wear is likely to occur.

An operation sometimes required on instrument work is the forming of a boss to provide sufficient metal for tapping a hole. First a small hole is punched about half the diameter of the finished hole, and the forming of the boss is done by the punch and die shown in Fig. 26. The hole in the die, A, is equal in diameter to the punch, B, plus twice the thickness of the material, and the punch enters the small hole previously punched and draws the surrounding metal down into the die forming the boss as shown. The end of the punch should be formed the shape of an acorn, and the edges of the hole in the die should be slightly rounded to remove the sharpness. Coining or cold pressing work calls for very robust tools and the use of a very powerful press, and is usually confined to small work such as medals, money, badges, and similar small ornamental articles.

In Fig. 27 is shown a tool for producing articles such as medals, the design being engraved on the underside of the punch, A, and the upper face of the forming pad, B, the edge or rim of the medal being formed by the hole in the die, C.

Reproducing Medals

The slug or blank is slightly smaller in diameter than the hole in the die, and is placed in the die resting on the forming-pad. As the punch descends on to the work the forming-pad is carried down until it reaches the bottom of the hole in the die. The slug is now completely enclosed, and the punch is

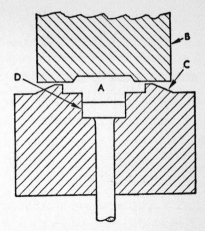

Fig. 28. In hot pressing a small gap is left between the punch B and the die C, where a fin or "flash" of surplus metal escapes, to be trimmed off later.

under very heavy pressure. The metal is made to flow into the crevices of the engraving on the punch and pad until the design is reproduced in the impression on the medal. As the punch rises after having done its work, the positive ejector forces the forming-pad to the top of the die and the finished work is ejected from the machine.

Hot Pressing

There is a limit to the extent to which even soft metals can be made to flow in the cold state, and when shapes are to be produced by pressing, which involves greater distortion of the metal, the slug or billet is heated to a forging heat before being placed in the die. The operation is then known as hot pressing, and in Fig. 28 is shown a tool for producing the part, A, with the tool in the closed position. A small gap is left where the faces of the punch, B, and die, C, meet each other to allow surplus metal to escape, leaving a thin fin all around the fin-

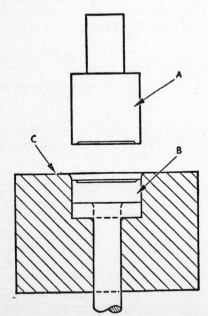

Fig. 27. In a coining die for medals the design is engraved on the under face of the punch A and the upper face of the forming pad B. The rim of the medal is formed by the hole in the die C.

ished work which can easily be trimmed off later. This fin is usually known as the flash, and serves two purposes. The first is to allow a slight excess of metal in the billet, to be sure the cavity is properly filled, and the second to act as a kind of safety-valve for the tool in case some billets are oversize.

If the shape of the work-piece is such that it is likely to stick in the punch or die, an ejector should be provided accordingly, as at D in this case. Whenever possible the work should be slightly tapered to facilitate ejection.

Owing to the heat at which they work, punches and dies for hot pressing should not be made of ordinary tool steel, but a steel especially made for the job, should be used.

A final operation to which many pressed parts are treated is tumbling to remove burrs and sharp edges. This is done in a machine which consists of a hexagonal box or barrel about 2 ft. in length with spindles on each end on which the box is slowly rotated. The parts to be treated are placed in the box along with a quantity of ball shot, the lid screwed down, and the box turned for a time with the work and shot rubbing together. For finer polish, sawdust or shavings may be used.

The time required to remove all the sharp edges will vary according to the size of the work, so the box may be opened periodically for examination; but a little experience with a particular class of work will suffice to show how long to allow.

PUNCHES AND PUNCHING

THE punches to be described here are those used by hand, as distinct from those used in machines. A description of each type will be given, together with an explanation of the purpose for which they are used.

The styles of hand-punches, like most other details in the machine shop have been developed from necessity and experience, and are the result of someone's ingenuity in finding a way to overcome a difficulty.

The Center Punch

The first punch to be described is the center punch, used, as its name implies, for marking the center of a point or position, usually for starting a drill. Referring to Fig. 29, A, this punch is made with a good solid shank to withstand the hammer blow, and tapers toward the point to allow the mark to be seen clearly. The shank is

knurled to provide a good finger-grip, and the top end is slightly chamfered to prevent the edge from becoming burred from constant hammer blows.

These punches are made of good-quality tool steel, hardened and tempered, and for preference should be left fairly hard at the bottom end to retain the sharp point and left tough rather than hard at the top to prevent the end from being chipped or cracked.

A good punch can be made from an old round file, ground to shape and suitably tempered, the file teeth providing a ready made knurl. For accurate marking, a punch should be turned in the lathe and the point ground perfectly true.

Point Angle of the Punch

When the center punch is used for marking the position of a hole to be drilled, the angle of the conical point

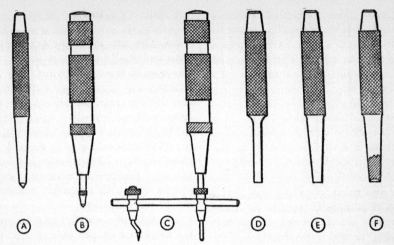

Fig. 29. Hand-punches. *A,* center punch; *B,* automatic center punch; *C,* spacing device for automatic center punch; *D,* pin-punch; *E,* nail punch; *F,* rivet punch.

is important. The point of the punch should be a sharper angle than the point of the drill, to insure the drill starting true.

For fine work, such as laying out dies and other tool-room work, center punches are used tapered down to a fine point, and a very light hammer is used. It is no easy matter to make a mark just where it should be to a fine degree of accuracy. For such work as tool-making the automatic center punch shown at Fig. 29, B, is very useful, as no hammer blow is used, the blow being applied by a spring mechanism inside the handle of the punch. The punch is placed in position on the work, and a steady downward pressure on the handle compresses the spring until the striker is automatically released and the blow is applied to the point. The force of the blow may be adjusted, and, when set, all marks made at that setting will be uniform in size.

When work is laid out for a machining operation, a line is scribed for the machinist to work to, and to make it

easier to see the line, fine dots are usually marked along it. For this and any other work where dots must be marked a uniform distance apart, the spacing device shown at C in Fig. 29 is valuable, as it not only keeps the dots a fixed distance apart but saves a good deal of time by eliminating the measurement which would otherwise be required. The attachment is supplied for use with the automatic center punch, and the points may be set any distance apart, so that once the first dot is marked, the pointer on the arm is placed on the dot and the punch is ready for the next one, and so on.

The pin-punch shown at D in Fig. 29 is used for driving out plain parallel pins such as dowel pins, and must be as long as the pin, and slightly smaller in diameter. As it is desirable to use a punch as large as possible for the size of pin, a set of punches is necessary to cover the range of sizes of pins. These punches are supplied in sets in a box, and it is a good practice to keep them in the box so that they can easily be found when wanted. As

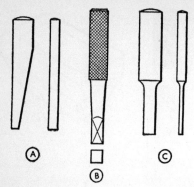

Fig. 30. Punches of the types here shown are usually known as drifts. Their uses are explained in the text.

these punches often have to stand a very heavy blow, it is advisable that a large radius should be left where the plain part meets the handle.

At E is shown the nail-set, a tool useful in woodworking for setting the head of a nail just below the surface, and also useful for removing taper pins from machine parts. The point of the punch is made slightly concave to prevent it from slipping.

The rivet punch or set shown at F, Fig. 29, is used for finishing off neatly the head of a rivet. The hollow, cupped end of the punch removes the hammer-marks and leaves a neat head.

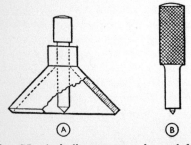

Fig. 31. A, bell-center punch used for marking for the center drill for work on the lathe; B, device for marking the center of a hole which has to be transferred from one part to another.

Drifts

In Fig. 30 are shown types of punches usually known as drifts, the one marked A being used for removing chucks and taper-shank drills from the drilling machine spindle or the lathe tailstock spindle. These drifts are made with a taper of about 1¾ in. per ft., and should always be used for removing taper-shank tools, as the deplorable practice of removing drill-chucks, etc., with a hammer can cause considerable damage.

The drift shown at B, Fig. 30, is used for forming a shaped hole such as the square hole in a solid tap-wrench. A round hole is drilled first, as large as possible, and the drift is then driven through the hole to form the shape required. This tool is really a simple form of broach, and it can be made quite easily for any shape required.

At C, Fig. 30, is shown a drift used for cutting through the thin fin left between the holes when a large hole or section is cut out of a block by the method of drilling a line of small holes round the shape to be cut out. The small holes cannot be drilled actually touching each other, as the drill would be likely to run from one hole to the next. For removing the fin between the holes a very satisfactory drift can be made from an old machine-saw blade.

In Fig. 31, A, is shown the bell-center punch used for marking the center of the end of a shaft or marking for the center drill for work on the lathe. The punch is a sliding fit in the bell, and when the bell is placed over the end of the shaft the punch is central, ready for a blow with a hammer. The use of this simple tool saves all the time which would otherwise be spent in marking out a center, and is probably more accurate.

At B, Fig. 31, is shown another similar device for marking the center of a hole when a hole is to be transferred from one part to another and cannot be drilled through both at once. The shank is made to fit the hole already drilled, and the point marks the center of the opposite hole ready for drilling when the first part is taken away.

For cutting washers and other parts from leather, a tool known as the *dinking punch* is used, a simple example being shown in Fig. 32, A. The punch is hollow, with a sharp edge, and is made the shape of the piece to be cut out. The angle of the cutting edge should be about 20 deg. to give a clean cut. When cut out, the pieces remain inside the punch, and are pushed out at the top by other pieces cut one after the other. The leather or other material to be cut is placed on a smooth level block of hard wood with the end-grain upward, and the punch is then placed on the leather and smartly struck with a mallet.

Larger sizes are made without a handle, and are just a plain outline of the shape to be cut, and used in a press

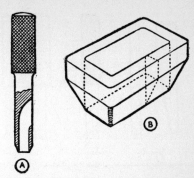

Fig. 32. A, dinking punch for cutting washers, etc., from leather; B, dinking die, used in fly-press or similar machine, for cutting paper, cardboard, cloth, and similar materials.

such as a fly-press or similar machine. The tool is then referred to as a *dinking die,* a typical example being shown at B in Fig. 32. These tools, made in a good quality tool-steel carefully hardened and tempered, are used for cutting many materials such as paper, cardboard, cloth, etc. as well as leather, and it is essential that the cutting edge be level all around the form and kept in the very best condition as regards keen sharpness.

CHAPTER 11

HEAT-TREATMENT OF METALS

RELATIVE HARDNESS OF METALS. SOFTENING STEEL. ANNEALING. HARDNESS
TESTING. NORMALIZING. TEMPERING. HIGH CARBON STEEL. MARTENSITE.
CASE-HARDENING. EFFECT ON STEELS. THE CYANIDE PROCESS. CARBURIZING.
NITROGEN-HARDENING. MALLEABLE IRON.

METALS possess relative hardness according to their nature, ranging from the softness of tin, gold, and lead to the extreme natural hardness of some rare metals, but so far as those used in engineering work are concerned, the hardness of practically all of them is controllable either by alloying or heat-treatment or both. Most metals increase in hardness with their strength, this being generally the case with steel. If a soft grade of iron or steel requires a hard surface, this can be given to iron by chilling the casting in the mold, while in the case of steel it is usually applied by case- or surface-hardening along lines which will be discussed in this chapter.

Softening Steel

If the steel is by nature too hard to machine economically, it is softened by heating to a temperature suitable to the particular steel, holding it at this temperature for awhile and then slowly cooling, this being spoken of as annealing. Most steels if heated and quenched in water acquire a degree of hardness according to their composition, and some acquire this condition by air-cooling. Some of the aluminum alloys harden up after working (*age-hardening*) by simply being left alone

for a few days. Copper and brass harden by being hammered or worked in a press. This makes the metal hard, weak, and brittle, and the condition is removed by heating, often followed by quenching, an operation referred to as annealing.

Through-Hardness

The more important parts of machinery are produced to a definite degree of hardness, and usually by some form of heat-treatment, and no general rules can be laid down. Through-hardness, in addition to serving no useful purpose, in many cases would render the part liable to failure from a shock load or from bending. Hardness is, therefore, of more importance on the surface of a finished part so that it will be able to resist wear. While through-hardness may be a certain indication of strength, it might, if excessive, be actually a source of weakness, apart from the fact that hard material is more difficult to machine. Thus, in general, mild carbon steels, which can be made hard by the appropriate heat-treatment, are usually case-hardened, as described presently.

The hardening of tools and their tempering to give the necessary hardness to resist fracture and the case-hardening of machine parts are not operations to be undertaken lightly. In this class of work considerable use is now made of alloy steels, the properties of which have already been set forth in Chapter 2. In the absence of instructions from the metallurgical department, the only reliable guide to the correct temperatures to which steel should be heated and the method of cooling, (oil- or water-quenching or air-cooling) is that given by the suppliers or found in the specification. Such terms as *cherry red, glass hard,* etc., are wholly misleading. Metals undergoing heat-treatment require heating in the appropriate type of furnace to the temperature indicated for that particular metal and to be kept at that temperature for the period specified. Hardness is a definite value according to the scale of hardness used in any particular shop.

Hardness Testing

Frequent reference has been previously made to the Brinell Hardness Number or, as it is usually written, the B.H.N. Actually hardness testing operates on the very simple procedure of making an impression on the surface of the metal, and, with a given pressure, the deeper the impression the softer the metal. For instance, in the Brinell system of hardness testing a hardened steel ball is pressed into the smooth surface of the metal making an indentation of a size that can be conveniently measured under the microscope. The diameter of this indentation has a definite relation to the hardness. Tables supplied by the Brinell machine manufacturers show these figures, and the hardness number is thus obtained. These machines for testing hardness, though of a delicate and

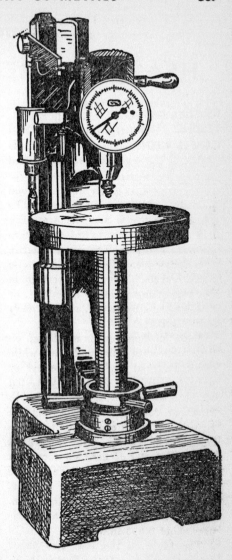

Fig. 1. Rockwell Hardness Tester. A dead weight acting through a series of levers impresses a diamond cone into hard metals or a $\frac{1}{16}''$ steel ball into softer materials and the depth of penetration measured. The hardness is indicated on the Rockwell dial gages. The harder the material the higher the Rockwell number.

somewhat complicated nature, reduce the actual operation of testing to one of simple routine.

Rockwell Testing

The Rockwell method of testing is probably the most common in use today. It is especially efficient and reliable on fully hardened steels. On this machine the hardness value is read directly on a dial and represents directly the penetration of a diamond point into the hardened material. The piece to be tested must have a clean and uniform surface in order to obtain accurate readings. The usual practice is to either grind both the place to be tested and the portion which rests upon the supporting pedestal or rollers, or to clean them by sand blasting, emery cloth, or filing.

Fully hardened steels are tested on the C scale with a diamond point, while softer material such as annealed or partially hardened steel may be tested on the B scale, using a small steel ball. However, for the softer materials, the Brinell method is considered more accurate and reliable. The Superficial Rockwell tester is used on very thin sheet or strip steels or to measure the hardness at the immediate surface, since it measures only about 0.0003 in. deep, while the standard C scale measures about 0.005 in. deep.

The table on the next two pages shows the relation of the Rockwell and Brinell scales as well as approximate tensile strengths.

Heat-Treatment

The heat-treatment of metals, and more particularly of modern steels, is, today, more or less an exact science based upon the theoretical principles of metallurgy, which are altogether too complex for discussion in the pages of this book.

For an understanding of what is to follow it is necessary to point out that the main constituents of steel are ferrite, cementite, pearlite, austenite, and martensite. Of these, the ferrite is a conglomeration of iron crystals which are soft, ductile, and weak. Cementite takes the form of crystals of iron carbide which are very hard and brittle. Pearlite is a combination of ferrite and cementite. Austenite is a solution of iron carbide usually obtained by heating the steel above what is known as the *critical temperature,* while martensite is another solution of iron carbide, but this is obtained by cooling the steel.

These different constituents and their effect on the condition of steel in the heat-treated condition can be properly understood only by those acquainted with the technical side of metallurgy, but, put briefly, if steel is heated and cooled slowly the pearlite and ferrite separate, whereas in rapid cooling, to be associated with the hardening of steel in general, a martensitic condition usually results. Conversely, if a steel is hard by nature by reason of its carbon or alloy content, it can be softened by heating and slow cooling, according to the directions of the steel-maker, so that it can be easily machined, the normal properties of such steels being usually restored by heating and allowing to cool in the air. This is commonly alluded to as *normalizing,* but should not be confused with what is termed annealing.

Normalizing

Normalizing consists of heating steels to approximately 100 deg. F. above the critical range and allowing

HARDNESS CONVERSION TABLE

BRINELL.		ROCKWELL.			
Dia. in mm., 3000 kg. load 10 mm. Ball.	Hardness No.	C 150 kg. load 120° Diamond Cone.	B 100 kg. load 1⁄16 in. Dia. Ball.	Shore Sclero-scope No.	Tensile Strength 1000 psi.
2.05	898	..	...	...	440
2.10	857	..	...	...	420
2.15	817	..	...	...	401
2.20	780	70	...	106	384
2.25	745	68	...	100	368
2.30	712	66	...	95	352
2.35	682	64	...	91	337
2.40	653	62	...	87	324
2.45	627	60	...	84	311
2.50	601	58	...	81	298
2.55	578	57	...	78	287
2.60	555	55	120	75	276
2.65	534	53	119	72	266
2.70	514	52	119	70	256
2.75	495	50	117	67	247
2.80	477	49	117	65	238
2.85	461	47	116	63	229
2.90	444	46	115	61	220
2.95	429	45	115	59	212
3.00	415	44	114	57	204
3.05	401	42	113	55	196
3.10	388	41	112	54	189
3.15	375	40	112	52	182
3.20	363	38	110	51	176
3.25	352	37	110	49	170
3.30	341	36	109	48	165
3.35	331	35	109	46	160
3.40	321	34	108	45	155
3.45	311	33	108	44	150
3.50	302	32	107	43	146
3.55	293	31	106	42	142
3.60	285	30	105	40	138
3.70	269	28	104	38	131
3.75	262	26	103	37	128
3.80	255	25	102	37	125
3.90	241	23	100	35	119
3.95	235	22	99	34	116
4.00	229	21	98	33	113

Figures in italics are an approximation and are to be used only as a guide.

HARDNESS CONVERSION TABLE—Cont'd

BRINELL.		ROCKWELL.			
Dia. in mm., 3000 kg. load 10 mm. Ball.	Hardness No.	C 150 kg. load 120° Diamond Cone.	B 100 kg. load 1/16 in. Dia. Ball.	Shore Sclero-scope No.	Tensile Strength 1000 psi.
4.05	223	20	97	32	*110*
4.10	217	*18*	96	31	*107*
4.15	212	*17*	96	31	*104*
4.20	207	*16*	95	30	*101*
4.25	202	*15*	94	30	*99*
4.30	197	*13*	93	29	*97*
4.35	192	*12*	92	28	*95*
4.40	187	*10*	91	28	*93*
4.45	183	*9*	90	27	*91*
4.50	179	*8*	89	27	*89*
4.55	174	*7*	88	26	*87*
4.60	170	*6*	87	26	*85*
4.65	166	*4*	86	25	*83*
4.70	163	*3*	85	25	*82*
4.75	159	*2*	84	24	*80*
4.80	156	*1*	83	24	*78*
4.90	149	..	81	23	*75*
4.95	146	..	80	22	*74*
5.00	143	..	79	22	*72*
5.05	140	..	78	21	*71*
5.10	137	..	77	21	*70*
5.15	134	..	76	21	*68*
5.20	131	..	74	20	*66*
5.25	128	..	73	20	*65*
5.30	126	..	72	...	*64*
5.35	124	..	71	...	*63*
5.40	121	..	70	...	*62*
5.45	118	..	69	...	*61*
5.50	116	..	68	...	*60*
5.55	114	..	67	...	*59*
5.60	112	..	66	...	*58*
5.70	107	..	64	...	*55*
5.75	105	..	62	...	*54*
5.80	103	..	61	...	*53*
5.85	101	..	60	...	*52*
5.90	99	..	59	...	*51*
5.95	97	..	57	...	*50*
6.00	95	..	56	...	*49*

Figures in italics are an approximation and are to be used only as a guide.

it to cool to room temperature in still air. This is most often applied to parts which have been forged, given severe cold working or otherwise strained, primarily to remove those strains and place the steel in suitable condition for further working or hardening. Normalizing cannot be performed on the types of steel which will harden when cooled in air. It is not usually done when the steel contains approximately 1 percent carbon or more, because these steels tend to increase the grain size under such conditions. Normalizing is sometimes followed by annealing, to obtain low hardness or very good machinability.

Annealing is usually performed on metals for the purpose of removing stresses, to induce softness, to change ductility or toughness, or to change the structure. The temperature of the operation and the rate of cooling depend upon the material and the purpose of the treatment. Full annealing consists of heating the steel 100 deg. F. above the critical range, holding at that temperature for about 1 hour for each inch of maximum thickness and allowing to cool slowly, usually in the furnace.

Furnaces

When hardening was mainly confined to tools and a few unimportant machine components, the pieces were simply heated in a blacksmith's fire and plunged into water, and while a skilled worker can get good practical results this way, such methods are no longer compatible with modern requirements. The men in the heat-treatment shop work to rule. Industrial furnaces are heated by gas, oil, or electricity and are under automatic control.

It must always be remembered that in an industrial heating furnace for any metallurgical work it is essential that actual contact with the work of the products of combustion be avoided, because while scaling must to a certain extent occur in a heating operation, the less there is on the parts, the less the cost of and work to remove it.

For the heavier classes of work, where lumps of steel have to be heated for forging and rolling operations, the pieces are handled in a re-heating furnace so designed that the ingots or billets are laid on a table and pushed into the furnace by a hydraulic or electric pusher, which also regulates the speed of the work through the furnace. During their passage the pieces are carried on water-cooled rails or skidbars. The hearth may be inclined right to the end of the furnace and the pieces there withdrawn, though in other cases it terminates some distance back from the end, so as to allow space for the material to be turned over. In most furnaces of this type which are heated by producer gas, the gas is fed to the furnace through burners placed in the top. This method throws the flame exactly where it is required, and leaves both sides and the end of the furnace free for the withdrawal of the material. After combustion, the waste products pass along the furnace, and into recuperators through ports at the end. The recuperators are placed directly under the furnace; they extend along the whole length of it, so that the length of the travel of the air and the products of combustion in the recuperators is approximately twice the length of the furnace. The heated air, after leaving the recuperator, is carried through passages into the double roof of the furnace and is there further heated before mixing with the gas. The type of burner used insures that no free air passes into the furnace.

HARDENING AND TEMPERING

IT HAS already been pointed out in these pages that any form of heat-treatment must, to be successful, be done strictly in accordance with the directions issued by the steel-makers or the plant metallurgical department. It is quite true that experienced tool-makers and those engaged in making razors, swords, surgical instruments, etc., acquire considerable skill in judging the correct temperature at which such parts can be plunged into water or oil or otherwise cooled to insure that the cutting edge is sufficiently hard to stand up under use without being so brittle as to risk breakage. That is, in effect, the essential operation, applied to anything from the end of a pickaxe to the blade of a surgeon's lancet, which is collectively referred to by the term *hardening and tempering*.

Some assistance may be had from color charts which show the different colors steel reaches when heated and at which the cooling operation may take place. Such instructions might be represented by, "quench from a cherry red and draw to a light straw"; but it must be impressed upon the reader that these old-time rule-of-thumb ideas have largely passed from high-class engineering, and any work of this kind, except that done by men of years of experience—work generally of a special nature—will as a rule only be undertaken by semi-skilled men strictly to rule and under supervision.

As already shown, carbon steels and alloy steels normally come to the shop in a soft or annealed condition in which they can be machined, and if they are forged they may be further annealed or normalized to correct any bad effects of the forging operation. Also it

has been shown that in dealing with alloy steels it is essential to comply with the makers' instructions, and some of these steels harden in air to a sufficient degree for this purpose.

Hardening Tool Steels

The common types of straight carbon or low alloyed steels which are intended for water quenching are usually heated to about 1450 deg. F. and then plunged directly and quickly into agitated water or brine. If the entire piece is to be hardened, it is important that the heating be uniform and thorough in order to accomplish this result. On small parts, such as hand tools, etc., it is common practice to heat only that portion of the tool which is to be hard, or sometimes to heat the whole piece, but to quench in the water only that portion which must be hard. If such differential hardening is to be done, it is important that the design be such that no weak section is located in that portion which would be only partially hardened. It is generally preferable to make a difference in hardness of any one part by tempering or drawing the portion desired soft to a much higher temperature than the hard part. The tempering operation is very important and must be performed on every piece which is hardened. Tempering should be done just as soon as the quenched part is cool enough to be comfortably handled in the bare hands. Tempering temperatures may vary from 225 deg. F. to as high as 800 deg. F., but usually about 300 deg. F. or 400 deg. F. is used. These temperatures can be judged by color, but modern practice definitely favors use of ovens or furnaces with accurate control of the temperature. The time of tempering is usually not less than 2 hours, but for heavy sections should be longer in proportion to size. This time can not be too long.

The common types of oil hardening tool and die steels are quenched in a special type of quenching oil from a temperature of about 1475 deg. F. With these it is important that they be tempered as soon as cool. The tempering range is usually 300 deg. F. to 450 deg. F. If any straightening is to be done on these types, it is easy to perform while the temperature from quenching is still about 500 deg. F., whereas if attempted while cold, it will usually cause fracture.

The high carbon-high chrome steels may be either quenched in oil or air. If in oil, the quenching temperature is usually about 1750 deg. F., whereas in air the temperature is usually about 1825 deg. F. These steels may be drawn over a wide range up to about 900 deg. F. without a great reduction in hardness. They maintain accuracy in size during hardening very well, especially when air cooled.

The newer types of air hardening steels are of two types, one of which may be hardened in air from about 1550 deg. F. and the other from about 1800 deg. F. With both of these, the tempering range is about 300 deg. F. to 400 deg. F.

High speed steels are usually hardened in oil or air from about 2350 deg. F. and are almost invariably preheated at about 1600 deg. F. The time at high heat is limited to that just sufficient to heat properly, as overheating will cause rapid grain growth and even *burning* of the edges. Tempering is usually done at about 1050 deg. F. However a wide variety of quenching temperatures and drawing temperatures are often combined to accomplish special desired values in toughness and hardness. Heating in special atmosphere, in neutral salt baths, quenching in hot lead at about 1000 deg. F., and other special devices are often used with high speed steel to accomplish good surface conditions, etc.

In all tool steels, it is important that the parts be handled both in heating and in quenching to avoid undue strains being set up which can so easily cause cracks and fractures. Experience and good judgment are very important in this work. It is always desirable to preheat tool steel so that it may not be forced through the range of transformation, or critical range at a high speed of heat absorption. It is often also desirable to protect the surface of intricate parts by packing them in a neutral material such as cast iron chips or spent carburizing compound during the heating operation. An indication of relation of heat colors to temperature is given in the tables on the next page.

Tempering a Cold Chisel

As an example of hand-tempering, take the case of a cold chisel. The essential operation is to heat it to bright red for, say, 1½ in. or so from the point, and then dip the point of the chisel in water. This must be just dipped, and moved up and down slightly to avoid a sharp line of demarcation between the hard and soft, which may, if it occurs, cause the hard end to shear off bodily when the chisel is put to use. As soon as the actual edge is quenched to cold, the chisel is removed rapidly to the anvil, laid with its hard end across the edge to support it, and both sides are rubbed with

TEMPER COLORS

CARBON TOOL STEEL

COLOR.	DEGREES FAHRENHEIT.	DEGREES CENTIGRADE.
Very Faint Yellow..................	420	215
Light Yellow......................	440	227
Straw Yellow.....................	460	238
Dark Yellow......................	480	250
Yellow-Brown....................	490	255
Spotted Red-Brown...............	510	265
Brown-Purple....................	520	270
Full Purple......................	540	280
Dark Purple.....................	550	288
Full Blue........................	560	293
Dark Blue.......................	570	300

HEAT COLORS

IN MODERATE DIFFUSED DAYLIGHT WITH APPROXIMATE TEMPERATURES

COLOR.	DEGREES FAHRENHEIT.	DEGREES CENTIGRADE.
White...........................	2250	1230
Light Yellow.....................	2100	1150
Yellow..........................	1950	1065
Lemon..........................	1830	1000
Orange..........................	1725	940
Dark Orange.....................	1630	890
Salmon..........................	1550	840
Bright Cherry....................	1450	790
Cherry..........................	1375	745
Dark Cherry.....................	1240	670
Blood Red.......................	1095	590
Faint Red.......................	985	530

a stone. This brightens it sufficiently for the operator to see the temper colors as they appear, coming up in straight lines across the shank.

Laying the edge of the chisel across the sharp edge of a cold anvil acts as a check to the tempering, because the heat that would be conducted to the cool end is absorbed by the anvil. As soon, therefore, as the edges are brightened and one can see what is happening, the job is lifted from the anvil so as to allow the conducted heat from the shank to have full play. When the right temper color reaches the actual edge, the whole tool is dipped and quenched. As another example, one can consider the common twist-drill, which is a more complex tool than a chisel or ordinary turning-tool. A drill is subject to considerable stress, especially when breaking through the under-side of a surface. This is due to the fact that it has then lost the support provided by the point. Twist-drills must be hardened along the whole length of their flutes, as they easily untwist if any part is left soft.

CASE-HARDENING

WHILE no definite rules can be laid down, it can be said in general that hardening and tempering is, in the main, a heat-treatment operation applicable to metal-working tools such as chisels, lathe-tools, milling-cutters, taps, dies, drills, drilling-bushings, gages, etc., the procedure being to machine the steel to certain limits while in the soft state and then to finish to size by grinding after hardening, where the common shop tolerance is over-size or under-size to $\frac{1}{1000}$ of an inch or what is in shop parlance + or − .001 in. One-thousandth of one inch is about the thickness of tissue-paper, and is measured for most practical shop purposes by a micrometer, which is fully dealt with in another chapter. In instrument and tool room work it may be necessary to work to closer limits, while a good deal of work is now being done on the metric system, where the corresponding unit is $\frac{1}{100}$ of a millimeter. The equivalent of $\frac{1}{1000}$ in. is very nearly .025 of a millimeter, as there are 25.40 millimeters to the inch.

Because hard steel tends to be brittle, through-hardness in machine parts is seldom called for and is usually undesirable. Furthermore, production from relatively cheap soft steels with the appropriate parts of the pieces surface-hardened is a cheap method which serves perfectly well for the average run of work. Surface-hardening is usually designated as case-hard-

ening, and though generally more applicable to the carburizing, heating, and quenching operations which are about to be discussed, the same result may be achieved by means of various other methods, such as nitrogen-hardening.

Principle of Case-Hardening

The basic principle of case-hardening is to apply, by what amounts to chemical absorption, more carbon to the steel at the surface than there is in the body. By heating the part for the right time and at the right temperature in contact with some case hardening or carburizing compound, this is brought about. Those parts of the piece which are not to be hardened are coated with some substance, or copper-plated to prevent this absorption of carbon. The average depth of the case is about $\frac{1}{32}$ in., though it will vary with the nature of the work. It is not intended that the actual case will wear to any appreciable extent, because actually in some work, like ball-bearings, there is no means of adjusting the wear, and when any appreciable wear has taken place, a ball-bearing is useless anyway. It is usual to provide for a grinding allowance when fixing the machining limits, this being done in the drafting room, and appearing on the print from which the operator works. The carburized part, being, in effect, hardening steel, can be hardened by the heating and quenching suited to the nature of the steel, without the body or core being materially affected. Steels used for case-hardening are usually supplied by the steelmakers specifically for the purpose, though they fall into two principal categories:

(1) Low-carbon mild steel.
(2) Nickel case-hardening steels.

Effect on Various Steels

Steels of class (2) give excellent results for all-round work, because, while they are somewhat more difficult to machine they are easier to caseharden. The low-carbon steels require care during treatment to insure good results. Quenches have to be severe to obtain a properly hardened structure, and the heating carefully controlled in order to minimize grain-growth. The higher nickel steels, on the other hand, are comparatively immune from graingrowth and as they call for less drastic quenches, are safe and easy to handle. They are useful in shops where conditions do not permit a close metallurgical control of the heating processes, and they are of value where distortion is a primary consideration, as with the thinner cases a single quench in oil from 1400 deg. F. after carburizing may be used instead of the doublerefining and quenching treatment.

Underlying Principles

It is the increasing of the proportions of pearlite which increases the hardness and tensile strength but decreases both the ductility and toughness; and increasing the coarseness of the pearlite enhances this effect. Martensite is the hardest constituent which can be produced in steel by heat-treatment alone, so that rapid rates of cool-

ing increase the hardness, but reduce the ductility and toughness.

To achieve a hard surface, a low-carbon steel is usually chosen, and while such steel, especially if alloyed with nickel, may be exceedingly tough, no amount of heat-treatment will convert it into a hard, wear-resisting condition. The process of case-hardening, therefore, consists of introducing carbon into the surface layers of the steel from anything between $10/1000$ in. thick to $1/16$ in. thick, according to requirements, and afterwards converting this high-carbon case into the hard or martensitic condition.

Carburizing

This is done in a simple manner, by heating the steel for several hours either in a case-hardening compound, a liquid such as cyanide (as in the cyanide bath process) or in ammonia gas (as associated with the nitriding process). During the carburizing operation the outer zones of the steel absorb carbon and a high concentration of carbide is built up. Then by heating the part to 1400 deg. F. and quenching, the case changes into the martensitic condition and becomes hard, and the part is in the case-hardened condition. The operation may be also performed in one stage by quenching direct from the carburizing temperature at 1750 deg. F., the slow cooling period being eliminated.

Grain-Growth

During the carburizing operation there is some degree of grain-growth in the steel, and in the case of .15 percent carbon steel which has been carburized for some hours at 1750 deg. F. then slowly cooled, both core and case will have a large grain. If the steel is then heated to 1650 deg. F.

and cooled immediately after it has attained this temperature, the core will acquire a small grain-size, whether it has been cooled in air or quenched, but the case will have been heated considerably above its upper change point, and will have thereby acquired considerable grain-growth. In order to refine the case, therefore, it is necessary to re-heat to about 1400 deg. F. and soak it at this temperature and then cool it. Thus, for the best work a double-quench treatment is to be recommended. This refining, though it adds to the cost of the work, gives a much better job, with a tougher core and a stronger case well blended into the core. The case-hardening steels used for the better classes of work usually contain nickel, as this allows of lower temperatures being used, and as the grain-growth is retarded, the refining may be omitted and the quenching done in oil, which is less drastic than water, and cuts down the risk of distortion. One could cite thousands of different parts which are produced from case-hardening steel, but the one shown in Fig. 2 actually shows a frequent result of bad work or indifferent steel, whereas a really good job should stand the exceptionally severe test indicated in Fig. 3. In practice, a case-hardened part would never be subjected to such drastic treatment.

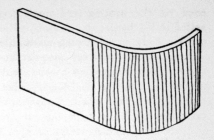

Fig. 3. Sample of mild-steel strip case-hardened in cyanide and tested by bending. The test is more severe than any ordinary conditions to which a case-hardened part would be subjected.

General Case-Hardening Practice

There is still some work being done by the old, time-honored method of packing it in boxes with any suitable case-hardening compound in such a manner that no two pieces will touch each other, and then heating at about 1700 deg. F. for the necessary period to give the required depth of case, the important thing being that this carburizing be done at as low a temperature as is consistent with the desired results, which should be as uniform as possible throughout the box. For the case-hardening steels there is a definite treatment for each one, and, of course, the parts will have been previously copper-plated or treated with a compound on the portions which are not to be carburized. There is nothing of interest to be said with regard to this operation beyond the necessity for working to rule, though men who have been engaged in it for some time acquire judgment with respect to heats, packing, and general handling which

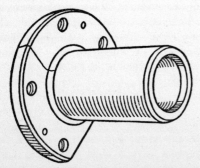

Fig. 2. Example of case-hardened work showing crack produced by uneven heating—a frequent result of faulty work or of indifferent steel.

prevents more than a very small percentage of rejects.

The result of this treatment is that the surface of the steel when carburized becomes high-carbon steel, with its ability to be hardened when quenched in water or oil. Therefore if the parts are taken from the furnace and quenched immediately, they will be hard on the surfaces. They will then be ready for use after cleaning, which removes scale or after grinding or polishing operations.

The Cyanide Process

Heating the parts by immersion in a liquid salt-bath is much more reliable. In this *cyanide* process, the parts are immersed in a bath of sodium cyanide, which is a perfectly good carburizing agent, and as the parts can be soaked in it in the molten state, most of the disadvantages of the older methods disappear. By regulating the time of immersion and the temperature of the bath, the required depth of case can be definitely applied and it is suitable for all depths of case up to $\frac{1}{32}$ in., and the case so formed has the outstanding advantage of blending exceedingly well with the core. It must not be assumed, because case-hardened parts are often finish-ground on the hard portion, that this is always necessary. It is called for primarily to counteract any effects of distortion, and it is not to be regarded as an essential cleaning-up operation. So that, provided the case is a good one, depth is not so important, as in modern precision machinery, $\frac{15}{1000}$ in. of wear, which is $\frac{1}{64}$ in. would be regarded as quite a large amount. In cyanide-hardening, which is generally suitable for depth of case up to $\frac{1}{32}$ in., about one-third is *glass-hard* and

two-thirds is in the form of a transition zone merging gradually into the core. Where a deeper case is called for, the process is modified by the addition to the bath of another element, known as *rapideep*. For average work immersion in the bath heated to 1750 deg. F. will give a case of .005 in. in 5 minutes, .015 in. in 30 minutes, .030 in. in 120 minutes, and so on, while in the modified treatment for a deeper case of .075 in., or approximately $\frac{5}{64}$ in., the soaking period would be 6 hours at 1650 deg. F. About half the depth of the case is *glass-hard*.

Liquid-Bath System

Carburizing by the liquid-bath system is ideal for all small parts, including small gears, and the carburized parts are noticeably free from distortion and scale. Good work does not depend on the skill and judgment of the operator to the extent that pack-hardened work does.

The general procedure for average-size light work for aircraft and automobiles is to put them in a jig and heat up to temperature gradually to a deep straw or blue color in a preheater, then lower into the bath for a few seconds, and then withdraw them. In this way a small quantity of melt is picked up, and this, in solidifying, raises the temperature of the piece. After carburizing, the charge is withdrawn and quenched in oil or cooled in air, as may be required. When cool enough to handle, the parts are removed from the jig and heat-treated according to requirements. For refining the case, the necessary reheating may be carried out in the same furnace as the carburizing after the temperature has been suitably reduced. This re-heating should be gradual.

Boxes filled with parts packed in case-hardening compound may be heated in any suitable type of industrial furnace, as already described, it being assumed that for high-grade work the temperature will be automatically controlled, or certainly very carefully watched by the operator, as the heat-treatment of modern steels is an exact science. The cyanide furnace consists essentially of a steel firebrick-lined shell with a flanged steel pot suspended from the top plate of the shell. The normal treatment is: (a) to carburize at 1700 deg.–1750 deg. F. and to quench directly in oil or water or cool in air. (b) To reheat to 1400 deg. F. and quench in water in small lots, but if the carburizing takes more than 2 hours there should be a re-heat between (a) and (b) and a quench in oil or water. Oil is always preferable for work not required to be glass-hard, as it prevents distortion.

Avoiding Bad Work

With suitable equipment, case-hardening is not normally a difficult operation as the treatment for any particular steel is well defined as the result of experience. There must always be a certain risk of distortion unless the parts are very simple in form, but this can be corrected by the final grinding operation. Annealing prior to final machining is also effective in reducing the risk of distortion. If the case is found to be cracked during the final inspection, it means the scrapping of a fairly costly part, and if such cracking occurs when the part is in use, there is likely to be a flaking off of very hard particles of metal, which would be a very serious matter in any delicate machine. Every possible precaution must be taken, therefore, to avoid this. It results from a sudden transition between the case and the core. The carbon content of the part, instead of dropping uniformly as the case is penetrated and merging gradually into the core, falls abruptly as the inner limit of the case is reached. The close proximity of two steels of differing carbon content will cause a high concentration of stress at this point, with the result that the case will separate from the core under slight provocation.

Cementite

Steel containing .9 percent of carbon is saturated, and if more carbon is introduced, it is not evenly distributed throughout the steel in a dissolved form, but occurs in a network of free cementite surrounding the grains. Cementite, as already stated, is a compound of iron and carbon, extremely hard and very brittle. This compound thus forms planes of weakness in the case.

The avoidance of warping in case-hardened parts is rather more a matter of planning the various operations on the part by the technical staff than the work of the operator. It is frequently due to strains left in the metal by previous working. These strains may be removed by annealing prior to final machining, but parts having thin walls or sections and any holes or slots, long shafts, and shanks with broad or thin flanges, are always liable to warp. The larger the job, the greater the danger of warping. Case-hardening steels are usually to be avoided, use being made of a grade of material with the lowest hardening temperature and mildest form of quench which will give the necessary mechanical and functional properties.

Equally important is the use of a suitable grade of steel. Cracking in hardening mainly affects steels hardened in water. With other steels, cracking usually indicates that either the material or its hardening treatment has been at fault. Again, while soft spots may be due to scaling, the most frequent cause is an unsuitable type of steel, having regard to the mass of the job. The remedy is to use a more drastic quenching medium, such as iced brine, or to use an alloy steel which enables a slower quench to develop a full and uniform hardness.

A final clean-up of the part by grinding, even if not essential, is often a worth-while operation, provided due care is taken not to heat the hardened part in grinding, as this would set up soft spots—a condition which may also come about by careless quenching.

Nitrogen-Hardening

This is another process of surface-hardening. It is based on the fact that if steel is heated to about 932 deg. F. in a current of ammonia gas, the surface will absorb nitrogen and become hard. Parts undergoing this treatment are placed in a gas-tight box of heat-resisting steel provided with inlet and outlet tubes for the circulation of the ammonia gas. The parts are loosely placed in the box without any packing material, the individual layers being separated by nickel wire-netting so as to allow free circulation of the gas. The box is then put into the electric furnace, the door sealed up and the furnace brought up to the required temperature. The ammonia is supplied direct from cylinders, and discharges through a water-bottle giving about ½ in. back pressure. The only require-

ments during nitriding are to insure that the flow of ammonia is maintained, and that the temperature of the furnace is kept constant.

Removing the Film

When the nitriding is completed, the furnace is allowed to cool down quickly to 700 deg. F., the box taken out, and the parts removed as soon as they are cool enough to handle. No further treatment of any kind is required, unless it is to remove the thin grey film on the surface. This can readily be done by buffing or lapping. Those portions which must be kept soft, such as threads, keyways, etc., are protected, by tinning, against the action of the ammonia gas.

Although there is a slight swelling during the operation, this process, which is simple, cheap, and reliable, is now being extensively employed because this can be provided for by the designer. There is no risk of distortion or cracking: no further work on the hardened surfaces is necessary, and, being exceedingly hard, they are very resistant to wear. Nitriding is also suitable for cast iron, and is thus a means of further extending the usefulness of alloy irons, hardened cylinder liners being a good example of this class of work. Steels for nitriding usually have a carbon content between .20 percent and .65 percent, and usually contain a small percent of aluminum.

Hardening Malleable Iron

The malleable iron casting may be an ideal means of producing machine parts at a very low cost, as they can be made more nearly to finished form than forging. These castings machine easily and no heat treatment is necessary but the wearing qualities are poor.

It is not practicable to carburize such castings to a depth exceeding .02 inch, as prolonged treatment causes complete solution of the graphitic carbon, and this would give a brittle result, especially in the center, when quenched. Well annealed castings can be case hardened to a depth of .015 inch.

The hot metal from which malleable castings are made is not so fluid as ordinary grey iron so it is customary to make the runners, risers, and gates extra large to allow the metal to flow easily into all parts of the mold.

CHAPTER 12

WELDING, SOLDERING, AND BRAZING

USES OF WELDING. RESISTANCE WELDING. REPAIRING CASTINGS. TYPES OF JOINTS. ARC WELDING. GAS WELDING. COPPER AND BRONZE. USE OF THE BLOWPIPE. ALUMINUM. SOLDERING. TOOLS AND METHODS. BRAZING. PREPARATION OF WORK.

THE elemental principle of welding is seen in a common operation performed by the blacksmith over the anvil, where, by heating the ends of two pieces of wrought iron or steel to a white heat and hammering them together, they can be welded together. In good work of this kind it should not be possible to detect the joint. If this kind of joint is tested in a testing machine to pull it apart, it would most likely fail at the weld rather than in the actual metal, but a good hammer weld should have about 75 percent of the strength of the metal.

Chain is commonly made by hammer welding, and the familiar joints for work of this nature are shown in Fig. 1.

Operations of this kind are confined largely to odd-shaped pieces made for mill-wrights and the maintenance staff in connection with repair work, although a good deal of it is associated with the requirements of shipyard work.

Wrought iron is a better welding material than steel, because when steel is heated, the parts become coated with oxide of iron in the form of a black scale, and if this is not removed the weld will be defective. In the case of wrought iron, the metal may be safely heated to a temperature which will melt the oxide, which is then forced out during the hammering. But as this is too high a temperature at which to work steel, it is necessary to

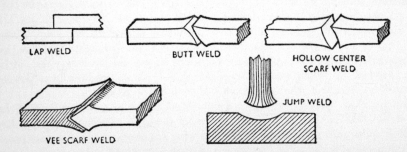

Fig. 1. Representative types of hand-made hammer welds as produced when using a blacksmith's forge. Good hammer welds should have about 75 percent of the strength of the metal. Chain is commonly made by hammer welding.

372

use a flux, usually borax. Borax powder and fine clean sand in equal parts makes a good flux, especially if mixed with 25 percent of iron (not steel) filings. In most cases, however, it is probably better to use one of the welding compounds which are sold specifically for different kinds of welding.

Welding of this kind can also be done in a forging press where pressure is applied in place of hammering. Extensive use is made of what is basically hammer welding in the fabrication of lap-welded pipe.

The pipe edges, suitably trimmed, are bent to the circle, the edges are heated by a gas flame and closed by hydraulic pressure in machines specially constructed for the purpose. The longitudinal seam of steel pipe is usually made in this way, although pipe is more often produced by a piercing and drawing operation from a piece of steel in present-day practice.

ELECTRIC WELDING

RESISTANCE welding is electrical welding done in machines, and is not usually to be regarded as a very skilled operation. Most of it is applicable to light work as a substitute for light riveting or soldering, and is classified as butt, flash, spot, and seam welding. The work is carried out by placing in contact the parts which require welding and passing a very heavy current at low voltage through them. The electrical resistance at the point of contact is high compared with the rest of the circuit, and the temperature at the joint rises rapidly. When welding temperature is reached, mechanical pressure is applied to join the metal into a sound weld.

Butt welding may be subdivided into slow butt welding and flash welding. In the slow weld the parts are brought into close contact and the current switched on. When welding temperature is reached, the parts are forced together, causing an upset at the weld. This method is used when welding solid uniform sections, and a typical machine is shown in Fig. 2.

For thin sections flash welding is used. In this process, the current is switched on and the parts brought together with only a slight pressure. Arcing takes place, and any unevenness at the ends burns away, while the whole area of the ends is rapidly raised to a high temperature. The application of a sudden heavy pressure forces out the burnt metal in the form of a thin fin, leaving only sound metal in the weld itself.

For light work, spot welding is now being used extensively as a substitute for riveting, to fasten two sheets of metal together by uniting them over an area equal to that of the rivet which would otherwise be used.

In this case, in a machine as shown in Fig. 3, the current is applied by means of two tips or electrodes between which two or more pieces are placed to be welded together. These electrodes are brought together by means of a hand-lever or pedal, or in certain types of machine by a power-driven mechanism.

Mechanical pressure is applied to them through a spring, and when the spring is compressed to a certain point a switch is closed automatically. Current then flows until welding temperature is reached, then the spring is further compressed, completing the weld

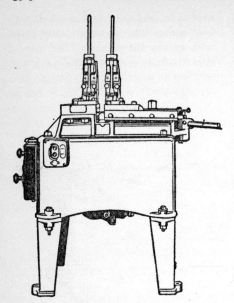

Fig. 2. Typical butt-welding machine used mainly for the welding of solid uniform sections.

it is not intended to form either a gas-tight or liquid-tight joint. For this purpose it is usual to make use of seam welding, which is done by passing the sheets between two copper disc electrodes which form part of the electrical circuit. The sheets become heated to welding temperature in the path of the electrodes, and the pressure between these completes the weld. This process is used in the manufacture of oil and paint drums, refrigerators, electric ovens, etc., and the materials for which it is best suited are mild steel and stainless steel. A maximum thickness of two $\frac{3}{16}$-in. steel sheets can be welded together.

In common with many other machines used in production work, it is essential, where a large number of parts must be produced, that the correct sequence of operations should be performed uniformly every time, and it is possible to do this by automatic

and cutting off the current. In the majority of machines at present in use, the operator has to judge the correct temperature, though this can now be done automatically by automatic spot welders.

Spot Welding

Spot welding is applied chiefly to the welding of steel from a few thousandths of an inch to half an inch thick, but brass, copper, and other non-ferrous metals of limited thickness may be welded safely. It can make as serviceable a joint as a riveted one, but

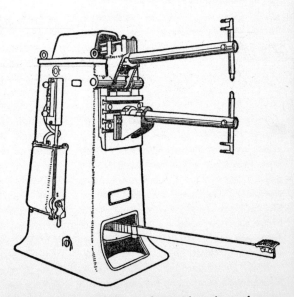

Fig. 3. Spot-welding machine. The electrodes are brought together by means of the pedal shown in the foreground.

means. A machine of this type, shown in Fig. 4, consists of a standard transformer and clamping gear, but with a special mechanism for welding. The parts to be welded are fixed in the machine with suitable clamps which may be either hand- or power-operated. The welding operation is then entirely automatic. There is a self-contained motor, driving the upset gear. This is set in motion, the slide is withdrawn slightly, the current switched on automatically, and then the slide moves slowly forward. When the parts to be welded make contact, flashing takes place, and this is continued for a certain time, allowing the two ends to become white hot in readiness for the final pressure. This is applied by means of a powerful spring, and the pressure is released after the welding has taken place.

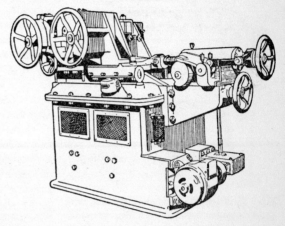

Fig. 4. For mass-production work an automatic welder of the type shown above is used.

Butt Welding

By means of machines like this thousands of welds can be made exactly alike, with the knowledge that the correct upsetting pressure has been applied to each one. The current is controlled by means of suitable cams on the driving shaft, and when the machine has once been set, no further adjustment is required when welding one kind of material.

Butt welding for comparatively heavy work is quite a recent development, sometimes referred to as flash-butt welding. The important thing is to have the faces of both parts being welded in contact over the whole section. Unless this condition is met, there is an uneven distribution of the current over the cross-section of the weld, and only some points of the cross-section are effectively welded. This is not so apparent in the welding of small parts, as the protruding points are generally very small, and shortly after the start of the weld, they are melted away, due to the higher pressure per unit of area. So that, the butt welding of objects with small cross-sections has always given good results. The abutting faces of large welds or those with complicated cross-sections must be carefully prepared and adjusted to each other before any actual welding is done.

The principal feature of the modern butt-welding machine for heavy parts, as shown on Fig. 5, is a means of applying considerable pressure, and in the particular one illustrated, in addition to the capstan wheel which operates the large screw through bevel gearing, there is a small motor driving the same gearing through a cone-clutch. The gearing is used when heavy sections are being welded where enough pressure cannot be applied by the capstan wheel. The amount of pressure applied is determined by the current fed to the motor and it is tripped automatically.

Operating a Butt Welder

The method of operation is as follows: Suitable contact blocks are provided to accommodate the work to be welded. These are fixed in the clamps by means of bolts provided for this purpose, the height of the clamps being varied by adjustment which is provided.

After the parts have been gripped in the machine the back stops are set; the parts are then moved apart by means of the capstan wheel. The plugs are set in their correct receptacles, No. 1 for the heaviest sections, No. 4 for the lightest, and intermediate ones for material between these thicknesses.

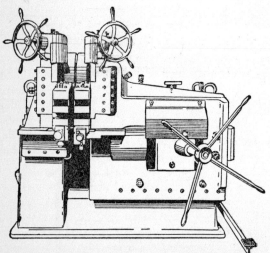

Fig. 5. Flash butt-welding machine for heavy parts. A feature of this machine is the method of applying considerable pressure which is obtained either by means of the capstan wheel or by an electric motor driving the same gearing through a cone clutch.

The current is turned on by means of the foot-switch, and the parts are then brought together by means of the capstan wheel. They are brought backward and forward several times to preheat the work slightly, then slowly brought forward during the flashing period.

When both ends are white hot the hand-wheel is turned rapidly. This brings the two parts into intimate contact, and further pressure is applied by the hand-wheel. The current is cut off, either automatically or by foot, at this stage.

In the case of heavy sections, the final upsetting pressure is applied by means of the motor. This is effected by the pedal operating the clutch connecting the motor to the upsetting gear.

Electric Arc Welding

Much the more important from an engineering standpoint are the means employed for joining metal sections, principally plate, to build up work such as that shown in Fig. 6 as a substitute for a casting. From the few simple pieces shown in Fig. 7, the pedestal on the left can be built up more cheaply than a comparable casting and the weight is less.

Another aspect of the extending application of welding is that in which an experienced operator can weld a broken piece back in place in a manner which renders the whole as serviceable as the original casting (Fig. 8).

Apart from work of

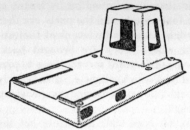

Fig. 6. Large bedplate built up by means of electric welding. The welded joints can be clearly seen.

this kind welding in general is applied to the joining of plates, bars, and fabricated sections of steel, copper, brass, and aluminum as an alternative to riveting.

Work which is met with in the shop is more like that illustrated, and in comprehensive work like the gear blank shown in Fig. 9, which weighs over 5 tons, the major portion of the work is preparation of the various sections to be welded, and the provision of jigs and other means of holding them in position during the welding operation.

The separate sections are cut and fabricated for assembly by the welder and the pieces set up for welding by "tack" welds.

Appreciable skill in welding can be acquired in a much shorter time than the skill of the tool-maker or engine-fitter, but the strength of a welded

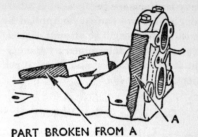

PART BROKEN FROM A

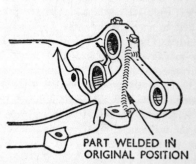

PART WELDED IN ORIGINAL POSITION

Fig. 8. How welding can be used to repair broken castings. *Above,* casting showing broken part; *below,* part welded in original position.

joint depends almost entirely on the skill of the welder. However, welding itself is simple enough. The plates come to the welder (that is, as far as the general run of work done in mild steel is concerned) in the form shown in Fig. 10, and the job of the welder is to run molten metal into the joints. Welds are classified as flat-butt welds, T welds, corner welds, and lap and

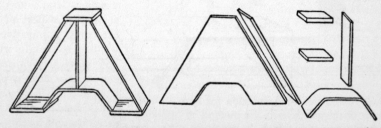

Fig. 7. Pedestal built up by means of welding. On the left the completed pedestal is shown, while on the right are seen the separate parts before being welded together. It can be produced cheaper than a comparable casting.

Fig. 9. Large gear blank for a double helical gear built up by welding. Its size can be judged by the man standing at the side.

fillet welds. The more usual methods are indicated in Fig. 11.

Electric Welding Procedure

If two rods of conducting material be connected to a suitable source of electric power, and be then placed in contact, the low electric resistance of the contact permits heavy current to pass; intense heat is produced, and this is sufficient to vaporize the conductors at the point of contact. On separating them slightly the current continues to flow through the vaporized material and an "arc" is produced, one or both of the electrodes being con-

tinually consumed to maintain the conducting vapor path.

A welding arc may be produced with either D. C. or A. C. and with carbon or metal electrodes, but a minimum difference in voltage must be present at the electrodes before the arc can be established with carbon electrodes; this is about 40 volts for D. C. and about 30 volts for A. C., but higher voltages are required to maintain stable arcs.

The essentials of a good weld are that the surfaces to be united be thoroughly fused and intimately mixed with the added metal, while the slag and oxide must be eliminated.

Lap joints, butt joints, and combinations of them are commonly used for joining plates. The edges of a butt joint must first be beveled and then melted from the bottom of the V upward, filling metal being run on to the bottom and sides of the V, and built up above the level of the plates.

The filling metal must always be suited to the metal to be united, for the weak point in a weld is the boundary between the original and the added metal. In many cases the formation of a hard brittle zone, due to too rapid cooling, can be avoided by preheating the work. The parts should be cleaned by mechanical means prior to welding, and where a joint must be welded in several layers, the flux should be

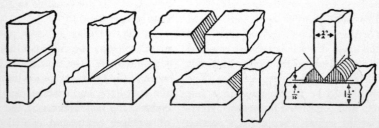

Fig. 10. How plates are prepared for welding. They come to the welder in the form shown above, and his job is to run molten metal into the joints.

chipped off each layer before the next layer is begun.

Application of Arc Welding

Arc welding is extensively employed for the joining of cast-iron, wrought-iron, and steel parts, for repairing

Factors Causing Faulty Work

In soldering, the metal is run into the joint at a low temperature which does not spoil the solder, but a welding operation is virtually a local casting of metal done under exceedingly bad conditions for the metal. There is

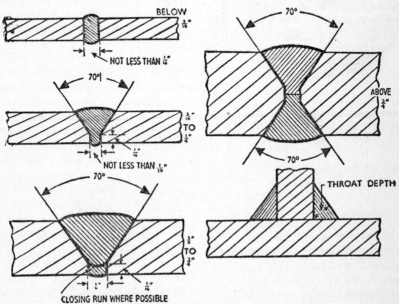

Fig. 11. Five types of electric arc welded joints.

castings, joining pipes, building tanks and barrels, connecting the members of steel structures, building up worn parts, such as rails, shafts, etc., as well as the different classes of work which have been mentioned previously.

The welding of a long seam should not be started at one end and continued in the same direction, because unequal expansion and contraction will result in distortion and severe stresses. The joint should be tack-welded in a few places and completed in sections, starting at the center, then doing a section on one side some distance away, then a similar section on the other side.

always the risk of weakness developing from strains and slag inclusions. A good deal depends on skillful use of the correct filler rods, etc., the manufacture of which is a specialized business, and it is not possible to give more than general rules.

In the welding of any particular metal, such as the various alloy steels, aluminum, etc., the best guide to good work is the instructions available from the suppliers, and with respect to procedure, the instructions of the makers of welding equipment can always be studied with advantage before undertaking the work.

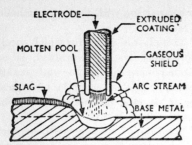

Fig. 12. Diagram showing the principal features of shielded arc welding.

In metallic-arc welding the essential principle is that an electric arc is maintained between a piece of wire—the electrode—and the work being welded. The heat generated by the arc fuses the electrode and the molten metal thus formed becomes a part of the metal being welded, so that at the face of the weld, there is an actual mixture of two liquefied metals to give, on solidification, a properly-fused joint. So metallic-arc welding is a miniature steel-making process, and just as ordinary steel production requires skilled metallurgical control, so must metallic-arc welding be carried out under strict inspection and control.

Protection of the Metal

The coating applied to the electrode wire largely determines the resultant quality of the weld and there are two distinct types of protection. First, there is the formation of a fusible slag. If this is ideal it will coat every globule of the weld metal with a skin which shuts out the air; secondly, there is the use of a chemically reducing gaseous envelope, which completely surrounds the arc.

It is important to note, however, that if not properly controlled and balanced, both the slag and the gas-shield can be responsible for an in-

ferior weld even though they may have adequately protected the weld metal during actual deposition. For instance, if the slag is not of the correct viscosity (stickiness), or is difficult to fuse, there is great danger of its being trapped in the rapidly cooling weld metal.

Again, if the slag is not right chemically, there may be a reaction of the slag in contact with the weld metal which will result in a poor weld.

Again, a gas-shield, if incorrectly applied, can cause blowholes in the

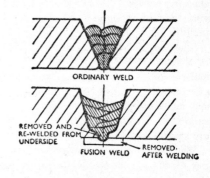

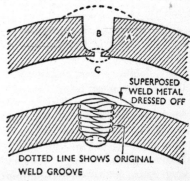

Fig. 13. The two upper illustrations show methods of welding heavy plate, while the lower shows how seams in boilers and drums are treated. The parent metal A is grooved while the groove B is filled in with weld metal by means of an automatic machine positioned outside the drum. The run of the weld metal C is done manually.

weld, and may be responsible for a poor, rough finish of the weld surface. Cracks in weld metal are known to have been caused by a too vigorous reducing action. The shielding of the arc is done by means of an inert gas which excludes air and does not itself enter into chemical combinations with the molten metal, as is shown in Fig. 12.

The heavy coating of the electrode is of such composition that, in the heat of the arc, it gives off a gas which envelops and completely shields the arc, preventing the air from combining with the molten metal and forming impurities likely to weaken the weld.

The electrode coating is consumed in the arc at a slower rate than the melting of the electrode. As a result of this, the coating extends beyond the metal core of the electrode and serves to direct and concentrate the arc stream.

The action of the arc on the coating of the electrode results in a slag formation which floats on top of the molten weld metal and protects it from the surrounding atmosphere while cooling. After the weld metal is sufficiently cooled the slag may be easily removed.

Form of Joint

An important factor in all welded joints is the groove. The plates come to the welder suitably formed (Fig. 10), the angle and size of the groove having been previously determined. The V and double-V grooves for flat-butt welding have already been noted, but in the welding of heavy boiler drums and high-pressure pipe, a U-form of groove is usually employed. This metallic arc fusion welding, which has been intensively developed by boiler makers, is shown in Fig. 13

in comparison with the more orthodox V weld.

This class of work, for which special equipment has been evolved, is entrusted to men of only the highest skill, and the finished work is later heat-treated to relieve strain, and the joints examined by X-ray.

Admittedly, welding skill, as such, is little more than an ability to direct the weld metal where it is needed without letting slag be trapped underneath it when it solidifies. That points to the necessity of a fairly wide V, the commonly included angle being one of 60 deg., but for thick sections, double-V, U and double-U forms are used. Generally speaking, the heavier the sections, the more care necessary in making the joint, apart from the fact that they are to be subjected to higher stresses.

At the bottom of the V the welds can be made in a single run; as the V is filled up, double and treble runs are required, and the overlapping of these is very important (Fig. 11). Too, in the matter of double-V joints, the gap becomes a matter of considerable importance.

It must be of a width which will allow the run at the bottom of the V to project just through to the other side without being so wide as to allow the metal to actually drop through. If it is too narrow, the metal will not penetrate far enough and a space is left in which slag will be included when the first run is put in from the other side.

Flat Surfaces

Running the metal to a flat surface —an art to be acquired only by practice—is essential here, too, because a convex surface causes slag to be trapped in the grooves at the side of the weld below the next run, and the greater the width of the groove the more important does this become, as it is at the sides of the joint that slag has its greatest weakening effect. When doing the other side of a double-V joint, there is a fin of metal which must be chipped out, so that for most practical purposes a gap of between $\frac{1}{8}$ in. and $\frac{3}{16}$ in. is allowed. While a wide groove is desirable from the standpoint of the slag inclusion, it increases the cost of the joint, and the commonly used 60 deg. angle satisfies the majority of cases.

Sometimes with thick plate, better results are obtained with 60 deg. at the root of the groove, changing to 45 deg., this being a stage toward the U-groove.

GAS WELDING

GAS welding, involving the use of the familiar acetylene torch, must not be regarded as just an alternative to arc welding, although it is true that a good deal of work can be done equally well by either method.

Basically gas welding, which requires the portable equipment shown in Fig. 14, is a method of applying the torch to a wire of suitable metal and melting it into the joint. To insure good work it is essential to handle the equipment carefully and to keep the welding tips clean. One should test the gas for purity by holding a piece of clean body paper, soaked in a dilute solution of silver-nitrate in the gas stream for a few seconds. If it shows rapid blackening, the blowpipe control valve should be opened gently until the flame just ceases to smoke. The oxygen control valve should then be turned on and the oxygen supply increased until a sharply-defined center cone is obtained.

The oxygen valve is then closed until there is a very faint haze around the outline of the center cone to obtain what is known as a neutral flame. In this condition, the blowpipe is burning equal quantities of oxygen and acetylene. It is generally advisable to have the slightest possible haze of acetylene around this center cone.

With the plates set up and held in position by such means as may be necessary, and the flame adjusted, the actual welding resolves itself into the really simple operation of melting the wire into the joint either by general movement to the left or the right, unless the work has to proceed in a vertical direction, although there is actually an appreciable difference between rightward or back-hand welding and leftward or forward welding, as indicated in Fig. 18.

Welding and Cutting Blowpipes

Most manufacturers make two distinct types of blowpipe, one for welding and one for cutting, although it is possible to use certain types for both welding and cutting. Each of these types is further classified into *low pressure* and *pressure* (high pressure) pipes.

Low pressure blowpipes make use of the *injector* principle. The oxygen passing through the small opening in the tip sucks the acetylene into the flow of gas. If properly designed, any change in the flow of oxygen will cause a corresponding change in the amount of acetylene.

In the pressure blowpipes, the oxygen and acetylene are both under pressure, which may be regulated independently at the respective cylinders as well as at the torch itself, so that the proportions of each can be carefully controlled.

The highest temperature is produced when the proportions of oxygen and acetylene are approximately equal. The flame from this combination has two sharply defined zones. The inside is a brilliant white cone from $\frac{1}{16}$ to $\frac{3}{4}$ in. long. Surrounding this is a larger cone of faintly bluish color.

Forward and Backward Welding

There are arguments in favor of the former, in which the welding rod precedes the blowpipe along the direction of the seam.

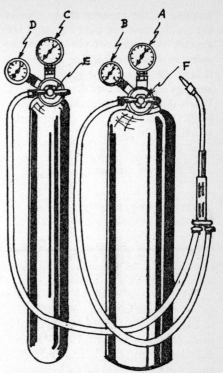

Fig. 14. Equipment used for acetylene welding. The cylinder on the left contains oxygen; that on the right acetylene. The various parts are as follows: A and C, high pressure gauges; B and D, low pressure gauges; E and F, adjusting screw.

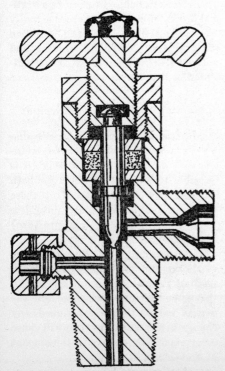

Fig. 15. Cross section of a Linde oxygen cylinder valve.

The blowpipe and the rod are in the same vertical plane, and are so held that their directions are approximately at right angles to each other. The movements of the blowpipe, and of the rod, are quite different from those used when the backward method of welding is practiced.

In backward welding the blowpipe points in the direction of the completed weld and moves steadily along the direction of the weld without any lateral motion at all. The welding rod, however, points in the opposite direction to the completed weld and is given

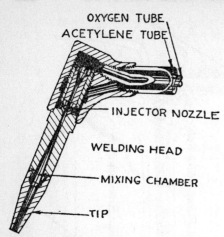

OXYGEN TUBE
ACETYLENE TUBE

INJECTOR NOZZLE

WELDING HEAD

MIXING CHAMBER

TIP

Fig. 16. Cross section of an Oxweld Type welding head.

a roughly circular progressive movement. The cone of the oxy-acetylene flame is directed toward the bottom of the seam, in order that the maximum amount of heat may be utilized to best advantage.

It is claimed in favor of backward welding that it is economical and enables a given run to be done with 30 percent less metal, and that the operator works to the best advantage. In certain circumstances, of course, such as the welding of seams of tanks, pipes, ducts, etc., where sections of appreciable weight are being erected in position, the welding has to be done in the vertical, and when the plate is over $3/16$ in. thick there are usually two operators on the work, the general procedure of which is illustrated in Fig. 19.

The square edges of the plates being joined will be noted, and they are suitable for mild steel plates up to $5/8$ in. thick. Thus, work on beveling the plates is eliminated and less filler rod is used. Backward welding in the horizontal can be done with square-edge

plates up to $5/16$ in. thick, but over this thickness a 60 deg. bevel is recommended.

Vertical Welding

Vertical welding can be done by a single operator at a rate of about 15 ft. per hour on $1/8$-in. plate, while the average speed for two operators on thicker plate is about 7 ft. per hour—according to thickness.

In this work, the initial operation is one of heating the edges sufficiently to fuse them through for their full depth, producing a small round hole between the edges, this hole being maintained as the welding proceeds. This is virtually forward welding, the rod being fed with the weld puddle in front of the blowpipe and preceding it up the seam.

In the case of the single-welder technique, the blowpipe has only one movement—forward up the seam—but if there is a large gap between the edges, it is desirable to impart a slightly semi-circular motion to the blowpipe in order to maintain both plate-edges in a state of equal fusion. The operator should check any tendency to lift the blowpipe from the weld or to allow the angles to alter as the work proceeds.

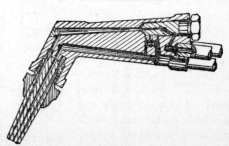

Fig. 17. Cross section of an Oxweld Type cutting head.

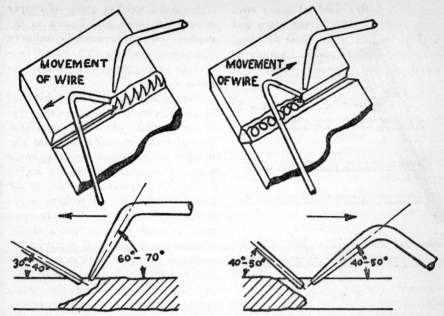

Fig. 18. The procedure followed in gas welding. *Left,* forward welding, and *right,* backward welding. In the former the welding rod precedes the blow pipe along the seam; in the latter the reverse is the case.

Work by Two Operators

In the case of two operators, both flames should be matched before starting the work, and in order to insure that both blowpipes are working at the same pressure and receiving an equal amount of gas, it is preferable for both blowpipes to be supplied from two outlets off the same gas supply.

When practicing, it is an excellent plan for a third person to be stationed in line with the edge of the test-pieces of plate, so that he can see both welders and check the blowpipe and rod angles. A few practice runs on these lines will soon get both welders working together.

While copper and bronze have long been successfully fabricated by brazing—an operation dealt with later in this chapter—modern welding methods are largely superseding it, as they

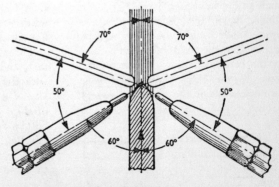

Fig. 19. Disposition of jets and metal for upward welding by two operators. Such a method is often necessary when fairly heavy sections have to be welded in position.

make for better work at lower cost. This class of work is not often met with in engine or machine building, because bronze is confined mainly to small parts or to large castings.

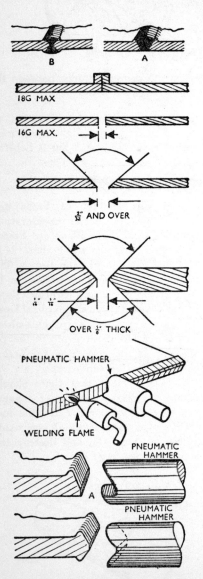

Fig. 20. On the top is shown the preparation of the plate for copper welding. The tools used are shown at the bottom.

A special welding grade of copper is now produced, and known as deoxidized copper, because the ordinary commercial grades contain a small percentage of oxygen in the form of cuprous oxide.

The cuprous oxide is not harmful in itself, because it occurs in the form of spheroidal particles distributed throughout the mass of the copper. The danger occurs when the copper is heated to temperatures in the region of the melting point. There is also the possibility that during welding a reaction may occur between the cuprous oxide and the reducing gases of the welding flame. This will result in the reduction of the oxide to metallic copper, and the production of water vapor, for example, within the metal, giving rise to inter-granular cracks and porosity, which make a weak and unsatisfactory weld.

For copper welding, special rods are used with a borax-compounded flux, and an absolutely neutral flame is essential. Plates are prepared for welding as shown in Fig. 20, where the flange on thin metal should be noted. With a height of about twice the thickness of the plate, this flange should have a square corner, as otherwise it will be impossible to obtain a flat sheet after welding.

The abutting edges may be in contact, and the metal may be run down with the blowpipe without the necessity of a welding rod. For thicknesses of sheet copper up to 16 gage, a plain butt weld may be used without any beveling. The plates should be separated before welding by a gap equal to about one-half of the thickness of the sheet. For plate up to $\frac{5}{8}$ in. thickness, a single bevel is necessary. The included angle of bevel should be 90 deg. (Fig. 20).

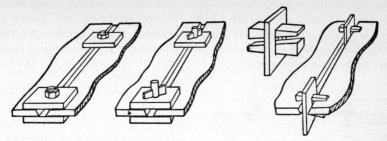

Fig. 21. Types of clamps used for maintaining the correct distance between the edges when welding long seams in copper plate.

Welding Long Seams

When welding long seams in copper plate it is essential to maintain the correct distance between the edges. For this purpose it is not advisable to tack-weld intermittently, because the copper is prone to hot-shortness, and the tack welds, not possessing very great strength at high temperatures, would be incapable of maintaining the edges in parallel alignment.

The only suitable method is that of taper spacing by means of suitable clamps (Fig. 21). Copper being a soft metal, the wedges should not be used in such a manner that they will be forced into the metal when the edges of the seam draw together as a result of expansion. A method which has been found successful when welding longitudinal seams on copper tanks is shown in Fig. 22.

Either the forward method of welding or the vertical method may be adopted, but work should not be started at the beginning of the seam. It should be started at a distance of about one-third of the total length from the end. Welding should then be carried out throughout two-thirds of the length of the seam in one direction.

Starting again at the previous starting point, the rest of the weld should be finished in the other direction, as shown in Fig. 22. A light hammering while the metal is still hot is helpful.

Bronze Welding

The zinc content of brass and bronze calls for special consideration, because when these alloys are heated up to the melting point there is a copious evolution of zinc fumes. The metal boils, causing blowholes to be formed, but by using a carefully regulated oxidizing flame a superficial layer of zinc oxide is formed on the bath of molten metal, which protects the remainder of the zinc from the action of flame, and prevents loss.

It is important that there should not be too great an excess of oxygen. Too much oxygen will cause the formation of a thick layer of zinc oxide on the molten bath, and destroy the fluidity of the rod.

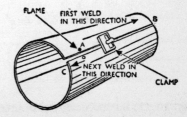

Fig. 22. Method of welding a long seam in a copper cylinder.

Preparation of the work is the same as that for steel, and forward welding with special fluxes sold for the purpose is recommended.

Cast Iron Welding

The welding of cast iron is applied mainly to repair work as already indicated, and it is not to be undertaken by anyone who happens to be handy with a blowpipe. It very often happens that the part has to be machined to restore it to its working condition, but when cast iron is welded with a steel or iron electrode the fusion point is extremely hard and non-machinable, and the surface can be finished only by grinding. For this reason, Monel metal electrodes are now being used, as with proper welding apparatus they give a surface capable of being machined as readily as can the parent metal.

The Monel metal rods supplied for the metallic arc welding of cast iron are coated with a special flux, while bare Monel metal is supplied for oxy-acetylene welding and refined powdered borax used as a flux. With gas welding, it is necessary to preheat the casting. Where possible, electric welding is recommended.

Monel flows differently from any other welding metal, so that an operator must accustom himself to its use, and not expect to obtain the best possible results with the first attempt.

Monel metal should always be deposited on a cold section of the casting, and a bead not longer than 2 in. laid at one time. Immediately upon breaking the arc, this bead should be carefully peaned with a light ball pean hammer. This produces a forged effect in the welded metal and relieves it of the strains due to cooling.

Use of Blowpipe

Bronze welding by the blowpipe is a good method of doing some kinds of repair work to broken castings, and, being done at a lower temperature than fusion welding, the time and cost of preheating are reduced. It is possible to carry out many repairs without dismantling the machinery.

The technique requires manganese-bronze rod and a special flux. Welding proceeds by the forward method, as explained previously.

Heavy sections may be vertically bronze welded by metal deposited into a series of cups formed by steel cleats placed across the V. These control the metal so that a larger blowpipe can be used, increasing the speed of working on section of 1 in. and over, where otherwise it is hard to avoid spilling the molten bronze. They also add to the strength.

The cast iron is tinned with the blowpipe pointing upward at 70 deg. to the surface. Then a clean cleat is placed into position and tinned. Bronze from one or more filter rods is then rapidly deposited, with the blowpipe pointing down into the bath.

Aluminum

Provided suitable rod and flux are used, aluminum welding is not a difficult operation. The preparation of the plates is the same as that to be associated with other non-ferrous metals. The flux is of primary importance, however, as aluminum has an invisible film of oxide on the surface which it is the primary purpose of the flux to remove. Heavy-gage work should be preheated.

As a general rule, the diameter of the welding rod should be approximately equal to the thickness of the work. Butt joints should always be employed, since better results are obtainable and there is less danger of the incomplete removal of the flux after welding than there is in the case of lap joints. For sheets below 20 gage it is recommended that the edges should be bent up at right angles and the resulting flange simply melted down to form the joint without the use of a welding rod. Above $\frac{1}{8}$ in., it is advisable to bevel the edges to insure the penetration of the weld metal.

On completion of the welding operation it is essential to remove all traces of flux. This can be done by brushing vigorously with hot water or by using a steam jet. Immersion in warm 5 percent nitric acid is recommended, to be followed by a thorough washing.

SOLDERING

SOLDERING comprises the uniting of two metals or alloys with the aid of a more soluble alloy or solder, or one with which they will more speedily join than with each other. It is customary to describe these more soluble alloys as soft solders, to distinguish them from the hard solders used for brazing (see Tables I, II and III). The types of metal that can be soldered include copper, nickel, tin, iron, lead, zinc, aluminum, and numerous of their alloys. It is also possible to solder nonmetallic substances together if they have first been provided with some form of metallic coating.

The first essential in good soldering is to insure that the metallic surfaces to be soldered are clean and completely free from dirt, grease, or adherent particles or films. Usually, the first operation is to clean the metals to be united, which is done either by hand with a file, a piece of sandpaper, or an emery cloth, or even a handful of sand, or, if available, by a pickling bath of acid or alkaline nature, which is especially suitable when dealing with large areas.

The next essential is correct heating of the soldering iron. This *iron* is not really of iron, but of copper (see Figs. 23–26). It must be *tinned,* or given a film of solder, before it can be used, and the commonest method of doing this, although not necessarily the most efficient, involves first a heating of the iron to a very dull red. Cleanliness of the tool is vital, so that it must next, while red hot, be swiftly filed on its faces to remove all dirt and oxide. It is then plunged into a flux, the purpose of which is to prevent the surfaces to be soldered from oxidizing, or to dissolve any oxides formed when the metal is heated. Zinc chloride is probably the commonest flux. Ammonium chloride is sometimes used with tin-lead solders applied at temperatures just above the melting point. Killed spirit is also used, while rosin and various preparatory fluxes are desirable for fine work on thin metal.

When fluxed, the soldering iron is brought into contact with a piece of solder, and the different faces are rapidly rubbed on a sheet of tin for the purpose of distributing the solder film evenly over the entire surfaces. If this work is correctly carried out, the point of the iron will be covered with an even film of solder. The evenness of this film must be maintained or the iron will not work properly. If the tinning

TABLE I
SOLDERING ALLOYS

TIN %	LEAD %	ANTI-MONY %	COPPER %	CADMIUM %	MELTING POINT DEG. F.	COMPLETE SOLIDIFICA-TION POINT DEG. F.
63	37				464	356
50	50	.12	.08		419	365
5	95				599	572
10–20	90–80				581–545	500–356
15–35	85–65				563–491	365
45	55				464–458.5	356
37.5	60	2.5			374	356
95	5				464	446
23	68			9	455	293
95		5			464	446
50	32			18	293	293
19	31	(50% bismuth)			203	203
13	27	(50% bismuth)		10	158	158
				95 (5% silver)	752	635
				50 (50% zinc)	617	509
				82.5 (17.5% zinc)	509	509

TABLE II
BRAZING ALLOYS

COPPER %	ZINC %	LEAD %	IRON %	TIN %	NICKEL %	MELTING POINT DEG. F.
50–53	Balance	.5	.1			1592.6–1616
52–53	"	.5	.1			1598–1616
Balance	45–50			3–5		1571
"	57–65		1.	5–9		1382–1400
"	55–59				7–9	1598
47	Balance				11	1697

TABLE III

SILVER SOLDERS

SILVER %	COPPER %	ZINC %	CADMIUM %	MELTING POINT DEG. F.	FLOW POINT DEG. F.
10	52	38		1508	1598
20	45	35		1427	1499
45	30	25		1247	1373
50	34	16		1283	1427
65	20	15		1283	1328
70	20	10		1337	1391
80	16	4		1364	1463
5			95	644	743
5		16.6	78.4	482	599
5.5			94.5 lead		
2.5	.25		97.5 "	563	671
50	15.5	16.5	18	1157	1157

is uneven, or even absent in places, the iron will have to be retinned.

The bit must never be heated to a temperature so great that the tinning is burnt off, since that will allow the iron to become oxidized and pitted. A simple test for correct temperature is to hold it about 6 in. from the cheek, when the heat from it should just be

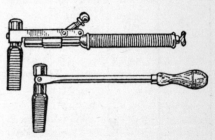

Fig. 24. Hatchet soldering irons. That above is a self-heating benzoline iron.

perceptible; some practice is necessary before this test can be applied with confidence. Another test is to touch the solder with the iron. Provided that both are clean, the solder should melt on contact.

The most effective tinning method is to employ a block of ammonium chloride or sal ammoniac, cut into oblong form, about 4 in. wide by 7 in. long by 1 in. thick, with a hollow gouged out of the upper flat surface (see Fig. 27). After cleaning and heating, the tool is inserted in this hollow and

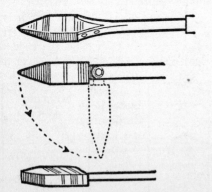

Fig. 23. *Top,* ordinary soldering iron; *center,* pivoted iron for awkward surfaces; *bottom,* internal iron for drums, churns, etc.

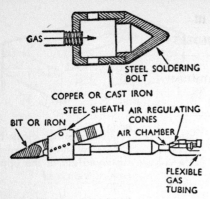

GAS →

STEEL SOLDERING
BOLT

COPPER OR CAST IRON

STEEL SHEATH   AIR REGULATING
                      CONES
BIT OR IRON
                AIR CHAMBER

FLEXIBLE
GAS
TUBING

Fig. 25. *Top,* gas-heated soldering bit. *Bottom,* the complete assembly of above showing the various parts.

pressed down firmly. The result will be the giving off of considerable quantities of white smoke or fume, and the sal ammoniac will liquefy on the surface. Each face of the iron should be treated thus, and a few drops of solder should then be melted into the hollow while the bit is still there. This tins the iron quickly and evenly. The same process should be repeated whenever the tinning is destroyed. Since ammonium chloride attracts moisture, it should be kept well away from all steel tools, which it will otherwise attack and corrode.

The next stage to be dealt with here, though of course it will, in point of time, precede the preparation of the

iron, is to prepare the joint to be soldered. Here again cleanliness is necessary and the surfaces of the joint must be cleaned as described earlier. The application of flux to these surfaces follows. A useful appliance for applying flux is shown in Fig. 28. The heated iron is then gripped in one hand and a piece of solder in the other. A small bead of solder is allowed to form on the joint, the iron is rested for a second on this to melt it, and is then passed over the edges quickly enough for these to acquire heat.

This, combined with the swift melting of the solder, creates a sound joint. Care is essential, because otherwise too much solder will make an ugly and bulky joint. The iron is moved lightly up and down the joint to spread the solder and cause the heat to soak thoroughly into the joint. If the iron is too cool the solder will be uneven, while if it is too hot the solder will not run smoothly.

The work must not be held in such a way that the flow of the solder is in the reverse direction to the inclination of the iron. In other words, the solder must flow downhill with the bit, not uphill against it (see Fig. 29).

The method of holding the iron is important. The elbow must be well away from the body, and the thumb right under the handle (see Fig. 29). The entire weight of the iron must be upheld and balanced on the thumb by the downward pressure of the lower portion of the hand.

Soldering irons are either plain—i.e., heated and applied by hand— electrically heated, gas-heated, alcohol-heated, or heated by means of a

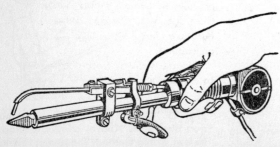

Fig. 26. Magazine electric soldering iron. Solder is fed to the bit by pulling the trigger.

thermit block. Gas stoves capable of having their temperatures regulated accurately are the best for plain irons, but coke, oil, or charcoal are also used. Coal causes too much dirt on the bit. For making a uniformly smooth joint in a long job, the hatchet iron (see Fig. 24) is valuable. The copper bolt is riveted in the eye of the iron shank, the bit, however, being able to revolve if desired. With this type of bit there is a greater area of contact with the metal, and therefore the whole joint is heated more thoroughly.

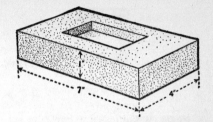

Fig. 27. Ammonium chloride block for tinning. It should be cut to the size given and a hollow gouged out of the upper surface as indicated

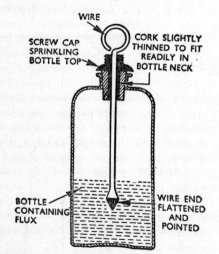

Fig. 28. Useful appliance for applying flux, showing the principal parts.

Soldering aluminum cannot be done with ordinary solders. Special solders are necessary. These do not flow as easily nor melt as quickly, and the ordinary soldering iron is therefore less suitable, since higher temperatures are essential. The blowtorch (see Fig. 30) is usually employed. Some aluminum solders (those containing phosphorus) need no flux. The fluxes available are numerous, stearin being the best. If an iron is used, it must be of aluminum or nickel, and not of copper.

Even greater cleanliness of both iron and work is essential. Soldering must be done swiftly, and the lap of the joint need not be so great, to allow for the more sluggish flow of the solder. The parts to be soldered must be tinned. Large parts are best prepared as shown in Fig. 31.

A preliminary heating of the work will facilitate operations. Certain aluminum solders and the work as well may have to be heated to a red heat before melting occurs.

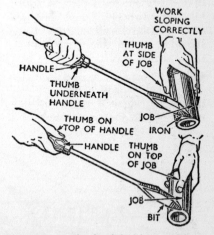

Fig. 29. Method of holding soldering iron and work. *Above*, correct method, *below*, wrong method. The thumb should be held under the handle of the iron as explained in the text.

Low-temperature solders (not above 700 deg. F.) are best. The blowtorch applies a flame directly to the surfaces to be joined, after which the solder, which is in the form of a stick or wire, is applied. The heat generated by the flame melts the metal solder, and the surplus is removed before it hardens.

BRAZING

BRAZING is the union of metallic surfaces by an interposed alloy film, and is sometimes termed hard soldering, as distinct from soft soldering. The surfaces to be brazed must be carefully cleaned, every trace of grease being removed. As a cleansing agent, carbon tetrachloride can be recommended. Gasoline is unsuitable, as parts cleaned with it retain a residual oil film.

A typical small-shop job is the brazing of tungsten-carbide tips on mild-steel shanks. For tools of large section, the tip should be set in its place on the shank, after a sliver or thin sheet of electrolytic copper, together with a small amount of unfused borax, have been laid on.

The entire job must then be transferred to the furnace. A cold tip should not be placed directly into a fierce heat, as this may cause it to crack. When the copper melts, the tip should be moved a little on its seat to make sure of a satisfactory joint. After this, the tool should be removed from the furnace, and the tip pressed gently into place. The tool must then be dipped in either powdered electrode carbon, or charcoal, to insure slow cooling without contact with the air.

An alternative method is to preheat the shank to about 1500–1800 deg. F., withdraw the tool, and clean the seat with a wire brush. Borax, copper, and tip are then placed in position and replaced in the furnace. The heating is continued until the copper melts, and the same procedure as outlined above then follows. The same methods can be used with the oxy-acetylene torch for small-section tools. This method has the advantage of eliminating slag due to the time necessary for heating up the furnace, while for the smaller and many-tipped tools it facilitates local heating. The tools should, of course, be cooled off in charcoal as above.

Preparation for Brazing

In ordinary forms of brazing, the joints are cleansed with a file, followed by em-

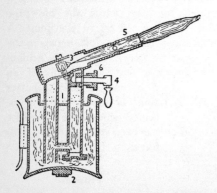

Fig. 30. Section through a soldering blowtorch for use with aluminum. 1, basin; 2, adjuster; 3, burner nipple; 4, regulator; 5, tube; 6, square for screwing up screw of regulator.

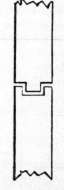

F i g .   3 1 . Method of fitting large aluminum parts for soldering. A small pointed flame should be used.

ery paper. Should it be necessary, they are then bound together with thin iron wire, or, if this method is inadequate, with clips. A flux of borax and water made into a stiff paste is then applied to the joint, which is then gently heated to eliminate moisture. The metal is then raised to a white heat, and the brazing alloy or spelter is plunged into the flux and applied to the joint, being rubbed on it until the spelter melts and begins to flow. The heat is then withdrawn.

It is advisable to cover almost the whole of the part being brazed with heat-conserving coke breeze or asbestos blocks. Small parts can be rested on a thick square sheet of asbestos.

Using a Blowpipe

The work should be so bound that the job can be reversed or moved during the operation without upsetting the relation of the parts. This facilitates flux and spelter application. The mouth blowpipe or the foot-bellows blowpipe can both be used for brazing, as can the gas blowpipe (Fig. 32). The former should be blown gently as continuity of air current must be sustained. Breathing should be through the nostrils and normal, but the cheeks should be tightly inflated to give a

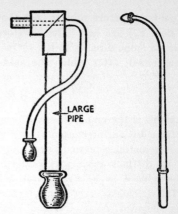

Fig. 32. *Left,* blowpipe for brazing hearth; *right,* mouth blowpipe.

steady pressure when blowing. The flame is obtained by holding the blast end of the blowpipe immediately over the source of heat—e.g., bunsen burner or alcohol flame, the tip of which it just contacts. The blast then throws forward a long bluish flame, which is hottest at its tip (see Figs. 32 and 33). The foot-bellows is employed mainly for the heavier work, and should embody a tray or trough of sheet iron provided with coke or coke breeze, or asbestos blocks, which are grouped round the part while the blowpipe flame is directed on to the joint. A small gap must be left between the parts to be joined, but this is seldom more than a few thousandths of an inch, and, in fact, a better joint is nearly always obtained when this clearance has been reduced to the minimum.

Fluxes

The brazing heat speedily oxidizes the metallic surfaces of the joint if exposed to the air; hence the use of

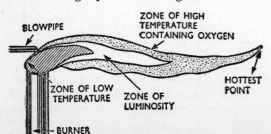

Fig. 33. Blowpipe flame. It is obtained by holding the blowpipe immediately over the flame, the tip of which it just touches.

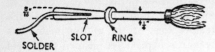

Fig. 34. Clip used to hold and apply silver solder.

flux, which can be either dry, paste, or a hot saturated solution. In the last two instances it is best applied by brush, to insure greater uniformity. If the flux is powdered or granulated, it is usually mixed with the brazing alloy. In brazing strip, wire, or rods, the ends to be joined should be dipped in a small tin of flux paste, or dry flux can be sprinkled on them.

Silver Soldering

In silver soldering, which is a form of brazing used for most non-ferrous metals and alloys, as well as for steel and iron, the flux is either borax or boric acid, or a combination of the two. The commercial fluxes on the market usually contain halogen salts or phosphates. For brazing stainless steel, which is much more difficult than soldering the same material, ground borax glass is the best flux. Fused borax is suitable for brazing proper. A clip for holding and applying the solder is shown in Fig. 34.

The spelter is best in wire or stick

Fig. 36. Preparation of copper rod for brazing. A dovetailed joint, as shown above, is advisable.

form, as powder is likely to be scattered by air-currents or the blast. Brazing spelters are usually of brass, and different compositions are necessary for the various types of metal, iron, brass, steel, copper, etc. If exceptional hardness in the joint is required, a little silver is sometimes added.

Fig. 35. Method of preparing metallic sheets for brazing.

Parts to be brazed can not only be heated by the mouth blowpipe or the foot-bellows blowpipe; but also by immersion in an alloy bath (termed dip brazing); by furnace; and by electrical resistance. This last is used mainly for parts of smaller dimensions or where a thin layer of the spelter can be inserted in the joint. This method has the advantage that it localizes the heat and also carries out the work with great speed.

In brazing metallic sheets, where very little forming work has to be carried out later, it is feasible to unite the seams edge to edge. If this is done, small nicks should be made along the edges with a file, separated by distances of about 1/2 in., as shown in Fig. 35. These enable the solder to flow through them, and make a sound joint.

If there is to be forming work after brazing, this method cannot be used, and it will be necessary to have the edges overlapping. To make a joint of this type, the edges must first be thinned along the ends which are to constitute the seams, roughly half an inch from the edge. Then, the overlapping of the two edges will make only a thickness equivalent to one thickness of the sheet. A small cramp must be cut in the top and bottom of the seam, and the opposite edge fitted in. Then the part should be securely fastened with wire to keep the joint firm.

In brazing copper rod, a dove-tailed joint is advisable, as shown in Fig. 36, as also in brazing key-stems, though here the dovetail must be narrower.

For brazing stainless steel, a rather higher temperature is required than that for ordinary steel. The part must be heated in advance to a temperature very nearly that of the molten spelter. A layer of borax deep enough for the piece to be dipped in it should be allowed to float on the surface of the metal, and after the parts have been preheated in borax, their dipping in the spelter should be deferred until the temperature of the molten metal has been reached. When dipped the parts should be taken out of the bath and allowed to cool. If a scum appears on the borax and sticks to the parts being dipped (this will impede adherence of the spelter) application of a little of the flux used for soft soldering stainless steel (zinc chloride and hydrochloric acid) should be applied to the parts before they are dipped. A clear path is then made in the borax. To remove the flux after hard soldering or brazing, the parts should be plunged into a 5 percent solution of caustic soda brought to boiling point.

CHAPTER 13

FORGING

HAND- AND MACHINE-FORGING. THE FIRE. HAMMERS AND TOOLS. ERECTING A HAMMER. FORGING ALLOY STEELS. DROP-FORGING. BOARD-HAMMERS. POWER-OPERATED DROP HAMMERS. MACHINE-FORGING. MAKING NUTS.

THE art of forging is one of the oldest in existence. Formerly an operation performed mainly on wrought iron, it is today to be associated not only with steel formed into the necessary rough shape from which tools and parts of machines and equipment will be machined, but quite a large business is done in the forging of aluminum alloys, and to a less extent the brasses and bronzes. Furthermore, hand-forging while associated with the time-honored trade of the blacksmith still has an important place in engineering work, especially in the shipyards and general shops. Machine parts, and more particularly those for the automobile, aircraft, and gun trades, are made in large numbers in drop-hammers and forging machines.

Hammering Wrought Iron

The early exponents of this ancient craft were well aware that wrought iron became relatively plastic at red heat and could then be hammered into any shape desired without detriment to the metal itself, and examples of this early work which have survived centuries are to be found the world over. Any machine part, tool, or utensil which does not originate in a casting and which cannot be economically machined from a fabricated section

must, with few exceptions, be formed to rough shape by a forging operation. Hand-forging, the trade of the blacksmith, is mainly one of hammering over the anvil parts which can be made more quickly and cheaply by manipulation under a power hammer.

In the forging machine, however, the procedure is to heat the stock, and with the end placed in the machine, the part undergoes a squeezing operation, after which, when so formed, it is sheared off the bar end, which is then pushed up into the machine again for a similar treatment. In the drop-hammer a lump of heated metal is placed in the lower die, and when the upper die is released to fall on it, the part is formed by one or two heavy blows, and is then complete so far as the forging operation is concerned, except for trimming to remove the *flash*.

Hand-Forging

The equipment for hand-forging is relatively simple, as the production of good work is almost wholly dependent upon the skill of the worker, and there are no really standardized tools. Many smiths make their own, and take good care that no one else uses them. The most important equipment in the forge shop is the hearth shown in Fig. 1, in which a coke fire is lit in the portion

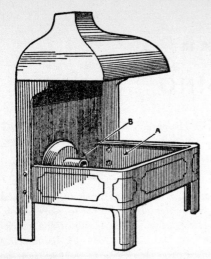

Fig. 1. A smith's hearth. The coke fire is lit at *A*, and air is admitted through the tuyere (*B*) to increase heat.

keep the fire clean and free from clinker. Other essential equipment is the anvil (Fig. 2), sufficiently familiar to call for little comment. It is usually mounted on a cast-iron stand, and while there are different forms, that shown —known as the single bick type—is the most usual. The average weight is about 250 lbs. Adjacent to it is a block with several holes in it of various forms and sizes, and grooves around it also of several sizes of V and ½-round forms. The purpose of the *swage-block* is to facilitate the formation of round, square and hexagon sections from the rough bar of iron of which the piece is being forged.

The Blacksmith's Tools

As hand-forging is essentially a hammering operation on a heated lump of metal, hammers of various weights and forms figure in the equipment, the heavier ones, or *sledge* hammers, being wielded by the smith's mate or *striker,* though really heavy hammering is now nearly always done by power-hammers. Then, what look like hammers to the first-day apprentice are a series of tools known by various names and shown in Fig. 3. Of these the Cold Sett (A) is used for nicking bars preparatory to cutting off a piece suitable for the work in hand, though this op-

(A) and by means of air admitted through the *tuyere* (B) under slight pressure an intense local heat can be applied to the piece of material placed in the fire. While the air is supplied at the required pressure by a blower or fan, usually serving several hearths, control of the blast to bring and keep the fire in good condition for the work being done calls for considerable skill. A trough of water may form part of the hearth, or it may be just a tank alongside. Its purpose is for cooling the tools or for any other work such as tempering.

The worker who is beginning the trade of the blacksmith should apply himself to the art of getting a good fire, for which a special grade of smith's coke is used. The main essential, however, is to have plenty of burning fuel between the outlet of the tuyere and the work being heated. The blast should not impinge on the metal in the manner of a blow-pipe, and a good deal of practice is necessary to

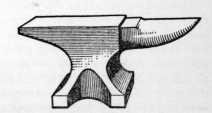

Fig. 2. Anvil here shown is that in most general use. It is usually mounted on a cast-iron stand, and weighs about 250 lbs.

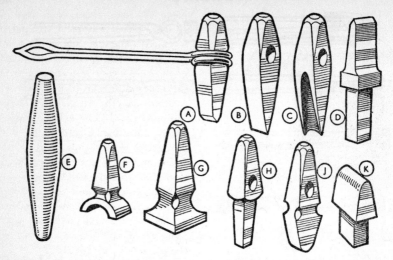

Fig. 3. Tools used in hand-forging are: A, the cold sett; B, the hot sett; C, the gouge, for curved cuts; D, the hardie; E, drifts; F, swages; G, flat-headed smoothing tool; H, punches; J, K, fullers.

eration would, in an up-to-date shop, be done by a power-driven shear or saw. The Hot Sett (B) is for cutting off surplus metal during the actual forging if that is required, while (C) is a similar tool for making a curved cut rapidly. It is known as a Gouge. The *Hardie* (D) fits in the square hole in the anvil, and is for the purpose of making any cuts in the metal while it is hot. There are also various punches (H) for making rough holes, hammers and tools with flat heads (G) for smoothing the surface of the work, as this finish may be quite sufficient in some cases, as for instance a lever on which the only actual machining may be the boring of a hole in the boss. The drifts (E) are for finishing holes, sometimes oval, while the swages (F) are used for drawing down the diameter of the round parts of forgings in conjunction with the swage-block. The two tools (J and K) are known as Fullers. They are always made in pairs, K being placed in the square

hole in the anvil, while J is held by the smith. Their purpose is the drawing down of the thin portion of a forging against a shoulder in such a manner as to avoid a sharp corner and to maintain the fiber or grain. This requirement is the reason for nearly all smith's tools being well rounded, as sharp angles in a forging are a source of weakness, just as they are in a casting, and, when required, they must be cut during machining. A smith will have, too, a whole array of tongs at his disposal, the more common of these being shown in Fig. 4.

Fig. 5 shows typical forged machine parts of medium size that would be done on the anvil in a general shop, though for mass production they can be very well made in a forging machine.

Although the production of work of the class shown in Fig. 5 by the hand-tools and equipment referred to calls for considerable acquired skill on the part of the smith and some hard work

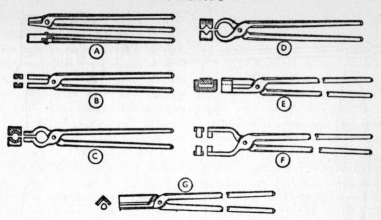

Fig. 4. Some common varieties of smith's tongs.

on the part of his mate if the forgings are of any size, the work does not present any great difficulty, and prior to the introduction of machinery into the forge the much heavier forgings shown in Fig. 6, which are typical of shipyards, were done by hand, or at the best with the help of a power-hammer (Fig. 7) for the roughing out, though actually this heavy class of forging is now done in hydraulic presses (Fig. 8). This view shows the manipulation of a heavy billet of steel which is being drawn down by a series of squeezes into what might be formed into a ship's propeller shaft or a gun-barrel. Hydraulic presses, however, are now used for producing the smaller forgings shown in Fig. 6 in one operation, much in the manner of a drop-

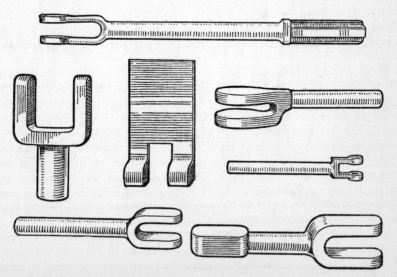

Fig. 5. Typical medium forged machine parts such as these can be made in a forging machine for mass production, or by hand on the anvil in a general shop.

hammer, but with a squeezing action in place of a heavy blow. On entering the forge though, one is more likely to meet with the power-hammer (Fig. 7), steam or air-operated, according to its type. These hammers have a very sensitive control, and the operator soon learns to vary his blows at will.

According to the actual work being done on the piece, the operator will use one or more of the tools shown in Fig. 9. A, B, C, and D are plain spring swages for round stock. E and F are top swages and G, H and I bottom swages. K is a spring necking tool, L a nobbler or flatting tool, M a hot cutter and N a cold cutter, O being a V tool for shouldering, etc.

The hammer shown in Fig. 7 has been developed in a whole number of different forms, principally with a view to compactness and more efficient operation, this being a *clear-space* air-hammer complete with motor-driven self-contained compressor. The overhanging form which leaves the front and sides of the pallets free to receive the work permits of long pieces being worked across the anvil.

Although these machines appear rough in comparison with a relatively delicate and complicated machine tool, such as a gear-cutter, they can quite easily be put out of order, or even wrecked, by a careless operator, and it takes time to acquire skill in their

Fig. 6. Heavy forgings of this kind, as needed in shipyards, were done by hand before the introduction of the hydraulic forging machine.

use. Among other things the operator should note the following points:

When erecting a hammer the anvil block should be set up above its lowest safe working position to allow for setting.

Precautions should be taken to prevent scale working down between the anvil block and base-plate, otherwise it will eventually find its way under the block and cause trouble.

Heavy hammering should be done as near as possible to the center of the pallets.

Unnecessary hammering on hard, thin, or cold material, or striking pallets together without anything between them should be avoided, and any pallet faces should be kept level so as to produce satisfactory forgings and avoid straining the piston rod.

In cases where the tup is guided by slides, these should be adjusted when necessary to take up wear and avoid more clearance than the heating of the tup necessitates.

This point has an important bearing on the life of the piston rod. The slides can normally be adjusted by inserting suitable packing strips.

The foundation for ordinary work should be so constructed as to allow a certain amount of spring, as otherwise the effect of the blow will be unnecessarily harsh, and may cause the breakage of the piston rod, or some other part of the hammer.

In cold weather it is a good precaution to lay a piece of hot metal on top of the tup before work begins.

Basic Principles of Drop-Forging

Most of the heavy work previously shown can be produced only by such operations because a comparable cast-

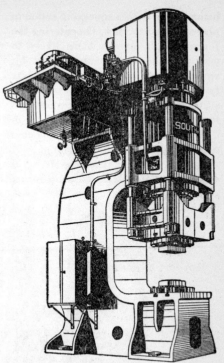

COURTESY LOBDELL CAR WHEEL CO.

Fig. 7. A power-hammer as used for roughing out heavy forgings of the type shown in Fig. 6.

ing would not suit the purpose of the finished article, but that does not necessarily apply to smaller pieces of the type shown in Fig. 10. As was pointed out in the sections dealing with alloy cast iron, malleable iron, and steel castings, it is now possible to cast parts like these in metal which has all the strength necessary to make a part to meet the service requirements, and no forging can approach the finished form of a casting, so that in general the part made from a forging will cost more.

Parts of the kind shown can, once the dies are made, be produced at a rapid rate, because as fast as the heated lumps of steel are taken out of the furnace they can be put into the hammer, pounded by it with dies to the required shape and then removed to have the surplus metal or *flash* cut off and then go to the machine shop.

For parts subjected to great stress this is probably the best all-round method of production for those produced from bar, because in this operation and, in fact, in most machine-forging work there is a plastic deformation of the steel, which refines the grain and consolidates the structure, if the work is skillfully done. Especially does this apply to forgings in alloy steel, where the necessary heating alone is a delicate operation. Many of these steels require great care in heating if the resulting forgings are to be satisfactory, for the range of temperature over which forging may be carried out without danger to the product is relatively narrow, and frequent reheating becomes necessary.

They are extraordinary carbon steels, and consequently require a greater pressure to bring about deformation, while the actual rate of deformation is also slower. The combined result of these various factors is that the forging of stainless and heat-resisting steels must be conducted slowly, due care being taken at all stages, having in mind that steel in the cast condition has a form dependent on the rate and direction of solidification.

The next requirement is suitable power for actuating the dies or tools, bearing in mind that the plastic or forgeable condition of wrought iron or steel can be retained for only a short time, especially in the case of articles having thin or light parts. This power must be capable of instantaneous application; it must be simple and ample, and the essential feature for producing the proper effect is that it must be of

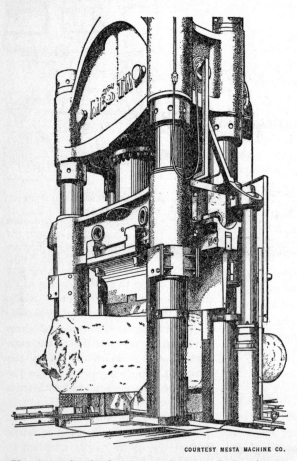

COURTESY MESTA MACHINE CO.

Fig. 8. Hydraulic forging machine in which a heavy billet of steel is being drawn down by successive squeezes into a forging that may become a gun barrel.

the same kind as the smith, with his limited physical strength, produces with hand hammer or sledge; that is to say, a perfectly elastic blow of sufficient force to produce an immediate and substantial effect upon the material, but, of course, of much greater power than would be possible in hand-forging.

Apart from the fact that a drop-forging operation combined with such heat-treatment as may be necessary produces a rough part in good physical condition, it also produces one with the minimum of material to be removed by machining, as the examples in Fig. 10 will show. These will be recognized as an automobile engine crankshaft in the upper view and axle parts in the two lower ones, while Fig. 11 shows some smaller forgings produced by this means for machine parts which can be very much more rapidly and cheaply produced by this means.

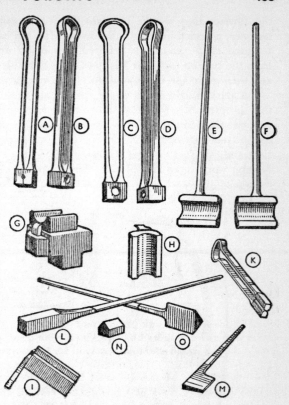

Fig. 9. Tools used with a power-hammer are here illustrated. *A, B, C, D* are plain spring swages for round stock; *E, F,* top swages; *G, H, I,* bottom swages; *K,* spring necking tool; *L,* nobbler or flatting tool; *M,* hot cutter; *N,* cold cutter; *O,* V tool for shouldering.

Construction and Working of Drop-Hammers

There is a difference between the hammers and presses already considered and the drop hammer. As the name implies, in the latter the hammer, or tup is lifted by some mechanical means and allowed to fall of its own weight. Moreover in practically all cases, the hammer is used with dies which form the part being forged.

Various means of lifting the hammer are used in the several types offered. Every manufacturer of drop hammers has his own design for each of the models which he offers the user. The underlying principles of the steam hammer may be followed from a study of Fig. 12.

The essential parts are the anvil, A, with its sow block, B. The lower half of the die in use is attached to this block with the impression facing upward. The upper half of the die is attached to the lower face of the ram, C, with the impression downward.

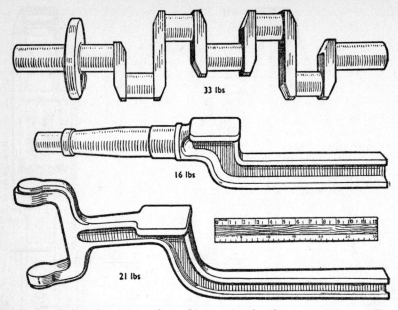

Fig. 10. Small drop-forgings such as these, once the dies are made, can be produced at a rapid rate by being pounded with dies by the drop-hammer to the required shape and then removed for the surplus metal to be cut off.

These two halves of the die must be carefully matched so that when they come together the piece to be formed will not be offset. The extra metal is squeezed out between the two halves of the die.

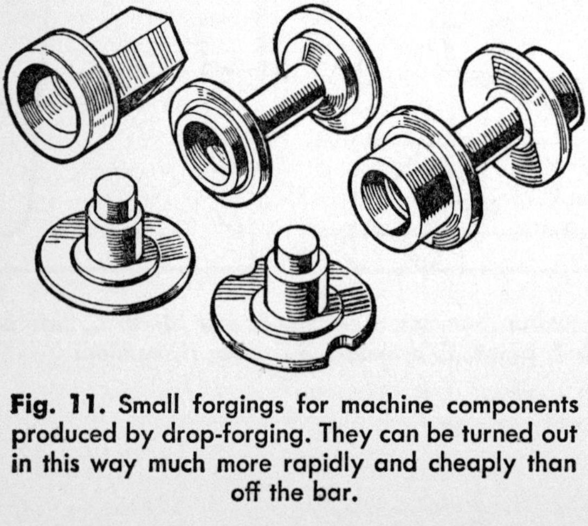

Fig. 11. Small forgings for machine components produced by drop-forging. They can be turned out in this way much more rapidly and cheaply than off the bar.

The ram is connected to the lower end of the piston rod, D, which is attached at its upper end to the piston, E. This is pushed up in the cylinder, F, by live steam which is admitted through a control valve, below the piston. It falls free and the blow depends on the weight of the hammer. The cylinder is attached to the top ends of the frame, G, of the hammer. Bolted to the top end of the cylinder is an auxiliary piston and cylinder to cushion the upward stroke of the hammer. See H.

Older methods of lifting the hammer are by means of air, ropes and boards. The air hammer is similar to the steam hammer. Where ropes are used they are fastened to the hammer at the lower

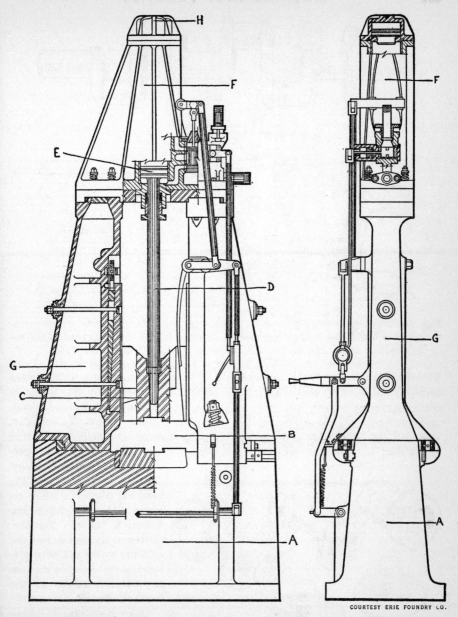

COURTESY ERIE FOUNDRY CO.

Fig. 12. Two views of a steam drop hammer. *A*, anvil; *B*, sow block; *C*, ram or hammer; *D*, piston rod; *E*, piston; *F*, cylinder; *G*, frame; *H*, cushion.

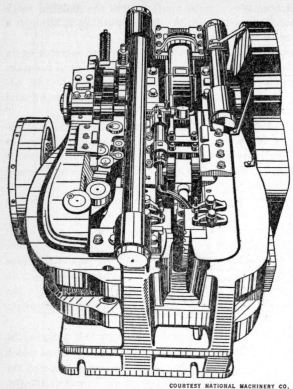

COURTESY NATIONAL MACHINERY CO.

Fig. 13. The forging machine, properly so-called, usually motor-driven through gearing, produces the forging by a squeezing motion and not by hammering.

may be hand-forged on the anvil, forged under a power-hammer, or drop-forged in dies, and each method has pretty well defined applications.

The typical forgings which are shown in Fig. 11 are very economically produced in the drop-hammer. While a drop-hammer is, in the nature of things, a forging machine, what is strictly designated as such is quite a different piece of equipment, as shown in Fig. 13. Usually motor-driven through gearing or otherwise, it produces the forging, mostly from the bar, not by a process of hammering at all, but by a squeezing motion. Thus it becomes an ideal machine for the production of forked parts (Fig. 5) and semi-hollow forgings of the class shown in Fig. 11.

This machine is quite old in conception and originated over 100 years ago for the purpose of making bolts.

In production of this kind the operator feeds a heated bar into the machine until it comes against a stop at the end and is guided by a stationary die. On the machine being put into motion, a movable die closes in on the bar, gripping it rigidly. The stop now rises and, as the ram of the machine advances, a plunger upsets the end of the bolt, forming a flat on each side of the upset end. The operator keeps his foot on the treadle, and as the movable die backs out, he rotates the rod one-sixth of a turn. This operation is

end and are wound up on drums at the top. The board hammer has boards fastened to the hammer. These boards are squeezed between rolls at the top of the frame. The friction of the rolls on the boards is sufficient to raise the hammer which is then released by separating the rolls.

Machine-Forging

From what has previously been said, it will be concluded that apart from any large forgings made by a relatively slow manipulation on large hydraulic forging presses, moderate-size pieces repeated until the head has been correctly formed. The operator now removes his foot from the treadle stopping the operation of the machine, when the dies remain in the open position, allowing him to remove the completed bolt.

The general procedure is to have the bars gripped with tongs and cut off to the desired length in a power-operated shear before heading. From this shear the bars are brought to the heating furnace, where one end is heated to the desired temperature. This furnace is placed as close to the forging machine as possible. The man who attends to the heating of the stock places the rods in a row, and as soon as the end to be headed reaches the proper temperature, he quickly removes the heated bar and passes it to the forging-machine operator, who at once places it between the dies, operates the machine, and forms the head.

Continuous-Motion Machine

For rapid production a continuous-motion machine is used, and again this may be either hand-fed or automatically fed. In machines of this kind the bar, which has been heated for a length of 4 or 5 ft., is fed through a shear in the face-plate block, and as the movable gripping die closes on the bar, a blank of the required length is cut off and held rigidly in the gripping dies. The head is then formed by the forward movement of the ram which carries the heading tool. After heading, the ram of the machine recedes, the gripping dies open, and a kicker, actuated by a connecting-rod from the main shaft, ejects the finished work from the dies, depositing it, through a chute, into a box.

As the dies open, the operator again pushes in the heated bar until it strikes the stop, and as the movable die advances, another blank is cut off and headed as before.

The machine runs continuously until the heated portion of the bar has been exhausted, when the operator takes another bar from the furnace and proceeds as before.

As the operation in a bolt-heading machine is one of upsetting the bar to form the hexagon or square head, it will be obvious that if the head were cut off and punched, a suitable size nut would be produced, and that, in fact, is the essential operation in the production of nuts for the appropriate size of bolt.

In making nuts by this process, the diameter of the round bar from which the nut is made should not exceed the root diameter of the thread in the finished nut, so a large upset is required to produce a full nut. When large nuts are produced in a plain forging machine, the usual method is first to form an upset on the end of the bar and then pierce the hole in the nut by punching the bar back, the metal removed to form the hole in the nut being thus attached to the bar. This

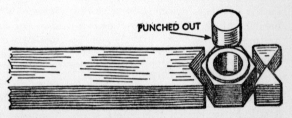

Fig. 14. Nuts can be produced as here shown by using rectangular section bar of the thickness of the nut, in a center-feed hot-pressed nut machine.

operation requires considerable pressure, but as little or no material is wasted, it is a very good method of production.

Another method of producing nuts is to use rectangular section bar of the thickness of the nut on the principle shown in Fig. 14, which shows a center-feed hot-pressed nut machine. A rectangular bar is heated to the correct temperature for a length of 4 or 5 ft. It is then brought to the machine and fed in from the side in front of the face of the main dies. A cut-off tool then moves up and shears the blank from the end of the bar, carries it into the main dies and presses it against a crowning tool, which has also advanced. The piercing tool now advances, punches the hole in the nut, and carries the wad into the cutting-off tool, then the cutting-off and piercing tools recede, an extractor forces the wad out of the punch at the same time as the nut is ejected from the dies. The ejector, which is operated by a lever and cam, prevents the nut from adhering to the crowning tool.

CHAPTER 14

FOUNDRY WORK

MOLDING SANDS. FOUNDRY BLACKINGS. MOLD MAKING. THE ODDSIDE. RAMMING. VENTING. RUNNERS AND RISERS. CORES. PATTERNS. BEDDED-IN MOLDS. LOAM MOLDS. FALSE ODDSIDES. PLATE MOLDING. MOLDING MACHINES. MULTIPLE MOLDS. MACHINE-MOLDED GEARS. MENDING-UP. PERMANENT MOLDS. MELTING IRON. POURING. FETTLING. MALLEABLE CASTINGS. CHILLED CASTINGS. NON-FERROUS METALS. GLOSSARY OF FOUNDRY TERMS.

A LARGE part of the work done by the man in the machine-shop has to do with castings of one kind or another, and it is necessary, therefore, that he should have at least some knowledge of the way in which they are produced. This chapter does not pretend to be a technical treatise on every aspect of the foundry; it is written more for the man who would like to know the general principles underlying the manufacture of castings.

An Old-Established Industry

The founding industry is probably the oldest branch of engineering, and it is certainly one of the most important. It was practiced by the craftsmen of the ancient Greek and Roman civilizations, and even earlier, and crude examples of the founder's work have been excavated from many ancient sites. Although modern methods have transformed it from a crude art into an exact science, it is interesting to note that the basic principles remain unchanged, and the molder of today uses methods very similar to those employed by the ancient founder.

Castings are made from patterns which are an exact facsimile of the article to be produced. The patterns are pressed into sand, and when removed leave their impression. Into this sand impression, or mold, molten metal is poured and allowed to cool. When it is removed it will be of the same shape as the mold, only slightly smaller owing to the contraction of the metal.

Before explaining how the mold is made, we will discuss the sand from which it is made.

Molding Sands

Molding sand must possess six main characteristics—porosity, plasticity, adhesiveness, cohesiveness, refractoriness, and strength when heated. It must be porous, in order to allow of the escape of any air, gases, or moisture present or generated in the mold when the hot metal is poured into it. It must obviously be plastic so that it can be shaped to the form of the pattern. It must be adhesive—i.e. capable of attaching itself to another body—so that it will cling to the sides of the box or flask in which it is molded or to the supports provided in the flask

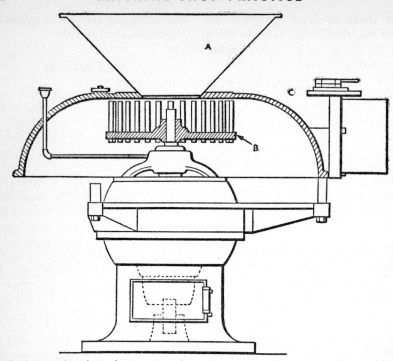

Fig. 1. A centrifugal sand-mixing machine. The sand, with any necessary additions, is thrown into the hopper A and falls to the plate B which has a number of vertical prongs bolted to it. This revolves at about 1500 revolutions per minute. The sand is thrown out of the machine through the plate C. A thorough mixture is obtained in this way.

for the purpose. Cohesion—or the ability of the particles to stick together—is necessary to allow the pattern to be removed without breaking the mold, and also to stand up to the flow of the molten metal as it enters the mold. Moreover, it must retain its cohesion on becoming hot. Refractoriness, or resistance to fusion by heat, is an obvious requirement in molding sands, for they have to stand exceedingly high temperatures and yet retain their stability. Moreover, a sand that is not refractory would affect the face of the casting and make it difficult, if not impossible, to machine.

Very few natural sands possess all these qualities in the right proportions,

so it is usual to make up the deficiency of a sand in any particular characteristic by mixing it with other sands or substances which possess that characteristic to a high degree. Most of the substances added to make up any deficiencies consist of loamy sands or sandstone which is crushed especially for the purpose. Some sands can be improved by mechanical means such as grinding, a process which will be explained later in this chapter.

Size and Shape of the Grains

The size and shape of the grains in any particular sand have a large bearing upon its strength and general character. Sands in which the grains are round are weaker than those in which they are sharp and irregular, because the round grains do not interlock or overlap with each other, whereas sharp, irregularly shaped grains do, especially when rammed together, forming a much stronger structure. Sharp-grained sands, having less clayey matter in their composition are often more porous and more easily vented—i.e., it is easier to make provision for the escape of the air and gases in the mold.

The size of the grains is also important. If the grains are large and regular in shape and size, the sand will be more porous than if the opposite were the case. Grains of equal size and irregular or angular in shape also favor porosity, while grains of unequal sizes and smooth surfaces do not, although they give a strong sand.

The size of grain does, of course, determine the smoothness of the mold surface, and for that reason large-grained sands are generally unsuitable when castings with very smooth skins are required. This difficulty can be overcome by using a fine sand on the face of the mold.

Some Natural Sands

Sands suitable for foundry work are found in several places. Natural sands which are suitable for foundry use are found in the vicinity of Albany, New York; Sandusky, Ohio; and Ottawa, Illinois, as well as other places. They are generally known merely as molding sand, and usually contain about 85 percent silica; about 8 percent alumina (clay) and the balance magnesia and other minerals. They are generally classed as (1) Sharp grained river sand, (2) Round grained lake sand.

The difference has been explained in the previous paragraph.

Sand Mixtures

Molds may be poured while moist, or they may be dried out in an oven before the metal is cast. These are known respectively as *green-sand* and *dry-sand* molds, and the sand mixtures used vary considerably. We will first of all consider green-sand mixtures.

For green-sand molds various materials are added to the natural sand with a view to making it more refractory. These substances separate the grains, thus making them less liable to burn together when they come into contact with the hot metal. They also make the sand more open, and allow the steam and gases to escape more readily from the mold.

Uses of Coal-Dust

Coal-dust is perhaps the most widely used substance, which accounts for the fact that most molding sand is black in color. Powdered charcoal, coke-dust, and anthracite are also used. These substances tend to make the sand more open, but at the same time they impair its cohesiveness and render it weaker. It stands to reason, therefore, that the mixing has to be done with extreme care. The addition of coal-dust is of great value in helping to cool the mold after it has been poured, for as soon as the molten metal comes into contact with sand containing coal it dries the face of the mold and begins to heat the sand. The coal-dust immediately gives off gas, the liberation of which, combined with the conversion of the water in the sand into steam, absorbs heat and cools the sand, thereby preventing the grains from becoming overheated and fusing. The amount of coal-dust used in molding sand varies not only with the character of the sand, but also with the type of work.

Moisture Content of Sand

The amount of moisture in a molding sand has a considerable effect not only upon the making of the mold, but also upon the behavior of the sand when the metal is poured. A mold may be perfect in all other respects and yet the casting may turn out to be a reject on account of the sand being too damp. Damp sand when rammed tight will not retain its porosity so well as drier sand; hence, the drier the sand that can be used without losing its cohesion, the better it will be.

It is impossible to give any hard-and-fast rules for the correct moisture content, because different sands require different amounts of moisture to enable them to be used; but the experienced molder will be able to determine for himself the quantity that gives the best results. In large foundries where a chemist is employed, the sand will be mixed under his supervision and delivered to the molders in the best possible condition.

This much, however, can be said: too little is better than too much, for there is nothing that will produce poor castings and castings with blowholes more readily than large quantities of steam in the mold, however well it may be vented.

Facing Sand

The purpose of facing sand is to form a smooth surface and prevent the mold from being washed away by the flow of the molten metal when pouring takes place. Facing sand is placed next to the pattern, and is then surrounded by used molding sand. Since it is the most important portion of the mold, this sand is usually composed of a mixture of high grade molding sand and carbon dust. The carbon dust is generally about 10 percent of the total volume. It is not possible to give mixtures for every type of work, but broad principles may be laid down. The first of these deals with the mixing. The various ingredients must be thoroughly intermingled. It is advisable as a rule to do the mixing in a separate shed with a good clean floor. Where more than one kind of sand is being use, they should be kept well apart to avoid the possibility of their getting mixed accidentally.

Where large quantities of sand are being mixed by hand, several men should be put on the job. In mixing the ingredients they should be spread in layers to form a mound finishing with the ingredient that is used in least quantity. The laborer should take a vertical slice from the mound and mix it well on the floor. The process should be continued until the mound has been used up.

Sand-Mixing Machines

In modern practice, especially when there are large quantities of sand to be mixed, mechanical mixers are employed. Fig. 1 shows a machine of this type.

Core Sand

Core sand differs from molding sand in several respects. First, it has to be handled when removed from the core-boxes, before being baked so it must be very adhesive. As cores are to a large extent surrounded by metal, it must be very free venting, otherwise the gases will be unable to escape, and blown castings are sure to result. This trouble is to a large extent removed by the fact that cores are usually dried, and consequently more porous than in the damp state. The difficulty is to retain sufficient cohesion after drying to enable them to be handled and withstand the pressure of the metal which is poured into the mold.

Additions to Core Sand

Various additions are made to core sand in order to make it meet these requirements. These include gums of various kinds, flour, powdered rosin, and oils of various descriptions. Syrup and water mixed, and even beer, are sometimes used. Core sand must not be mixed too wet, or it will adhere to the sides of the core-box, especially if the box is a wooden one, and rough cores will result. Small cores should be made with a finer sand than large ones, although the type of casting will determine this.

Dry-Sand Mixtures

Dry-sand molds are dried in an oven before the metal is poured into them, and consequently the mixture of the sand varies somewhat from that used in green-sand molds. Only the heavier types of sand of a close clayey texture will retain their coherence when dried. The usual green-sand mixtures would pulverize and break up under the action of the heat.

Horse manure, straw, or cow hair is frequently added to dry sand to render its otherwise close texture sufficiently open for venting. Dry-sand

molds are made in much the same way as green-sand ones (to be described later), but, being dried before pouring, less gas is generated, and they are therefore safer. The face of the mold is generally thoroughly blackened before drying.

Parting-Sand

Parting-sand is used to prevent the surfaces between the halves of a mold from sticking to one another when the two parts of the flask are separated. It also prevents the sand from sticking to the pattern. It is sprinkled on the surface of the drag before the cope is rammed up, as will be described later.

It is composed of burnt sand, pulverized blast furnace slag, brick dust, or very fine grained sand. It is important that it should not contain any material which would draw or retain moisture. It may be sprinkled on by hand or shaken from a bag.

Facing

In order to prevent the molten metal from coming into actual contact with the sand on the face of a mold and producing sandburns on the face of the casting, the mold is frequently painted or dusted. Various substances may be used for this purpose, including charcoal, lamb black, coke dust, plumbago, black lead, or graphite. These substances, which are all more refractory than the molding material, are nearly all some form of carbon. They may be applied wet or dry, according to the nature of the mold, and for use in the wet state some adhesive is employed, clay, gum, syrup, and other substances being mixed with the water used. When applied wet, they are usually

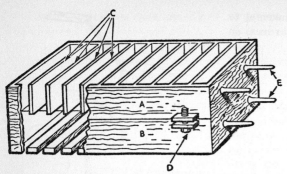

Fig. 2. Simple type of two-part molding-box, consisting of a top, or cope, A, and a bottom, or drag, B. The bars C are provided to retain the sand in the box. The two parts are held in register by means of the pin D. The handles E are for purposes of handling.

painted on to the mold with a brush. Facing used dry is dusted over the face of the mold.

All facings must, of course, be fairly porous, for they must not close up the pores of the mold.

Making the Mold

Molds are made in sand from patterns which are the exact facsimile of the article to be produced. They are slightly larger, in order to allow for the shrinkage of the metal on cooling and for any later machining that may be necessary. The patterns are pressed or buried in the sand, and when removed leave their impression. Into this impression molten metal is poured and allowed to cool. When it is removed it will be found that it will be of the same shape as the mold, only smaller owing to shrinkage. This is allowed for in the pattern.

While it is a simple matter to press or bury a pattern into the sand, to remove it presents some difficulties. In order to make this easier, molds are usually made in a box in two or more

sections, the former being the more common for most types of work.

The boxes in which the molds are made are known as flasks. These consist of frames of wood or metal, two such frames being required to make a mold. These boxes fit accurately together, and are provided with pins to insure an exact fit when they are put together. The accuracy with which these parts fit is of the greatest importance, as will be seen later. Any displacement of the parts will produce inequalities on the surface and in the thickness of the casting.

Fig. 2 shows a simple type of two-part flask. The part, A, is the top, or cope; B is the bottom, or drag; the bars, C, are provided to locate the two halves of the box, and the handles, E, are used to lift the boxes.

Making the Oddside

In making the mold, the cope is placed joint upwards on the bench or floor and strickled off roughly. The pattern is then embedded in the sand up to the joint, which is usually somewhat about the half-way line. At this stage the cope is used only to support the pattern while the drag is rammed and the joint made. This support is known as the oddside.

The drag is now placed on the cope, and facing-sand sieved on to the uncovered part of the pattern. This sand is rammed evenly round the pattern, special care being taken to avoid hitting the latter with the rammer. This, apart from causing possible damage to the pattern, would be detrimental to the mold owing to uneven hardness on the surface.

Ramming

The object of ramming the sand is to consolidate it, thereby preventing the cavity of the mold from being enlarged by the pressure of the metal without making it so hard as to obstruct the free passage of air and gases escaping from the mold. The sand must be rammed evenly and to the same density all over, otherwise the metal may swell at the soft spots and produce a casting that is not true to pattern. Again, if any part of the face is rammed too hard, the gases may stay in the metal and cause blow-holes in the casting. If hard ramming is necessary it must be done not on the facing sand, but on the sand behind the face, and the dangers arising from it prevented by the free use of the vent wire, for the harder the ramming the more the venting that will be necessary. Fig. 3 shows three types of rammers in common use.

When the facing sand round the exposed part of the pattern has been

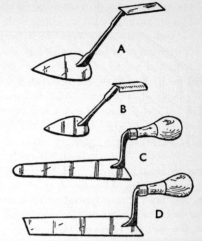

Fig. 4. Trowels used in making molds. *A,* heart-shaped trowel; *B,* gate knife used for cutting gates and runners; *C* and *D,* two types of trowel used for purposes of jointing.

rammed, floor sand, or backing sand, is added to fill the drag to the top. This is rammed up evenly all over and may be rammed somewhat harder than the sand on the face.

The flask is then turned over, the cope being now on the top and the drag beneath it. The cope is lifted from the drag and the sand knocked out. The joint must now be carefully made and troweled smooth, great care being taken with the sand near the edge of the pattern. It is sometimes as well at this stage to lift the pattern very slightly to make sure that it does not lift the sand at the edges with it.

Use of Parting-Sand

Parting-sand is next dusted over the surface to prevent the two halves of the flask from sticking when they are separated for the removal of the pattern. The cope is replaced on the drag, and facing-sand riddled into it, as was

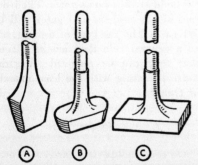

Fig. 3. Types of rammers in general use in the foundry. *A* and *B,* two forms of pegging rammers used for general ramming; *C,* flat rammer used for final ramming.

done in the case of the drag. When rammed, backing-sand is added as before and rammed up evenly all over.

The pattern is now completely buried in the sand, but before the two halves of the flask are separated for its removal, provision must be made for the free escape of gases and steam that will be generated when the hot metal comes into contact with the damp sand. The method of venting varies with the weight of the casting and the nature of the mold, small castings being frequently cast without any vents at all, whereas in very heavy ones numerous vents may be necessary.

Venting

Broadly speaking, venting consists of providing holes from the top of the flask to within about one-eighth of an inch of the mold-face. They are usually made with some form of thin wire, which is pushed through the sand, and which, when withdrawn, leaves channels for the free passage of air and steam contained in, and generated by, the contact of the hot metal with the mold. The need for careful venting is due to several causes: the expansion of the air contained in the pores of the mold, steam and gas caused by the water vapor coming into contact with the hot metal, on the coal dust and other ingredients of which the sand mixture is formed.

When the venting is completed, the cope and drag may be separated. This is a very delicate operation, and must be done with great care. If the joint has been properly made it will be found that, when the cope is lifted the pattern is left in the drag, from which it must now be removed. It may sometimes be found necessary before lifting the pattern to loosen it by rapping

it gently. This usually makes it separate cleaner and more easily. The operation of removing the pattern is known as drawing.

Cutting the Runner

We now have the two separated halves of the flask each containing the impression of half of the pattern, but before the mold can be finally closed a runner, or channel, for the metal, must be cut through the cope to the mold. There are various means of doing this, perhaps the most common being by pushing a piece of thin tubing through the cope from the mold-face outwards. This removes the sand in much the same way as an apple-corer removes the core from an apple. In certain cases the runner is rammed up with the cope. This is done by inserting a piece of round stick into the cope while the ramming is being done, and afterwards removing it when the parts of the box have been separated.

Runners may be led directly into the mold, or they may be placed some distance away and a channel cut from them to the mold at the most suitable spot. The channels from the runner to the mold are known as *gates*. The position of the runners and gates will be determined by the type of casting, but as a general rule they are so placed that they can be removed from the finished casting with the least amount of trouble.

Risers

On some molds risers are cut. These are provided for in exactly the same way as the runners, and their purpose is to remove any dirt or slag formed by the oxidation of the metal from the mold. The metal when it is poured runs through the mold and out through the riser, taking any dirt or sand with it. Risers, like runners, may be led off directly from the mold, or they may be connected with it by gates. The metal contained in the riser serves as a feeder when the metal in the mold shrinks in cooling. This makes a better casting. Fig. 5 illustrates a section through a mold showing both these channels.

In order that the metal may be poured easily down the runner, a runner cup or basin is cut either directly into the sand in the top of the cope or in a separate box used for the purpose. This acts as a funnel into which the metal is poured, and provides for a constant flow of metal to the mold. A section through such a cup is illustrated in Fig. 6.

It should be noted that, if molds are not cast immediately they are closed, some form of covering should be placed over the runners and risers to prevent any sand or other material from finding its way into the mold via these

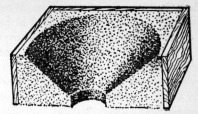

Fig. 6. Section through runner cup, or sand funnel, through which the metal is poured into the runner. It may be made in a separate box or hollowed out in the sand of the cope.

channels. This would obviously be detrimental to the casting.

When the mold has been closed it is ready for casting, but before the actual pouring is done it is necessary to clamp, bolt, or weight the two parts of the flask together, so that they cannot be forced apart by the pressure created by the head of metal in the runners and risers. This may be considerable, and in big castings may run into tons. Should the mold lift, the metal will escape through the joint and ruin the casting. Another result might be that the casting would be thicker and not true to pattern. Fig. 7 illustrates the general arrangement of a mold ready for casting, with runner-cups and weights in position.

Cores

The mold described above is of the simplest form, producing merely a solid piece of metal. Many castings are more complicated and have hollow portions, sometimes of very intricate design. The water-jacket of an internal-combustion engine is a good example. Whether simple or intricate the hollow portions are made by inserting cores into the mold to

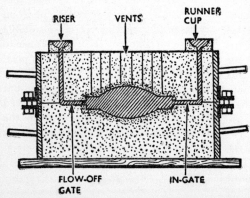

Fig. 5. Section through completed mold showing the runner, down which the metal is poured, and the riser, which is provided to rid the mold of dirt, etc. The channels cut from the runner into the mold and from the mold to the riser are known respectively as in-gates and flow-off gates.

form the exact shape of the hollow part of the casting. These cores are made of sand. It stands to reason that damp sand molded into any particular shape would not possess sufficient strength to be handled easily. The cores are, therefore, frequently reinforced, and special binders are added, as already described, which, baked, give additional strength.

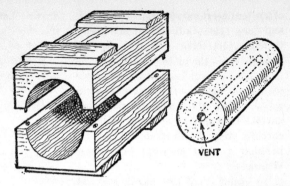

Fig. 8. *Left,* simple core-box made in two parts, used for the production of cylindrical cores. *Right,* core as it would appear when removed from the box. Note the central vent.

Core-Boxes

Cores are made in boxes. These are somewhat similar to the flask in principle, but are usually made from solid wood. They are made in two or more parts into which the sand is rammed. The core-box is in fact a mold, and the process of making a core is the exact reverse of that entailed in making a mold.

After ramming the sand into the core-box, the two halves are separated and the core is turned out. It is then placed in an oven and baked, after which it is ready to be placed in the mold. Fig. 8 shows a simple core-box together with the core that has been made in it.

The cores rest in the mold in recesses especially made for the purpose. These recesses are added to the pattern in the form of projections known as core-prints. Fig. 9 illustrates a simple pattern with core-prints and also the impression left by these prints in a sand-mold.

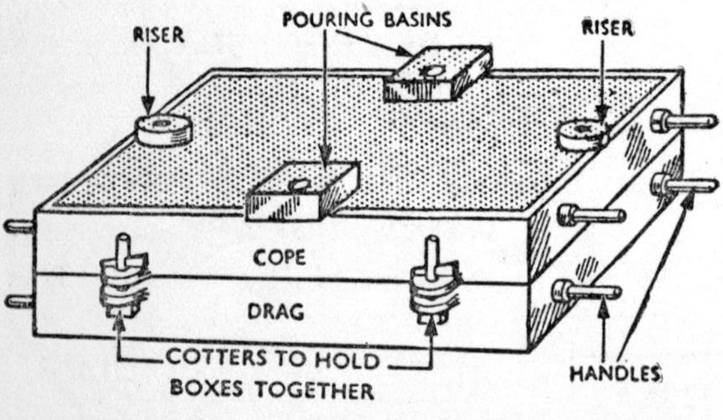

Venting of Cores

Although cores are thoroughly dried out in an oven before being placed in the mold, it is still necessary to provide means of escape for the gases generated when the metal comes into contact with them. Venting is of extreme importance so far as the core is concerned, for the larger part of it is

Fig. 7. General arrangement of a mold after it has been closed and is ready for casting. It is provided with two runners and two risers, and the two parts of the flask are cottered together to prevent them becoming separated by the head of metal in runners and risers. On many jobs weights are used in place of the cotters.

often entirely surrounded by metal, and any gas failing to get away through the vents will stay in the metal, thus causing blow-holes.

A core is vented in a similar manner to a mold—that is to say, it is provided with channels through which the gases escape. These are made in the core in its green, or damp, state by pushing a wire through the center. Where the core is not straight, string is frequently rammed up in the box with the core and removed when the core is completed, but before it has been removed from the box.

Use of Wax String

It is essential that molten metal cannot find its way into these vents and block them up, as this might result in the bursting of the core, owing to the fact that the gases have no free means of escape.

With very intricate cores the venting is frequently done by means of wax-coated string. The wax melts when the core is in the drying oven, and when it is removed the strings can easily be pulled out.

Cods

Strictly speaking, a core is any portion of a mold which produces a hole through or a hollow in a casting, and although most cores are made entirely separate from the mold, hollow parts in a casting are often produced by up-standing parts left in the mold when the pattern is

drawn. These projecting portions fulfill the functions of cores, and are known as *cods*.

Where large cods are left behind in the mold when the pattern is drawn they may have to be reinforced with wires to prevent them breaking away.

It is usually desirable to arrange the mold in such a way that the cod is left in the drag. This is done for the simple reason that it is obviously easier and safer to draw the pattern upward from the cod than to draw the cod away from the pattern in the cope. In machine molding, dealt with later on, turn-over machines are used in cases where large cods have to be drawn.

Patterns

A pattern is a facsimile of the casting to be produced, and its manufacture calls for a very high degree of skill on the part of the pattern-maker, as well as a sound knowledge of

Fig. 9. *Above*, simple pattern with core-prints. The core fits into and is supported by the impressions left in the sand by these prints. *Below*, impression left by the pattern.

foundry practice. The pattern-maker decides the manner in which the casting is to be molded and where the joints are to be made in the mold.

The first requirement of a good pattern is that it should be removed from the sand without disturbing the mold. To achieve this the faces are tapered slightly, the taper in use being generally about $\frac{1}{8}$ in. to the foot. When the shape of the pattern is such that the taper will not work, as in a pattern that is wider at the bottom than at the top, then *loose pieces* or cores are used to meet the particular case. These loose pieces are fixed to the pattern by means of pins, which are removed as soon as the sand has been rammed round the loose piece to hold it in position in the mold.

Loose Pieces

When the pattern is drawn, the loose pieces are left behind in the sand and drawn out into the cavity left in the mold by the removal of the pattern. See Fig. 10.

Generally speaking, patterns are made of wood, but where very large numbers of molds have to be made from a single pattern, as in the case of mass-production jobs, metal patterns are used. These have a highly polished surface to make them draw easily.

Core-Boxes

Core-boxes and patterns are sometimes made together in one piece, the pattern being made in two parts and hollowed out inside to form the core-box. These dual-purpose patterns, however, are only used in small types of work and never in repetitive jobs.

Care of Patterns

Patterns are expensive to make, and should be handled carefully if they are to be maintained in good condition. They must be stored in a properly ventilated building where the temperature is even, otherwise they may warp and become unserviceable.

It is best to number each pattern, together with its loose pieces, if any, and core-boxes, store them in a rack with the number painted on the outside. In this way much time may be saved in finding the pattern when it is wanted. When patterns come from the pattern-maker they have a smooth surface. Frequent use in the foundry will, in time, tend to roughen them, so it is desirable that they should be looked over periodically and treated, if necessary, with applications of varnish or shellac.

Other Types of Molds

Very heavy castings, or castings of a considerable depth or area, may be molded in the foundry floor. In such cases the floor itself acts as the drag, and this may be covered with a cope, or the mold may be cast open. Open sand castings usually have a very rough surface, and only castings in which this is not important are made in this way.

It stands to reason that when molding patterns in the sand of the foundry floor, the lower faces of the mold which are formed underneath the pattern cannot be easily rammed, for, unlike molds made in a box, there is no means of providing an oddside.

Preparing the Bed

In making a bedded-in mold a smooth surface is first made on the sand and the level carefully checked. The sand is then dug up and loosened to a sufficient depth and the pattern beaten into it with heavy wooden mallets. The pattern is then removed and an inch or two of facing sand riddled into the impression. The pattern is then replaced and beaten down again. The sand round the pattern is then thoroughly packed with the rammer, after which it is smoothed off and the joint face made ready to receive the cope. Parting-sand is then dusted over the joint and the cope rammed up in the normal manner. The mold is then opened, the pattern removed, and runners and risers cut as for box-molds.

Bedded-in molds have to be made with great care, for it is a difficult matter to make the lower half of the mold of even density all over. They call for considerable skill on the part of the molder, because if the sand is of unequal density, the metal is liable to swell over the softer portions and produce castings that are not true to pattern. The lower half of a bedded-in mold is difficult to vent, and consequently the best type of sand for use with this work is one which possesses a large proportion of sharp sand of a free-venting type. Cinders or other such loose material are sometimes placed beneath the mold.

Loam Molds

Where a mold has to be modeled to the required shape without the use of

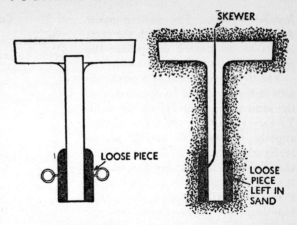

Fig. 10. Where patterns must be of such a shape that they cannot be drawn from the sand owing to projections, loose pieces are employed to get over the difficulty. These are detachable from the pattern and drawn separately after the pattern has been taken from the mold. *Left*, pattern showing loose pieces; *right*, the loose pieces being removed from the mold by means of a skewer.

a pattern or with patterns only of such portions as depart from the general sectional form, some sort of plastic material, possessing considerable adhesiveness, must be used. Clayey sand, or loam, is used for molds of this type. The wet loam is daubed on to brick supports built up in the rough shape of the mold, and, in addition, iron plates and supports are used to give it sufficient strength and rigidity to stand up to the weight of the metal when poured. The mold is thoroughly dried before pouring takes place.

The apparatus used in the production of these molds is simple, and consists of spindle bars, striking-boards, and the like, which are used in shaping the mold. The making of loam molds calls for great skill.

Molds of this type are generally used only for very heavy castings or in cases where the cost of the pattern for a single mold would be prohibitive.

Fig. 11 shows plan and sectional views of a loam mold in course of construction. A is the striking-bar, B the striking-board, C socket for striking-bar, and D the loam-bricks forming the skeleton of the mold.

We have explained earlier in this chapter that an oddside is the support upon which the pattern stands while the drag is being rammed up, and shown how this may be made in the cope, the sand being knocked out after

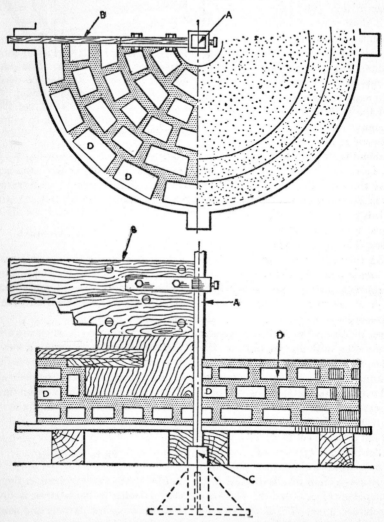

Fig. 11. Loam mold in plan and section. These molds are built up from loam, or clayey sand on a skeleton structure and modeled to the required shape by means of striking-boards. Usually very large molds, where the cost of a complete pattern would be prohibitive, are made in this way. They are thoroughly dried out before pouring begins. The letters indicate, A, striking-bar; B, striking-board; C, socket for striking-bar; D, bricks forming skeleton of mold.

the drag has been rammed. Sometimes, however, false oddsides are used to save the time and trouble involved in having to make a fresh sand oddside for each mold.

STRUTTING TO REINFORCE ODDSIDE

PLASTER ODDSIDE

Fig. 12. Section through plaster oddside, showing the drag rammed up. The use of a false oddside saves considerable time, as it obviates the necessity of making a new oddside for each mold. When making the oddside the plaster need not fill the box, but need only be sufficiently thick to withstand ramming.

False Oddsides

These false oddsides may be made of several substances. They may be of clayey sand blackened or painted on the surface, or of plaster of Paris. The latter substance is perhaps the more suitable, as it will stand up longer against wear and is less likely to become chipped or damaged. These oddsides do not form part of the mold, but only assist in the molding operations.

Plaster oddsides may be made as follows. A drag is filled with sand and strickled off. The pattern is then bedded in up to the joint and the sand carefully sleeked. A cope is then put on top of the drag, and graphite or some similar substance dusted over the pattern to prevent the plaster from adhering to it. A suitable mixture of plaster may now be poured in to cover the pattern. It need not fill the box, being poured only to a depth which is sufficient to withstand ramming.

When the plaster has set, the cope may be removed, when it will be found that a plaster impression of one half of the pattern has been left. This may be reinforced on the underside by means of wooden struts, if necessary.

When making a mold by this means, the pattern is first placed in the oddside, and the drag put on top and rammed up. The boxes are then turned over and the oddside removed. If only one false oddside is used, the second half of the pattern is rammed up in the usual way.

Use of Two Oddsides

Frequently two false oddsides are used in making a single mold—one for each half. This considerably reduces the molding time, especially in the making of the joints.

It will be realized, when the following section on plate molding has been studied, that false oddsides very much resemble pattern plates in their application. Fig. 12 shows a section through a false oddside showing the drag rammed up.

Plate Molding

Much time can be saved in the making of molds if the pattern is divided in half across the parting and mounted in halves on two plates with parallel sides of the same shape as the parting.

The use of plates enables the molder to handle the patterns rapidly and with certainty, for he is relieved of the task of making the joint between the two parts of the mold, the plate providing its own joint when the flask is rammed up. In addition, the patterns can be drawn quickly, as the plate overlaps the side of the box, and the pins which hold it in position act as guides during the drawing operation. Provided the patterns are satisfactory, practically no mending up of the mold is necessary.

Pattern plates are generally made of wood or metal, and the patterns may be mounted in halves either on both sides of a single plate or on one side of two plates. Fig. 13 shows a plate with half a pattern on each side in plan and section.

The sequence of operations entailed in making a mold from such a plate are as follow: The plate is placed on the cope and the drag on top of the plate. Facing-sand is sieved in and rammed up, and backing-sand added to fill the box, and the sand strickled off. The flask is next turned over and the cope rammed up in the same manner. The cope is then lifted off and the pattern or patterns on the plate drawn by lifting the plate off the drag.

Provision of Gates

Where a number of patterns are mounted on one plate, the gates—i.e. the channels from the runner to the molds—are allowed for on the pattern plate and made as part of the mold. These are shown in Fig. 13. Runners and risers are now cut, and runner cup added. The mold is then finished and ready to be closed, weighted, and cast.

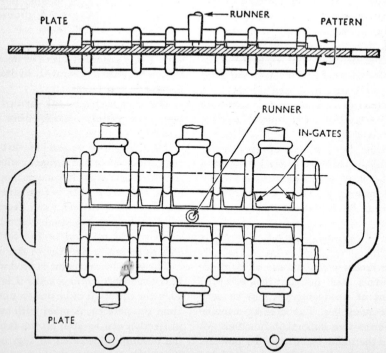

Fig. 13. Plan and sectional views of a double-pattern plate on which several patterns are mounted. The gates into each mold are allowed for in the pattern.

Metal patterns are frequently used in plate-molding where large numbers of molds are required from one plate. They are highly burnished to facilitate drawing.

Single-sided pattern-plates are used chiefly in conjunction with molding-machines. The halves of the pattern must be very carefully positioned so that when the two halves of the flask come together the two halves of the mold register exactly.

Use of Snap-Flasks

Snap-flasks are flasks which are hinged at one corner so that they can be opened and the mold removed. Molds are made in these flasks, but not cast in them, and their use in foundries engaged in repetitive work effects a great saving in flasks, which are very expensive. Molds are made in snap-flasks in precisely the same way as in ordinary ones. Fig. 14 shows a typical snap-flask with a locking device A. It is hinged at B, and the two parts are held in register by the pins C. These are triangular in section and fit into a movable slide D. The grooves E are provided for the retention of the sand in the flask. Snap-flasks are largely used in connection with the molding of patterns from plates.

Machine Molding

In recent years the use of molding-machines has become the accepted means of producing castings in very large quantities. The molding-machine performs two important functions—it rams the mold and draws the pattern, no specialized knowledge or skill being required on the part of the oper-

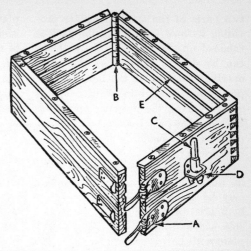

Fig. 14. By using a snap-flask such as that shown above, a considerable saving in flasks may be effected. When the mold is completed the flask is opened and the mold removed. The main parts shown are: A, locking device; B, hinges; C, pins to hold parts in register; D, slide to take pins; E, grooves to retain sand in flask.

ator. There are many types of machine in use—manually operated, hydraulic, pneumatic and electric.

These again can be sub-divided into two main types: straight-draw and turn-over.

The straight-draw machine lifts the mold away from the pattern, whereas the turn-over, as its name implies, turns the mold over before drawing and draws the pattern away from the mold. The former is used where there is no weight of sand in the form of cods adhering to the face of the mold.

The turn-over machine is used where heavy sand projections make it impossible for the mold to be drawn upward from the pattern. A mold with such a projection can be seen on the table of the machine illustrated in Fig. 20 D. We will now deal with these types of machine in turn.

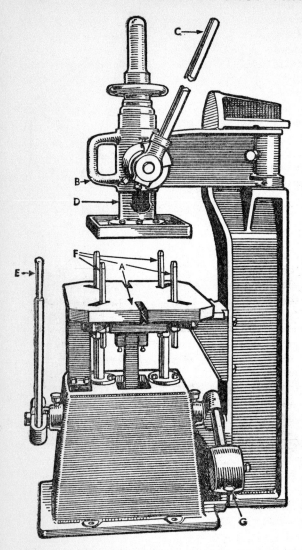

Fig. 15. Hand-operated straight-draw molding machine. The pattern is fixed to the table A and the flask placed over it and filled with sand. It is then roughly rammed round the edges of the box. The squeeze head B is then swung over into the position shown above, and the lever C pulled forward. This operates the squeeze through the ram D, and squeezes the mold. The pattern is drawn by the four pins F, which rise when the handle E is moved from left to right. The weight of the box on the pins is counterbalanced by the weight G.

Hand-Operated Machines

Hand machines are usually of simple design and are, as a rule, only employed in the manufacture of the smaller types of castings. In some cases they consist only of a table with an attachment for drawing the pattern, the mold being rammed by hand as with floor work. On other machines the ramming is done by a squeezing device, the pressure being obtained by mechanical leverage of some form or other. An example of a hand-squeeze straight-drawn machine is illustrated in Fig. 15.

Straight-Draw Machine

The pattern is fixed to the table, A, and the flask is placed over the pattern and filled with sand. It is then roughly rammed round the edges of the flask, usually with the handle of a shovel. The squeeze head, B, is then swung over the mold in the position shown in Fig. 15, and the lever, C, is pulled forward, applying the pressure through a crank to the ram, D. This causes the squeeze head, B, to descend and pack the sand in the flask. The arm is then lifted by returning the lever, and the head swung clear of the machine. The handle, E, is then moved from left to right, and through a crank raises the four pins, F. These are so adjusted as to register with the four corners of the box, and thus, when the pins are raised, the box is lifted from the pattern. During the drawing process it is customary to rap the pattern plate with a mallet to assist the draw. The weight of the box on the four pins is counterbalanced by the weight, G, enabling a very steady pattern draw to be obtained.

The mold is then lifted from the pins and the latter returned to their original position by moving the lever, E, from right to left. This completes the cycle of operations, and the machine is ready to receive the next flask.

Use of Two Machines

It is often the practice to employ two machines in the production of a single mold, half being made on one machine and half on the other. It follows, therefore, that considerable care must be taken by the pattern maker in mounting the patterns accurately, so that when the molding-boxes are mated the two halves of the mold will register exactly. A turn-over machine will very often work in conjunction with a straight-draw if one half of the mold has a cod that is difficult to draw and the other has not.

Assuming that each operator works at approximately the same speed, the molds

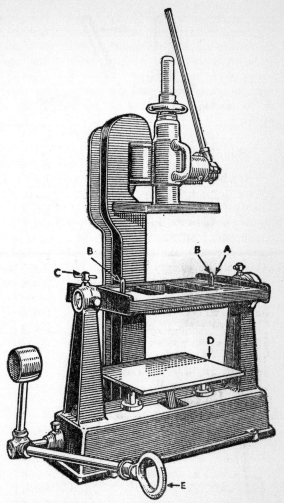

Fig. 16. The turn-over machine, shown above, differs from the straight-draw in that it draws the mold away from the pattern in a downward direction. It is used mainly where the mold contains large sand projections, or cods. The pattern is fixed to the main table A and the box placed over it. The method of ramming and squeezing is exactly the same as with the straight-draw machine (Fig. 15). After squeezing, the flask is clamped to the table by means of the pins B, and the table turned over through 180 deg. and locked in position by the screw C. The draw-table D is raised by the lever E to support the underside of the flask when the clamps are released and the draw-table lowered away.

may be closed as soon as they have been removed from the machine, had the runners cut, and any cores inserted. It is often the practice, particularly where there are a large number of cores to set, to employ a third man to do the coring and closing up of the molds.

Hand Turn-Over Machines

The pattern on this type of machine is fixed to the main table, A (Fig. 16). The method of ramming and squeezing is precisely the same as with the straight-draw machine just described. After squeezing, the flask is clamped to the table by means of the pins, B, and the table turned through 180 deg. The table is locked in position after being turned over by the screw, C.

The draw-table, D, is next raised by lifting the lever E until it supports the under-side of the flask, when the clamps B are released and the mold drawn away from the pattern in a downward direction by lowering the lever, E. During this operation the pattern plate is rapped with a mallet as before. The mold is lifted from the draw-table and the main table turned back again to its normal position ready for the next job.

Power-Operated Machines

The next machines to be dealt with are those operated by power, the simplest form of which is the squeeze-machine. These differ from the hand-machines only in that the squeezing operation and the pattern draw are worked by power, hydraulic, pneumatic, and electrically driven machines being the most usual.

A popular type of power-machine is the pneumatic, or compressed-air type.

Its popularity arises from the fact that it covers a very much wider range of molds than the others, and in addition can successfully handle many types of mold that cannot be made on the other machines.

Advantages of Air-Machines

The main advantage the air-machine possesses over its competitors is the fact that it does not rely for ramming on direct squeezing pressure only but has a shaking device, usually termed the *jolt* which enables any depth of sand to be rammed, whereas with plain squeeze-machines there is a definite limit to the depth of sand that can be rammed. Furthermore, a very much more uniform ramming density is obtained when a jolt is employed, resulting in considerable improvement in the quality of the castings.

Pneumatic Straight-Draw

Both straight-draw and turn-over machines may be power-operated, and we will first of all describe a pneumatic straight-draw machine as illustrated in Fig. 17. This machine has a table, A, to which the pattern-plate is fixed. The flask is placed over the pattern in the usual manner, and the lever, B, moved to the jolt position. This causes the table to rise and fall rapidly and has the effect of ramming the sand in the flask. While the table is in motion the sand is shoveled into the flask, and when it is full the arm, C, is swung into position above the flask and the lever, D, depressed. This operates the squeeze-piston, which lifts the table and squeezes the mold against the presser-plate, E. The squeeze-lever, D, is then returned to its original position and the arm, C, swung clear of the table. The lever, B, is now moved to the draw position, which causes the four pins, F, to rise and lift the mold from the pattern in exactly the same way as in the case of the manual type.

During the first part of the draw the pins rise slowly, and gradually increase in speed as the mold gets clear of the pattern. While the drawing operation is in progress the table is automatically shaken by a vibrator beneath it. This replaces the rapping of the pattern-plate in the manual machines and insures an easy and clean drawing action. The mold is removed from the pins and the draw-lever returned to neutral. That completes the cycle of operations.

How the Air-Machine Works

A very brief description of the internal construction of this machine will give the reader a clearer understanding of its method of working.

Fig. 18 is a sectional drawing of the body of the machine illustrated in Fig. 17. The main cylinder is cast with the frame, A. This is accurately machined and ground to take the squeeze-piston, B. This piston is bored out in the center with a similar cylinder in which moves another piston, C. The piston, C, is fixed to the

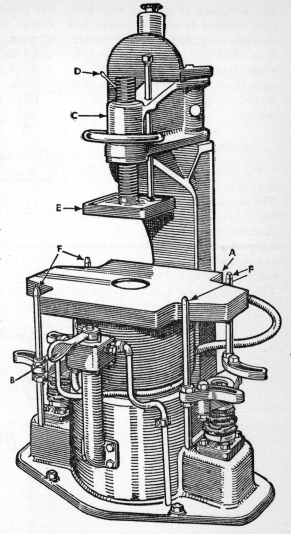

Fig. 17. Pneumatic straight-draw molding machine. Besides performing the squeezing and pattern-drawing automatically, this machine possesses two features not included in the hand-operated type. These are the jolting device, for ramming the sand, and the vibrator, which assists in drawing the pattern cleanly. The main features are shown above: A, the pattern table; B, lever for operating the jolt; C, squeeze-head arm; D, lever for operating squeeze; E, presser-plate; F, pins for lifting box.

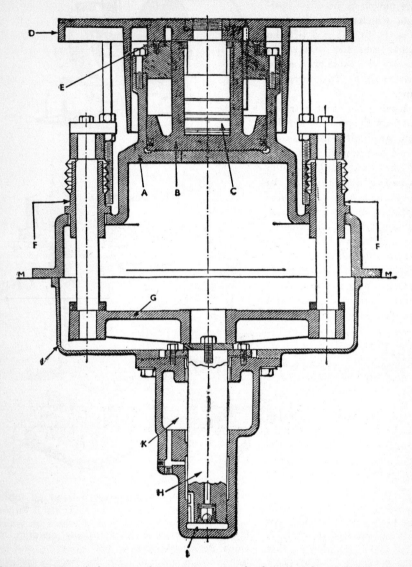

Fig. 18. Sectional drawing of pneumatic straight-draw machine, showing details of the operations. A, frame containing main cylinder; B, squeeze piston; C, table piston; D, table; E, jolt anvil; F, draw-rod guides; G, bridge coupling draw-rods; H, draw-piston; J, casing; K, oil reservoir; L, draw cylinder; M, ground level.

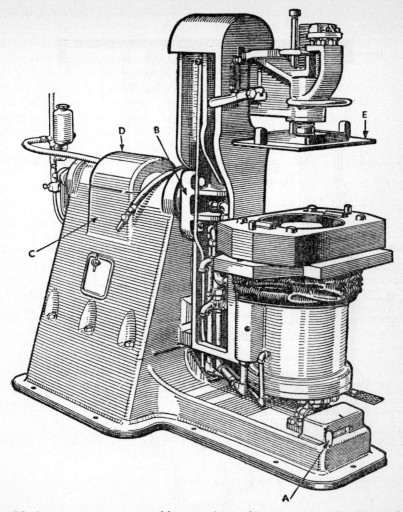

Fig. 19. Pneumatic turn-over molding machine, showing pattern fixed on table. The method of operation is similar to the straight-draw, but the machine is turned over before the pattern is drawn. *A*, lever operating turn-over; *B*, shaft on which machine rotates; *C*, main housing; *D*, housing cover; *E*, squeeze-plate.

table, D, which in its normal position, rests on the anvil, E.

The Jolt-Cylinder

When air is admitted into the jolt-cylinder, the jolt-piston rises about 1½ in., in which position it uncovers an exhaust port which allows both piston and table to fall, the table hitting the anvil, E, with a sharp blow. This up-and-down movement of the table continues throughout the jolting process at approximately three hundred strokes a minute.

When the squeeze pressure is applied to the main piston, B, the table and jolt-piston are lifted upward and the flask on the table pressed against the squeeze-plate, the table-pressure on the small machine illustrated amounting to about three tons.

The draw-rods that lift the mold from the pattern operate through two guides, F, which are attached to and coupled together through a bridge, G. This is in turn fixed to a solid piston,

H, the whole being housed in the casing, J.

The reservoir, K, is filled with oil, and when the pattern draw-valve is moved, air pressure is applied to this reservoir, forcing the air down the channels situated immediately below and allowing it to enter the chamber, L. This causes the piston to rise, thus effecting the draw.

The pneumatic turn-over machine is

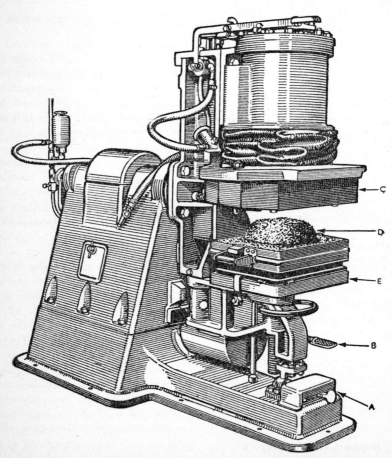

Fig. 20. Pneumatic machine in turned-over position, showing the mold after the pattern has been drawn. A, turn-over lever; B, draw-lever; C, pattern; D, mold; E, squeeze-plate. The mold shown affords a good illustration of the use of the turn-over machine, for it would be difficult to draw the projection, or cod, upward from the pattern without it becoming separated from the parent mold.

illustrated in Fig. 19. The method of operation is similar to that described for the straight-draw machine in so far as the jolting and squeezing of the mold are concerned. After the squeeze pressure has been applied, the lever, A, is moved, which causes the machine to rotate through 180 deg. about the shaft which is coupled to the column at B.

The machine is then in the position illustrated in Fig. 20. The lever, B, is depressed, causing the table and the pattern, C, to rise and leave the mold, D, on the squeeze-plate, E. The mold is then taken off the machine.

The lever, A, is then moved back to the neutral position, causing the machine to turn back.

The construction of the machine so far as the jolt and squeeze are concerned is identical with that of the straight-draw illustrated in Figs. 17 and 18.

Turn-Over Mechanism

The turn-over mechanism consists of a shaft running through the main housing, C (Fig. 19). This shaft is coupled to the column at B. A sprocket-wheel is keyed to the shaft under the cover, D, over which passes a chain connected to two pistons situated in the lower part of the housing. The turn-over valve merely allows the air to pass from one cylinder into the other, thus rotating the sprocket and causing the machine to revolve.

Hoppers and Conveyors

Molding machines, and particularly those of the power-operated type, turn out molds at a considerable speed, and it is frequently the practice in large foundries to employ hoppers to keep the machines supplied with sand. These hoppers are placed over the table and filled by means of conveyors at a speed proportionate to the speed of the machine. In such foundries other conveyors are usually used to carry away the finished molds from the machine to be cast. It need scarcely be added that in such cases continuous pouring is always employed.

Machines for Multiple Molds

The use of molding machines in small foundries frequently causes difficulties through lack of sufficient floor space, for even if the molding machines themselves do not occupy a great deal of room, considerable space is necessary for the finished molds and the many empty flasks.

This problem, which arises through the speed with which the machines turn out the molds, is sometimes solved by multiple molding. Machines are used which are capable of making two half molds in a single half-flask. The flasks are stacked one on top of the other, a complete mold being formed at each joint; and the whole stack is poured through a single runner, gates being provided for each mold. All the runners are made wider at the top than the bottom, so that when pouring begins the metal will fill the bottom box first, the boxes above being filled in turn as the metal rises. Reference to Fig. 21 will make this point clear.

Machines used for multiple molds sometimes consist of a pattern plate, with one half of the pattern on it, and a squeeze head which carries the other half of the pattern. The half-flask is placed on the pattern plate, a sand-frame placed on it, and filled with sand. The presser head is then brought

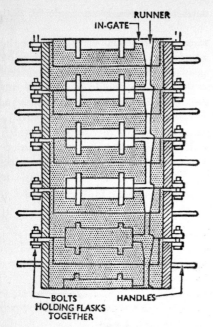

Fig. 21. Special machines are sometimes employed which mold two halves of a mold, half on each side of a half box. The boxes are then stacked on each other, a complete mold being formed at each joint, and the stack is poured through a single runner. The diagram illustrates the principle of this system.

over the half-flask and the mold squeezed in the usual manner. A half-mold is thus made on both sides of the half-flask at one operation. Only comparatively small castings are made in this way, for it is doubtful whether the quantity of sand required to fill a large half-flask could be satisfactorily rammed to stand any real weight of metal.

Machine-Molded Gears

Machines are largely employed for molding all kinds of spur, worm, bevel, miter, and helical gears, complete patterns for which would cost a con-

siderable sum. The patterns in use on such machines consist only of a single tooth-space or short segment of the periphery known as the tooth-block (see Fig. 22). This block is attached to a bracket on the machine as shown in Fig. 23. By repeating the mold of the tooth-block the required number of times molds may be made for gears of any diameter. Core-boxes are employed for molding the arms.

Details of the Machine

The mold is made in a circular molding-box which is carried on the revolving table of the machine as shown at A, Fig. 23. The table is revolved by means of the handle, B, which, through a bevel gear, C, turns one of the two parallel horizontal shafts under the

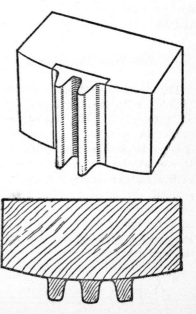

Fig. 22. Tooth-blocks used for molding gears. They consist of a short segment of the periphery of the gear to be molded.

table. At the other end of this shaft is a change-gear, E, on the other shaft. The latter carries the worm, F, in the center, which actuates the dividing-gear, G, attached to the under-side of the table.

By this means the table can be turned through any required fraction of the circumference of a circle with great accuracy, thereby repeating the mold of the tooth-block. It stands to reason that for each tooth the table must turn through an angle of $\dfrac{360,}{x}$ where $x =$ the number of teeth in the wheel. The method of regulation is by means of change-gears, and is similar to the method adopted in a thread-cutting lathe and explained in Chapter 4.

The tooth-block, H, is attached to the lower end of the carrier, I, which slides in the guides, J, and is counter-balanced by the weight, K. By turning the handle, L, the carrier may be

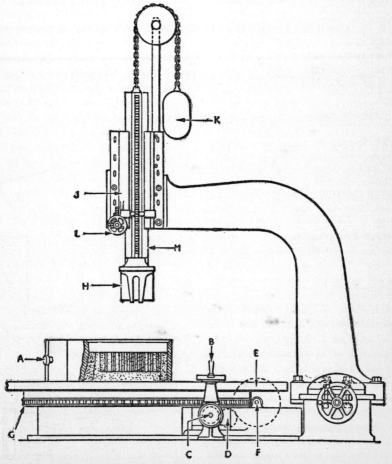

Fig. 23. Main features of a gear-molding machine. A, revolving table; B, handle for revolving table; C, bevel gear; D and E, change-gears; F, worm; G, dividing-gear; H, tooth-block; I, carrier; J, guides; K, weight; L, turning-handle.

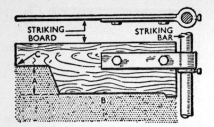

Fig. 24. Striking-board used to prepare the bed for molding gears. *A*, depth of face of gear; *B*, bottom edge of board that strikes the bed; *C*, top edge of board that strikes the mold-joint.

racked up and down to any desired height.

Molding Operations

The gear is molded by placing the box on the machine-table and preparing a bed with a striking-board which fits on to a central spindle in the table. This is shown in Fig. 24, *A* being equal in depth to the depth of the face of the gear. The bottom edge, *B*, strikes the bed, and the top edge, *C*, the joint of the mold. The spindle and striking-board are then removed, and the tooth-block, having been screwed to the carrier, is set to the correct radius and lowered until its face bears on the sand-bed.

Facing-sand is next rammed between the teeth of the block, and if the wall of the bed is sloping, as would be the case if it were made with the striking-board in Fig. 24, the slope is also filled up. The ramming should be done with a small wooden pegging rammer to avoid damaging the pattern. A flat rammer is used for the top, and the joint scraped and sleeked with a trowel. The teeth are vented and the pattern is lifted clear of the mold. Gentle rapping during lifting will help the pattern to come away cleanly. The table is then revolved through one space, lowered into position, and the operation repeated until the circle is complete.

As the tooth-block molds a ring of teeth only, the interiors of the gears have to be formed with cores. These are made in core-boxes and put into the mold before it is closed.

Making the Cope

Copes for flat gears may be rammed up on a flat surface, but copes for bevel gears or gears that are not flat may be made by means of a striking-board or rammed up in a reverse mold. Copes made by the latter method are generally more satisfactory, as they can be rammed up harder than by a striking board.

When the copes are struck direct, a striking-board is used which produces a surface similar to the top of the mold the cope has to fit. This board must be so adjusted that its upper surface is in the plane of the joint between the two parts of the mold. Fig. 25 shows a striking-board for striking a cope direct.

For ramming a cope up in a reverse mold a hard sand-bed is first made and the surface struck up to shape with a reverse board, as shown in Fig. 26. The cope is now put on, parting-powder added, and rammed up as if on a pattern.

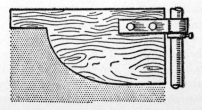

Fig. 25. Striking-board used for striking a cope direct.

Machines for molding gears may be either bench types, as shown in Fig. 23, or floor machines. The latter are used for molding gears up to 25 ft.

Mending-Up of Molds

Few sand-molds, with the possible exception of those made on molding-machines from plates or from very good patterns, are perfect when the pattern has been withdrawn. Faults of various kinds are liable to arise, the most common being caused through rough patterns, patterns made without sufficient taper, or through bad workmanship; and the result is that when the pattern is withdrawn from the mold, parts of the mold become fractured or broken off. Bad ramming is a frequent cause of bad molds, or rapping too vigorously while withdrawing the pattern may break down weak parts of the mold or weaken them to such an extent that they wash off when the metal is poured. Jerking of the pattern while drawing it may also cause portions of the mold to be broken or to become loosened.

Cutting Out Soft Spots

All parts broken or loosened through these or any other causes must be made good, and in addition any parts of the mold that are found on examination to be either too hard or too soft must be cut out and remade. If the mold is seriously damaged it is often quicker in the long run to remake it completely.

If the damage is small it is generally better to patch it by hand rather than with a trowel, for the latter tends to sleek the mold and close the pores, thereby impairing the venting. When applying new sand to the mold, as little water as possible must be used in

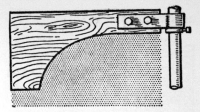

Fig. 26. When a cope is rammed up in a reverse mold a sand-bed is made and struck to the required shape by means of a suitable striking-board such as that shown above.

assisting the sand to adhere to the parent mold, as this may chill the metal in that part of the mold and cause hard spots on the casting.

Use of Sprigs

In cases where the edges have suffered badly it is often a good plan to replace the pattern in the mold and make the repairs with the pattern in place. When this is done the sand should be well troweled to make it cohere. In this instance the use of the trowel is not injurious to the mold, as the metal does not come into contact with the sleeked surfaces.

Sprigs or small pins may be used to strengthen weak parts of the mold. These are small pins which are pushed into the sand below the surface and the holes filled in and made good. In some molds specially bent irons are used as strengtheners.

Permanent Molds

For certain types of work, particularly in the manufacture of bedsteads, sand-molds are replaced by permanent ones made of metal, usually iron. The cost of such molds is obviously heavy, but where articles have to be produced in very large quantities, the time saved

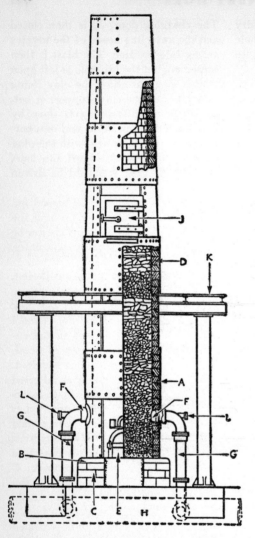

in making a fresh mold for each casting fully justifies the cost.

Non-chilling brands of iron are usually used in making castings in permanent molds, and the molds into which it is poured may be either cold or hot. It will generally be found that the best results are obtained if the molds are kept at a temperature of about 300 deg. F. The metal must be very hot when cast, and the castings must be turned out of the molds at approximately an orange-red color.

Soft iron cores are used in conjunction with permanent molds. These must be removed before the casting begins to contract, otherwise they will be gripped fast and it will be impossible to remove them.

Melting Iron

Iron for foundry purposes is melted in a furnace known as a cupola. This is a blast furnace, and a simple type is illustrated in Fig. 27. It consists of a boiler-plate shell, A, which rests on a base-plate, B, supported on a brick platform, C. The shell is lined with firebricks, D, and the iron base is covered with fireclay sloped slightly in the direction of the tap-hole in front of which a channel is fixed to carry the metal to the ladle. The cupola is generally

Fig. 27. Cupola, or furnace for melting iron. It consists of a shell A standing on a base-plate B supported by a brick platform C. The shell is lined with firebrick D. The fire is lighted through the opening E and the blast is led into the cupola through the tuyeres F and from the supply pipe G, which, in turn, connects with the main supply pipe H. The furnace is fed through the charging door J from the charging platform K. When the charging door is closed the swiveling heads of the tuyeres are swung into position and the blast turned on, the tap-hole being left open to allow the clay lining to dry. The metal, which begins to run after about 15 minutes of full blast, is observed through the mica sight-holes L.

built on the outside of the foundry wall, the channel from the tap-hole being carried through the wall into the molding shop.

On the side of the cupola shell opposite to the tap-hole is an opening covered by a plate, E, through which the fire is lighted and the furnace cleaned out when necessary. The blast is led into the cupola by means of the tuyeres, F, each of which has a swiveling head resting on the supply pipes, G, which take the air from the main supply pipe, H.

The materials are fed to the furnace through the charging hole, J, placed at a suitable height above the charging platform, K.

Filling the Cupola

A fire is lighted in the bottom, and a charge of coke added. When this is well alight filling begins. A charge of iron of suitable weight is put in, together with a suitable flux. Another layer of coke is added and followed by a further charge of metal. The proportion of coke may vary between eight and twenty pounds of coke per hundred pounds of iron, according to the requirements of the cupola. Alternate charges of coke and iron are then added to fill the cupola.

Lining the Tap-Hole

This is done two or three hours before the blast is put on. During this period the various openings in the cupola are left open to assist combustion and allow it to become warmed throughout. Before the blast is turned on for melting down the metal, the tap-hole is lined with clay, and the plate, E, Fig. 27, packed round the edges with sand.

The charging door, J, is then closed and the swiveling heads of the tuyeres swung into position. The blast is then turned on, but the tap-hole is left open at this stage to allow the clay lining to dry before the clay stopper, or bot, is put in. The stopping is done by sticking the bot on to the end of a bot-stick, and the latter held with the plug pointing downward toward the hole, in which position it should be driven home.

Full blast may now be turned on, and in about a quarter of an hour the metal begins to run down. This can be observed through the mica sight-holes, L, in the tuyeres.

When sufficient metal has collected, the bot is knocked out of the tap-hole with the sharp point of the bot-stick and the metal run down the channel into a ladle. As the metal in the cupola sinks, additional charges of metal, coke and flux are added as required.

Metal from the cupolas is collected in ladles and poured from these ladles into the mold. Ladles of various types are illustrated in Fig. 28. A is a hand ladle holding about half a hundredweight, used for very light casts; B is a two-man ladle for heavier work; C is a crane ladle for casting up to a ton of metal; and D a heavy crane ladle capable of holding from one to twelve tons. The ladle shown at C is tipped direct by means of the handle, while that at D is a geared type and is tipped by turning the wheel.

Ladles are lined with fireclay, and must be thoroughly heated before the metal is run into them. This is done in the case of small ladles by heating them over a coal or coke fire, but with the larger types a fire is lighted within them. When they have been filled the metal is protected with coal-dust or charcoal and covered with a plate.

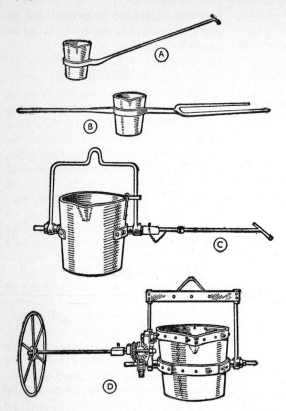

Fig. 28. Types of ladles used in the foundry. *A,* hand ladle for light casts; *B,* two-man ladle for heavier work; *C,* crane ladle for casting up to a ton of metal; *D,* heavy crane ladle with geared tipping device, capable of holding from one to twelve tons of metal.

All material used for covering the metal while collecting, or foreign matter thrown up by the metal, must be skimmed off before pouring begins, and in addition it is customary to hold a rectangular bar of iron across the mouth of the ladle during the actual pouring to keep back any dirt or other matter which remains floating on the surface of the metal and which, if it were allowed to enter the mold, would prove detrimental to the quality of the finished casting.

Temperature of the Metal

The temperature of the metal while being poured is of the greatest importance, as it influences the shrinkage of the casting during solidification. The lowest temperature at which the mold can be completely and properly filled is the best temperature at which to pour. This will, of course, vary with different types of mold, being influenced by the distance the metal has to run, the thickness of the mold, and other factors.

Pouring the Metal

Pouring must be done steadily, and a constant stream of metal must be maintained until the operation is complete. Any iron entering the mold in driblets is liable to become chilled and cause marks on the castings. In view of this, the runner-cup or pouring basin is closed by a stopper and metal poured in until the basin is full.

The stopper is then removed, and the flow of the metal from ladle to basin must be sufficiently rapid to keep the basin full until casting is complete. A basin that is kept full in this way will also prevent foreign bodies from entering the mold, as these will float on the top of the metal.

When pouring very heavy molds a sand channel is sometimes made from the cupola to the mold and the metal poured without the use of ladles.

Feeding of Molds

Feed-gates are frequently provided in molds to compensate for the contraction of the metal as it cools and to supply fresh metal to make up the deficiency, thus stopping shrinkage of the casting. They are therefore cut in those parts of the mold where the mass of metal is greatest and the total contraction is large. If metal is not supplied in this way the castings may turn out to be spongy, or drawn and twisted, because of stresses set up during cooling.

Feed-gates are vertical passages cut through the cope to the mold. Like runners, they are provided with a cup or basin-shaped cavity at the top. Feeding is done by means of an iron rod $\frac{1}{4}$ in. or $\frac{3}{8}$ in. in diameter, which is first heated by dipping it in the hot metal in the ladle. As soon as the mold is full, the rod is put into the molten metal in the head of the feed-gate and moved up and down in a regular manner, care being taken to avoid touching the sides of the gate or pushing it in so far as to touch the mold. The pumping movement of the feeder-rod keeps a passage open in the center of the metal and allows metal in the feeder-basin to pass down into the mold. Feeding is continued until the iron clings to the rod, which should then be removed with as little disturbance to the metal as possible.

In cases where the runner runs direct into the mold the latter may be fed through the runner, although this should only be done in cases where very clean metal is used. Fig. 29 shows a mold being fed as described.

When castings are cool enough to be removed from the sand the boxes are knocked and the castings allowed to cool down uniformly. The cooling process should not be hurried, and on no account should artificial cooling be resorted to.

Fettling

The castings are now ready to be cleaned up and finished. When they are removed from the mold they have several unwanted projections in the shape of runners, risers, feed-gates, etc. These are removed, in the case of iron, by nicking them with a chisel and snapping them off. Non-ferrous runners are sawed off, and steel ones removed by means of the oxy-acetylene cutting process. The core-holes should then be cleaned out and any fins removed with a cold chisel.

Cores are cleaned out by means of drifts or otherwise. The use of a wire brush on the exterior faces of a casting will remove any sands adhering to it, while sand-blasting is also employed for this purpose. Castings that are not too delicate may be cleaned by tumbling in a rattler, and even fragile castings, if properly filled, may be treated in this way.

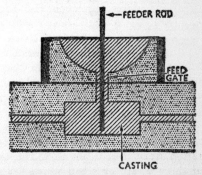

Fig. 29. Feeding a mold. The pumping action of the feeder-rod keeps a passage open in the center of the metal and allows the metal in the feeder-basin to pass down into the mold. Feeding compensates for the contraction of the metal as it cools.

Mixing Iron

Cast iron is readily recognizable by its brittleness and its inability to bend without breaking. When being machined, the chips are small, brittle crumbs, and parts of the casting may be so hard that they cannot be touched with a machine tool or a file. There are, however, various grades of cast iron, and these are produced by mixing different types of iron in the cupola or other melting furnace so that the best type for the job can be obtained.

A good proportion of foundry scrap is generally employed in such mixtures, ranging from light shop scrap, such as runners, risers, etc., from small castings, to heavy shop scrap, which consists of heavy defective castings, heavy runners, and the like. This scrap may be mixed with a suitable quantity of new iron, or pig iron, different grades of which can be bought.

Alloying

In addition, iron is frequently alloyed with nickel, chromium, and other metals to give it special heat-resisting, durable, or other properties. The question of the composition and alloying of cast iron is dealt with fully in Chapter 2, to which the reader should refer for further information on this subject.

It should be noted that any scrap to be used for re-melting should be sorted over before being used. The use of dirty scrap, or scrap which has a large quantity of sand adhering to it, can only prove detrimental to the quality of the metal. In addition, special care should be taken while sorting to see that any unsuitable metal is removed.

Malleable Castings

Although castings are normally rather hard and brittle when removed from the sand, it is possible to produce castings that are less brittle and very tough. These qualities are produced largely by prolonged annealing (see Heat-Treatment of Metal), but annealing can only be really satisfactory if suitable iron is used in the first place.

Malleable castings are made in green-sand molds, and although the method of making the mold is the same as for any other type of casting, there are one or two points which, if borne in mind by the molder, will help to insure the success of the finished article.

A good fine facing sand should be used to produce a good *skin* or face on the casting; a mixture of cement and plumbago makes a good facing. It is also well to remember that the iron used for malleable castings tends to shrink to a greater extent than the ordinary iron, and larger gates and risers should therefore be provided. Shrink heads or feeders should be larger for the same reason, and they should be made wider at the bottom than at the top. This is done because metal for malleable castings is not very fluid and is liable to set rather quickly, especially in the narrow neck of the runner, riser or feed-gate, and will thus impede the passage of feed metal to the casting.

Heat of Ladles

Ladles for malleable iron should be hotter than those used for ordinary grey iron, and they are frequently heated by filling them with metal from the cupola, allowing them to stand until they have become thoroughly heated through, and then pouring the metal back into the cupola. Some furnaces are provided with an aperture near the tap-hole for this purpose.

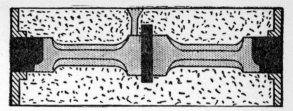

Fig. 30. In order to produce a durable and hardwearing surface on certain faces of a casting, iron chills are inserted into the mold, as shown above. The diagram illustrates a mold for a truck wheel with chills for the tread and axle.

Chilled Castings

In cases where certain faces of a casting are required to stand up to considerable wear while the body of the casting remains soft, chills are put into the mold as shown in Fig. 30. The molten metal coming into contact with the chill becomes very rapidly cooled; this prevents the formation of free carbon near the chilled surface and results in a very hard and durable surface.

Chills are made of iron, a close, strong grey iron, with a high melting point being the most suitable. They are usually dressed or blackened before use with a thin wash of blacklead or other substance that will not interfere with the cooling effect of the chill. Sometimes they are not dressed, but allowed to form a thin coating of rust, and smeared over with a little oil before being put into the mold as explained later.

The depth of the chilling effect may be regulated by the thickness of the chills. Skin chilling can be effected by means of chilling plates from half to one inch thick.

Chills sometimes crack through unequal heating, and if this is to be avoided, the molds should be filled as quickly as possible so that the whole surface of the chill may be similarly affected. Larger gates than for ordinary molds are therefore necessary.

The face of the chill that comes into contact with the casting should be carefully prepared in the first instance and thereafter kept in good condition. Frequently these faces are machined for accuracy and also to remove the outer skin of the iron. The removal of this skin is generally desirable because being cast iron, it is often of a slightly different composition from the interior, and if not removed might cause cracks or other blemishes to form on the surface. When chills are being machined, the greatest care should be exercised to avoid coarse tool marks.

On very smooth surfaces it is difficult to get the blacking to adhere properly, and in addition, the molten metal coming into contact with them will not lie quietly. In order to overcome these difficulties the smoothness may be removed by carefully rusting the surface, but no more than a very thin layer should be allowed to form. For this purpose chills are often exposed to the weather, or they may be treated with a very dilute solution of sal-ammoniac. Sometimes urine is used to produce the film of rust. The chill should be rusted uniformly over the surface, which is then rubbed over by hand.

Repairing Damage to Chills

It will be obvious to the reader that chills have to withstand very severe conditions. They must, therefore, be frequently inspected and kept in good order. Rough patches are liable to appear on the surface, and these must be rubbed down. A little blacking may be used as a filler where the damage is slight. Chills that have been in use for a long time lose their chilling properties and are liable to produce defects in the casting. This is due to the annealing effect of the hot metal coming into contact with them.

In order to reduce the danger of fracture, chills should be heated in a stove before being put into dry-sand molds, and the metal should be poured before they have had time to cool.

Brass, aluminum, and other non-ferrous metals are cast in sand molds in much the same way as iron. The making of the mold is in most cases the same as for iron, although, in the brass the flasks are usually poured vertically instead of horizontally. It is usual, when making molds for brass castings, to provide several in-gates from a central runner, while the runner itself should be somewhat wider than that used for iron.

With aluminum the most important point is the pouring temperature of the metal. This metal readily overheats, but if satisfactory castings are to be obtained, the temperature should not be allowed to rise very much above the melting point. Before pouring, the dross and dirt should be carefully skimmed off, and the metal given a vigorous stir. It should then be poured quickly into the mold in a steady stream.

Green-sand molds are generally used, and the cores are often made from sawdust with resin as a binding agent. With this metal hard cores tend to produce cracked castings, owing to the fact that they do not contract to the same extent as the metal itself. It is desirable to remove them from the sand as soon after pouring as possible. Owing to the lightness of the metal, heavy runners and risers are essential.

GLOSSARY OF TERMS USED IN THE FOUNDRY

ADHESIVENESS. The ability of particles of sand to cling to some other material.

BACKING SAND. Sand used to fill flasks after facing-sand has been used to cover the pattern.

BEDDED-IN MOLD. Mold the bottom half of which is made in the sand in the floor of the foundry. It may be covered with a cope, or cast open, according to the type of work.

BLOWN CASTINGS. Castings in which bubbles, or blowholes, have been caused through gases, steam, etc., generated when the mold is cast, finding their way into the molten metal.

BOT. Clay wedge used in a cupola to stop the hole through which the metal is run.

COD. A sand projection left behind in the mold by some patterns. Strictly speaking, it is a core, but instead of being inserted separately into the mold, it forms part of the mold itself.

COHESIVENESS. The ability of particles of sand to cling together.

COPE. The top half of a molding-box.

CORE. Sand facsimile of the interior, or hollow, portions of a casting.

CORE BOX. Box in which cores are rammed up and shaped.

DRAG. The bottom half of a molding-box or flask. It is rammed up before the cope.

FACING. Materials used in the foundry for painting the surface of a finished mold in order to produce a smooth skin on the casting.

FACING-SAND. Sand used to form the faces of a mold.

FALSE ODDSIDE. Permanent oddside made of plaster or other material. See Oddside.

FEEDING. Process of assisting metal to run into a mold to make up for any contraction of the metal as it cools.

FETTLING. Cleaning up, trimming and finishing of castings after they have been taken out of the sand.

FLASK. A complete molding-box, consisting of two or more parts. The term is often loosely applied to a half box.

FLOW-OFF GATE. Channel cut from the mold to the riser.

GATE. Channel by which metal may enter or leave a mold. See In-Gate; Flow-off Gate.

GREEN SAND-MOLD. Mold made and cast in damp sand. The opposite of a dry sand-mold, which is dried in an oven before it is poured.

IN-GATE. Channel cut from the bottom of the runner into the mold. It is used in cases where the runner does not enter the mold direct.

LADLE. Receptacle into which molten metal is run from the cupola and from which metal is poured into a mold.

LOOSE PIECES. Undercut portions of a pattern which are made separate from and fixed on to the pattern by pins or other means, in order that they may be left behind in the sand when the pattern is withdrawn and removed separately from the mold.

MOLD. Impression of the article to be cast. It is usually made in sand, but may be of metal.

MULTIPLE MOLDS. Molds which are stacked on top of each other and cast through a single runner. Each half box contains a half mold on each face.

ODDSIDE. Support used for supporting a pattern while the drag is being rammed up.

PATTERN. Facsimile of the article to be produced. It may be of wood, metal or other material, and is made larger than the casting to allow for contraction.

PRINT. Wooden projection put on to a pattern to provide supports for the cores in a mold.

RAPPING. Tapping of the pattern with a mallet in order to loosen it as it is drawn from the mold.

RISER. Channel from a mold used to carry foreign matter out of the mold or to assist in feeding the casting as it cools.

RUNNER. The channel down which the metal is poured into a mold.

SLEEK. Term meaning to make smooth. It is applied to the troweling of a sand surface.

SNAP-FLASK. Molding-box, hinged on one side so that it may be opened to allow the finished mold to be removed.

SPRIGS. Small pegs of wood or metal

used to strengthen weak portions of a mold or to assist in the mending up of a damaged mold.

STRICKLE. Piece of wood by means of which surplus sand is removed from a molding-box or other surface. Strickles may also be used to shape sand surfaces in the mold.

VENT. Channel made in the sand in the vicinity of a mold to allow steam, gases, etc., generated when sand and molten metal come into contact with one another, to escape.

WASTER. Faulty casting.

CHAPTER 15

MEASURING AND TESTING

LAYING-OUT WITH RULE, SCRIBER, DIVIDERS AND TRY SQUARE. USE OF TAMMELS. THE SURFACE PLATE. MEASURING WITH CALIPERS. PRINCIPLES AND USE OF THE MICROMETER AND VERNIER. VERNIER PROTRACTORS. DIAL, CYLINDER, AND FEELER GAGES. THREAD GAGES. PLUG GAGES. RADIUS GAGES. PRINCIPLES OF TESTING. ANGLE PLATES. THE SPIRIT LEVEL. THE PLUMB-BOB. USE OF TANGENT TABLES. LIMITS AND CLEARANCE. NEWALL LIMITS. ANGLES AND TAPERS.

I**N ORDER** to measure anything, a standard must be fixed, and the American standard of length is the foot. This is one-third of a standard yard, the distance between two marks on a bar especially prepared and preserved for the purpose of establishing a standard length. Every instrument which measures length in some way reproduces the standard length or some fraction of it. It is evident that for accurate work the material from which the instrument is made must be inextensible and hard-wearing. Thus, a fabric tape measure or a wooden rule cannot be used for really accurate measurement.

The Steel Rule

The simplest instrument for measuring is the rule, and for engineering jobs it is made of steel. Stainless steel is superior to other types, as it does not rust with handling. Probably the most convenient rule for general purposes is 12 in. long, $1\frac{1}{8}$ in. wide and $\frac{1}{32}$ or $\frac{3}{64}$ in. thick. For small jobs a pocket rule 6 in. x $\frac{1}{2}$ in. x $\frac{1}{64}$ in. thick is very useful. Folding rules are not recommended for close measurements, continuous steel rules being available in many lengths. The choice of graduations is great, but for the 12-in. rule $\frac{1}{8}$ in., $\frac{1}{16}$ in., $\frac{1}{32}$ in. and $\frac{1}{64}$ in. scales will be found convenient, as will $\frac{1}{32}$ in., $\frac{1}{64}$ in., $\frac{1}{50}$ in. and centimeter scales for the 6-in. rule. One scale having decimal parts of an inch is desirable. A thin, flexible 12-in. rule is often handy for measuring along slightly curved surfaces where a straight rule would not work.

The graduations should be fine, clear, and cut right up to the edge of the rule. Always have the graduations as near the work as possible (see Fig. 1). When measuring in $\frac{1}{64}$ in. or $\frac{1}{100}$ in. the use of a pocket magnifying-glass will be of some assistance. If the first graduation occurs on the end of the rule as in Fig. 1, constant use wears away the end until the first inch is actually a bit short. When this happens, accurate measurements can be taken by starting at the 1-in. mark and subtracting 1 from the rule reading. A worn rule could not, of course, be serviceable for a job of the type shown in Fig. 1.

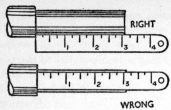

Fig. 1. To have the graduations as near the work as possible, use the rule as shown above, not below.

The Scriber

For making lines on the work when marking off, a good scriber is required. Do not bother to make one, it is not worth while. A first-class tool with a hardened and tempered renewable point can be purchased cheaply. To reduce the possibility of error, the scriber should be held against the rule or straight-edge as shown as Fig. 2.

Note that the use of a scriber, center punch, or similar marking instrument, on almost all aircraft fittings is prohibited unless the marks made can be removed during manufacture. This is because scratches, and the like, on the surface of stressed parts may start a structural failure.

Dividers

These are essentially scribers for marking arcs and circles, hence the points should be hard and sharp. Small radii should be struck with small dividers, since large dividers spring excessively when the points are very close together. Convenient sizes are 3-in. and 6-in.

Dividers may also, as their name implies, be used for dividing distances into a number of equal parts. They are generally used when a rule is not applicable, and in this event trial-and-error methods are adopted. The dividers are set to the approximate required distance, and this is stepped off along the line to be divided. If a large number of divisions are required, three or four attempts will have to be made before the required setting is obtained.

Where possible a light center punch makes a good center for the dividers when marking an arc or a circle.

Another use for dividers is transferring dimensions from a rule to the work. When doing this, one point should be placed on the 1-in. graduation of the rule, and the other set to the required dimension, allowing for the difference in the rule reading.

Spring dividers are easily the most convenient to use, and for average work two sizes—3-in. and 6-in.—will be found satisfactory.

The Try-Square

This instrument is used for setting and checking lines or faces which have to be at right angles to some other plane. To use the square it is necessary to have some plane of reference such as a surface plate, marking-off table, or machined face on the work.

For average jobs the type of square having a fairly heavy base or stock and a relatively thin blade is most used.

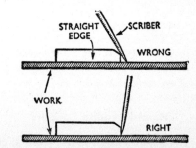

Fig. 2. How a scriber should be held against a straight-edge to reduce the chance of error.

The blade may be graduated if required, and in the large sizes the square may then be used in conjunction with a surface-gage for marking heights on vertical faces.

As the large sizes usually form a part of the shop equipment, a small square with a 4-in. or 6-in. blade will be found sufficient for most individual tool-kits.

A square may be checked by setting off a perpendicular to a perfectly straight edge such as can be found on a surface plate, and then turning the

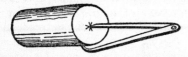

Fig. 3. For centering a bar, hermaphrodite or jenny calipers, or odd legs, are used as shown here.

square over so that the stock points in the opposite direction. The blade should be absolutely parallel to the perpendicular. If a surface plate is employed for this purpose, a convenient way of doing the job is to clamp a narrow machined bar, previously checked with a micrometer for parallelism, to the face of the plate, using the square on one edge of the bar for setting. If the square is turned over and used on the other side of the bar, the error, if any, between the blade and the bar can be checked with feeler-gages. The actual amount of error will be half of that shown by the test.

A scriber should not, of course, be used on the plate surface.

Hermaphrodite Calipers

Hermaphrodite calipers, jennies, or odd legs as they are variously termed, are used for centering bars, taking distances from the edges of holes or

plates, and similar jobs. The method of centering a bar is shown in Fig. 3, while Fig. 4 illustrates the method of marking a line parallel to the edge of a surface. It will be noted that two types are shown, that in Fig. 4 being the most adaptable and convenient for general purposes, as it has an adjustable leg.

Surface-Gage

When scribing horizontal lines on a vertical surface, a tool known as a surface-gage is used for holding the scriber. The latter is mounted so as to facilitate setting, and a fine adjustment is provided by a screw on the heavy base. Movement of this screw swings the scriber through a small arc, and so varies the height (see Fig. 5). A plane surface is required when using the surface-gage, although some makes have movable pins in the base which act as guides when the gage is used along a machined edge.

If extreme accuracy is not required, duplicate parts may be marked off at the same time with a surface-gage to insure uniformity, the gage being set either to a rule or to a master part.

Although it is made for marking on vertical or nearly vertical faces, the surface-gage can also be adapted to scribing on horizontal surfaces. A further advantage is the provision of a V in the base for resting the latter on a bar, so that dimensions may be set

Fig. 4. Method of marking a line parallel to the edge of a block with adjustable-leg calipers.

off from the bar to some other part of the work.

The size of the gage is dictated by the job in hand, but it is possible to purchase one with interchangeable spindles about 9 in. and 12 in. long, and these sizes may safely be recommended for average work.

Trammels

It is impracticable to employ calipers and dividers for laying off and checking dimensions of several feet. A very convenient method of doing this with reasonable accuracy is to employ trammels for the purpose. A pair of trams or trammel heads are used with a beam of convenient length to suit the job. Generally, each head carries two clamping-screws, one for fixing the position of the head on the beam, and the other for fixing the position of the scribing-point in the head. On most trammels the point of the scriber is ground eccentrically with the outside diameter to facilitate fine adjustment when setting.

Trammels are generally used in conjunction with a large steel rule, which may be from 3 to 10 ft. long. It is a simple matter to measure by this means a distance of several feet with an error of less than $\frac{1}{64}$ in.

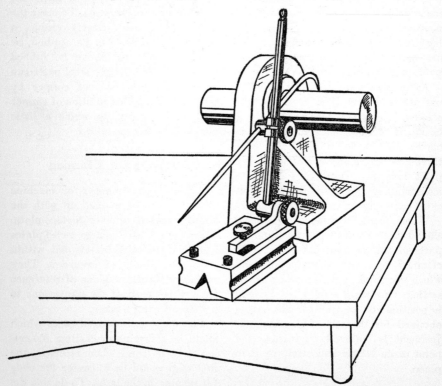

Fig. 5. For marking horizontal lines on horizontal or vertical surfaces, the scriber is held in a surface-gage. A screw in the base of the gage varies the scriber's height by swinging it through a small arc.

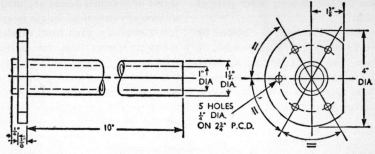

Fig. 6. To find the center of a flanged forging or casting such as that shown here, it would be placed in V blocks and half the diameter subtracted from the over-all height as measured by the surface-gage.

An additional feature which may be added to trammels is a pair of caliper legs. These are very useful for many jobs where inside or outside dimensions are to be checked, since the legs can be turned around for either case and the distance of the application point from the beam can be varied.

As trammels are usually sold without the beam, it is a good plan to select a type which does not require a beam of special section. On some makes, the heads are provided with three grooves, in any one of which the point may be clamped to facilitate measuring in awkward places—a decided advantage in some circumstances.

When using trammels, the beam should be as rigid as possible, and all parts of the head should be securely clamped to avoid slight movements which might affect the accuracy of the setting. One tram should be clamped in position and an approximate setting obtained for the other. The final adjustment is obtained by turning the point in its holder and clamping it in place.

Preparing Work for Marking Off

In machine-drawing, dimensions are taken about center or datum lines, and the first job when marking off is to reproduce these lines on the surface of the metal to provide a basis for subsequent measurements. To make the lines on the work clearly visible, a coat of whitewash can be applied, or ordinary white chalk can be rubbed into the surface. Bright steel parts can be given a thin coat of copper by treating them with a solution of copper sulphate in water, to which a little nitric acid has been added.

Marking Off a Forging

A very large number of machine parts have to be marked off with the aid of a surface table or surface plate. These are essentially large metal plates having surfaces which are flat within very close limits of accuracy. They serve as a datum or plane of reference from which most of the dimensions to be laid off can be taken.

Fig. 6 shows a flanged piece which might be a forging or casting. Assuming it to be solid when received, the first step would be to center the ends for turning in the lathe. To do this the forging would be placed in V blocks and the center height found by subtracting half of the diameter from the over-all height as measured with the aid of the surface-gage. If the work is not very regular a mean height may be taken by repeating the process in two or three places. The center height having been arrived at, center lines may be marked on either end with the surface-gage. The try-square may be used to set the first center line vertical prior to marking the second one.

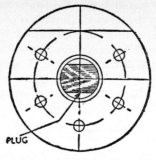

PLUG

Fig. 7. Final marking out of the finished job of which the earlier stage is shown in Fig. 6.

is a template for a portion of the shell-plating for an airplane. In a case like this it is convenient to cut the sheet for the template to the correct shape before marking the positions of the rivet-holes if these are around the edge only. Otherwise the entire job should be laid out.

If the job comes back from the lathe turned, bored, and faced, the remainder of it can be marked off. To do this the center will again be required for marking the pitch-circle for the bolt-holes. A plug of lead or hard wood can be wedged in the bore and the center marked on this as before. At the same time center lines can be marked on the flange. Set the dividers and mark the pitch-circle on the flange, using the center on the plug. With the same setting for the dividers step off the hole centers around the pitch-circle, starting with a hole on the vertical center line of the flange.

Now set the surface-gage to the top of the pitch-circle and scribe a horizontal line tangent to it for the flat on the flange. This done, the job may be removed from the blocks, the hole centers marked with center punches and the holes marked out with dividers. The finished job is shown in Fig. 7.

Marking Off a Large Template

Some jobs cannot be done with the aid of a surface plate, and must be laid out in the flat. An example of this

A datum line can be scribed along one edge with the aid of a straight-edge and a scriber. Perpendiculars to this line may be erected as follows: Mark a point on the line as near as is practicable to the edge of the sheet, and with the trammels, set from a rule, mark along this line another point four units distant from the first. A unit may be any convenient dimension, and for this job we can call it 1 ft. The points will, therefore, be 4 ft. apart. Set the trammels to a dimension of three units (in this case 3 ft.) and scribe an arc where the perpendicular is likely to fall, using the first point as center. With the trammels set at 5 units (5 ft.), and using the second point as center, scribe another arc intersecting the first. If the intersection point and the first point are joined by a straight line, the latter will make an angle of 90 deg. with the line first laid down (see Fig. 8). This is because $3^2 + 4^2 = 5^2$, a familiar condition for a right-angled triangle. The method can be applied to many jobs, using dividers or trammels, the units being selected to suit the size of the work.

If the trammels are set to the 5 ft. 1 in. dimensions shown in Fig. 8, an arc can be scribed as indicated. To obtain the position 6 in. distant from the perpendicular, a line parallel to it is required. To do this, scribe two arcs of 6-in. radius at convenient points and draw the parallel tangent to both arcs. From where this line cuts the arc of 5 ft. 1 in. radius a line may be scribed to the point on the datum line. Measure 7 ft. 4 in. along the datum line, erect a perpendicular as before and measure up 5 ft. 6 in. and complete the marking out of the template profile, after which it may be cut out. If hand-holes and so on are to be included, the marking out of these should be done before cutting the profile, as it is easier on a job of this description to work to a line rather than to a cut edge.

In Fig. 9 further details of the marking out are shown. Another method of erecting a perpendicular can be adopted if desired for laying out

the two rows of rivets indicated. The method is as follows: Measure the 3-ft. dimension from the template profile and along the datum line, marking a point, A, on the latter. With this point as center, scribe arcs of any convenient radius at B and C on the datum line. Then with a larger radius scribe two arcs, centers, B and C, intersection at point, D. Join the points, D and A, to obtain the perpendicular.

By simple measuring along the perpendiculars and the edge of the profile with which they are parallel, the line of rivets 3 ft. 8 in. from the datum can be located.

Similarly, the center line of the hand-hole can be marked in position and a distance of 4 ft. 1 in. measured along it. At this point and one 9 in. from it, 3-in. radii will mark the ends of the hole. Two lines tangent to these

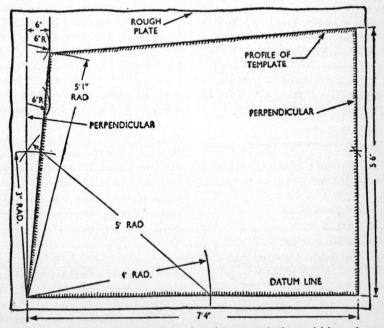

Fig. 8. Illustrating the method, explained in the text, which would be adopted for marking out with straight-edge, scriber, and trammels a large template for such a job as a portion of the shell-plating for an airplane.

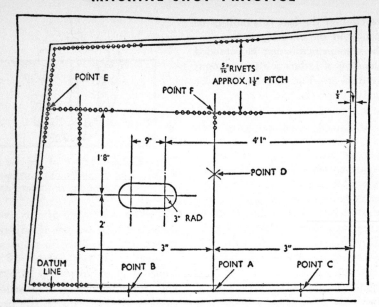

Fig. 9. Further stage in the marking out of the large template illustrated in Fig. 8. Full explanations are given in the text.

radii will give the hole-outlines. Note that radii are marked in first, then lines tangent to them added.

Rivet-hole centers at points such as E and F should be marked before the remainder are spaced out with dividers.

Hints about Radii

When joining two radii with a common tangent, the straight-edge should be used outside the radii so that the latter are not covered by it. If this is done it will be found easier to blend the straight line into the curves.

A common occurrence in marking out is blending a radius into two other radii, as in Fig. 10. Too often this is done by trial and error instead of using the simple method shown here. The two radii for which centers are given are struck first. With the same centers two other radii are struck, the dimensions of each being equivalent to the sum of one of the radii given and the radius with which it must blend. The

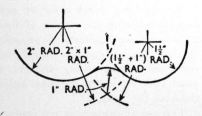

Fig. 10. By the use of the method illustrated here, it is easy to blend a radius accurately into two other radii.

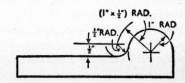

Fig. 11. The principle of Fig. 10 applies also to blending a radius with a straight line and an arc, as shown here.

intersection of the last two radii gives the center of the blending radius.

The same principle may be extended to blending a radius with a straight line and an arc. Fig. 11 shows how the method is applied.

Measuring with Calipers

Calipers, either spring or firm-joint types, are convenient tools for measuring a number of jobs which are not required to be extremely accurate. Firm-joint calipers have two legs fastened together with a rivet or bolt of special design. To give a smooth joint thin fiber-washers are interposed between the legs, and when purchasing calipers this point should be looked for.

The legs of inside calipers are curved outward at the extremities to facilitate measuring small holes, while outside caliper legs have a large curve inward to increase their capacity for large work.

Firm-joint calipers are adjusted approximately by the hands and then set to the *feel* of the work by tapping them on a metal surface. It is a common practice when opening calipers by this means to tap the top of the joint. It is better, if possible, to tap the inside of the legs, as repeated blows, though light, tend to burr the edges of the joint. Care should be taken when using calipers to hold them square across the job, or an incorrect reading will be obtained. The interference between the work and the instrument should be very slight, as distortion of the legs occurs if force is used. The application of calipers for good results calls for a certain amount of practice.

Spring calipers are provided with an adjusting screw which moves the legs against the tension of the spring.

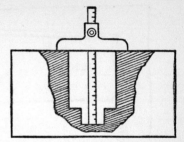

Fig. 12. An example of the use of the depth-gage, a convenient instrument for measuring holes, shoulders, etc.

The chief advantage of this over the firm-joint type is ease of adjustment. Quick nuts are fitted to many spring dividers, and they consist of a nut which is split completely in two and held by a conical sleeve under the pressure of the spring. If this pressure is removed by holding the legs together with the fingers, the nut is released from the screw and can be moved into any position along its length without being rotated. This is particularly advantageous in inspection work, where many varying diameters have to be checked.

Either inside or outside calipers can be set to a rule or to a standard part, the latter being the most accurate. If the standard has a very smooth surface and the work surface is less smooth, more resistance will be offered by the work to the movement of the calipers, and allowance has to be made for this.

Mistakes can easily arise by accidentally altering the setting of these tools when laying them down after checking the job, and it is a good plan, particularly with spring dividers, to check the setting each time before checking the work.

The use of calipers is not confined to cylindrical work. They can often be employed to advantage in checking rectangular holes, parallel faces, and so on. Convenient sizes for the tool-kit are 3 in. and 6 in.

The Depth-Gage

A very useful device for measuring the depth of holes, shoulders and the like is the depth-gage. This is essen-tially a narrow rule (or sometimes a rod) to which a sliding head can be clamped. The head forms a convenient marker in places where the rule must be held at a distance from the point being measured. Fig. 12 shows an example of the use of this tool.

PRECISION INSTRUMENTS

IN PRACTICE it is not possible to make a machine part to an exact dimension. There is always an error, however slight it may be. The permissible extent of this error depends on the job. Thus, to measure the pitch of rivets with a rule is a recognized practice, as an error of, say $\frac{1}{64}$ in. is not of great importance. To measure a ball race housing with a rule, however, would be out of the question, as it is quite impossible to obtain the required accuracy, since the permissible error must be expressed in thousandths of an inch.

While it is not possible to measure .001 in. (one-thousandth of an inch) with a rule, because of the limitations of our eyesight, it is not by any means an inconsiderable dimension. An ordinary one dollar bill, for example is not considered very thin, although its thickness is only about .004 in.

The Micrometer

To divide a distance of 1 in. on an instrument scale into one thousand parts is obviously impracticable, and some method of magnifying the graduations must be resorted to. This is achieved by dividing the instrument scale directly into $\frac{1}{40}$ in. graduations and then subdividing each of these as required. One-thousandth part is $\frac{1}{25}$ of $\frac{1}{40}$; hence it is necessary to divide each fortieth into 25 parts.

In the case of the micrometer the division is achieved as follows: the body of the instrument functions as a nut in which a screw can be operated. This screw or spindle does the actual measuring, and it possesses 40 threads per inch, of a very high degree of accuracy. One full turn of the screw causes it to move backward or forward $\frac{1}{40}$ in. and obviously $\frac{1}{25}$ of a turn will cause it to move $\frac{1}{25}$ of $\frac{1}{40}$, or .001 in. All that is now required is a convenient method of gaging $\frac{1}{25}$ of one turn, and this is provided by an attachment to the screw known as the thimble. This has 25 marks equally spaced around its circumference and suitably numbered, so that the number of marks which have passed a fixed line on the body or frame of the micrometer can easily be counted. Fig. 13 will help to clarify the above description.

Micrometers can also be obtained for measuring in the metric system. These have a screw or spindle with 20 threads per cm., so that one complete revolution of the thimble moves the spindle .5 mm. Apart from this, the form of construction and method of use are the same as for an instrument calibrated in inches fractions.

The instrument frame is of forged steel and is designed to give maximum rigidity. The two gaging faces are the end of the spindle and the face of a stud or anvil which is fixed to the frame opposite the spindle.

Construction of the Micrometer

The main nut is carried in a barrel fixed to the frame, while a loose-friction-fitting sleeve is pushed over the outside of the barrel, and it is this sleeve which carries the datum line and fixed graduations. The object of graduating a loose sleeve instead of the barrel proper is to provide a convenient method of adjustment for the zero setting of the instrument. This is generally considered to be an improvement on the other method of adjustment, where the anvil is screwed into the frame and can be moved backward or forward, after loosening a locking-screw which holds the threaded end of the anvil tight in the split end of the frame.

When the gaging faces are in contact, it is a simple matter to turn the sleeve with the special spanner until the datum line coincides with the zero graduation on the thimble.

The Datum Line

The datum line on the sleeve is graduated along its length in $1/40$ ths of an inch, to indicate the number of whole turns which the spindle has made from zero. Every fourth graduation is numbered, starting from zero. Thus the numbers may be read off as tenths of an inch, since four times $1/40$ of an inch is equal to $1/10$ of an inch.

The thimble is a sort of tubular cover which is fastened to the outer end of the spindle and moves with it, providing a medium for indicating the micrometer setting.

As was previously mentioned, the circumference of the thimble is divided into 25 equal parts. Every fifth division is numbered, starting from zero, hence the end of the twenty-fifth division coincides with zero. This will be understood if it is remembered that the zero mark indicates the beginning

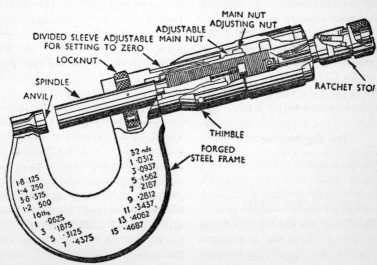

Fig. 13. Construction of the micrometer, an instrument for measuring small parts such as thousandths of an inch by magnifying the graduations. The body of the instrument acts as a nut, in which a measuring screw or spindle operates. The text fully explains the method of operation and reading.

or end of a full turn, and that the twenty-fifth mark must do likewise.

The main nut, in addition to the internal thread of $\frac{1}{40}$-in. pitch, has an external thread which tapers toward its extremity. Four slots in the threaded portion make it possible to reduce the internal diameter of the main nut by means of an adjusting nut, and so compensate for any wear which might take place between the main nut and the spindle.

With the aid of a locking-ring provided on the spindle it is possible to lock the instrument at any desired setting and use it as a snap gage (see Fig. 13).

The Ratchet-Stop

With such a fine thread on the spindle it is evident that only a slight pressure on the thimble will result in considerable force being exerted on the frame. This can lead to inaccurate readings, and to overcome the difficulty the ratchet-stop has been fitted. This is a small extension to the thimble, which it drives through the medium of a ratchet device. The ratchet always slips at the same pressure, and so results in uniform readings being obtained, in addition to preventing any distortion of the frame. It is an essential feature for micrometers which are arranged to measure in ten-thousandths of an inch.

Special Frame Shapes

For some work where the dimensions have to be taken in awkward places it is desirable to have a micrometer with a frame which is narrow at the anvil. Because of the necessity for rigidity it is not practicable to reduce the width of the frame cross-section, and so it is relieved locally. Another type of frame is very shallow, to permit insertion into holes of comparatively small diameter such as the bore of a milling cutter when the thickness of the center boss is to be measured.

Opposed to this is a frame which is very deep and made expressly for measuring sheet-metal. The depth of the frame makes it possible to take readings at a reasonable distance from the edge of the metal sheet.

Checking for Wear

After considerable use a micrometer will show some slight signs of wear. To test if wear is present, hold the frame firmly and endeavor to move the spindle endwise without turning it. If this can be done the thread is worn, and the play must be taken up by turning the adjusting nut which is concealed under the thimble (Fig. 13). Unscrewing the spindle to the limit of its travel will facilitate this. When the thread is correctly adjusted, the spindle will rotate freely but without end-play.

A piece of notepaper can next be nipped very gently between the gaging faces of the anvil and spindle and pulled out against this pressure. This is a very satisfactory way of cleaning the faces preparatory to checking the zero setting. To do this, screw in the spindle until the gaging faces are in contact. The zero mark on the thimble should now coincide with the datum line on the barrel sleeve. If not, the sleeve can be turned with the special wrench provided for this purpose until the setting is correct.

On some makes of instruments the anvil is clamped in position by a screw, and adjustment is effected by moving the anvil endwise after loosening the screw. If the anvil itself is screwed into the frame and has to be turned to effect adjustment, it must not on any account be forced against the end of the spindle, otherwise the frame will be distorted.

The Use of Standards

Micrometers for measuring dimensions in excess of 1 in. are provided with a mechanism similar to a 1-in. micrometer. Thus a 1-in. micrometer will measure from 0 to 1 in., while the next sizes measure from 1 in. to 2 in. to 3 in. respectively, and so on. This necessitates the use of standards for checking purposes.

For checking a 1-in. to 2-in. instrument, a 1-in. standard is required, and this usually takes the form of a disc or roller. When the micrometer is set at zero, the gap between the gaging faces should be exactly the same as the standard.

If a standard is not available, new ball or roller bearings can be used in an emergency for setting micrometers measuring in thousandths, since these bearings are accurate to one ten-thousandth of an inch.

It sometimes happens that the spindle thread wears more in some part of its length than elsewhere. If errors due to this are suspected, the micrometer should be tested with a series of standards ranging through its capacity.

The presence of dust and grit on the thread will greatly reduce the useful life of the micrometer, and precau-

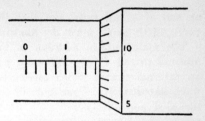

Fig. 14. The micrometer setting here is read as .100 + (.025 × 3) + .009, that is, .184 in. or other units.

tions must be taken to keep the instrument clean. When not in use, it should be kept in a case. Whether a case is available or not it is a good plan to wrap the tool in a piece of thin material dampened with light machine oil when the micrometer is not in use.

Reading the Micrometer

Micrometer readings are always expressed in decimals, and future references to various settings will take account of this fact. For convenience it is usual to engrave a table of decimal equivalents on either the frame or the thimble of the instrument, and this may be used when fractional dimensions have to be used.

The sleeve of the instrument has marked on it major divisions representing tenths of an inch—that is, .100 in. each. Every major division is subdivided into four minor divisions, and these obviously will represent .025 in. each.

The thimble is divided into 25 parts around its circumference, and as one full turn of the spindle is equal to one minor division on the sleeve, then one division on the thimble will be .001.

Thus, to read the setting as shown in Fig. 14, count the number of tenths (major divisions), add the number of minor divisions multiplied by 25, and then add the number on the thimble.

Fig. 15. The micrometer user should keep in mind the meaning of the minor graduations, as here marked.

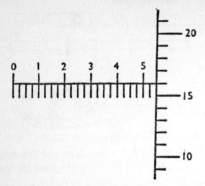

Fig. 16. Using the mental picture method, it will immediately be seen that the reading here is .525 + .016 = .541.

Thus the setting in Fig. 14, is .100 + (.025 × 3) + .009, which equals .100 + .075 + .009 = .184 in.

The "Mental Picture" Method

The process is simplified if the operator forms a mental picture of the graduations as shown in Fig. 15. An effort should be made to memorize this until the figures come to mind automatically. Applying the method to Fig. 16, it will be seen that the barrel reading is .525 and this plus the thimble reading of .016 is .541, which is the required setting.

Similarly in Fig. 17 the sleeve-reading is .825, while the thimble-reading is .009, a total of .834.

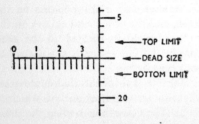

Fig. 18. The text explains how the micrometer, as shown here, may be used for checking accuracy of work between assigned limits.

Those who are not familiar with reading a micrometer can obtain good practice in this by measuring the thickness of feeler-gages (mentioned in a later section). The advantage in this lies in the fact that the thickness of the gages are stamped on them, and so the readings obtained can be checked. It is not advisable to use more than three leaves at one time for this purpose, and it is essential that they should all be perfectly clean.

To operate a small micrometer (up to 2 in.) comfortably with one hand, hold the thimble between the thumb and first finger of the right hand, and hook the third finger into the loop of the frame, allowing the instrument to rest in the palm of the hand. The work can then be manipulated with the left hand. This, of course, is not necessary on large jobs which rest on the bench or are fixed in a machine.

Fig. 17. In this example the sleeve reading of the micrometer is .825, the thimble reading .009: total .834.

Measuring between Limits

On inspection work particularly, parts often have to be checked in quantity to specified limits. For example, the diameter of an acceptable pivot pin may range from ⅜ in. + .002 in. to ⅜ in. − .002 in. That is, a smallest diameter of .373 in. and a largest diameter of .377 in.

In cases like this, do not measure each pin and mentally calculate the difference between actual and permissible dimensions. A much quicker and easier method is to make a mental note of the top and bottom limits on the thimble of the micrometer and when measuring each part observe whether the actual size falls inside or outside of these limits.

Reference to Fig. 18 will make this clear. Imagine an arrow pointing to the graduation two thousandths above .375, and another arrow pointing to the graduation two below .375. Any pin which gives a reading outside the top limit is too big, and any pin which gives a reading outside the bottom limit is too small. Thus it is unnecessary actually to read off the diameter of each pin, and when two or three hundred or more parts are to be checked this is a decided advantage.

Purchasing a Micrometer

The temptation to buy a cheap instrument is to be discouraged. Good-quality micrometers are a sound investment, as they embody a number of features such as hardened threads, fine, clear-cut graduations and so on. They are also, of course, more reliable and accurate. If there is any chance of the micrometer being needed for use in confined spaces or for measuring in ten-thousandths of an inch, instruments specially made for these purposes can be obtained. In any event the incorporation of a ratchet stop is to be recommended.

For 0–1 in. micrometers steel cases are available. Micrometers must never be carried loose in the pocket; in fact, the pocket is no place for any fine tool.

Special Micrometers

One of the most used of the special micrometers is that for measuring internal dimensions. As may be seen in Fig. 19, it is essentially a measuring

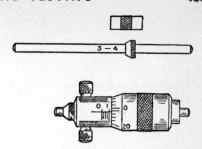

Fig. 19. Special micrometers of this type are used for measuring internal dimensions.

head similar to that on an ordinary micrometer, but generally with only $\frac{1}{2}$-in. movement. Extension rods are provided which make the instrument applicable over a wide range of sizes. When extension rods are used, care must be taken to have a clean joint, or errors will result.

Some practice is necessary to use this instrument, as the results are greatly affected by the *feel* of the contact between the tool and the work. When using long extensions the heat of the hands can cause incorrect readings if transmitted to the rods; hence they should be handled carefully. This instrument may also be used for measuring the distance between machined faces or the height of a surface above the table and so on.

Two types are available, one with marks on the rods which are intended to register with similar marks on the head, and the other with collars on the rods intended to butt up to the head extremity. The latter is the easiest to set accurately.

Another style of internal micrometer has two small jaws, one of which is fixed. The other moves when the thimble is turned, and as the opening increases, the barrel disappears inside the thimble. In consequence, the graduation must be read in the opposite

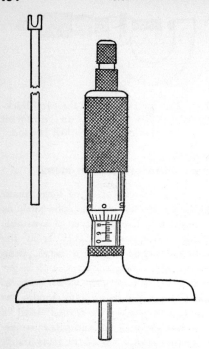

Fig. 20. A depth-gage (see Fig. 12) may be provided with a micrometer head for accurate measurement.

there while the spindle is screwed down until it just contacts the work. It is here that care is necessary, as it is possible to lift the head off the work slightly by screwing the spindle too far. A depth-gage can be used only in places where there is a satisfactory seating for the instrument head, and the bottom of the hole, slot, or shoulder being measured is parallel with the spindle. The cutter rests on this while it is being adjusted, and a true reading is insured.

For Measuring Screw-Threads

The screw-thread micrometer, of which an illustration is shown in Fig. 21, has been developed especially for measuring the pitch diameter or effective diameter of V-type screw-threads. The spindle has a conical end with a rounded point to clear the thread root, while the anvil has two V-points to suit the thread being measured. A particular anvil is applicable only to a limited number of threads, and a range of micrometers is therefore necessary to meet all requirements. When using this micrometer it is necessary to subtract the theoretical depth of the thread

direction to those on a standard instrument, and if not used frequently confusion may arise from this. Attention should therefore be paid to this point when using the appliance.

The Micrometer Depth-Gage

The ordinary depth-gage described in a previous section and illustrated in Fig. 20, has been elaborated by the addition of a micrometer head. This must be used with care, as it is an easy matter to obtain an incorrect reading if the spindle is adjusted carelessly. In use, the spindle is screwed back to a point where it will clear the bottom of the hole or shoulder being gaged. The instrument head is then placed across the top of the hole and held

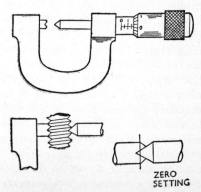

Fig. 21. Screw-thread micrometers, for measuring pitch diameter of V screw-threads, have conical-ended spindles.

being measured from the outside diameter of the screw. The result is the reading for the micrometer. Accurate thread-cutting in the lathe is facilitated by this instrument, as the possibility of cutting too deep is greatly reduced.

Measuring Tubes

The wall-thickness of tubing has frequently to be determined exactly, and obviously an ordinary micrometer will not serve for the purpose. An instrument having a spherical radius on the anvil as shown in Fig. 22 is available for work of this description, and it is generally known as the ball micrometer. In use, the anvil is inserted inside the tube, and the end of the spindle then contacts the outside, the end of the spindle being flat as in the normal pattern. Some makers supply a special adaptor which can be fitted to an ordinary micrometer anvil to convert it into a ball-type instrument.

For Surface Work

Surface grinding is facilitated by means of a special micrometer designed to eliminate the necessity for removing the work from the machine. The heavy base carries a micrometer head arranged in a vertical position so that the spindle may be screwed down on to the work-face. The base of the instrument rests on the chuck or table of the machine, and care must be exercised to maintain a clean contact, or errors will result. Magnetic chucks must be switched off before the micrometer is used on them or it will be damaged. By taking a reading before commencing operations and then checking at intervals, the amount of metal being removed can be easily measured.

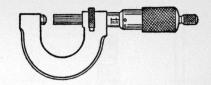

Fig. 22. For measuring the wall-thickness of tubes or pipes, an instrument with a spherical-ended anvil is used.

Measuring Sheet-Metal

For rapid measuring of large quantities of relatively thin jobs such as sheet-metal, a micrometer is available which varies considerably from the usual pattern. It has a large, deep frame with a ring for the fourth finger and a protruding grip which rests in the palm of the hand. The spindle has an eight-start screw-thread with a travel of only $\frac{1}{4}$ in., and this is consequently the capacity of the instrument. The outer end of the spindle carries a pointer which travels over a dial as the spindle rotates. The dial is of a large diameter so that the graduations of .001 in. are easily read. As only one turn is required for $\frac{1}{4}$-in. travel of the spindle, the capacity of the tool can be read directly from the dial. The rapidity with which the spindle can be adjusted is a great advantage when making repetitive measurements, as is also the fact that only one hand is required to operate the instrument.

Another micrometer of special design is intended for fine bench work. The frame is suitable for attaching to a baseboard, and it carries the spindle in a horizontal position. Readings in ten-thousandths are easily taken off a thimble of unusually large diameter ($1\frac{1}{2}$ in.), this being necessary to accommodate the graduations.

Although they are not very common, there are on the market micrometers

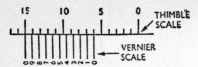

Fig. 23. The application of a vernier scale to a micrometer makes it possible to measure accurately tenths of the thimble divisions, that is, ten-thousandths of an inch. Each vernier division is equivalent to nine-tenths of a thimble division.

which have numbered dials similar to those on a cyclometer. The dials present different numbers as the micrometer setting is altered, and thus the reading is given directly to three decimal places without any mental calculation being necessary. This type is very convenient to read, but as it is also expensive, it is not often used.

The Vernier

Although the term vernier is loosely applied to mean almost any vernier

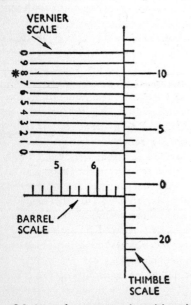

Fig. 24. Use of a vernier placed beside a main scale to measure tenths of the main scale divisions. See text.

caliper or protractor, it is actually the name of a special auxiliary scale used for measuring fractions of small divisions on standard instrument scales. It is evident that if, on an ordinary micrometer, a device is provided for accurately measuring tenths of the thimble divisions, the vernier can be used for measuring in ten-thousandths of an inch.

The vernier scale consists of a number of divisions corresponding to the

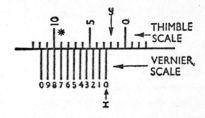

Fig. 25. The vernier micrometer reading here given is .650 + .023 + .0008 = .6738.

fraction of the main division required. Thus, if the main divisions are to be subdivided into ten parts there will be ten divisions in the vernier. The full length of the vernier is made equal to one less than a similar number of divisions of the main scale. Hence on a micrometer the vernier scale of ten divisions is nine thimble divisions in length, as is shown in Fig. 23. Each vernier division is, therefore, equivalent to nine-tenths of a thimble division, or, expressed differently, each vernier division is one-tenth short of a thimble division, two vernier divisions are two-tenths short of two thimble divisions, and so on.

If the vernier is placed alongside the main scale (Fig. 24) to that the seventh graduation of the vernier coincides with a main scale graduation, then seven divisions on the vernier will be shorter than seven divisions of the thimble by seven-tenths of one of the latter divisions. In other words, the distance between the zero line on the vernier (marked x) and the previous graduation on the thimble (marked y) is seven-tenths of a thimble division. If the micrometer measures in inches, this distance will represent a movement of the spindle equal to .0007 in.

Reading the Micrometer Vernier

It is not necessary to bear all this in mind when using the vernier. Sim-

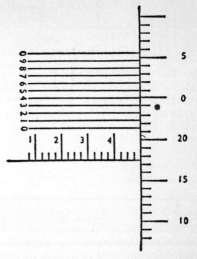

Fig. 27. This vernier micrometer reading is .4750 + .0170 + .0003, or .4923.

Fig. 26 gives a further example of a vernier micrometer reading. In this case the reading is .825 + .012 + .0004, or .8374 in. In Fig. 27 the reading shown is .4750 + .0170 + .0003,

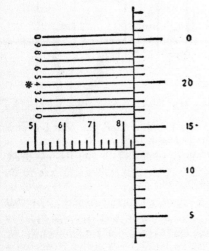

Fig. 26. In this example the vernier micrometer reading is .825 + .012 + .0004, totaling .8374 in.

ply observe the number of the vernier graduation which coincides with the main-scale graduation, and (in the case of the micrometer) this represents the fourth figure of the decimal reading. Thus in Fig. 25 the reading is .650 + .023 + .0008, or .6738. Note that the disposition of the vernier scale at a distance from the datum line has no bearing on the results, providing that it registers zero when the datum line coincides with a thimble graduation.

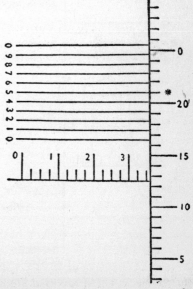

Fig. 28. The vernier micrometer reading here is .3500 + .0120 + .0005 = .3625.

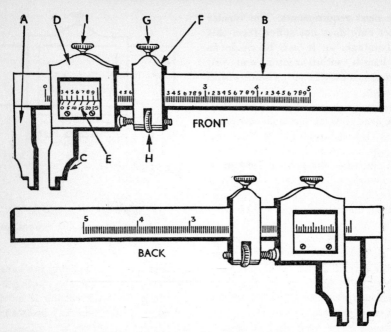

Fig. 29. The vernier caliper rule consists of a rule B with a fixed jaw A at one end and a sliding head, with a second jaw C integral with its frame D. Adjustment is effected by moving the vernier scale E endwise. F, clamp which can be locked to the rule by the knurled screw G. H, knurled nut which moves sliding head. I, screw which locks head to rule.

or .4923 in., and in Fig. 28 it is .3625.

One disadvantage of the micrometer is that the range of each instrument is, for practical reason, limited to 1 in. in most cases, and it is therefore necessary to have several instruments to

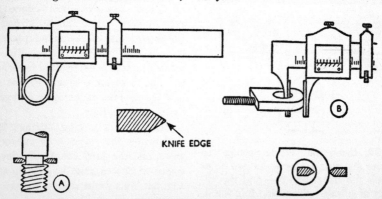

Fig. 30. The knife-edge vernier has jaws which are reduced to a very narrow edge, useful for measuring in restricted places or on a curved surface. Here it is shown at A measuring the undercut of a screw, and at B the amount of metal on an eye-bolt radius.

cover most requirements. The vernier caliper rule does not suffer from this disadvantage, as it can be made to any length within reason and will measure accurately anywhere within its range.

It consists essentially of a rule having a fixed jaw at one end and fitted with a sliding head (Fig. 29). A second jaw is integral with the sliding head, and when the jaws are closed on to the work, a datum line and vernier on the head indicates the dimension required on the rule-scale. Referring to Fig. 29, the fixed jaw, A, will be seen to be made in one piece with the rule, B. The sliding head actually consists of several parts. The jaw, C, is integral with the frame of the head, D, and adjustment of the instrument for wear is effected by moving the vernier scale, E, endwise after slackening the attachment screws.

It is not possible to set the tool accurately by sliding the head along with the fingers, and so a fine adjustment is provided. After setting the head approximately, a clamp, F, can be locked to the rule by means of the

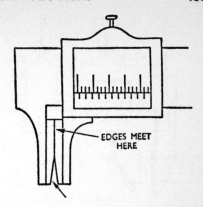

Fig. 31. The knife-edge vernier is liable to develop a gap at the extremities of the jaws, as here.

knurled screw, G. Turning the knurled nut, H, then moves the sliding head gradually until the setting is correct. If required, the head may be locked to the rule by the screw, I.

Types of Vernier Caliper

Two types of jaw are in common use, and the type is indicated by the name given to the instrument. Thus a *knife-edge* vernier caliper rule (generally termed just a knife-edge vernier) has jaws which are reduced to a very narrow edge. These are useful for measuring in restricted places or on curved surfaces, as in Fig. 30, where the tool is being used to measure the undercut on a screw in one case and the amount of metal on an eyebolt radius in the other.

Because the gaging surface is so narrow on this type it is subject to wear, and the jaws eventually develop a gap at the extremities, as shown in Fig. 31. This point should be watched, as errors can easily result from this defect.

The other type of jaw gives rise to the name *inside vernier,* as it is in-

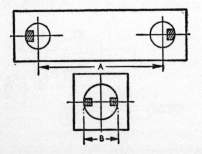

Fig. 32. Using the "inside vernier" to measure the distance between two holes —given the dimension A—and the diameter of a hole—dimension B in the illustration. The outside faces of the jaws are curved to make the radius of the smallest hole into which they can be inserted.

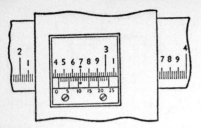

Fig. 33. The reading shown here is 2 in. (major scale) + .4 in. + .025 in. + .011 in. (vernier): total 2.436 in.

tended mainly for checking internal dimensions, such as the diameter of bores and so on. Usually the jaws have two gaging faces, and can be applied also to external measuring. Fig. 32 shows the application of this type of jaw to measuring a bore diameter. It will be seen that each jaw has a radius to accommodate the curvature of the work. This radius is equal to that of the smallest hole the jaws will enter. The method of checking hole-centers is also indicated. The dimension shown as A in Fig. 32 relates to the hole spacing, and dimension, B, to the diameter of a hole.

Some inside verniers have only one rule-scale, and this reads zero when the jaws are in contact. At this point it is evident that the outsides of the jaws are not at zero, and so the dimension indicated on the scale is not correct for inside measurements. The jaws are usually each about ⅛ in. thick, and the exact dimensions for the two must be ascertained with a micrometer and added to the rule reading when using the outside gaging faces. There are, however, a number of instruments with a scale on each side of the rule, the one on the obverse side being for external measurements, and that on the reverse side for internal measurements. It is thus possible to take *direct* readings of internal

measurements without having to make any allowance for the thickness of the jaws.

The range of the caliper rule for measuring diameters is limited by the length of the jaws unless the measurement is made across the end of the work-piece. The range of applications is very wide, however, and includes measuring hole-centers, long work-pieces, the distance between shoulders on shafts, and so on.

Reading the Vernier Caliper

The inch divisions on the rule-scale are divided into tenths of an inch, and these are further divided into four parts, which will be each equal to .025 in. Thus, there are graduations for direct reading of inches, tenths of inches and units of 25-thousandths. Vernier caliper rules are also supplied with metric (cm.) calibration, but they are precisely the same in principle as the generally-used pattern for measuring in inches. The vernier is applied in the same manner as in the case of the micrometer, to indicate the number of thousandths to be added to complete the reading, the only difference being that on the vernier rule 25 vernier divisions are equal to 24 scale divisions.

To obtain the reading add the inches, tenths of inches, and 25-thousandths together, and then add the number of thousandths indicated by the scale graduation which coincides with a vernier graduation. In Fig. 33 the reading is made up of 2 in. + .4 in. + .025 in. + .011 in., which makes the total of 2.436 in. Similarly, Fig. 34 shows an instrument set at 1.395. The first part of the reading in this case is shown by the zero mark on the vernier to be 1 in. + .3 in. + (.025 × 3) in., while the vernier gives the off thousandths as .020, making a total of 1.395. Counting up in the same way, Fig. 35 shows a setting of 4.732.

Adjusting a Vernier Rule

Although it does not happen very often, it is sometimes necessary to adjust a vernier. This is effected by releasing the two small attachment

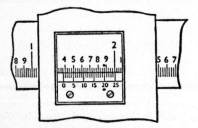

Fig. 34. This vernier reading is 1 in. + .3 in. + (.025 × 3 in.) + .020, a total of 1.395 in.

screws which hold the vernier scale to the sliding head and then setting the jaws together. This done, the vernier zero graduation may be set opposite the scale zero mark and the screws tightened up.

It is advisable to check all precision instruments of this type at intervals by setting them to zero and observing the reading. In this way the chances of wear on the jaws causing trouble are minimized.

Purchasing a Vernier

For the tool-kit, an instrument with a scale about 4 in. long is a convenient size. The type must necessarily depend on the work for which the tool is required, but a knife-edge vernier will generally be found to be the most useful. There are on the market some cheap verniers which measure in $\frac{1}{128}$ in. These are useful for approximate

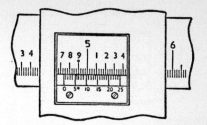

Fig. 35. In this example the reading is 4 in. + .7 in. + (.025 × 1) in. + .007, or 4.732 in.

work, but do not give satisfactory results on accurate work. In any case it is better to have measurements in decimals rather than in fractions.

The Vernier Protractor

The problem of measuring angles accurately has always been an acute one, since the instruments used must be kept to reasonable dimensions for convenience in handling, so the graduated scale cannot be very large. This means that very accurate setting is required, as the greater the length over which the angle is extended, the greater the linear error for a given angular error.

One way of reducing the possible error is to make easy the accurate reading of the instrument setting, and this is done in some cases by fitting a vernier scale to the protractor. It is proposed to deal here with the appli-

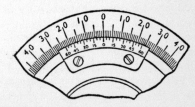

Fig. 36. On the vernier protractor, as shown here, one vernier division is 1½ deg. (5 min.) shorter than two main scale divisions.

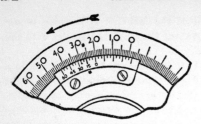

Fig. 37. Vernier protractor reading 20 deg. 15 min.

cation of the vernier scale only. Further details of the protractor will be found in a later section.

The majority of protractors are graduated from 0 to 90 deg. reading in two directions, and it is therefore necessary to have a vernier scale which will also read in both directions. Actually the usual vernier attachment has two distinct scales with a common zero, and care must be taken to read the vernier in the same direction as the main scale.

On a protractor it is a common practice to make 12 divisions of the vernier equal to 23 divisions of the major scale, instead of 11 divisions, as might be expected. This is because the close proximity of the degree graduations to one another would make the shorter scale difficult to read. The basic principle remains exactly the same, however, as in practice one vernier division is $\frac{1}{12}$ of one degree (five minutes) shorter than two scale divisions, as can be seen in Fig. 36.

If the application of the vernier to the protractor is considered in exactly the same way as the application of the vernier to the caliper rule, it will be readily understood. Similarly, in reading the protractor it is not necessary to memorize the fundamental principle. Simply note the number of degrees on the major scale, and then, reading in the same direction and starting at 0 on the vernier scale,

count the number of spaces to a line on the vernier which coincides with a line on the major scale. For each of these spaces five minutes must be added to the number of degrees read off the major scale in order to obtain the full reading.

Reading a Vernier Protractor

Referring to Fig. 37, the number of whole degrees between zero on the major scale and zero on the vernier will be seen to be 20. Also between zero on the vernier and a line on the vernier which coincides with a line on the major scale there are three spaces. As each of these represent five minutes, the full reading is 20 deg. + $(3 \times 5 \text{ min.}) = 20$ deg. 15 min.

Fig. 38 shows another example of reading a vernier protractor. In this case the reading is taken in the opposite direction to the one given previously. The number of whole degrees between the two zero marks is 37, and the number of spaces on the vernier is 10. Hence the reading is 37 deg. + $(10 \times 5) = 37$ deg. 50 min.

Dial Gages

There are many types of instruments fitted with dials for gaging in thousandths or ten-thousandths of an inch. Almost all of these are used in a

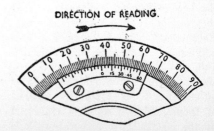

Fig. 38. This vernier protractor reads 37 deg. + $(10 \times 5) = 37$ deg. 50 min.

comparative sense only; that is, they measure variations between different articles or parts of articles, but do not actually measure principal dimensions.

The commonest of these instruments is usually known as a *clock gage* or test indicator, and it is applicable to a very large number of jobs. The needle of the indicator is moved by a small lever or contact point which acts

bed of the lathe, it is possible to ascertain if the work is parallel with the bed.

If it is necessary to set up work in a milling machine so that it is at right angles to the machine arbor or spindle, the gage may be attached to some convenient point so that the work slides under the contact point when the machine-slide is traversed. Any lack of

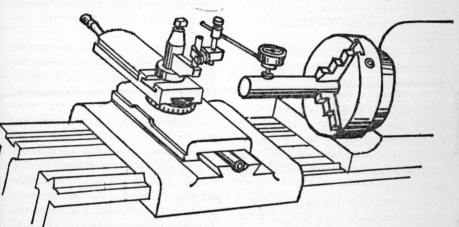

Fig. 39. The clock-gage or test indicator is often used for truing up work in the lathe. The indicator is attached to the lathe saddle or tool-post, the contact point resting on the work.

through a train of gears in order to magnify the motion imparted to it by variations in the work. One job for which the instrument is used very often is truing-up work in the lathe or similar machines. As will be seen from Fig. 39, the indicator is attached to the lathe saddle or tool-post, so that the contact point rests on the work. Eccentricity of the latter as it rotates will cause a movement of the needle, and, as a little thought will show, the actual amount by which the work is off-center will be half of the number of thousandths of an inch traversed by the needle. If cylindrical work is held stationary in the chuck and the saddle is traversed up and down the

parallelism between the work and the slide will be indicated on the dial.

The Zero Setting

The majority of these gages are so arranged that the calibrated dial may be turned into any position required to make the needle register zero. This is an advantage, as the zero reading may be set to coincide with the correct dimension, and plus or minus discrepancies are then shown directly by the needle.

As an example of this, it is often required to set a work-piece face parallel with the marking-off table. After setting it approximately, the clock gage, mounted on a suitable support, is set to read zero when the contact point is touching one extremity of the work-face. The gage is then moved to other parts of the work-face and corrections are made for the variations as shown by the needle. Thus, if the needle indicates on the plus side of zero, the work is too high in the new position, and *vice versa*.

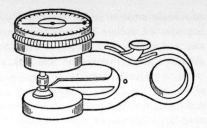

Fig. 41. Dial-sheet gage, used for checking thickness of sheet-metal. The first finger is placed in the ring, and the lever depressed by the thumb.

The Bench Dial-Gage

For repetitive work a dial-gage is available which can be set up on the bench. This is shown in Fig. 40, and it consists of a heavy base carrying a surface plate or platen, A, and also a machined pillar, B, on which the gaging-head slides. The vertical travel of the contact point is small, but by adjusting the position of the head on the pillar the capacity of the instrument

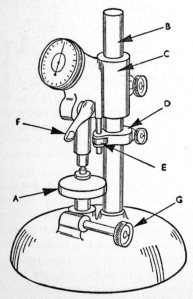

Fig. 40. Bench dial-gage. A, platen; B, pillar on which gaging head slides; C, D, clamps; E, nut; F, lever; G, screw governing platen height.

is varied at will. The head comprises a large clamp, C, which carries the dial, and a smaller clamp, D. When setting the instrument, a standard gage or pattern is placed on the platen, the contact point brought up to it and the small clamp is tightened on the pillar. The position of the large clamp is then adjusted by turning the milled nut, E, until the contact point is about midway in its travel, and the large clamp is then locked. If required, the height of the platen may be varied by loosening the screw, G.

The lever, F, may then be depressed in order to lift the contact while the standard gage is removed and a work-piece inserted. This lever does not affect the reading in any way, and should always be used when inserting or removing a test-piece. On some makes it is possible to turn the calibrated dial to read zero, and this should be done when the standard gage is in position.

Very accurate instruments of this type with a somewhat different indicating arrangement have been developed, and are frequently known as comparators. Some of these measure in ten-thousandths of an inch, and it is possible to estimate to hundredths of thousandths because of the large graduations. One form of indicator consists of a scale on to which a circle of light is projected. A hair-line appears across the center of this circle. With the standard gage in position the instrument is adjusted until this line coincides with the zero graduation. Two small pointers can then be set to indicate the highest and lowest limits of accuracy on the scale, and any workpiece which causes the hair-line to fall in between these two pointers is acceptable for size.

Dial-Sheet Gage

When large batches of sheet-metal have to be checked for thickness, a useful tool is the dial-sheet gage. This is shown in Fig. 41, and to use it the first finger is placed in the ring while the work is inserted, when the lever may be released. Care must be taken when using this tool not to tilt it while measuring. The back-plate should rest quite flat on the work, or errors will result. If the dial is set to zero when there is nothing in the gage, direct measurements in thousandths may be taken. It may be noted that on almost all dial-gages, when the needle makes more than one revolution, the reading will still be correct if the number of whole revolutions is multiplied by the dial range and the answer added to the reading indicated by the needle.

Cylinder Gage

The cylinder gage was devised primarily for ascertaining variations in the bores of internal-combustion-engine cylinders, but it can be applied to any similar work. A high degree of accuracy is called for in cylinders of this type with respect to diameter and parallelism of the bores. Hence great care is necessary in taking measurements. As can be seen from Fig. 42, the

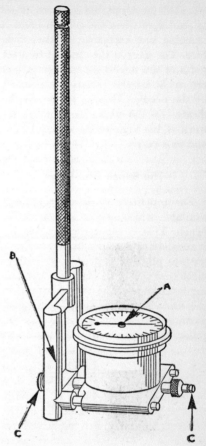

Fig. 42. The cylinder gage has a dial indicator A mounted on a sledge B. One of the two contact points C is situated between the runners of the sledge.

gage has a dial indicator, A, mounted on a *sledge*, B, which acts as a guide when the instrument is in use. There are two contact points, C, one of which is situated between the runners of the sledge. Interchangeable extension rods of varying length may be attached to the other contact in order to vary the range of the tool. To apply the gage a suitable length rod is fitted, and the gage is inserted in the cylinder, where it is carefully traversed up and down in several positions while the action of the needle is observed. If the actual diameter of the bore is required, it is necessary to remove the instrument and measure across the contact points with a micrometer. On an instrument provided with a locking device for the needle this should be used before removal, when the dimension may be obtained straight away. If no such device is provided, the gage must be removed carefully and the number of revolutions of the needle counted. When using the micrometer the needle is made to travel through the same number of turns until it gives the same reading as in the cylinder.

Care is necessary in the use of these gages, as they must be applied only on the diameter of the cylinder bore, and, in addition, the sledge must be kept parallel with the bore axis.

When used for checking purposes the dial may be turned so that it registers zero when the gage is set to a micrometer. If the instrument is then placed in the bore and readings taken in various positions, the error will be shown as plus or minus, according to which side of the zero mark the needle indicates. To avoid any chance of error in this direction it is a common practice to mark + and − signs on the dial.

THICKNESS GAGES

IT OFTEN happens in machine shop practice that a very small gap between two parts has to be measured accurately. The easiest way of doing this is by inserting a slip of metal which is just the right size and then ascertaining the thickness of the slip. In practice a number of blades of different thicknesses are assembled together in a convenient holder, as is shown in Fig. 43.

For work where a large number of parts have to be set to the same gap it is possible to obtain the feeler-gage stock in coils like steel ribbon. This may be used with a holder devised to grip the ribbon so that it may be fed out as required.

The thicknesses of blade in common use range from .0015 in. to .025 in., but it is not necessary to have a gage with every intermediate size for ordinary work. The usual pattern has a number of blades which can be arranged in combinations to give all the desired sizes. Thus .005 in. can be made up of .003 in. and .002 in., while

.007 in. can be made up of .004 in. and .003 in. It is always advisable to use a minimum number of blades in a combination to reduce the possibility of error due to imperfect contact between the blade-faces. For example, as .009 in. can be obtained by using .006-in. and .003-in. blades, it should not be made up of .002 in. + .003 in. + .004 in.

Applications of Feeler Gages

The applications of the feeler gages are very numerous, and new ones arise from time to time. A common application is gaging the clearance between an internal-combustion-engine piston and the cylinder wall. This clearance has to be maintained within very close limits as, if it is excessive, the efficiency of the engine will suffer, whereas insufficient clearance will result in seizure when the piston expands with heat. The clearance has to be correct over the whole length of the piston, and so very long feeler blades are required to measure it. For normal work very long blades are inconvenient and easily broken, hence fairly short blades are to be recommended.

Modern production methods involve the use of fixtures for supporting the work in many operations, such as milling. In order to make certain that the work-piece is to size after the operation is carried out, the fixture is provided with a setting-block. The machine-table is set so that when the block is directly beneath the milling-cutter a small gap (usually .010 in.) exists between them. The gap is checked for accuracy with a feeler

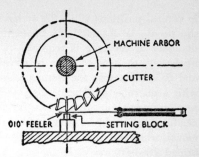

Fig. 44. Method of setting a milling cutter, using a feeler gage.

case a straight-edge is placed along the original surface and the feeler is then inserted between the straight-edge and the bottom of the groove.

Setting jobs up square is often facilitated if a set of feelers is used along

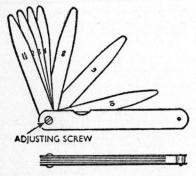

Fig. 43. A set of feeler gages.

gage, and, if incorrect, the height of the table is adjusted until a very slight drag is felt when the feeler is inserted. During this operation the milling-cutter is, of course, stationary, and care must be taken to have the cutting edge in such a position that it does not approach nearer to the setting-block when turned through a fraction of a revolution (see Fig. 44).

If the cutter were set directly to the block, the setting operation would be much more difficult, and most probably the cutter or block would be damaged.

Another operation in which feeler gages are useful is the machining of shallow grooves or recesses. In this

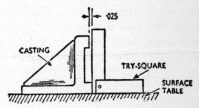

Fig. 45. How a casting may be set up squarely by using a set of feelers in conjunction with a try-square.

with the try-square. An example of this is the casting shown in Fig. 45. This has two steps, one of which is .025 in. below the level of the other, and to set it up a 25-thousandth feeler is used between the lowest step and the try-square blade.

For average work a set of feelers about 4 in. long and having approximately 10 leaves is very satisfactory. If the leaves are ½ in. wide and taper to ³⁄₁₆ in. or thereabouts at the extremity, they can be used in fairly restricted places. An adjusting screw is provided on the holder, and this should be set so that only light pressure is

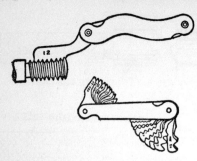

Fig. 46. Gages used for checking the pitch of screw-threads.

exerted on the blades. If the screw is kept too tight, the thinnest blades will be buckled when they are moved. A film of light machine oil should be kept on the blades to prevent rust.

Thread Gages

The screw pitch gage, Fig. 46, generally described loosely as a thread gage, has several leaves secured in a holder very similar to that on a set of feeler gages. Each leaf or blade possesses several teeth, which are accurately shaped to the profile of a standard thread form. A particular gage is applicable only to threads of the form for which it is designed—that is, American Standard, Whitworth, or some similar standard type. The leaves of the gage are made to suit the pitches of any screw thread of the correct form, and it should be noted that the diameter of the screw has no connection with the application of the gage.

Each blade is stamped with the number of threads per inch which it represents and also, in some makes, with the double depth of thread expressed in thousandths of an inch. This latter is useful if a tap drill size is required, and the tap can be measured on its outside diameter. By subtracting the double depth of thread from the tap

measurement the required drill size can be found.

To determine the pitch of a thread with the aid of this gage, the threads should be cleaned, and then the teeth of the gage should be tried against them until a blade is found which matches exactly. It is advisable to hold the screw up to a light so that very small gaps between the thread and the gage teeth can be seen. A mistake can be made if care is not taken in this, because, on fine threads particularly, a gage one size more or less than the screw-thread is only very slightly different. As the difference becomes more apparent over a long length it is also advisable to make use of the full length of each blade, if possible.

A distinct improvement on the original pattern is a gage which incorporates a positive stop for the blades. In the old type a selected blade has to be held with the fingers, as the holder does not control it at all. This is a nuisance when checking small nuts and so on, as the space for the fingers is very restricted. In the newer type a blade can only move until it is fully extended when it meets a stop, and in this position it can be manipulated by the holder (in a similar fashion to a pen-knife). This feature is well worth the extra price that is charged for it.

Thread Plug Gages

There are two types of thread plug gages. The commonest type (Fig. 47) is simply a length of screw very accurately ground to the correct size and fitted with a handle. In the small sizes the screw-thread and the handle are machined in one piece.

The end of the gage just described is the *Go* end. This means that if it will just screw smoothly into the work, then the latter is the correct size. The opposite end of the gage is usually *No Go,* and the application of this will be described later on in this chapter.

Operating Plug Gage

When using this type of gage in the shops the machining must be carried out until the gage will enter the work. If taps are being used for the threading operation this is not especially difficult, as it is only necessary to proceed cautiously with the third tap, and to try the gage in the work at frequent intervals. Plenty of the correct lubricant, where this is called for, greatly assists the production of good threads and helps clean the job so that the gage can be correctly applied. On stainless steel this last point cannot be over-stressed as it is a very easy matter to seize a plug gage in a workpiece if small chips are present from the thread-cutting operation.

If the thread is being cut with a thread-cutting tool in the lathe, how-

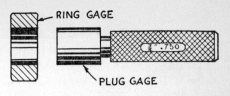

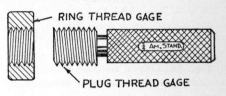

Fig. 47. Types of gages used for internal and external measurements.

ever, the plug gage is not applicable until the tops of the threads have been given the correct form, as the sharp V would contact only the bottom of the thread on the gage.

From the foregoing it will be apparent that while the plug gage tells us when the job is the correct size, it does not tell us how much metal to remove when it is below size. This leaves an element of chance in the machining operation, and a gage has been designed to overcome this.

Radius Gages

On many jobs, particularly in the aircraft industry, sharp corners on the work have to be eliminated and certain radii are called for. The only satisfactory way of checking the correctness of these is with the aid of a radius or fillet gage.

Gages of this type are shown in Fig. 48. Their application is also made clear. The majority of the gages are made with a convex and concave radius of the same size on one blade.

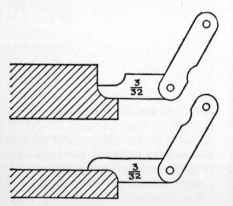

Fig. 48. Example of a radius gage.

PRINCIPLES OF TESTING

THE routine inspection and testing of parts which are produced in quantity is carried out, not so much to find out if they are right, as to determine by how much they are wrong. In commercial production it is not practicable to produce parts which are absolutely correct in every dimension. The difficulty is overcome by setting limits for the variations from standard, these limits depending on the class of work and the functions of the various parts. In cases where limits are not established, a certain amount of judgment must be exercised in deciding whether the job is acceptable or otherwise. The proposed use of a part generally dictates the permissible errors, and it is always a good plan, where doubt exists, to investigate the job from this standpoint, since an error which would inevitably scrap one part might be regarded as quite trivial in the case of a part serving a different purpose.

On machine-drawings, dimensions are invariably taken about center lines which act as planes of reference (a line may be regarded as the edge or section of a plane). On the job these lines are often in thin air or imaginary (as in Fig. 6), and it is not possible to measure the position of anything by using them as datum lines. In order to carry out any testing, therefore, new planes of reference must be established. The surface plate or marking-off table serves this purpose, as by simply turning the work through 90 deg. either the horizontal or vertical center lines can be set parallel with the surface plate.

The establishing of a datum plane or plane of reference is an essential feature of all marking-out and testing operations where linear dimensions are concerned. The principal reason for this is to be found in the fact that it is much easier to locate a point on the work by measuring its horizontal and vertical coordinates than by any other method. This is made clear in Fig. 50, where the two holes in the bracket are to be checked for position.

If the bracket is set on the surface table as shown in Fig. 49, and a bar is inserted in each hole, it is a simple matter to ascertain the height of the respective hole or, in other words, its vertical ordinate. This figure may then be checked against the drawing, which gives one dimension as 6 in. and the other as $6\frac{1}{2}$ in.

Vertical Ordinates

As far as possible all dimensions are taken in a vertical direction, as this is much more convenient than measuring at right angles to a vertical plane. In order to check in a vertical direction the dimensions shown on the drawing as horizontal ordinates, the work is turned through 90 deg. and clamped to an angle plate as shown in Fig. 50. In this case the height of the lower edge of the bracket is ascertained and subtracted from the height arrived at for the hole-centers. The ordinates for the hole-centers from the table in this case are 6 in. and 10 in. respectively. Whichever of the two positions the bracket is in, it is a simple matter to check the position of any point.

Checking Hole-Centers

The hole-center lines through the bracket must be parallel with the surface table if the check is to be accurate. The easiest way to verify this is to compare the heights above the table of the two extremities of each of the bars, which should protrude about 3 or 4 in. beyond the bracket at each side. If the bars are parallel with the table the heights of the respective ends will, of course, be identical. The method of checking to the top of a bar with a surface gage or scribing block is shown in Fig. 5.

We can now consider supporting the work. Many jobs are not provided with a convenient flat face such as that shown in Figs. 49 and 50, and various methods are adopted to set them up in the correct position. This, of course, must be done so that the theoretical center lines are as nearly parallel to the table surface as can be determined by measuring from suitable portions of the work. This *setting up,* as it is called, is often the most difficult part of testing. Various methods of support are adopted, and of these the V block is one of the most useful. Its application is made clear in Fig. 6, where it is supporting a cylindrical object. For accurate work V blocks are made in pairs, and on no account should odd ones be used, even though they appear to be similar. Slight variations between two V blocks used on

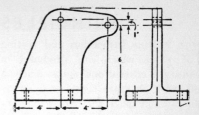

Fig. 49. The height of the holes in this bracket can be found by inserting a bar and using a scribing block or height gage as described in the text.

the same job will result in the work being out of parallel with the table.

Machine Parallels

For work which is not cylindrical, and which possesses suitable plane surfaces, machine parallels are frequently employed. These, too, are generally made in pairs and stamped with identification letters or numbers, to avoid confusion. Many of these parallels are hardened and ground very accurately, and they may be used as packing in cases where the work must be raised a definite amount.

Very often when the work is of an awkward shape it has to be bolted to some support before checking can be carried out. The angle plate is useful in these cases. It consists of a rigid L-shaped casting (Fig. 50), which is accurately machined to an angle of 90 deg. Each machined face has slots cut in it through which bolts may be passed for securing the work. Extra heavy work pieces demand that the angle-plate be clamped or bolted down to the surface table, but for small work the weight makes this unnecessary.

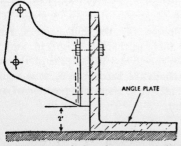

Fig. 50. To find the dimensions shown as horizontal in a vertical direction, an angle-plate is used, as here.

Angle-Plates

Some work has to be set at a particular angle to the surface table, and

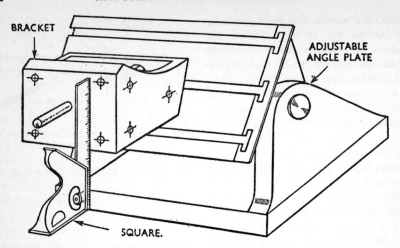

BRACKET

ADJUSTABLE
ANGLE PLATE

SQUARE.

Fig. 51. The adjustable angle-plate consists of a small plate arranged to pivot on a horizontal axis and supported by a base-plate.

this is often effected by bolting it to an adjustable angle-plate. As can be seen from Fig. 51, this consists of a small plate arranged to pivot on a horizontal axis and supported by a base-plate. Generally one of the trunnions on the base-plate is graduated in degrees so that the inclination of the top plate to the surface table may be measured. Accurate setting of this type of angle-plate can be achieved with the aid of a sine-bar, as will be explained in a later section.

Small screw-jacks are made specially for supporting awkward and heavy work. A big advantage in using these is that the height of the job can be adjusted at will by simply turning the screw of the jack. Adjustable parallels serve a somewhat similar purpose. They are made in two parts which fit together, the joint being at an angle to the parallel faces. By sliding one part on the other, the inclined joint causes a variation in the width of the parallel, and a set-screw secures the parts accurately in the required position.

The Combination Square

This is an extremely useful tool for many jobs. It incorporates all the essential features of the try-square, miter-square, protractor, and center-square. Fig. 52 illustrates all the parts which are required to fulfill these functions. To use the instrument as a try-square the blade, A, is inserted into the head, B, and clamped in position with the thumb-nut. The head can be set in any position along the length of the blade and, as the blade is graduated exactly the same as a rule, measurements from shoulders and the like can be taken with it in exactly the same manner as with a depth gage. Generally a small scriber, E, is concealed in the square head, and it can be removed for marking-off jobs and so on.

If the blade is fixed in the square head, the tool is very convenient for marking-off purposes, when a surface gage or scribing block is being used, as the blade may be held vertical by the head. A small clip is now available which fits across the head and, by resting on the table, supports the square, thus increasing the stability of the instrument when standing on the narrow edge of the head. Angles at 45 deg. are easily measured, as one edge of the square head is machined to this angle for the purpose.

The center square, C, is intended for marking the centers of round or square stock (Fig. 53). The head is arranged so that the blade bisects the angle between the machined faces; hence it is only necessary to mark lines in two places on the end of the work, and the intersection point is the center required. For accuracy the end of the bar should be trimmed of all burrs, and also the two marks should be approximately at right angles to one another.

For measuring angles the protractor head, D, is used, and the blade may be clamped in this in any desired position. The scale is divided up in one-degree graduations, but it is possible to estimate angles to half of one degree, and this is accurate enough for average work. Most protractor scales are divided into 180 deg. in both directions, and the tool may be set to any desired angle.

The Spirit-Level

It is possible to obtain the square and protractor heads with integral

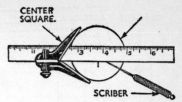

CENTER SQUARE.

SCRIBER →

Fig. 53. Center square, used for marking the centers of round or square stock. See figure 52.

spirit-levels, and for jobs where it is necessary to have one part of the work level or plumb, this is a very convenient feature. To set work plumb it is only necessary to lay the blade of the square on it, when the spirit-level should be horizontal in the square head.

There are many irregular jobs which have to be set up on the surface table so that some part is horizontal. It is not always possible to use height- or surface-gages for checking this, and very often an accurately made spirit-level is used for the purpose. Good-quality levels have glasses which carry graduations intended to give some indication of the variation of the work from the horizontal plane. These graduations are not usually calibrated, since the error is really an angle, and not a linear dimension. It is, however, often convenient to have some idea of the linear discrepancy which a graduation represents. The best way to obtain this is to place the instrument on a level surface-plate and insert feeler gages under one end until the required dimension is found.

This must, of course, be compared with the overall length of the instrument base when used as a basis for measurement. Thus, if the base is 10 in. long and a .001-in. feeler causes the bubble to move one graduation, on a work-piece 30 in. long a vertical discrepancy of .006 would be indicated

Fig. 52. Combination square. A, blade; B, square head; C, center square; D, protractor head; E, scriber.

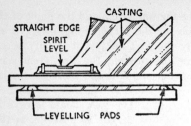

Fig. 54. Using level and straight-edge to test height of leveling pads.

when the bubble was two graduations off center. This method is frequently useful in measuring the effect of a variation from the horizontal.

The work to be set level may have only two small leveling pads (or machined faces) set at some distance apart, the space in between being irregular. In cases like this a straight-edge is placed on the two points and the level is used on the upper edge of it (Fig. 54). Obviously the two edges of the straight-edge must be parallel for accurate work, and must also be of a reasonable width. For average work planed mahogany straight-edges are suitable, but accurate jobs call for something more reliable. Bright drawn

mild-steel bar, 1 to 3 in. wide (depending on the length), and not less than ¼ in. thick, is often useful, but it should not be machined unless this is essential, as warping occurs from relieving the skin stresses. Precision work is executed with the aid of hardened and precision-ground straight-edges. It is usual to mark points on these where supports should be used if the weight of the straight-edge is likely to cause distortion when supported elsewhere.

It is possible to have a job horizontal in one direction but tilted when viewed from another point. Thus, if a rectangular piece of plate be laid on a surface table it will be horizontal, but if two equal-thickness packing-pieces are inserted under adjacent corners, then the plate will be tilted. Since the packing-pieces are equal in thickness, however, the edge of the plate which has been raised will still be horizontal, providing, of course, that the pieces are the same distance from the edge. It often occurs that the work is tilted in this manner, and when this happens care is necessary to avoid errors in

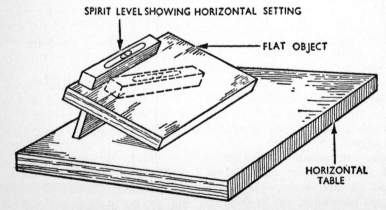

Fig. 55. To test accurately the level of a piece of work which appears horizontal in one direction and tilted from another viewpoint, it is essential that the spirit-level be kept parallel. For explanation of diagram see the text.

leveling, as the spirit-level must be kept parallel to the vertical plane in which the work appears horizontal. Usually some rib stiffener or similar protrusion can be found to act as a guide for the instrument. The reader will appreciate the point better if he experiments with a flat object. Raise one edge of the object slightly and place a level (a cheap one will do) as shown in Fig. 55. Arrange the object until the level shows a horizontal setting. Now move the level into the position shown by the dotted lines, and it will be seen that it no longer shows a level setting. In the figure the point is exaggerated for clarity, but it will be obvious that the result depends on the position in which the instrument is placed.

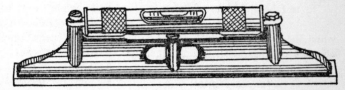

Many good quality instruments are fitted with small cross-levels for setting in both directions. If protection covers are supplied, they should always be placed over the glasses when not in use.

The Plumb-Bob

Despite its simplicity, the plumb-bob is a very useful device and in careful hands can give excellent results when a job has to be set vertical or when points one above the other have to be aligned.

There are actually two ways in which the bob can be used. By one method all measurements are taken from the plumb-line, and in this case the bob may be any convenient mass, such as a large nut or similar object. By the second method the line is used

for the top datum and the point of the bob for the bottom (Fig. 58). To apply the first method it is only necessary to suspend the line from some convenient point and measure from it to the points which must be vertical (Fig. 57). The line should always be as fine and smooth as possible, as this

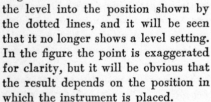

Fig. 56. Adjustable bench levels. Levels such as these are accurate and very sensitive.

makes for ease in measuring (linen thread is excellent for the purpose). If the line touches both points it is possible to deflect it and obtain incorrect results.

Trouble is generally experienced with a long line, owing to swinging of the bob. This is easily remedied by allowing the end of the bob to dip into a small can of machine oil, which will damp the oscillations.

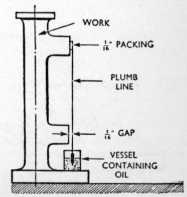

Fig. 57. The plumb-bob is used by setting the line from some convenient point and measuring from it to the points required to be vertical.

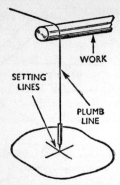

Fig. 58. The plumb-line may be used for the top datum and the bob-point for the bottom.

It may not be evident at first sight, but when measurements are to be taken from the point of a bob, it must be accurately made, particularly if the measurements are to be exact. This is because the center of gravity of the bob always hangs in line with the string and the spot where the string is attached to the bob. If the point of the bob does not also lie in this line it will not indicate the correct position. This is made clear in Fig. 59. It is also desirable that the center of gravity of the bob should be as low as possible, and this is achieved in the high-quality types by making them hollow and partially filling them with mercury.

Testing with the Surface Gage

The checking of work with a scribing block or surface gage is only a variation of marking off, and reference to the section which deals with this will make the matter clear. Instead of marking the centers of holes, however, the usual plan is to mark the edges as shown in Fig. 60. This is also a convenient guide when marking out the positions of holes which are to be

drilled. In this case four marks are put in, making a square with the hole in the exact center.

Even the best scribing blocks have a number of shortcomings, and when really accurate work is required some other instrument is needed for measuring vertical dimensions from the surface plate or table. This instrument is known as the vernier height gage, and is shown in Fig. 61. A fairly heavy base, A, supports a beam, B, which is graduated in exactly the same manner as a vernier caliper rule (see earlier section for method of reading). The sliding head, C, also resembles the sliding head on the caliper rule, the main difference being that provision is made for clamping a scriber, D, on to the moving jaw. The height gage can actually be used as a caliper rule if the work is measured between the faces, E and F.

The scriber can be clamped as shown for checking to the top surface of a bar or similar object, or it can be

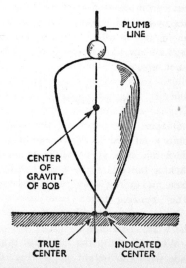

Fig. 59. Unless the point of the plumb-bob is in line with its center of gravity it will not center accurately.

clamped in the inverted position for checking to the under side. It is actually possible to set the scriber in several positions, and as the manner of graduating the rule in relation to it is not identical with all instruments, the one being used should be studied to determine if any alteration from the scale-reading is necessary.

Position of Scriber

It is usual to make height gages so that when the sliding head is set at zero the scriber is exactly 1 in. above the surface plate on which the instrument is standing. Some makes go further than this, and the beam carries two scales, one reading zero when the faces, E and F, are in contact, and the other starting at the minimum gap between the scriber and the table. The gage is made so that the height of the scriber above the table is an exact figure. Do not rely on this with anything but a new instrument. The reason is that continual sliding of the gage on the surface table wears the base until the figure is no longer exact, and checks show that an error of .010 in. is not beyond the bounds of possibility. There are two ways of overcoming this difficulty. One is to measure the actual distance with slip-gages and allow for the error. The other and more satisfactory method is, when possible, to place the work on parallels or similar packing-pieces, measure the height of these and subtract the result from any other reading taken from the scale whenever a height above the base of the work is required.

When checking the height of a surface with the height gage (Fig. 62) the result depends to some extent on the feel of the operator. By fitting a small indicator dial gage (specially

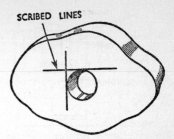

Fig. 60. When using a scriber for hole-marking it is usual to mark the edges, not the center.

made for the purpose) this feel is eliminated. The method of finding the vertical distance between two holes is as follows. After inserting close-fitting bars into the holes, the instrument is set so that when the contact point of the indicator is moved over the upper

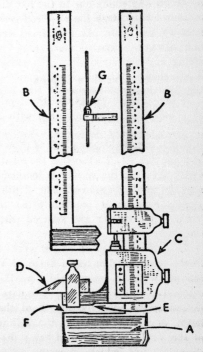

Fig. 61. Vernier height gage. A, base; B, beam; C, sliding head; D, scriber; E, F, faces; G, attachment for measuring hole depths.

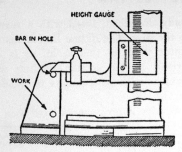

Fig. 62. Using the vernier height gage to check a surface height.

surface of the top bar the indicator dial reads zero at the highest point. At this setting the scale-reading is noted. The process is repeated for the lower bar, and the scale-reading for this is then subtracted from the one previously noted, allowance being made for any difference in the bar diameters. This gives the required centers. Checks from plane surfaces are carried out in a similar manner.

Measuring Hole Depths

It sometimes happens that the depth of a hole has to be measured with a height gage. For this job a special fitting is obtainable, and this is shown at G in Fig. 61. To use this the small clamp securing the scriber is loosened and the scriber removed. The depth-gaging attachment is then fitted in place of the scriber and secured with the clamp.

An improved type of height gage of fairly recent design has a beam of V section, which is more rigid than the original rectangular form. A square-thread screw runs the length of the beam, and is concealed in the hollow of the V. The sliding head has a disengaging nut which operates when two release levers are depressed between thumb and first finger. This permits the head to slide freely to obtain

an approximate setting, after which the nut is allowed to re-engage the central screw. Rotating a small knurled nut which protrudes from the base causes the screw to turn and provides a means for obtaining a fine adjustment in a very convenient manner. It is advisable with any height gage to clamp the sliding head in position on the beam with the screws provided, once the required setting is obtained. A further precaution is to check the setting after tightening the clamping screws, as sometimes the action of tightening causes the sliding head to move slightly.

Testing Angles

The most-used tool for testing angles is the ordinary protractor. Everyone is familiar with its simplest form, in which it appears as a semi-circle (or full circle) of metal or celluloid on which lines are engraved to indicate degrees. While this type finds application in the drafting room, where it can be laid on the paper, it is of little use in the shops. The type of protractor which the shops usually employ is actually based on the ordinary try-square. This latter is really an instrument for measuring one angle only—that is, 90 deg.—while the protractor is an instrument for measuring any angle (including 90 deg.). If this fact is borne in mind the method of application of the protractor will present no difficulty.

The Protractor

Fig. 63 shows the construction of an ordinary instrument. The base or stock, A, is integral with a disc, B, which is fitted with a pivot at the center and carries a datum line, D. On this pivot the dial, C, is allowed to rotate when the clamping nut, E, is released. A second nut, F, clamps the blade, G, rigidly to the dial, C. The blade can be moved lengthwise or replaced by one of a different length when F is released. To set the protractor it is only necessary to release E, turn B until the line D is opposite the required angle, and then tighten E. Always check the tightness of the clamping-nuts before using the tool. As with the height gage and similar tools, it is advisable to check the readings when everything is tightened up. Sometimes it is necessary to subtract the angle given from 90 deg. or 180 deg. in order to obtain the correct setting for the protractor. The manner in which the scale is graduated determines when this is necessary.

Combination Protractor

The protractor which forms a unit of the combination square is essentially the same as the instrument just described. The outstanding difference lies in the length of the bases, as will be seen from Figs. 52 and 63. Both types have their uses, but for general work the combination pattern has fewer applications, because it is often necessary to "get right into the corner," which the long base will not allow.

Vernier Protractor

For precision work neither of the instruments just described is satisfactory, as they cannot be set to a degree of accuracy much finer than 30 minutes. As the principal difficulty is due to the limitations of the human eye, an improved type of scale-reading is provided by the vernier protractor. This is simply a protractor of the type already described, fitted with a vernier on the disc. The datum line forms the center zero on this scale, as is described in the section dealing with verniers with instructions on reading the device.

Sundry improvements have been incorporated in the vernier protractor from time to time, and one of the best-known makes now has a fine adjustment which is operated by depressing and turning the center one of three knurled nuts protruding from the center of the tool. The lower nut locks the dial at the required setting, and the upper nut clamps the blade in its slot. In this instrument the blade is fitted into a slot in the side of the dial and the latter is graduated through 360 deg.

Optical Types

Another type of precision protractor has no visible scale, and the necessary accuracy in the reading is obtained by optical means. When the tool is held up to the light and the eye applied to a small eye-piece, a section of the dial, highly magnified, can be seen behind the hair-line which constitutes the datum. As with the vernier protractor, one division on this instrument usually represents 5 minutes.

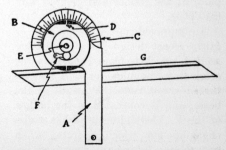

Fig. 63. Universal bevel protractor: A, base; B, disc; C, dial; D, datum line; E, F, clamping nuts; G, blade.

Unless the protractor is vertical to the plane from which the angle is being measured, the results will be inaccurate. This usually means that the base must be kept flat on the surface of the work or table.

The Sine Bar

The sine bar is a very simple device, which utilizes trigonometrical ratios in conjunction with a height gage to determine the value of an angle to a very close degree of accuracy. In Fig. 64 the height P divided by the length H is equal to the sine of the angle θ.

Obviously if we know H and can measure P, we can calculate the value of sin θ. The sine of any particular angle is a constant value, and tables of these values for all angles between 0 deg. and 90 deg. are in universal use. To obtain the angle, therefore, all that is required is a table of sines from which the angle may be read directly. In practice it is only necessary to move the decimal point in the value for P. Thus if P is found to be 3.764 in., then sin θ is .3764, and the tables give an angle of 22 deg. 7 min. as corresponding to this value. This method is more accurate than using a protractor which only measures in units of 5 min.

Fig. 65 shows a sine-bar in use. The distance, H (Fig. 64) is between the

centers of the cylinders, A, but, as these are of equal diameter, it also holds good between the points where the height gage contacts them. The latter are firmly attached to the bar, B, and the whole is made as accurately as possible. By placing one cylinder on the surface plate and placing gage-blocks under the other cylinder, the flat face of the bar may be set at any required angle to the surface plate. Some handbooks have tables of constants for 4- and 5-in. sine bars from which the angle can be obtained directly without dividing P by H.

Finding Angles by Tangent Tables

It sometimes happens that a drawing gives an angle between two hole-centers and some other part of the work. An example of this is shown in Fig. 66, where the distance between the perpendiculars is given as 7 in. and the angle as 24 deg. 21 min. It is always easier to check linear dimensions than to check angles and so, if possible, angles should always be measured in this way. In Fig. 66 the height P divided by the length B (in this instance 7 in.) gives the tangent of the angle, which in this case is 24 deg. 21 min., or $\frac{P}{B}$ = tan 24 deg. 21 min. or $\frac{P}{7}$ = tan 24 deg. 21 min.

Therefore,

P = 7 tan 24 deg. 21 min.

= 7 × .4525.

= 3.1675 in.

The tangent of an angle is obtained from tables in the same way as the sine. If suitable allowances are made for the hole sizes it becomes a simple matter to check the positions of the holes when bars are inserted. Should the angle be required and the dimen-

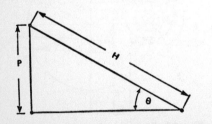

Fig. 64. The sine of the angle θ is found by dividing the height P by the length H.

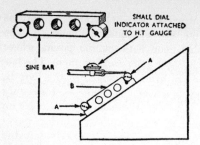

Fig. 65. How a sine-bar is used for angle-finding.

sions P and B are known, the process is simply reversed.

It may be noted that it is possible to lay off an angle accurately on a flat surface if the perpendicular distance P is obtained by the method outlined and measured with dividers. Further information on the use of trigonometrical ratios can be found in any book dealing with workshop calculations.

Limits and Clearances

In the earlier days when two parts had to fit together one was produced and the other was made to suit it. This procedure is very expensive when large quantities are being made, because a great deal of labor is involved in assembling the parts. In addition to this, interchangeability, which is essential when spare parts have to be supplied, is non-existent under this system.

The modern solution to the problem is the imposing of limits on the manufacturing errors. Thus, the designer may say, "I would like this shaft to be 3 in. in diameter, but if it happens to be .003 in. over-size or .004 in. under-size then we may use it, because it will still serve its purpose without causing trouble in assembly or in operating the machine." The dimensions of 3.003 in. would be termed the

high limit for the diameter, and similarly the dimension of 3 in. − .004 = 2.996 in. would be termed the low limit. The difference between the two (i.e., .007 in.) is termed the *tolerance,* and represents the range of error permissible in the work.

On machine drawings the limits may be expressed in two ways, thus:

$$\vert\!\leftarrow\ 3''\ ^{+\ .003''}_{-\ .004''}\ \rightarrow\!\vert \qquad \vert\!\leftarrow\ ^{3.003''}_{2.996''}\ \rightarrow\!\vert$$

the former being the most popular, as it indicates the desired figure (i.e., 3 in.), which the latter does not. In this connection it is advisable to work to standard size, since the limits given are concessions intended to lower production costs. If the limits are correctly selected, then they must be adhered to, and the work which falls outside of the limits must be rejected, or trouble will result.

Shafts and Holes

While limits are imposed on jobs of all shapes and sizes, they are more often met with on shafts and the holes into which the shafts must fit. (The term shafts in this case includes bolts, pins, and so on.) In this connection there are several different types of fits, each for a specific purpose. These are:

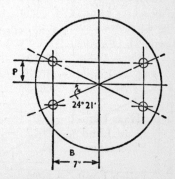

Fig. 66. Example of drawing giving angle measurement from which height can be found.

NEWALL LIMITS

	TOLERANCES IN STANDARD HOLES						
Class	Nominal Dia.	Up to ½ in.	9/16–1 in.	1 1/16–2 in.	2 1/16–3 in.	3 1/16–4 in.	4 1/16–5 in.
A	High Limit Low Limit Tolerance	+.0002 −.0002 .0004	+.0005 −.0002 .0007	+.0007 −.0002 .0009	+.0010 −.0005 .0015	+.0010 −.0005 .0015	+.0010 −.0005 .0015
B	High Limit Low Limit Tolerance	+.0005 −.0005 .0010	+.0007 −.0005 .0012	+.0010 −.0005 .0015	+.0012 −.0007 .0019	+.0015 −.0007 .0022	+.0017 −.0007 .0024
	ALLOWANCES FOR FORCED FITS						
F	High Limit Low Limit Tolerance	+.0010 +.0005 .0005	+.0020 +.0015 .0005	+.0040 +.0030 .0010	+.0060 +.0045 .0015	+.0080 +.0060 .0020	+.0100 +.0080 .0020
	ALLOWANCES FOR DRIVING FITS						
D	High Limit Low Limit Tolerance	+.0005 +.0002 .0003	+.0010 +.0007 .0003	+.0015 +.0010 .0005	+.0025 +.0015 .0010	+.0030 +.0020 .0010	+.0035 +.0025 .0010
	ALLOWANCES FOR PUSH FITS						
P	High Limit Low Limit Tolerance	−.0002 −.0007 .0005	−.0002 −.0007 .0005	−.0002 −.0007 .0005	−.0005 −.0010 .0005	−.0005 −.0010 .0005	−.0005 −.0010 .0005
	ALLOWANCES FOR RUNNING FITS						
X	High Limit Low Limit Tolerance	−.0010 −.0020 .0010	−.0012 −.0027 .0015	−.0017 −.0035 .0018	−.0020 −.0042 .0022	−.0025 −.0050 .0025	−.0030 −.0057 .0027
Y	High Limit Low Limit Tolerance	−.0007 −.0012 .0005	−.0010 −.0020 .0010	−.0012 −.0025 .0013	−.0015 −.0030 .0015	−.0020 −.0035 .0015	−.0022 −.0040 .0018
Z	High Limit Low Limit Tolerance	−.0005 −.0007 .0002	−.0007 −.0012 .0005	−.0007 −.0015 .0008	−.0010 −.0020 .0010	−.0010 −.0022 .0012	−.0012 −.0025 .0013

1. *Force fits*. Mechanical pressure is required for assembly, and, once assembled, no dismantling is likely to be necessary. As the shaft is larger than the hole in this case, *interference fit* is a general term also applicable.

2. *Driving fits*. These are a little less tight than force fits, and one part can be driven into the other. This is also an interference fit.

3. *Push fits*. Slight manual effort is required to assemble the parts in this case. A push fit is suitable for detachable or locating parts, but not for moving parts. As the clearance is small or negligible this is termed a *transition fit*.

4. *Running fits*. These are suitable for moving parts such as axles and so on. All running fits are clearance fits.

The first three are distinct classifications, but there are several classes of running fits for different types of work, since the clearance between the parts may be large or small.

System of Limits

In order to obtain some degree of standardization in the industry, several systems of limits have been devised. To simplify the process it has been found necessary to make either the shaft or the hole as nearly accurate as possible to the nominal size, and to vary the remaining factor in order to obtain the required fit. If the shaft is constant and the hole varied the system is said to have a *shaft basis*. If the hole is constant and the shaft varies, the system has a *hole basis*. The latter is generally adopted in this country because it is much easier to produce a shaft to any odd size than to make an odd-size hole.

One of the best-known hole-basis systems is known as the Newall Sys-

tem, and despite certain shortcomings it is probably the most used. In this system the holes are classified as A and B fit, the tolerances in the former being smaller than in the latter. Force, driving and push fits are lettered F, D and P respectively, while running fits are in three classes—X, Y, and Z in order of merit, a Z fit being the finest of the three. A Table of Newall limits is to be found on page 492, and reference to it will show that the holes have plus and minus limits. This is known as a bilateral system. A unilateral system varies in one direction only.

Some manufacturers do not use the Newall System at all, while others use the A and B limits for holes and impose their own limits on the shafts.

Gaging Holes

The methods for testing the diameters of shafts to close limits has been made clear in previous sections of this work. The method usually adopted for gaging holes is as follows: A gage is made from a hardened steel cylinder (Fig. 67) very accurately ground to that diameter which represents the bottom limit for the hole. When this gage is a smooth, light, push fit in the hole being tested (the hole must, of course, be clean), then the work is considered satisfactory, providing that the hole is round. This last observation must be stressed, because an elongated or an irregular hole, due perhaps to *chatter* in the reamer or carelessness

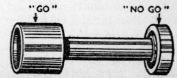

Fig. 67. "Go" and "No Go" plug gage of hardened steel for hole gaging.

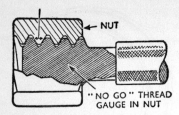

Fig. 68. How a "No Go" thread gage checks the effective diameter of a screw-thread.

on the part of the operator, can be very much over-size and still be of such dimensions in some directions as to prohibit inserting the gage at all.

It is also possible in some cases to produce a hole which is larger inside than at the ends, particularly if the hole is long and produced by hand. Sometimes a plain elongation can be measured with an inside vernier caliper or with a micrometer having two jaws similar to those on the vernier.

The end of the gage described is the *Go* end, and is usually so stamped. The opposite end is stamped *No Go*, and when this enters the work at all, the latter is unsatisfactory, as this gage is made to the diameter which represents the top limit of the hole. Here again discretion is required, as a long hole may be slightly bell-mouthed and will contain the *No Go* plug gage for only a very small percentage of its length. In some cases this would be quite acceptable, and after a little experience on this kind of work it is not difficult to arrive at a decision.

It is possible to have a *Go* thread plug-gage a nice fit in the thread and yet have the thread quite unsatisfactory from a strength point of view. This is because the thread-flanks can be cut away and made narrow without affecting the diameter of the thread root (i.e., the greatest diameter in the

nut-thread). The effective diameter of the thread (see screw-thread micrometer) is affected by this so the *No Go* thread-gage is often stamped "No Go Eff. Dia." It will be seen from Fig. 68 that this gage is relieved at all points except the thread-flank which it is checking.

For average-size male threads a gage has been devised which eliminates the necessity of screwing the work in and out. Known as the Wickman gage, it consists essentially of a C-shaped frame carrying two pairs of jaws (Fig. 69). The outermost pair of jaws are ground to the thread profile (something like a screw-pitch gage blade, but much more robust), and are adjusted so that a bolt which can be passed between them is the correct size. The next pair of jaws form the *No Go* part of the gage, and actually check the effective diameter of the work. Hence anything which passes through the second pair should be rejected.

Another type of gage for male threads is a variation of the Wickman gage. In place of the fixed jaws, rollers ground to the thread profile are fixed to the frame of the gage. The method of application is exactly the same as with the Wickman gage. When using either pattern the work must not be

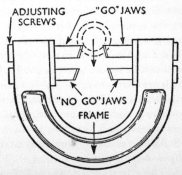

Fig. 69. Wickman gage with two sets of jaws for "Go" and "No Go."

forced or rotated when attempting to pass it between the gaging points. Cleanliness is also essential, as with any gaging operation.

Caliper Snap Gages

A caliper snap gage (Fig. 71) is usually a C-shaped frame with two flat faces, one on each jaw, ground so that the distance between them will

"GO" JAW
FULL THREAD
FORM

"NO GO" JAW
RELIEVED TO
CHECK PLANES

Fig. 70. In the Wickman gage the "Go" jaws have the full thread form, the "No Go" jaws are relieved.

permit the gage to fit smoothly on to a part which is the correct size. (The ordinary micrometer may be used as a snap gage if the spindle is locked when the setting is correct.) For repetitive work where one dimension (e.g., a shaft diameter) has to be checked very frequently, the snap gage is a great help. For production, a gage which is made to the correct dimension only is frequently used. For inspection, however, a double-gage is required—that is, *Go* and *No Go*. In one type the *No Go* check is made between two faces which are farther inside the jaws than the other two (Fig. 72), while another type has a double frame with gaging-faces at each end.

Suitable for most work, adjustable caliper snap gages are available (Fig. 73). These possess a C-shaped frame, as do the fixed type, but in place of

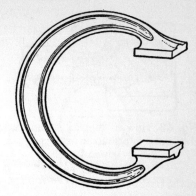

Fig. 71. Caliper snap gage for repeated checking of a single dimension.

the usual jaws four cylindrical jaws are inserted in holes in the frame, and endwise movements of these by means of a screw provide the necessary adjustment. The ends of the cylindrical jaws are the gaging surfaces. This type of gage has much in common with the Wickman thread gage, the principal difference being that the latter has a thread-form gaging surface. When adjusting these snap gages, slip gages are used for setting purposes as shown in Fig. 73.

Special Gages

Very often some part of a job which is unusual in shape has to be produced

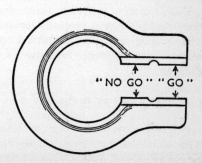

"NO GO" "GO"

Fig. 72. Double snap gage: the "No Go" check is made by the inner faces.

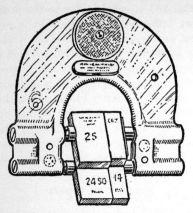

Fig. 73. Adjustable caliper snap gage; the jaws are adjusted by a screw action.

to close limits. Thus, a rectangular hole for a locating block may have to be accurate within .005 in. In cases like this it is not usually sufficient to measure the length and breadth of the hole, as it may be slightly out of square or have over-size radii in the corners. The most satisfactory job is achieved with gages made to the correct dimensions and fitted with handles for convenient application to the work.

A taper plug gage (Fig. 74) is an example of a special gage. The gaging limits are indicated by marks or flats ground on the end of the gage in such positions that the distance the gage enters the work can be observed.

Profile gages are also made for checking the shape of specially formed jobs such as are often produced by form-tools in the lathe (see section on Turning).

Slip and Block Gages

For tool-room and other precision work the ordinary methods of measuring are not always sufficiently accurate. For example, a snap gage may be required to check a shaft diameter to a

tolerance of .002 in., and it is evident that the gage must be made to a much greater degree of accuracy if it is to serve its purpose. A slip gage presents the simplest possible means of measuring in tenths of thousandths, and it consists merely of a small rectangular slip or block of hardened steel, two opposite faces of which are ground and lapped so that the distance between them is within a few millionths of an inch of the nominal size of the gage.

Although a set of gages comprises only a comparatively small number of slips, they are so graded that a great number of combinations may be made to give dimensions increasing in steps of .0001 in. up to the capacity of the set. The faces of the slips are dead parallel and so flat that they may be "wrung" together. Thus, if two slips are selected, wiped clean with chamois skin, and then placed one on the other with a slight sliding action, they will adhere, and some force will be required to separate them. The importance of cleaning the gages before wringing them together cannot be over-estimated, as dust or grit not only leads to inaccurate readings, but also causes abrasion of the slips and shortens their useful life. As far as possible, the slips should be handled by the ends, as perspiration of the fingers often causes rusting to occur. By assembling in a frame a combination of slips making up the required dimension

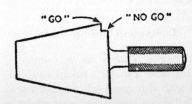

Fig. 74. Taper plug gage; the limits indicated by marks, as shown.

with a special bar at each end of the pile, a snap gage can be built up (Fig. 75).

Gage Bars

An extension of the gaging principle is afforded by bars in varying lengths

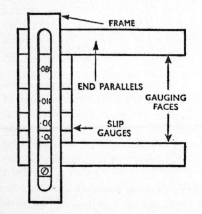

Fig. 75. How a snap gage may be built up from a combination of slips in a frame.

which can be screwed together to check long work. Another device which is sometimes used is a small tripod base on to which one or more of these bars can be screwed so that they stand vertical. Slip gages are then wrung on to the upper end of the top bar and the whole is used as a form of height gage.

As the accuracy of a combination is affected by the number of slips in it, the smallest possible number should always be used.

Compound Sliding-Table

A device known as a compound sliding-table can be used in conjunction with slip gages when holes are to be drilled or bored very accurately in relation one to the other. The table

(Fig. 76) is very similar to the ordinary lathe saddle or slide-rest in action, as it possesses two V-slides working at 90 deg. and actuated by square thread screws. Each slide has a fixed and a moving stud between which slip gages may be inserted to ascertain the movement of the slide. By setting up the work on the table and fixing the table to a drilling or boring machine very accurate results may be obtained.

Angles and Tapers

Angles occur so often in so many different branches of industry that anyone who has no knowledge of trigonometry (the mathematics of angles) sooner or later feels handicapped by the deficiency. For the ordinary workman in the shop, trigonometry need not be difficult; indeed, it is extremely simple if one or two rules are remembered. The reader has already been introduced to two "trig" ratios in the previous section, the sine and the tangent. There is one more to complete a trio which will serve for most jobs in the shop. The three ratios are derived as follows:

In any right-angled triangle (that is, a triangle having one angle of 90 deg.) we may label the sides as shown in Fig. 77, where the upright side is termed the perpendicular (abbreviated to P), the lower side is the base

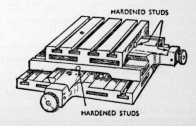

Fig. 76. Compound sliding-table, used with slip gages for accurate hole-drilling.

(B) and the remaining side is the hypotenuse (H). If we consider the angle X, that is, the angle opposite the perpendicular, we can obtain three simple ratios which will always hold good for this angle. Thus, if we take the length of the perpendicular, P, and divide it by the length of the hypotenuse, H, we will obtain a figure which will always be correct for the

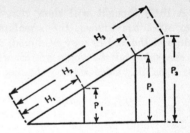

Fig. 78. The ratio between the respective sides is the same for all right-angled triangles: that is, perpendicular divided by hypotenuse, base divided by hypotenuse, and perpendicular divided by base are constants.

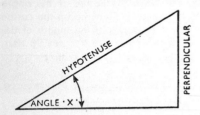

Fig. 77. In a right-angled triangle the upright side is called the perpendicular, the horizontal side is called the base, and the side opposite the right angle is called the hypotenuse.

right-angled triangle under consideration regardless of the lengths of P or H. In Fig. 78 the application of this is made clear. We have said that $\frac{P}{H}$ for the angle X remains constant hence:

$$\frac{P_1}{H_1} = \frac{P_2}{H_2} = \frac{P_3}{H_3}$$

This constant value of $\frac{P}{H}$ is called the sine of the angle X, and if the triangle in Fig. 79 is examined, it will be seen that:

$$\frac{P}{H} = \frac{1}{2} = \frac{P_2}{H_2} = \frac{P_2}{6}$$

$$\text{or } \frac{P_2}{6} = \frac{1}{2}$$

so that $P_2 = 3$

To test the argument:

$$\frac{P_1}{H_1} = \frac{1}{2} \quad \text{and}$$

$$\frac{P_2}{H_2} = \frac{3}{6} = \frac{1}{2} = \text{sine X.}$$

In exactly the same way: $\frac{B}{H} = $ cosine of the angle X (generally written cos X), and $\frac{P}{B} = $ tangent of the angle X (written tan X).

It must be emphasized that the terms sine, cosine, and tangent do not possess any hidden significance. They are nothing more than convenient names which have been given to the ratios to which they refer.

The values of the three ratios for angles between 0 deg. and 90 deg. have been calculated and tabulated in a convenient form, and are reproduced, together with notes on how to use them, on pages 528–531.

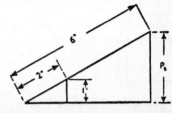

Fig. 79. The sine of an angle is the ratio of perpendicular to hypotenuse (in this case $\frac{3}{6}$ or $\frac{1}{2}$): the cosine is the ratio of base to hypotenuse, and the tangent is the ratio of perpendicular to base.

A little thought will show that if two sides are known, the remaining side and the angles may be found, or if one side and the angle are known, the remaining sides may be obtained.

Memory Aids

Two simple mnemonics (or memory aids) which will help to avoid mistakes will be found extremely useful. These are:

1. Always draw the little triangle with the perpendicular on the right-hand side, and the angle on the left-hand side, and label the sides P, B and H as shown in Fig. 77, also marking in the known dimensions. If the other angle is being dealt with, turn the work round so that the required angle is on the left-hand side. On no account must the sides be labeled differently from the manner shown in Fig. 77.

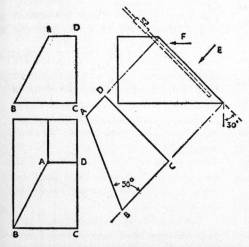

Fig. 81. Showing a block machined at two different angles. The angle between *AB* and *BC* is given as 50 deg., but this applies only in the direction of the arrow *E*. In the direction of the arrow *F*, the angle is quite different; it is a compound of the two angles 50 deg. and 30 deg.

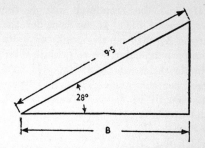

Fig. 80. Since the cosine of the angle is *B/H*, we can by looking up the cosine in the table, work out the length of the base. In this case: $B/9.5 = \cos 28$ deg. $= .8829$; $\therefore B = 8.387$.

2. The ratios are easily remembered if written down thus:

$$\text{sine} = \frac{P \text{ eter's}}{H \text{ orse}}$$

$$\text{cosine} = \frac{B \text{ rings}}{H \text{ ome}}$$

$$\text{tangent} = \frac{P \text{ eter's}}{B \text{ read}}$$

Think of the whole as "sine, cosine, tangent. Peter's Horse Brings Home Peter's Bread," and write the lines one under the other as shown. Elementary, perhaps, but undoubtedly very useful. After some practice, of course none of this procedure will be necessary.

An example in the use of the cosine is shown in Fig. 80, where the angle and the hypotenuse are given and the length of the base is required. As the hypotenuse, H, is given and B is required, the ratio used must include these two, and so the cosine is selected because:

$$\frac{B}{H} = \cos 28 \text{ deg.}$$

Looking up the value of cos 28 deg. in a table of cosines we get

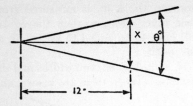

Fig. 82. Illustrating two methods of expressing degree of taper—by the angle included between the tapering lines, and by the taper per foot at 90 deg. to the center line of the taper.

$$\frac{B}{9.5} = .8829.$$

Multiplying both sides by 9.5,
$$B = .8829 \times 9.5 = 8.387.$$

Applications of the sine and tangent were mentioned in the section on testing (see sine bar), and the novice should experience little difficulty in applying the rules to ordinary problems. It is important not to attach any great significance to the unfamiliar terms used, as the whole of the work mentioned in this section is really very little more than plain arithmetic.

Resultant or Compound Angles

A not uncommon source of error in jobs which incorporate two or more angles is the failure on the part of the workman to realize that an angle alters in apparent size when viewed from different points. Very often an angle is shown on a machine-drawing

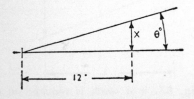

Fig. 83. The illustration shows two further methods of expressing taper—by the half angle, and by the taper per foot given at 90 deg. to one side.

in an unusual projection, and when this happens a wary eye should be kept on the position in which the angle is checked.

Fig. 81 shows a block which is machined at two different angles. The angle between the sides AB and BC is given as 50 deg., and the novice might be tempted to stand the block flat on its base BC and check this angle from the surface plate in the normal manner. This would be wrong, because the angle of 50 deg. is given in the direc-

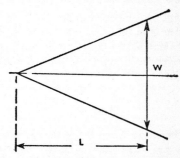

Fig. 84. To find the width of the taper at any given number of inches from the point, divide the taper per foot by 12, and multiply by the required number of inches.

tion of arrow, E, and despite the fact that it is still the same corner of the work, the angle in the direction of arrow, F, is not by any means the same thing. To check the angle, E, the block could be laid on the face, CD, and then the protractor used along the edge, AB, in the position shown by the dotted lines.

Actually in the example given it is fairly evident that there is some difference in the angles, but there are many jobs in which the snare is far from obvious. Even "old hands" have been known to make mistakes in this connection.

The angle seen in the direction of arrow, F, may be described as a re-

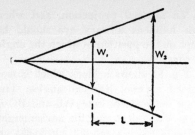

Fig. 85. If the widths of the taper at two positions and the distance between them are known, the taper per foot can be calculated as explained in the text.

sultant or compound of the two angles 50 deg. and 30 deg., and it is possible to calculate its value. The method, however, is beyond the scope of this work.

Tapers

There are three ways in which tapers are expressed: (1) By the included angle. (2) By the half angle. (3) By the taper per foot given at 90 deg. to the center line of the taper.

The first method is illustrated in Fig. 82, where the angle is shown symmetrical about the center line.

Methods 2 and 3 are shown in Fig. 83.

It will be observed that the width, X in., depends on the length of the taper and is proportional to it. Hence, if the width is wanted at a point 8 in. from the end (Fig. 84), the taper per foot is first divided by 12 to bring it to taper per inch. Suppose, for example, that the taper per foot is $\frac{1}{4}$ in., then the taper per inch will be:

$$\frac{1}{4} \times \frac{1}{12}$$

and the taper per 8 in. will be:

$$\frac{8}{4 \times 12} = \frac{1}{6} \text{ in.}$$

So that if the 8 in. is measured from the point, the width will be $\frac{1}{6}$ in. If,

however, the 8 in. is measured from some other position, then the $\frac{1}{6}$ in. will have to be added to the width at this point.

If, as in Fig. 85, two widths and the distance between them are known, and

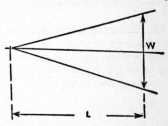

Fig. 86. If the width of the taper at a given point and the taper per foot are known, the distance from the end can be calculated as shown above.

the taper per foot is required, then, supposing that L = 9 in., $W_1 = \frac{1}{4}$ in. and $W_2 = \frac{1}{2}$ in., the taper per 9 in. will be:

$$\frac{1}{2} \text{ in.} - \frac{1}{4} \text{ in.} = \frac{1}{4} \text{ in.}$$

and the taper per inch is

$$\frac{1}{4} \times \frac{1}{9} = \frac{1}{36}.$$

The taper per foot, therefore, is

$$\frac{12}{36} = \frac{1}{3} \text{ in.}$$

The width at a point may be given, together with the taper per foot, the distance from the end being required (Fig. 86). In this case, first find the

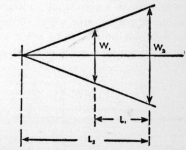

Fig. 87. If a width is required at a known distance from a known width, it can be calculated either by the formula given in the illustration, or as described in the text.

TABLE I
ANGLES AND TAPERS
Half Angles ∢ (See Footnote)

TAPER PER FOOT.	TAPER PER INCH.	ANGLE (DEG. AND MIN.).	TAPER PER FOOT.	TAPER PER INCH.	ANGLE (DEG. AND MIN.).
$\frac{1}{32}$	.00260	.09	$1\frac{3}{16}$	.09896	5.39
$\frac{1}{16}$	.00520	.18	$1\frac{7}{32}$	.10156	5.48
$\frac{3}{32}$	.00781	.27	$1\frac{1}{4}$	.10417	5.57
$\frac{1}{8}$	.01042	.36	$1\frac{9}{32}$	.10677	6.06
$\frac{5}{32}$	.01302	.45	$1\frac{5}{16}$	.10938	6.15
$\frac{3}{16}$	.01562	.54	$1\frac{11}{32}$	.11198	6.23
$\frac{7}{32}$	.01823	1.03	$1\frac{3}{8}$	.11458	6.32
$\frac{1}{4}$	.02083	1.12	$1\frac{13}{32}$	.11719	6.41
$\frac{9}{32}$	.02344	1.21	$1\frac{7}{16}$	.11979	6.50
$\frac{5}{16}$	.02604	1.30	$1\frac{15}{32}$	.12240	6.59
$\frac{11}{32}$	.02865	1.38	$1\frac{1}{2}$	.12500	7.07
$\frac{3}{8}$	.03125	1.47	$1\frac{17}{32}$	.12760	7.16
$\frac{13}{32}$	.03385	1.56	$1\frac{9}{16}$	.13021	7.25
$\frac{7}{16}$	.03646	2.05	$1\frac{19}{32}$	.13281	7.34
$\frac{15}{32}$	.03906	2.14	$1\frac{5}{8}$	.13542	7.43
$\frac{1}{2}$	.04167	2.23	$1\frac{21}{32}$	.13802	7.52
$1\frac{7}{32}$	.04427	2.32	$1\frac{11}{16}$	.14063	8.00
$\frac{9}{16}$	.04688	2.41	$1\frac{23}{32}$	.14323	8.09
$1\frac{9}{32}$	.04948	2.50	$1\frac{3}{4}$	.14583	8.18
$\frac{5}{8}$	.05208	2.59	$1\frac{25}{32}$	.14844	8.27
$2\frac{1}{32}$	.05469	3.08	$1\frac{13}{16}$	.15104	8.35
$1\frac{1}{16}$	.05729	3.17	$1\frac{27}{32}$	.15365	8.44
$2\frac{3}{32}$	.05990	3.26	$1\frac{7}{8}$	.15625	8.53
$\frac{3}{4}$	.06250	3.35	$1\frac{29}{32}$	.15885	9.02
$2\frac{5}{32}$	.06510	3.43	$1\frac{15}{18}$	.16146	9.10
$1\frac{3}{16}$	.06770	3.52	$1\frac{31}{32}$	.16406	9.19
$2\frac{7}{32}$	.07031	4.01	2	.16667	9.28
$\frac{7}{8}$	.07292	4.10	$2\frac{1}{4}$	.18750	10.37
$2\frac{9}{32}$	.07552	4.19	$2\frac{1}{2}$	.20833	11.46
$1\frac{5}{16}$	.07813	4.28	$2\frac{3}{4}$	.22916	12.54
$3\frac{1}{32}$	.08073	4.37	3	.25000	14.02
1	.08333	4.46	$3\frac{1}{2}$	.29167	16.16
$1\frac{1}{32}$	.08594	4.55	4	.33333	18.26
$1\frac{1}{16}$	.08854	5.04	$4\frac{1}{2}$	.37500	20.33
$1\frac{3}{32}$	.09115	5.12	5	.41667	22.37
$1\frac{1}{8}$	.09375	5.21	6	.50000	26.34
$1\frac{5}{32}$	.09635	5.30			

Note.—The figure given in the column "Taper per inch" is also the tangent of the angle in the third column.

Included angles up to that for 2-in. taper per foot may be read directly from the above table for most work, as the error does not exceed 4 minutes. Thus, from the table the angle corresponding to a taper of 2 in. per foot is 9 deg. 28 min.

The actual included angle for the same taper per foot is 9 deg. 32 min., hence the error is 4 minutes in this case. For smaller angles the error is much smaller than this.

For more accurate work and for tapers exceeding 2 in. per foot proceed as follows:

A. *Given the taper.*
  1. Divide the given taper per foot by 2.
  2. Find the corresponding angle in the above table.
  3. Multiply this angle by 2.

taper per inch. Suppose the taper per foot is $\frac{1}{4}$ in., then taper per inch is

$$\frac{1}{4} \times \frac{1}{12} = \frac{1}{48} \text{ in.}$$

For every time $\frac{1}{48}$ in. will divide into the given width there will be an inch in the length required; hence if the given width is $\frac{3}{16}$ in.

$$\frac{3}{16} \div \frac{1}{48} = \frac{3 \times 48}{16} = 9 \text{ in.}$$

If, as in Fig. 87, a width is required some distance from another width which is known, first work out the length to the point as in Fig. 86, and then find the new width as in Fig. 84. Alternatively, use the formula given under the figure.

All the methods outlined are applicable to both of the tapers shown in Figs. 82 and 83. It will also be appreciated that in the case of Fig. 82 the widths could be diameters and the work cylindrical.

Calculating Tapers by Angles

When the taper is measured by the angle, it is necessary to use trigonometry to calculate the various dimensions.

It will be seen from Fig. 83 that the taper per foot divided by 12 gives the

B. *Given the angle.*
  1. Divide the given angle by 2.
  2. Find the corresponding taper in the above table.
  3. Multiply this taper by 2.

tangent $\frac{P}{B}$ of the angle. (This does not refer to Fig. 82.) Hence, given the taper per foot, it is a simple matter to find the angle. Alternatively, if the angle is given, the taper per foot is

Tan (angle) $\times$ 12.

Hence, if the angle is known, and the width is required, find the taper per foot and proceed as before.

When dealing with tapers of the type shown in Fig. 82, the calculations which are based on trigonometry must be worked out on the half angle, as this forms part of a right-angled triangle. Similarly, the taper per foot must be divided by 2, as the taper at one side of the center line is half of the total taper.

TABLE II
INCLUDED ANGLES ◁

ANGLE (DEG.).	TAPER PER INCH (IN.).	TAPER PER FOOT (IN.).	ANGLE (DEG.).	TAPER PER INCH (IN.).	TAPER PER FOOT (IN.).
1	.01746	.20952	24	.42511	5.10132
2	.03492	.41904	25	.44338	5.32056
3	.05238	.62856	26	.46174	5.54088
4	.06984	.83808	27	.48016	5.76192
5	.08732	1.04784	28	.49866	5.98392
6	.10482	1.25784	29	.51724	6.20688
7	.12232	1.46784	30	.53590	6.43080
8	.13985	1.67820	31	.55464	6.65568
9	.15740	1.88880	32	.57350	6.88200
10	.17498	2.09976	33	.59242	7.10904
11	.19258	2.31096	34	.61146	7.33752
12	.21020	2.52240	35	.63060	7.56720
13	.22787	2.73444	36	.64984	7.79808
14	.24557	2.94684	37	.66920	8.03040
15	.26330	3.15960	38	.68866	8.26392
16	.28108	3.37296	39	.70824	8.49888
17	.29890	3.58680	40	.72794	8.73528
18	.31676	3.80112	41	.74776	8.97312
19	.33468	4.01616	42	.76772	9.21264
20	.35265	4.23180	43	.78782	9.45384
21	.37068	4.44816	44	.80806	9.69672
22	.38876	4.66512	45	.82842	9.94104
23	.40690	4.88280			

The problem then reduces itself to a form similar to the previous one, where the angle does not enter into the calculations.

CHAPTER 16

MACHINE DRAWING

TYPES OF DRAWINGS. DRAFTSMAN'S EQUIPMENT. DRAWING TO SCALE. PROJECTION. DIMENSION LINES. METHOD OF INDICATING MATERIALS, ETC. TYPES OF KEYS AND KEYWAYS. LIMITS. FITS. PREPARING DRAWINGS AND BLUEPRINTS. TRUE-TO-SCALE PRINTS.

AN UNDERSTANDING of the work of the drafting room will make the reading of blueprints easier. Generally speaking, the drafting room is sub-divided into Design, Detail, and Jig-and-Tool sections. The design draftsman lays out on his drawing-board the general lines of the machine, and works out calculations, the stresses and strains on the different parts, so that each may have sufficient strength for its use and be made of the material suitable for the purpose.

These requirements may necessitate many preliminary drawings and designs before the final design is decided upon. The final layouts will be passed to the detail draftsman, whose duty it is to make drawings of every single piece needed in the machine, so that each piece may be made in the shop, and every part treated as an individual item. In this way much of the complication of an elaborate drawing is reduced.

The detail drawing will give every requirement of the particular piece: complete dimensions, together with the tolerances that may be allowed for each dimension; the material from which it is made; the number required; whether or not the part is to be heat-treated, plated, etc.; its drawing number or part number—in fact, complete details of the part for its manufacture, subsequent assembly, and re-ordering, if it should ever need replacing.

Jig-and-Tool Designing

With modern large-scale production the detail drawing will pass to the Jig-and-Tool division before it goes into the shop. The Jig-and-Tool designer will decide with which machine-tool the part can be best produced; he will design the jigs, fixtures, gages, or special tools needed, so that by the time the detail drawing reaches the shop a complete sequence of machining operations has been planned, and the shop will use the detail drawing and the tools to produce the particular part, and keep within the machining tolerances which have been laid down.

Even simple machines have many parts, but a product such as an airplane, with many thousands of parts, will require the preparation of many thousands of detail drawings.

Draftsman's Equipment

Drawings are made on drawing paper of standard sizes, usually in multiples of $8\frac{1}{2} \times 11$ inches.

The most conspicuous part of the drafting room equipment is the drawing-board, of which an example is shown in Fig. 1. In more elaborately equipped offices this may be superseded by a drafting-machine or drafting-table (see Fig. 2). On a drafting-machine the board may easily be tilted to any angle and the T-square is replaced by a pivoted arm, which, by a system of parallel links, enables lines to be drawn horizontally, vertically, or at any angle. Other widely-used drawing-instruments are also illustrated and named in Fig. 3. Initial lines are made with pencils obtainable in graduated grades of hardness, H, 2H, 3H, etc. These grades are also available in leads to fit spring-bows and compasses. Inked lines are produced by means of a ruling-pen, or the penpoint of spring-bows or compass, using India ink, the water-proof variety being generally favored.

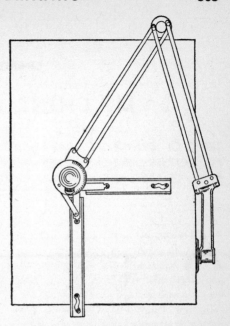

Fig. 2. Universal drafting machine of the mid anchor type.

Fig. 1. The drawing board is the most conspicuous feature of the drafting room equipment. This collapsible board with instrument tray and side attachment for standing inks, etc. is a typical example.

When laying out the drawing, it is not always possible, because of the size of the part, to make the drawing actual size; therefore, the drawing must be made to scale. In order that this operation may be done with less chance of error, a scale is used, generally of boxwood, divided along its edges into different scales—full-size, half-size, quarter-size, etc.,—so that the actual dimension at the reduced scale may be laid out directly without calculation (see Fig. 4).

Owing to alterations or other causes, a dimension sometimes appears on a drawing that is not correctly to scale; it is customary in

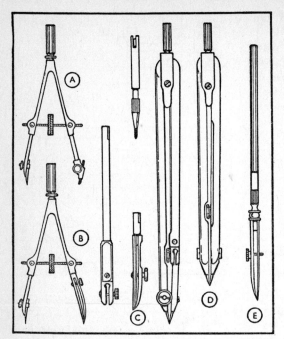

Fig. 3. Drawing instruments in common use. A, pencil spring-bow; B, pen spring-bow; C, compass half set with lengthening bar; D, dividers; E, ruling pen.

this case to add the letters N.T.S. (Not-to-scale) after the dimension.

If a dimension cannot be found on a drawing, it should never be measured on the blueprint to find out what it is. When drawings are reproduced

as blueprints, part of the process requires the print to be washed in water, and this causes shrinkage of the paper, making the blueprint out of scale. Always work to the dimensions as laid out, or "when in doubt, ask" is the best motto.

Before going on, a description of engineering sketches and the general rules of projection is advisable. Fig. 5 shows an isometric sketch of an angle bracket and Fig. 6 an elbow connection. It is not often that such sketches are sent to the shop, but when simple objects are wanted it is sometimes a quick way of making a drawing that is also a complete record.

Sketches should carry sufficient dimensions to enable the part to be made. When complicated parts are to be manufactured, a *projection* drawing must be used.

When a drawing is received in the shop it usually, except in intricate cases, contains three different views;

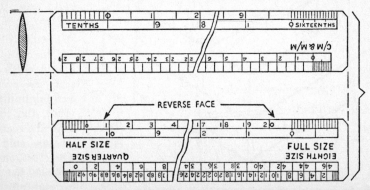

Fig. 4. By the use of a scale rule of this kind, scale drawings can be measured without the need for calculating scale dimensions.

front view, side view, and top view; all of the same part.

The drawing is started by placing the side view in such a position as to necessitate the use of as few dotted lines as possible when drawing front and top views.

In all drawings those lines which cannot be seen when looking at the object are represented by dotted lines.

Considerable use is made of center lines, which are always drawn passing through the center of holes or symmetrical bodies. It is usual to project center lines to connect the different views, and this greatly facilitates reading the drawing.

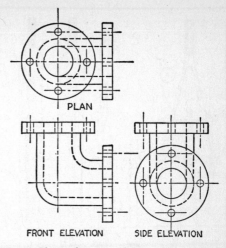

PLAN

FRONT ELEVATION   SIDE ELEVATION

Fig. 6. These drawings for an elbow connection illustrate the method of projection.

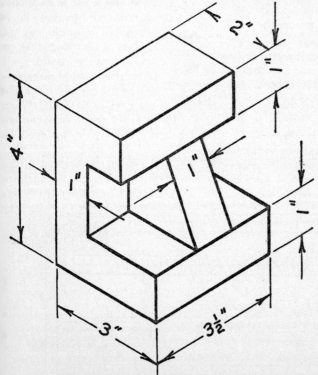

Fig. 5. An isometric view of an angle bracket showing the heavy shade lines sometimes used to give depth to a sketch.

Dimension lines are drawn as full but faint lines, and it is usual to show the dimension lines outside of the drawing itself unless, in so doing, the dimension line will tend to cause confusion; then the dimension is inserted within the drawing. Because of the complication caused by an elaborate drawing and the many times it is possible to insert the same dimension in different views, the practice is to show each dimension only once. Therefore, one must examine the drawing carefully to obtain all the dimensions.

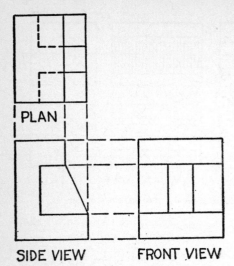

SIDE VIEW   FRONT VIEW

Fig. 7. An angle bracket is shown here in a projection having the least amount of invisible lines.

Owing to the complicated nature of many drawings, it is often advisable to show a portion of the object in section—i.e., an imaginary cut is made through the portion of the object where it is desired to show more detailed construction. Where this imaginary cut occurs the material thus cut is cross-hatched with diagonal lines at 45 deg., as Fig. 8. It is then possible to omit the dotted lines representing the invisible portions thus making the drawing more understandable. Liberties are sometimes taken in sections to make the drawing clearer, and one must become accustomed to these. For instance, the section may cut through nuts and bolts, rivets, solid shafts, etc., but such items are never shown in section, and will appear on the drawing as if they have been placed in the hole that accommodates them (see Fig. 9).

Indication of Materials

From time to time various methods have been adopted to indicate in the section-drawing the various materials used. An early method was to color the section to represent the material. Later, various combinations of lines were employed. These conventions and many others can be secured in the form of a pamphlet from the American Society of Mechanical Engineers.

For instance, it is possible to specify

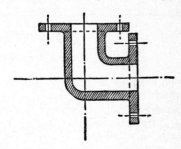

Fig. 8. Section through an elbow connection, showing method of shading to indicate a metallic section.

at least a dozen different steels, and the modern method is to show by section-lining all the ferrous metals with faint full lines and nonferrous metals with dotted lines, and to indicate by an accompanying schedule the materials which are to be employed.

The various conventional methods of indicating screw-threads are shown in Fig. 10. These may be for right or left

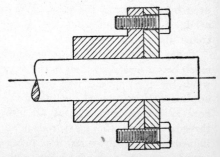

Fig. 9. In a sectional view showing nuts and bolts, shafts, etc., such items are not shown in section but in elevation as illustrated here.

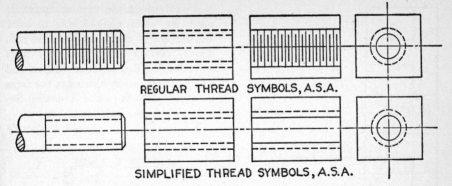

REGULAR THREAD SYMBOLS, A.S.A.

SIMPLIFIED THREAD SYMBOLS, A.S.A.

Fig. 10. Various ways of indicating screw threads in section.

hand, and this is always indicated. All threads are measured over the outside diameter of the screw, and the number of threads per inch is indicated unless the thread is of a standard pattern accepted as universal practice, when it can be indicated by its name and size.

In this category are the American Standard screw threads, with an angle of 60 deg. between threads.

Pipe Thread

The pipe thread has been handed to us from the early installation of screwed pipes, and this thread, unlike all other, is not measured over its extreme diameter. A pipe thread is measured by the bore of the pipe, so that a 1-in. A.S.P. thread is 1.3 over its extreme diameter.

Today pipes and tubes are made of much better materials than in the days when the pipe thread was originally applied, and one should not accept the bore as the measurement of all pipe threads. Unless the measurement is indicated on the drawing, it is necessary to refer to a standard list to obtain the correct outside diameter to suit the respective pipe thread specified on the drawing. The various

thread profiles are shown in the chapter on cutting screw threads.

Flats, Squares, and Tapers

The conventional method of indicating flats and squares on round bodies is illustrated by Fig. 11, while the method of showing tapers is as Fig. 12. A taper is defined as the alteration in diameter, over a definite length, measured along the center line. It is extremely difficult to caliper or otherwise measure a taper at its smallest diameter, and the best practice is to indicate the maximum diameter, this being easily measured, and then to indicate the taper. Where a taper is very grad-

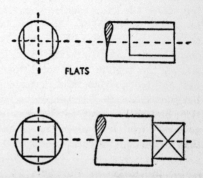

FLATS

Fig. 11. Methods of indicating flats and squares on round stock.

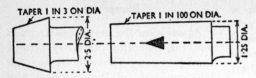

Fig. 12. How tapers are indicated. The graduated taper on the center line is exaggerated in drawing for the sake of clarity.

ual, and the large and small ends are not easily seen from the drawing it is usual to indicate on the center line an exaggerated taper (see Fig. 12).

Keys and Keyways

A key is used to secure a pulley or gear to a shaft, so that the shaft may receive or transmit motion from or to the pulley or gear. Where the key can be easily withdrawn it is referred to as a *loose key,* but when it is permanently fixed to the shaft it is known as a *feather.* There is the sunk key, flat key, saddle key, Woodruff key, round key, and splined shaft. All these have their uses, and are illustrated in Fig. 13.

Limits

As it is necessary to manufacture parts within given limits of accuracy, so that the fitting of spare parts is assured and an efficient job produced, all dimensions indicated on drawings must be given limits of accuracy beyond which the dimension should not vary. Various methods are adopted to indicate limits, but only an outline of the various methods can be given here.

The most popular way is to express the actual limit thus:

$2\frac{1}{2}$ in. $\pm$ .005 in. But as limits are usually shown in thousandths of an inch, some drafting rooms omit the cypher and express the dimension simply as $2\frac{1}{2} \pm 5$. A further method is to indicate dimensions that are not of any great degree of accuracy in fractions, and to specify important dimensions in decimals. Thus, $2\frac{1}{2}$ in. would represent a reasonable tolerance, but 2.5 in. would represent an accurate dimension.

Fits

The whole scope of limits has been tabulated (see Chapter 15) and drawn up in easily-accessible tables and textbooks, giving the various required fits. Of the systems in use, the Newall is the most popular. Under this system it is agreed that any hole is made to

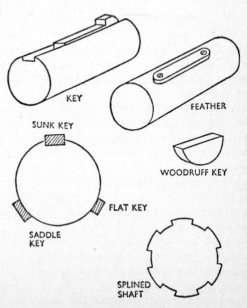

Fig. 13. Types of key and an end elevation of a splined shaft.

standard dimension, plus or minus a very fine margin. This is easily produced by the use of standard reamers, and the system allows for the various degree of fits being made on the shaft or fitting portion. Thus we have forced fits, when both tolerances will be $\frac{+}{+}$; push fits, when both dimensions are $\frac{-}{-}$, but to a very fine degree only running fits of two or three classes, depending on the type of fit required —whether it is an accurate tool fit, or a fine rotating fit, or a rough rotation fit. In all the cases mentioned the tolerances will be $\frac{-}{-}$.

Many shops adopt their own system of limits, generally based on the Newall table and the various fits are indicated on the drawings by giving the desired dimension together with the maximum and minimum variations from standard.

Prints from Drawings

As observed earlier in this section, the draftsman prepares his original drawing on drawing-paper. The drawing is then checked and rechecked by checkers and is then passed on to the tracing room. A tracing is made in ink on tracing-cloth—a transparent material which will withstand wear and tear. Because it is cheaper, tracing paper has, to a large extent, replaced cloth. Using this transparent original, it is possible to reproduce photographic copies by placing sensitized paper at the back of the transparent original and exposing to light. This simple operation has led to the complicated blue-printing machinery, the only object of which is to produce a far greater output of prints by electrical exposure than is possible by daylight exposure.

Blueprints

At one time the most popular print was the blueprint, correctly termed ferro-prussiate. The only reason for the popularity of the blueprint was that ferro-prussiate paper was the least expensive of all the sensitized papers. As cheaper processes were evolved, giving a print of different color, it has been superseded by other methods, although the name *blueprint* is still used. All that is necessary after exposing the ferro-prussiate paper to the light is to wash in water and hang up to dry.

Black-and-White Prints

Many prefer the clearer contrast of black and white, and therefore use higher-priced sensitized paper to achieve this end. The so-called black-and-white prints may, in practice, vary in color from a brown to a deep purple. This type of print is not so likely to fade as the blue print, and is not subject to the same amount of shrinkage. The process does not call for any prolonged washing, and by some methods the print is produced by ammonia vapor, which does not even damp the prints, so that the scale of the original drawing is preserved. The cost of these prints is slightly higher than that of blue prints, but when allowing for the elimination of washing and drying the time saved more than offsets the higher cost of the sensitized paper.

True-to-Scale Prints

It frequently happens that copies must be made from drawings that are on opaque material, and in recent years the *Reflex* process has come into wide use. Using this process, the light is first passed through the printing paper, and the lines of the original are reflected back, giving a print in reverse. Thus, white lines are given on a black back-ground. The process uses photographic bromide papers, and is therefore costly, but when copies must be produced and time will not permit of a tracing to be made, it is very valuable. This class of print is extremely useful in copying documents of a valuable nature that have to be safeguarded against the possibility of loss or damage through fire or other causes.

Abbreviations

The following abbreviations are frequently used on drawings.

A.S.A.—Am. Standards Assn.
B.B.—Ball bearings
B.C.—Bolt circle
Bab.—Babbit metal
Br.—Brass
Bz or Bro.—Bronze
C'bore—Counterbore
C.I.—Cast iron
C.L.—Center line
Cop.—Copper
C.P.—Circular pitch
C.R.S.—Cold rolled steel
Csk.—Countersink
CtoC—Center to center
D—Diameter
D.F.—Drop forging
D.P.—Diametral pitch
EF—Extra fine (threads)

f—Finish
ff—File finish
Fil.—Filister
G.I.—Galvanized iron
Gr.—Grind
Hd.—Head
H.D.G.—Hot dipped galvanized
Hex.—Hexagonal
Hrd. & Gr.—Harden and grind
L.H.—Left hand
Mal. I.—Malleable iron
M.S.—Machine steel
N.—National (Am.) Std.
NC—National Coarse (Th'ds)
NF—National Fine (Th'ds)
No. or #—Number
O.D.—Outside diameter
P—Pitch
Pat.—Pattern
Pcs.—Pieces
P.D.—Pitch diameter
Phos. Bro.—Phosphor bronze
lb. or #—Pounds
R—Radius
Rd.—Round
Req.—Required
R.H.—Right hand
S. or ST.—Mild steel
S.C.—Steel casting
Sc.—Screw
S.Forg.—Steel forging
Std.—Standard
S.Tube—Steel tubing
T.—Teeth
Thd.—Thread
T.S.—Tool steel
W.I.—Wrought iron

TABLES AND USEFUL DATA

THE METRIC SYSTEM

In 1866 the United States passed a law making legal the meter, the only standard of measurement that has been legalized by the United States Government. The United States yard, which is the most common standard of measurement in this country, is defined by the relation: $1 \text{ yard} = \dfrac{3600}{3937}$ meter.

The metric system is convenient in that it is based on multiples of ten, so that when it is necessary to change from one unit to another—e.g., millimeters to centimeters—one has only to multiply or divide by a multiple of ten. Conversions may be carried out in accordance with the tables on the next few pages.

Measures of Length

10 millimeters (mm.)	= 1 centimeter (cm.).
10 centimeters	= 1 decimeter (dm.).
10 decimeters	= 1 meter (m.).
1000 meters	= 1 kilometer (Km.).

Square Measure

100 square millimeters (mm.^{2})	= 1 square centimeter (cm.^{2}).
100 square centimeters	= 1 square decimeter (dm.^{2}).
100 square decimeters	= 1 square meter (m.^{2}).

Surveyor's Square Measure

100 square meters (m.^{2})	= 1 are (ar.).
100 ares	= 1 hectare (har.).
100 hectares	= 1 square kilometer (Km.^{2}).

Cubic Measure

1000 cubic millimeters (mm.^{3})	= 1 cubic centimeter (cm.^{3}).
1000 cubic centimeters	= 1 cubic decimeter (dm.^{3}).
1000 cubic decimeters	= 1 cubic meter (m.^{3}).

Dry and Liquid Measure

10 milliliters (ml.)	= 1 centiliter (cl.)
10 centiliters	= 1 deciliter (dl.).
10 deciliters	= 1 liter (l.).
100 liters	= 1 hectoliter (Hl.).

1 liter = 1 cubic decimeter = the volume of 1 kilogram of pure water at a temperature of 39.2 degrees F.

Measures of Weight

$$
\begin{aligned}
10 \text{ milligrams (mg.)} &= 1 \text{ centigram (cg.).} \\
10 \text{ centigrams} &= 1 \text{ decigram (dg.).} \\
10 \text{ decigrams} &= 1 \text{ gram (g.).} \\
10 \text{ grams} &= 1 \text{ decagram (Dg.).} \\
10 \text{ decagrams} &= 1 \text{ hectogram (Hg.).} \\
10 \text{ hectograms} &= 1 \text{ kilogram (Kg.)} \\
1000 \text{ kilograms} &= 1 \text{ (metric) ton (T.).}
\end{aligned}
$$

Metric and English Conversion Table

Linear Measure

1 kilometer = 0.6214 mile.

$$
1 \text{ meter} = \begin{cases} 39.37 \text{ inches.} \\ 3.2808 \text{ feet.} \\ 1.0936 \text{ yard.} \end{cases}
$$

1 centimeter = 0.3937 inch.
1 millimeter = 0.03937 inch.

1 mile = 1.609 kilometer.
1 yard = 0.9144 meter.
1 foot = 0.3048 meter.
1 foot = 304.8 millimeters.
1 inch = 2.54 centimeters.
1 inch = 25.4 millimeters.

Square Measure

1 square kilometer = 0.3861 square mile = 247.1 acres.
1 hectare = 2.471 acre = 107,640 square feet.
1 are = 0.0247 acre = 1076.4 square feet.
1 square meter = 10.764 square feet = 1.196 square yard.
1 square centimeter = 0.155 square inch.
1 square millimeter = 0.00155 square inch.

---

1 square mile = 2.5899 square kilometers.
1 acre = 0.4047 hectare = 40.47 ares.
1 square yard = 0.836 square meter.
1 square foot = 0.0929 square meter = 929 square centimeters.
1 square inch = 6.452 square centimeters = 645.2 square millimeters.

Cubic Measure

1 cubic meter = 35.314 cubic feet = 1.308 cubic yard.
1 cubic meter = 264.2 U. S. gallons.
1 cubic centimeter = 0.061 cubic inch.
1 liter (cubic decimeter) = 0.0353 cubic foot = 61.023 cubic inches.
1 liter = 0.2642 U. S. gallon = 1.0567 U. S. quart.

---

1 cubic yard = 0.7645 cubic meter.
1 cubic foot = 0.02832 cubic meter = 28.317 liters.
1 cubic inch = 16.383 cubic centimeters.
1 U. S. gallon = 3.785 liters.
1 U. S. quart = 0.946 liter.

Weight

1 metric ton = 0.9842 ton (of 2240 pounds) = 2204.6 pounds.
1 kilogram = 2.2046 pounds = 35.274 ounces avoirdupois.
1 gram = 0.03215 ounce troy = 0.03527 ounce avoirdupois.
1 gram = 15.432 grains.

---

1 ton (of 2240) pounds) = 1.016 metric ton = 1016 kilograms.
1 pound = 0.4536 kilogram = 453.6 grams.
1 ounce avoirdupois = 28.35 grams.
1 ounce troy = 31.103 grams.
1 grain = 0.0648 gram.

---

1 kilogram per square millimeter = 1422.32 pounds per square inch.
1 kilogram per square centimeter = 14.223 pounds per square inch.
1 kilogram-meter = 7.233 foot-pounds.
1 pound per square inch = 0.0703 kilogram per square centimeter.
1 calorie (kilogram calorie) = 3.968 B.T.U. (British thermal unit).

DECIMAL EQUIVALENTS OF FRACTIONS OF AN INCH

Fraction	Decimal	Fraction	Decimal	Fraction	Decimal
$\frac{1}{64}$	0.015 625	$\frac{11}{32}$..	0.343 75	$\frac{43}{64}$	0.671 875
$\frac{1}{32}$..	0.031 25	$\frac{23}{64}$	0.359 375	$\frac{11}{16}$....	0.687 5
$\frac{3}{64}$	0.046 875	$\frac{3}{8}$........	0.375	$\frac{45}{64}$	0.703 125
$\frac{1}{16}$....	0.062 5	$\frac{25}{64}$	0.390 625	$\frac{23}{32}$..	0.718 75
$\frac{5}{64}$	0.078 125	$\frac{13}{32}$..	0.406 25	$\frac{47}{64}$	0.734 375
$\frac{3}{32}$..	0.093 75	$\frac{27}{64}$	0.421 875	$\frac{3}{4}$........	0.750
$\frac{7}{64}$	0.109 375	$\frac{7}{16}$....	0.437 5	$\frac{49}{64}$	0.765 625
$\frac{1}{8}$......	0.125	$\frac{29}{64}$	0.453 125	$\frac{25}{32}$..	0.781 25
$\frac{9}{64}$	0.140 625	$\frac{15}{32}$..	0.468 75	$\frac{51}{64}$	0.796 875
$\frac{5}{32}$..	0.156 25	$\frac{31}{64}$	0.484 375	$\frac{13}{16}$....	0.812 5
$\frac{11}{64}$	0.171 875	$\frac{1}{2}$........	0.500	$\frac{53}{64}$	0.828 125
$\frac{3}{16}$....	0.187 5	$\frac{33}{64}$	0.515 625	$\frac{27}{32}$..	0.843 75
$\frac{13}{64}$	0.203 125	$\frac{17}{32}$..	0.531 25	$\frac{55}{64}$	0.859 375
$\frac{7}{32}$..	0.218 75	$\frac{35}{64}$	0.546 875	$\frac{7}{8}$......	0.875
$\frac{15}{64}$	0.234 375	$\frac{9}{16}$....	0.562 5	$\frac{57}{64}$	0.890 625
$\frac{1}{4}$........	0.250	$\frac{37}{64}$	0.578 125	$\frac{29}{32}$..	0.906 25
$\frac{17}{64}$	0.265 625	$\frac{19}{32}$..	0.593 75	$\frac{59}{64}$	0.921 875
$\frac{9}{32}$..	0.281 25	$\frac{39}{64}$	0.609 375	$\frac{15}{16}$....	0.937 5
$\frac{19}{64}$	0.296 875	$\frac{5}{8}$......	0.625	$\frac{61}{64}$	0.953 125
$\frac{5}{16}$....	0.312 5	$\frac{41}{64}$	0.640 625	$\frac{31}{32}$..	0.968 75
$\frac{21}{64}$	0.328 125	$\frac{21}{32}$..	0.656 25	$\frac{63}{64}$	0.984 375

Table of Decimal Equivalents of a Foot Corresponding to Inches and Fractions of Inches.—Assume, for example, that it is required to find the equivalent of $6\frac{7}{32}$ inches in decimals of a foot. Locate $\frac{7}{32}$ in the left-hand column and follow the horizontal line until the column headed "6" is reached. The figures 0.5182 read off in this column are the decimals of a foot corresponding to $6\frac{7}{32}$; in other words, $6\frac{7}{32}$ inches equals 0.5182 foot.

TABLE FOR CONVERTING MILLIMETERS INTO INCHES

MILLI-METERS.	INCHES.	MILLI-METERS.	INCHES.	MILLI-METERS.	INCHES.	MILLI-METERS.	INCHES.	MILLI-METERS.	INCHES.
1	0.0394	51	2.0079	101	3.9764	151	5.9449	201	7.9134
2	0.0787	52	2.0472	102	4.0157	152	5.9842	202	7.9527
3	0.1181	53	2.0866	103	4.0551	153	6.0236	203	7.9921
4	0.1575	54	2.1260	104	4.0945	154	6.0630	204	8.0315
5	0.1968	55	2.1653	105	4.1338	155	6.1023	205	8.0708
6	0.2362	56	2.2047	106	4.1732	156	6.1417	206	8.1102
7	0.2756	57	2.2441	107	4.2126	157	6.1811	207	8.1496
8	0.3150	58	2.2835	108	4.2520	158	6.2205	208	8.1890
9	0.3543	59	2.3228	109	4.2913	159	6.2598	209	8.2283
10	0.3937	60	2.3622	110	4.3307	160	6.2992	210	8.2677
11	0.4331	61	2.4016	111	4.3701	161	6.3386	211	8.3071
12	0.4724	62	2.4409	112	4.4094	162	6.3779	212	8.3464
13	0.5118	63	2.4803	113	4.4488	163	6.4173	213	8.3858
14	0.5512	64	2.5197	114	4.4882	164	6.4567	214	8.4252
15	0.5905	65	2.5590	115	4.5275	165	6.4960	215	8.4645
16	0.6299	66	2.5984	116	4.5669	166	6.5354	216	8.5039
17	0.6693	67	2.6378	117	4.6063	167	6.5748	217	8.5433
18	0.7087	68	2.6772	118	4.6457	168	6.6142	218	8.5827
19	0.7480	69	2.7165	119	4.6850	169	6.6535	219	8.6220
20	0.7874	70	2.7559	120	4.7244	170	6.6929	220	8.6614
21	0.8268	71	2.7953	121	4.7638	171	6.7323	221	8.7008
22	0.8661	72	2.8346	122	4.8031	172	6.7716	222	8.7401
23	0.9055	73	2.8740	123	4.8425	173	6.8110	223	8.7795
24	0.9449	74	2.9134	124	4.8819	174	6.8504	224	8.8189
25	0.9842	75	2.9527	125	4.9212	175	6.8897	225	8.8582
26	1.0236	76	2.9921	126	4.9606	176	6.9291	226	8.8976
27	1.0630	77	3.0315	127	5.0000	177	6.9685	227	8.9370
28	1.1024	78	3.0709	128	5.0394	178	7.0079	228	8.9764
29	1.1417	79	3.1102	129	5.0787	179	7.0472	229	9.0157
30	1.1811	80	3.1496	130	5.1181	180	7.0866	230	9.0551
31	1.2205	81	3.1890	131	5.1575	181	7.1260	231	9.0945
32	1.2598	82	3.2283	132	5.1968	182	7.1653	232	9.1338
33	1.2992	83	3.2677	133	5.2362	183	7.2047	233	9.1732
34	1.3386	84	3.3071	134	5.2756	184	7.2441	234	9.2126
35	1.3779	85	3.3464	135	5.3149	185	7.2834	235	9.2519
36	1.4173	86	3.3858	136	5.3543	186	7.3228	236	9.2913
37	1.4567	87	3.4252	137	5.3937	187	7.3622	237	9.3307
38	1.4961	88	3.4646	138	5.4331	188	7.4016	238	9.3701
39	1.5354	89	3.5039	139	5.4724	189	7.4409	239	9.4094
40	1.5748	90	3.5433	140	5.5118	190	7.4803	240	9.4188
41	1.6142	91	3.5827	141	5.5512	191	7.5197	241	9.4882
42	1.6535	92	3.6220	142	5.5905	192	7.5590	242	9.5275
43	1.6929	93	3.6614	143	5.6299	193	7.5984	243	9.5669
44	1.7323	94	3.7008	144	5.6693	194	7.6378	244	9.6063
45	1.7716	95	3.7401	145	5.7086	195	7.6771	245	9.6456
46	1.8110	96	3.7795	146	5.7480	196	7.7165	246	9.6850
47	1.8504	97	3.8189	147	5.7874	197	7.7559	247	9.7244
48	1.8898	98	3.8583	148	5.8268	198	7.7953	248	9.7638
49	1.9291	99	3.8976	149	5.8661	199	7.8346	249	9.8031
50	1.9685	100	3.9370	150	5.9055	200	7.8740	250	9.8425

TABLE FOR CONVERTING MILLIMETERS INTO INCHES

MILLI-METERS.	INCHES.	MILLI-METERS.	INCHES.	MILLI-METERS.	INCHES.	MILLI-METERS.	INCHES.	MILLI-METERS.	INCHES.
251	9.8819	301	11.8504	351	13.8189	401	15.7874	451	17.7559
252	9.9212	302	11.8897	352	13.8582	402	15.8267	452	17.7952
253	9.9606	303	11.9291	353	13.8976	403	15.8661	453	17.8346
254	10.0000	304	11.9685	354	13.9370	404	15.9055	454	17.8740
255	10.0393	305	12.0078	355	13.9763	405	15.9448	455	17.9133
256	10.0787	306	12.0472	356	14.0157	406	15.9842	456	17.9527
257	10.1181	307	12.0866	357	14.0551	407	16.0236	457	17.9921
258	10.1575	308	12.1260	358	14.0945	408	16.0630	458	18.0315
259	10.1968	309	12.1653	359	14.1338	409	16.1023	459	18.0738
260	10.2362	310	12.2047	360	14.1732	410	16.1417	460	18.1102
261	10.2756	311	12.2441	361	14.2126	411	16.1811	461	18.1496
262	10.3149	312	12.2834	362	14.2519	412	16.2204	462	18.1889
263	10.3543	313	12.3228	363	14.2913	413	16.2598	463	18.2283
264	10.3937	314	12.3622	364	14.3307	414	16.2992	464	18.2677
265	10.4330	315	12.4015	365	14.3700	415	16.3385	465	18.3070
266	10.4724	316	12.4409	366	14.4094	416	16.3779	466	18.3464
267	10.5118	317	12.4803	367	14.4488	417	16.4173	467	18.3858
268	10.5512	318	12.5197	368	14.4882	418	16.4567	468	18.4252
269	10.5905	319	12.5590	369	14.5275	419	16.4960	469	18.4645
270	10.6299	320	12.5984	370	14.5669	420	16.5354	470	18.5039
271	10.6693	321	12.6378	371	14.6063	421	16.5748	471	18.5433
272	10.7086	322	12.6771	372	14.6456	422	16.6141	472	18.5826
273	10.7480	323	12.7165	373	14.6850	423	16.6535	473	18.6220
274	10.7874	324	12.7559	374	14.7244	424	16.6929	474	18.6614
275	10.8267	325	12.7952	375	14.7637	425	16.7322	475	18.7007
276	10.8661	326	12.8346	376	14.8031	426	16.7716	476	18.7401
277	10.9055	327	12.8740	377	14.8425	427	16.8110	477	18.7795
278	10.9449	328	12.9134	378	14.8819	428	16.8504	478	18.8189
279	10.9842	329	12.9527	379	14.9212	429	16.8897	479	18.8582
280	11.0236	330	12.9921	380	14.9606	430	16.9291	480	18.8976
281	11.0630	331	13.0315	381	15.0000	431	16.9685	481	18.9370
282	11.1023	332	13.0708	382	15.0393	432	17.0078	482	18.9763
283	11.1417	333	13.1102	383	15.0787	433	17.0472	483	19.0157
284	11.1811	334	13.1496	384	15.1181	434	17.0866	484	19.0551
285	11.2204	335	13.1889	385	15.1574	435	17.1259	485	19.0944
286	11.2598	336	13.2283	386	15.1968	436	17.1653	486	19.1338
287	11.2992	337	13.2677	387	15.2362	437	17.2047	487	19.1732
288	11.3386	338	13.3071	388	15.2756	438	17.2441	488	19.2126
289	11.3779	339	13.3464	389	15.3149	439	17.2834	489	19.2519
290	11.4173	340	13.3858	390	15.3543	440	17.3228	490	19.2913
291	11.4567	341	13.4252	391	15.3937	441	17.3622	491	19.3307
292	11.4960	342	13.4645	392	15.4330	442	17.4015	492	19.3700
293	11.5354	343	13.5039	393	15.4724	443	17.4409	493	19.4094
294	11.5748	344	13.5433	394	15.5118	444	17.4803	494	19.4488
295	11.6141	345	13.5826	395	15.5511	445	17.5196	495	19.4881
296	11.6535	346	13.6220	396	15.5905	446	17.5590	496	19.5275
297	11.6929	347	13.6614	397	15.6299	447	17.5984	497	19.5669
298	11.7323	348	13.7008	398	15.6693	448	17.6378	498	19.6063
299	11.7716	349	13.7401	399	15.7086	449	17.6771	499	19.6456
300	11.8110	350	13.7795	400	15.7480	450	17.7165	500	19.6850

TABLE FOR CONVERTING MILLIMETERS INTO INCHES
(Continued)

MILLI-METERS.	INCHES.	MILLI-METERS.	INCHES.	MILLI-METERS.	INCHES.	MILLI-METERS.	INCHES.	MILLI-METERS.	INCHES.
501	19.7244	551	21.6929	601	23.6614	651	25.6299	701	27.5984
502	19.7637	552	21.7322	602	23.7007	652	25.6692	702	27.6377
503	19.8031	553	21.7716	603	23.7401	653	25.7086	703	27.6771
504	19.8425	554	21.8110	604	23.7795	654	25.7480	704	27.7165
505	19.8818	555	21.8503	605	23.8188	655	25.7873	705	27.7558
506	19.9212	556	21.8897	606	23.8582	656	25.8267	706	27.7952
507	19.9606	557	21.9291	607	23.8976	657	25.8661	707	27.8346
508	20.0000	558	21.9685	608	23.9370	658	25.9055	708	27.8740
509	20.0393	559	22.0078	609	23.9763	659	25.9448	709	27.9133
510	20.0787	560	22.0472	610	24.0157	660	25.9842	710	27.9527
511	20.1181	561	22.0866	611	24.0551	661	26.0236	711	27.9921
512	20.1574	562	22.1259	612	24.0944	662	26.0629	712	28.0314
513	20.1968	563	22.1653	613	24.1338	663	26.1023	713	28.0708
514	20.2362	564	22.2047	614	24.1732	664	26.1417	714	28.1102
515	20.2755	565	22.2440	615	24.2125	665	26.1810	715	28.1495
516	20.3149	566	22.2834	616	24.2519	666	26.2204	716	28.1889
517	20.3543	567	22.3228	617	24.2913	667	26.2598	717	28.2283
518	20.3937	568	22.3622	618	24.3307	668	26.2992	718	28.2677
519	20.4330	569	22.4015	619	24.3700	669	26.3385	719	28.3070
520	20.4724	570	22.4409	620	24.4094	670	26.3779	720	28.3464
521	20.5118	571	22.4803	621	24.4488	671	26.4173	721	28.3858
522	20.5511	572	22.5196	622	24.4881	672	26.4566	722	28.4251
523	20.5905	573	22.5590	623	24.5275	673	26.4960	723	28.4645
524	20.6299	574	22.5984	624	24.5669	674	26.5354	724	28.5039
525	20.6692	575	22.6377	625	24.6062	675	26.5747	725	28.5432
526	20.7086	576	22.6771	626	24.6456	676	26.6141	726	28.5826
527	20.7480	577	22.7165	627	24.6850	677	26.6535	727	28.6220
528	20.7874	578	22.7559	628	24.7244	678	26.6929	728	28.6614
529	20.8267	579	22.7952	629	24.7637	679	26.7322	729	28.7007
530	20.8661	580	22.8346	630	24.8031	680	26.7716	730	28.7401
531	20.9055	581	22.8740	631	24.8425	681	26.8110	731	28.7795
532	20.9448	582	22.9133	632	24.8818	682	26.8503	732	28.8188
533	20.9842	583	22.9527	633	24.9212	683	26.8897	733	28.8582
534	21.0236	584	22.9921	634	24.9606	684	26.9291	734	28.8976
535	21.0629	585	23.0314	635	24.9999	685	26.9684	735	28.9369
536	21.1023	586	23.0708	636	25.0393	686	27.0078	736	28.9763
537	21.1417	587	23.1102	637	25.0787	687	27.0472	737	29.0157
538	21.1811	588	23.1496	638	25.1181	688	27.0866	738	29.0551
539	21.2204	589	23.1889	639	25.1574	689	27.1259	739	29.0944
540	21.2598	590	23.2283	640	25.1968	690	27.1653	740	29.1338
541	21.2992	591	23.2677	641	25.2362	691	27.2047	741	29.1732
542	21.3385	592	23.3070	642	25.2755	692	27.2440	742	29.2125
543	21.3779	593	23.3464	643	25.3149	693	27.2834	743	29.2519
544	21.4173	594	23.3858	644	25.3543	694	27.3228	744	29.2913
545	21.4566	595	23.4251	645	25.3936	695	27.3621	745	29.3307
546	21.4960	596	23.4645	646	25.4330	696	27.4015	746	29.3700
547	21.5354	597	23.5039	647	25.4724	697	27.4409	747	29.4094
548	21.5748	598	23.5433	648	25.5118	698	27.4803	748	29.4487
549	21.6141	599	23.5826	649	25.5511	699	27.5196	749	29.4881
550	21.6535	600	23.6220	650	25.5905	700	27.5590	750	29.5275

TABLE FOR CONVERTING MILLIMETERS INTO INCHES
(Continued)

MILLI-METERS.	INCHES.	MILLI-METERS.	INCHES.	MILLI-METERS.	INCHES.	MILLI-METERS.	INCHES.	MILLI-METERS.	INCHES.
751	29.5669	801	31.5354	851	33.5039	901	35.4728	951	37.4409
752	29.6062	802	31.5747	852	33.5432	902	35.5117	952	37.4802
753	29.6456	803	31.6141	853	33.5826	903	35.5511	953	37.5196
754	29.6850	804	31.6535	854	33.6220	904	35.5905	954	37.5590
755	29.7243	805	31.6928	855	33.6613	905	35.6298	955	37.5983
756	29.7637	806	31.7322	856	33.7007	906	35.6692	956	37.6377
757	29.8031	807	31.7716	857	33.7401	907	35.7086	957	37.6771
758	29.8425	808	31.8110	858	33.7795	908	35.7480	958	37.7165
759	29.8818	809	31.8503	859	33.8188	909	35.7873	959	37.7558
760	29.9212	810	31.8897	860	33.8582	910	35.8267	960	37.7952
761	29.9606	811	31.9291	861	33.8976	911	35.8661	961	37.8346
762	29.9999	812	31.9684	862	33.9369	912	35.9054	962	37.8739
763	30.0393	813	32.0078	863	33.9763	913	35.9448	963	37.9133
764	30.0787	814	32.0472	864	34.0157	914	35.9842	964	37.9527
765	30.1180	815	32.0865	865	34.0550	915	36.0235	965	37.9920
766	30.1574	816	32.1259	866	34.0944	916	36.0629	966	38.0314
767	30.1968	817	32.1653	867	34.1338	917	36.1023	967	38.0708
768	30.2362	818	32.2047	868	34.1732	918	36.1417	968	38.1102
769	30.2755	819	32.2440	869	34.2125	919	36.1810	969	38.1495
770	30.3149	820	32.2834	870	34.2519	920	36.2204	970	38.1889
771	30.3543	821	32.3228	871	34.2913	921	36.2598	971	38.2283
772	30.3936	822	32.3621	872	34.3306	922	36.2991	972	38.2676
773	30.4330	823	32.4015	873	34.3700	923	36.3385	973	38.3070
774	30.4724	824	32.4409	874	34.4094	924	36.3779	974	38.3464
775	30.5117	825	32.4802	875	34.4487	925	36.4172	975	38.3857
776	30.5511	826	32.5196	876	34.4881	926	36.4566	976	38.4251
777	30.5905	827	32.5590	877	34.5275	927	36.4960	977	38.4645
778	30.6299	828	32.5984	878	34.5669	928	36.5354	978	38.5039
779	30.6692	829	32.6377	879	34.6062	929	36.5747	979	38.5432
780	30.7086	830	32.6771	880	34.6456	930	36.6141	980	38.5826
781	30.7480	831	32.7165	881	34.6850	931	36.6535	981	38.6220
782	30.7873	832	32.7558	882	34.7243	932	36.6928	982	38.6613
783	30.8267	833	32.7952	883	34.7637	933	36.7322	983	38.7007
784	30.8661	834	32.8346	834	34.8031	934	36.7716	984	38.7401
785	30.9054	835	32.8739	885	34.8424	935	36.8109	985	38.7794
786	30.9448	836	32.9133	886	34.8818	936	36.8503	986	38.8188
787	30.9842	837	32.9527	887	34.9212	937	36.8897	987	38.8582
788	31.0236	838	32.9921	888	34.9606	938	36.9291	988	38.8976
789	31.0629	839	33.0314	889	34.9999	939	36.9684	989	38.9369
790	31.1023	840	33.0708	890	35.0393	940	37.0078	990	38.9763
791	31.1417	841	33.1102	891	35.0787	941	37.0472	991	39.0157
792	31.1810	842	33.1495	892	35.1180	942	37.0865	992	39.0550
793	31.2204	843	33.1889	893	35.1574	943	37.1259	993	39.0944
794	31.2598	844	33.2283	894	35.1968	944	37.1653	994	39.1338
795	31.2991	845	33.2676	895	35.2361	945	37.2046	995	39.1731
796	31.3385	846	33.3070	896	35.2755	946	37.2440	996	39.2125
797	31.3779	847	33.3464	897	35.3149	947	37.2834	997	39.2519
798	31.4173	848	33.3858	898	35.3543	948	37.3228	998	39.2913
799	31.4566	849	33.4251	899	35.3936	949	37.3621	999	39.3306
800	31.4960	850	33.4645	900	35.4330	950	37.4015	1000	39.3700

EQUIVALENTS OF INCHES IN MILLIMETERS

In.	0	1/16	1/8	3/16	1/4	5/16	3/8	7/16	In.
0	.000	1.587	3.175	4.762	6.350	7.937	9.525	11.112	0
1	25.40	26.987	28.574	30.162	31.749	33.337	34.924	36.512	1
2	50.799	52.387	53.974	55.561	57.149	58.736	60.324	61.911	2
3	76.199	77.786	79.374	80.961	82.549	84.136	85.723	87.311	3
4	101.60	103.19	104.77	106.36	107.95	109.54	111.12	112.71	4
5	127.00	128.59	130.17	131.76	133.35	134.94	136.52	138.11	5
6	152.40	153.98	155.57	157.16	158.75	160.33	161.92	163.51	6
7	177.80	179.38	180.97	182.56	184.15	185.73	187.32	188.91	7
8	203.20	204.78	206.37	207.96	209.55	211.13	212.72	214.31	8
9	228.60	230.18	231.77	233.36	234.95	236.53	238.12	239.71	9
10	254.00	255.58	257.17	258.76	260.35	261.93	263.52	265.11	10
11	279.39	280.98	282.57	284.16	285.74	287.33	288.92	290.51	11
12	304.79	306.38	307.97	309.56	311.14	312.73	314.32	315.91	12
13	330.19	331.78	333.37	334.96	336.54	338.13	339.72	341.31	13
14	355.59	357.18	358.77	360.36	361.94	363.53	365.12	366.71	14
15	380.99	382.58	384.17	385.76	387.34	388.93	390.52	392.11	15
16	406.39	407.98	409.57	411.16	412.74	414.33	415.92	417.50	16
17	431.79	433.38	434.97	436.55	438.14	439.73	441.32	442.90	17
18	457.19	458.78	460.37	461.95	463.54	465.13	466.72	468.30	18
19	482.59	484.18	485.77	487.35	488.94	490.53	492.12	493.70	19
20	507.99	509.58	511.17	512.75	514.34	515.93	517.52	519.10	20
21	533.39	534.98	536.57	538.15	539.74	541.33	542.92	544.50	21
22	558.79	560.38	561.96	563.55	565.14	566.73	568.31	569.90	22
23	584.19	585.78	587.36	588.95	590.54	592.13	593.71	595.30	23
24	609.59	611.18	612.76	614.35	615.94	617.53	619.11	620.70	24
25	634.99	636.58	638.16	639.75	641.34	642.93	644.51	646.10	25
26	660.39	661.98	663.56	665.15	666.74	668.33	669.91	671.50	26
27	685.79	687.38	688.96	690.55	692.14	693.72	695.31	696.90	27
28	711.19	712.77	714.36	715.95	717.54	719.12	720.71	722.30	28
29	736.59	738.17	739.76	741.35	742.94	744.52	746.11	747.70	29
30	761.99	763.57	765.16	766.75	768.34	769.92	771.51	773.10	30
31	787.39	788.97	790.56	792.15	793.74	795.32	796.91	798.50	31
32	812.79	814.37	815.96	817.55	819.14	820.72	822.31	823.90	32
33	838.18	839.77	841.36	842.95	844.53	846.12	847.71	849.30	33
34	863.15	865.17	866.76	868.35	869.93	871.52	873.11	874.70	34
35	888.98	890.57	892.16	893.75	895.33	896.92	898.51	900.10	35
36	914.38	915.97	917.56	919.15	920.73	922.32	923.91	925.50	36
37	939.78	941.37	942.96	944.55	946.13	947.72	949.31	950.90	37
38	965.18	966.77	968.36	969.94	971.53	973.12	974.71	976.29	38
39	990.58	992.17	993.76	995.34	996.93	998.52	1000.1	1001.7	39
40	1016.0	1017.6	1019.2	1020.7	1022.3	1023.9	1025.5	1027.1	40
41	1041.4	1043.0	1044.6	1046.1	1047.7	1049.3	1050.9	1052.5	41
42	1066.8	1068.4	1070.0	1071.5	1073.1	1074.7	1076.3	1077.9	42
43	1092.2	1093.8	1095.4	1096.9	1098.5	1100.1	1101.7	1103.3	43
44	1117.6	1119.2	1120.8	1122.3	1123.9	1125.5	1127.1	1128.7	44
45	1143.0	1144.6	1146.2	1147.7	1149.3	1150.9	1152.5	1154.1	45
46	1168.4	1170.0	1171.6	1173.1	1174.7	1176.3	1177.9	1179.5	46
47	1193.8	1195.4	1197.0	1198.5	1200.1	1201.7	1203.3	1204.9	47
48	1219.2	1220.8	1222.4	1223.9	1225.5	1227.1	1228.7	1230.3	48
49	1244.6	1246.2	1247.8	1249.3	1250.9	1252.5	1254.1	1255.7	49
50	1270.0	1271.6	1273.2	1274.7	1276.3	1277.9	1279.5	1281.1	50

EQUIVALENTS OF INCHES IN MILLIMETERS (Cont'd)

In.	½	9/16	5/8	11/16	¾	13/16	7/8	15/16	In.
0	12.700	14.287	15.875	17.462	19.050	20.637	22.225	23.812	0
1	38.099	39.687	41.274	42.862	44.449	46.037	47.624	49.212	1
2	63.499	65.086	66.674	68.261	69.849	71.436	73.024	74.611	2
3	88.898	90.486	92.073	93.661	95.248	96.836	98.423	100.01	3
4	114.30	115.89	117.47	119.06	120.65	122.24	123.82	125.41	4
5	139.70	141.28	142.87	144.46	146.05	147.63	149.22	150.81	5
6	165.10	166.68	168.27	169.86	171.45	173.03	174.62	176.21	6
7	190.50	192.08	193.67	195.26	196.85	198.43	200.02	201.61	7
8	215.90	217.48	219.07	220.66	222.25	223.83	225.42	227.01	8
9	241.30	242.88	244.47	246.06	247.65	249.23	250.82	252.41	9
10	266.70	268.28	269.87	271.46	273.05	274.63	276.22	277.81	10
11	292.09	293.68	295.27	296.86	298.44	300.03	301.62	303.21	11
12	317.49	319.08	320.67	322.26	323.84	325.43	327.02	328.61	12
13	342.89	344.48	346.07	347.66	349.24	350.83	352.42	354.01	13
14	368.29	369.88	371.47	373.06	374.64	376.23	377.82	379.41	14
15	393.69	395.28	396.87	398.46	400.04	401.63	403.22	404.81	15
16	419.09	420.68	422.27	423.85	425.44	427.03	428.62	430.20	16
17	444.49	446.08	447.67	449.25	450.84	452.43	454.02	455.60	17
18	469.89	471.48	473.07	474.65	476.24	477.83	479.42	481.00	18
19	495.29	496.88	498.47	500.05	501.64	503.23	504.82	506.40	19
20	520.69	522.28	523.87	525.45	527.04	528.63	530.22	531.80	20
21	546.09	547.68	549.27	550.85	552.44	554.03	555.61	557.20	21
22	571.49	573.08	574.66	576.25	577.84	579.43	581.01	582.60	22
23	596.89	598.48	600.06	601.65	603.24	604.83	606.41	608.00	23
24	622.29	623.88	625.46	627.05	628.64	630.23	631.81	633.40	24
25	647.69	649.28	650.86	652.45	654.04	655.63	657.21	658.80	25
26	673.09	674.68	676.26	677.85	679.44	681.03	682.61	684.20	26
27	698.49	700.07	701.66	703.25	704.84	706.42	708.01	709.60	27
28	723.89	725.47	727.06	728.65	730.24	731.82	733.41	735.00	28
29	749.29	750.87	752.46	754.05	755.64	757.22	758.81	760.40	29
30	774.69	776.27	777.86	779.45	781.04	782.62	784.21	785.80	30
31	800.09	801.67	803.26	804.85	806.44	808.02	809.61	811.20	31
32	825.49	827.07	828.66	830.25	831.83	833.42	835.01	836.60	32
33	850.88	852.47	854.06	855.65	857.23	858.82	860.41	862.00	33
34	876.28	877.87	879.46	881.05	882.63	884.22	885.81	887.40	34
35	901.68	903.27	904.86	906.45	908.03	909.62	911.21	912.80	35
36	927.08	928.67	930.26	931.85	933.43	935.02	936.61	938.20	36
37	952.48	954.07	955.66	957.25	958.83	960.42	962.01	963.60	37
38	977.88	979.47	981.06	982.64	984.23	985.82	987.41	988.99	38
39	1003.3	1004.9	1006.5	1008.0	1009.6	1011.2	1012.8	1014.4	39
40	1028.7	1030.3	1031.9	1033.4	1035.0	1036.6	1038.2	1039.8	40
41	1054.1	1055.7	1057.3	1058.8	1060.4	1062.0	1063.6	1065.2	41
42	1079.5	1081.1	1082.7	1084.2	1085.8	1087.4	1089.0	1090.6	42
43	1104.9	1106.5	1108.1	1109.6	1111.2	1112.8	1114.4	1116.0	43
44	1130.3	1131.9	1133.5	1135.0	1136.6	1138.2	1139.8	1141.4	44
45	1155.7	1157.3	1158.9	1160.4	1162.0	1163.6	1165.2	1166.8	45
46	1181.1	1182.7	1184.3	1185.8	1187.4	1189.0	1190.6	1192.2	46
47	1206.5	1208.1	1209.7	1211.2	1212.8	1214.4	1216.0	1217.6	47
48	1231.9	1233.5	1235.1	1236.6	1238.2	1239.8	1241.4	1243.0	48
49	1257.3	1258.9	1260.5	1262.0	1263.6	1265.2	1266.8	1268.4	49
50	1282.7	1284.3	1285.9	1287.4	1289.0	1290.6	1292.2	1293.8	50

EQUIVALENTS OF SQUARE CENTIMETERS IN SQUARE INCHES

SQ. CM.	.0	.1	.2	.3	.4	.5	.6	.7	.8	.9
0	—	.01550	.03100	.04650	.06200	.07750	.09300	.10850	.12400	.13951
1	.15501	.17051	.18601	.20151	.21701	.23251	.24801	.26351	.27901	.29451
2	.31001	.32551	.34101	.35651	.37201	.38751	.40301	.41852	.43402	.44952
3	.46502	.48052	.49602	.51152	.52702	.54252	.55802	.57352	.58902	.60452
4	.62002	.63552	.65102	.66652	.68203	.69753	.71303	.72853	.74403	.75953
5	.77503	.79053	.80603	.82153	.83703	.85253	.86803	.88353	.89903	.91453
6	.93004	.94554	.96104	.97654	.99204	1.00754	1.02304	1.03854	1.05404	1.06954
7	1.08504	1.10054	1.11604	1.13154	1.14704	1.16254	1.17804	1.19355	1.20905	1.22455
8	1.24005	1.25555	1.27105	1.28655	1.30205	1.31755	1.33305	1.34855	1.36405	1.37955
9	1.39505	1.41055	1.42605	1.44156	1.45706	1.47256	1.48806	1.50356	1.51906	1.53456
10	1.55006	1.56556	1.58106	1.59656	1.61206	1.62756	1.64306	1.65856	1.67406	1.68956

EQUIVALENTS OF SQUARE INCHES IN SQUARE CENTIMETERS

SQ. IN.	.0	.1	.2	.3	.4	.5	.6	.7	.8	.9
0	—	.6451	1.2903	1.9354	2.5805	3.2257	3.8708	4.5160	5.1611	5.8062
1	6.4515	7.0965	7.7416	8.3868	9.0319	9.6770	10.3222	10.9673	11.6125	12.2576
2	12.9027	13.5479	14.1930	14.8381	15.4833	16.1284	16.7736	17.4187	18.0638	18.7090
3	19.3541	19.9992	20.6444	21.2895	21.9346	22.5798	23.2249	23.8701	24.5152	25.1603
4	25.8055	26.4506	27.0957	27.7409	28.3860	29.0312	29.6763	30.3214	30.9666	31.6117
5	32.2568	32.9020	33.5471	34.1922	34.8374	35.4825	36.1277	36.7728	37.4179	38.0631
6	38.7082	39.3533	39.9985	40.6436	41.2887	41.9339	42.5790	43.2242	43.8693	44.5144
7	45.1596	45.8047	46.4498	47.0950	47.7401	48.3853	49.0304	49.6755	50.3207	50.9658
8	51.6109	52.2561	52.9012	53.5463	54.1915	54.8366	55.4818	56.1269	56.7720	57.4172
9	58.0623	58.7074	59.3526	59.9977	60.6428	61.2880	61.9331	62.5783	63.2234	63.8685
10	64.5137	65.1588	65.8039	66.4491	67.0942	67.7394	68.3845	69.0296	69.6748	70.3199

EQUIVALENTS OF METERS IN FEET

METERS.	.0	.1	.2	.3	.4	.5	.6	.7	.8	.9
0	—	.3281	.6562	.9843	1.3124	1.6404	1.9685	2.2966	2.6247	2.9528
1	3.2809	3.6090	3.9371	4.2652	4.5933	4.9213	5.2494	5.5775	5.9056	6.2337
2	6.5618	6.8899	7.2180	7.5461	7.8742	8.2022	8.5303	8.8584	9.1865	9.5146
3	9.8427	10.1708	10.4989	10.8270	11.1551	11.4831	11.8112	12.1393	12.4674	12.7955
4	13.1236	13.4517	13.7798	14.1079	14.4360	14.7640	15.0921	15.4202	15.7483	16.0764
5	16.4045	16.7326	17.0607	17.3888	17.7169	18.0449	18.3730	18.7011	19.0292	19.3573
6	19.6854	20.0135	20.3416	20.6697	20.9978	21.3258	21.6539	21.9820	22.3101	22.6382
7	22.9663	23.2944	23.6225	23.9506	24.2787	24.6067	24.9348	25.2629	25.5910	25.9191
8	26.2472	26.5753	26.9034	27.2315	27.5596	27.8876	28.2157	28.5438	28.8719	29.2000
9	29.5281	29.8562	30.1843	30.5124	30.8405	31.1685	31.4966	31.8247	32.1528	32.4809
10	32.8090	33.1371	33.4652	33.7933	34.1213	34.4494	34.7775	35.1056	35.4337	35.7618

EQUIVALENTS OF FEET IN METERS

FEET.	.0	.1	.2	.3	.4	.5	.6	.7	.8	.9
0	—	.03048	.06096	.09144	.12192	.15240	.18288	.21336	.24384	.27432
1	.30480	.33527	.36575	.39623	.42671	.45719	.48767	.51815	.54863	.57911
2	.60959	.64007	.67055	.70103	.73151	.76199	.79247	.82295	.85342	.88390
3	.91438	.94486	.97534	1.00582	1.03630	1.06678	1.09726	1.12774	1.15822	1.18870
4	1.21918	1.24966	1.28014	1.31062	1.34110	1.37158	1.40205	1.43253	1.46301	1.49349
5	1.52397	1.55445	1.58493	1.61541	1.64589	1.67637	1.70685	1.73733	1.76781	1.79829
6	1.82877	1.85925	1.88973	1.92020	1.95068	1.98116	2.01164	2.04212	2.07260	2.10308
7	2.13356	2.16404	2.19452	2.22500	2.25548	2.28596	2.31644	2.34692	2.37740	2.40788
8	2.43836	2.46884	2.49931	2.52979	2.56027	2.59075	2.62123	2.65171	2.68219	2.71267
9	2.74315	2.77363	2.80411	2.83459	2.86507	2.89555	2.92603	2.95651	2.98699	3.01747
10	3.04794	3.07842	3.10890	3.13938	3.16986	3.20034	3.23082	3.26130	3.29178	3.32226

EQUIVALENTS OF CUBIC CENTIMETERS IN CUBIC INCHES

CU. CM.	.0	.1	.2	.3	.4	.5	.6	.7	.8	.9
0	—	.006103	.012205	.018308	.024411	.030514	.036613	.042719	.048822	.054924
1	.061027	.067130	.073232	.079335	.085488	.091541	.097643	.103746	.109849	.115951
2	.122054	.128157	.134260	.140362	.146465	.152568	.158670	.164773	.170876	.176978
3	.183081	.189184	.195287	.201389	.207492	.213595	.219697	.225800	.231903	.238005
4	.244108	.250211	.256314	.262416	.268519	.274622	.280724	.286827	.292930	.299033
5	.305135	.311238	.317341	.323443	.329546	.335649	.341751	.347854	.353957	.360060
6	.366162	.372265	.378368	.384470	.390573	.396676	.402779	.408881	.414984	.421087
7	.427189	.433292	.439395	.445497	.451600	.457703	.463806	.469908	.476011	.482114
8	.488216	.494319	.500422	.506525	.512627	.518730	.524833	.530935	.537038	.543141
9	.549243	.555346	.561449	.567552	.573654	.579757	.585860	.591962	.598065	.604168
10	.610271	.616373	.622476	.628579	.634681	.640784	.646887	.652989	.659092	.665195

EQUIVALENTS OF CUBIC INCHES IN CUBIC CENTIMETERS

CU. IN.	.0	.1	.2	.3	.4	.5	.6	.7	.8	.9
0	—	1.639	3.277	4.916	6.554	8.193	9.832	11.470	13.109	14.748
1	16.386	18.025	19.663	21.302	22.941	24.579	26.218	27.856	29.495	31.134
2	32.772	34.411	36.050	37.608	39.327	40.965	42.604	44.243	45.881	47.520
3	49.158	50.797	52.436	54.074	55.713	57.352	58.990	60.629	62.267	63.906
4	65.545	67.183	68.822	70.461	72.099	73.738	75.376	77.015	78.654	80.292
5	81.931	83.569	85.208	86.847	88.485	90.124	91.763	93.401	95.040	96.678
6	98.317	99.956	101.594	103.233	104.872	106.510	108.149	109.787	111.426	113.065
7	114.703	116.342	117.980	119.619	121.258	122.896	124.535	126.174	127.812	129.451
8	131.089	132.728	134.367	136.005	137.644	139.282	140.921	142.560	144.198	145.837
9	147.476	149.114	150.753	152.391	154.030	155.669	157.307	158.946	160.585	162.223
10	163.862	165.500	167.139	168.778	170.416	172.055	173.693	175.332	176.971	178.609

EQUIVALENTS OF CENTIMETERS IN INCHES

CM.	0	1	2	3	4	5	6	7	8	9
0	—	.394	.787	1.181	1.575	1.969	2.362	2.756	3.150	3.543
10	3.937	4.331	4.724	5.118	5.512	5.906	6.299	6.693	7.087	7.480
20	7.874	8.268	8.661	9.055	9.449	9.843	10.236	10.630	11.024	11.417
30	11.811	12.205	12.598	12.992	13.386	13.780	14.173	14.567	14.961	15.354
40	15.748	16.142	16.535	16.929	17.323	17.717	18.110	18.504	18.898	19.291
50	19.685	20.079	20.472	20.866	21.260	21.654	22.047	22.441	22.835	23.228
60	23.622	24.016	24.409	24.803	25.197	25.591	25.984	26.378	26.772	27.165
70	27.559	27.953	28.346	28.740	29.134	29.528	29.921	30.315	30.709	31.102
80	31.496	31.890	32.283	32.677	33.071	33.465	33.858	34.252	34.646	35.039
90	35.433	35.827	36.220	36.614	37.008	37.402	37.795	38.189	38.583	38.976

DECIMAL EQUIVALENTS OF FRACTIONS OF AN INCH

Decimal Equivalents of 6ths, 12ths, and 24ths of an Inch

Fraction	Decimal	Fraction	Decimal	Fraction	Decimal	Fraction	Decimal
1/24	0.041 667	7/24	0.291 667	13/24	0.541 667	19/24	0.791 667
1/12	0.083 333	2/6	0.333 333	7/12	0.583 333	5/6	0.833 333
3/24	0.125	9/24	0.375	15/24	0.625	21/24	0.875
1/6	0.166 667	5/12	0.416 667	4/6	0.666 667	11/12	0.916 667
5/24	0.208 333	11/24	0.458 333	17/24	0.708 333	23/24	0.958 333
3/12	0.25	3/6	0.5	9/12	0.75		

Decimal Equivalents of 7ths, 14ths, and 28ths of an Inch

Fraction	Decimal	Fraction	Decimal	Fraction	Decimal	Fraction	Decimal
1/28	0.035 714	2/7	0.285 714	15/28	0.535 714	11/14	0.785 714
1/14	0.071 429	9/28	0.321 429	4/7	0.571 429	23/28	0.821 429
3/28	0.107 143	5/14	0.357 143	17/28	0.607 143	6/7	0.857 143
1/7	0.142 857	11/28	0.392 857	9/14	0.642 857	25/28	0.892 857
5/28	0.178 571	3/7	0.428 571	19/28	0.678 571	13/14	0.928 571
3/14	0.214 286	13/28	0.464 286	5/7	0.714 286	27/28	0.964 286
7/28	0.25	7/14	0.5	21/28	0.75		

INCHES INTO DECIMALS OF A FOOT

INCH.	0	1	2	3	4	5	6	7	8	9	10	11
						DECIMALS OF A FOOT.						
....	.....	0.0833	0.1667	0.2500	0.3333	0.4167	0.5000	0.5833	0.6667	0.7500	0.8333	0.9167
1/32	.0026	0.0859	0.1693	0.2526	0.3359	0.4193	0.5026	0.5859	0.6693	0.7526	0.8359	0.9193
1/16	.0052	0.0885	0.1719	0.2552	0.3385	0.4219	0.5052	0.5885	0.6719	0.7552	0.8385	0.9219
3/32	.0078	0.0911	0.1745	0.2578	0.3411	0.4245	0.5078	0.5911	0.6745	0.7578	0.8411	0.9245
1/8	.0104	0.0938	0.1771	0.2604	0.3438	0.4271	0.5104	0.5938	0.6771	0.7604	0.8438	0.9271
5/32	.0130	0.0964	0.1797	0.2630	0.3464	0.4297	0.5130	0.5964	0.6797	0.7630	0.8464	0.9297
3/16	.0156	0.0990	0.1823	0.2656	0.3490	0.4323	0.5156	0.5990	0.6823	0.7656	0.8490	0.9323
7/32	.0182	0.1016	0.1849	0.2682	0.3516	0.4349	0.5182	0.6016	0.6849	0.7682	0.8516	0.9349
1/4	.0208	0.1042	0.1875	0.2708	0.3542	0.4375	0.5208	0.6042	0.6875	0.7708	0.8542	0.9375
9/32	.0234	0.1068	0.1901	0.2734	0.3568	0.4401	0.5234	0.6068	0.6901	0.7734	0.8568	0.9401
5/16	.0260	0.1094	0.1927	0.2760	0.3594	0.4427	0.5260	0.6094	0.6927	0.7760	0.8594	0.9427
11/32	.0286	0.1120	0.1953	0.2786	0.3620	0.4453	0.5286	0.6120	0.6953	0.7786	0.8620	0.9453
3/8	.0313	0.1146	0.1979	0.2813	0.3646	0.4479	0.5313	0.6146	0.6979	0.7813	0.8646	0.9479
13/32	.0339	0.1172	0.2005	0.2839	0.3672	0.4505	0.5339	0.6172	0.7005	0.7839	0.8672	0.9505
7/16	.0365	0.1198	0.2031	0.2865	0.3698	0.4531	0.5365	0.6193	0.7031	0.7865	0.8698	0.9531
15/32	.0391	0.1224	0.2057	0.2891	0.3724	0.4557	0.5391	0.6224	0.7057	0.7891	0.8724	0.9557
1/2	.0417	0.1250	0.2083	0.2917	0.3750	0.4583	0.5417	0.6250	0.7083	0.7917	0.8750	0.9583
17/32	.0443	0.1276	0.2109	0.2943	0.3776	0.4609	0.5443	0.6276	0.7109	0.7943	0.8776	0.9609
9/16	.0469	0.1302	0.2135	0.2969	0.3802	0.4635	0.5469	0.6302	0.7135	0.7969	0.8802	0.9635
19/32	.0495	0.1328	0.2161	0.2995	0.3828	0.4661	0.5495	0.6328	0.7161	0.7995	0.8828	0.9661
5/8	.0521	0.1354	0.2188	0.3021	0.3854	0.4688	0.5521	0.6354	0.7188	0.8021	0.8854	0.9688
21/32	.0547	0.1380	0.2214	0.3047	0.3880	0.4714	0.5547	0.6380	0.7214	0.8047	0.8880	0.9714
11/16	.0573	0.1406	0.2240	0.3073	0.3906	0.4740	0.5573	0.6406	0.7240	0.8073	0.8906	0.9740
23/32	.0599	0.1432	0.2266	0.3099	0.3932	0.4766	0.5599	0.6432	0.7266	0.8099	0.8932	0.9766
3/4	.0625	0.1458	0.2292	0.3125	0.3958	0.4792	0.5625	0.6458	0.7292	0.8125	0.8958	0.9792
25/32	.0651	0.1484	0.2318	0.3151	0.3984	0.4818	0.5651	0.6484	0.7318	0.8151	0.8984	0.9818
13/16	.0677	0.1510	0.2344	0.3177	0.4010	0.4844	0.5677	0.6510	0.7344	0.8177	0.9010	0.9844
27/32	.0703	0.1536	0.2370	0.3203	0.4036	0.4870	0.5703	0.6536	0.7370	0.8203	0.9036	0.9870
7/8	.0729	0.1563	0.2396	0.3229	0.4063	0.4896	0.5729	0.6563	0.7396	0.8229	0.9063	0.9896
29/32	.0755	0.1589	0.2422	0.3255	0.4089	0.4922	0.5755	0.6589	0.7422	0.8255	0.9089	0.9922
15/16	.0781	0.1615	0.2448	0.3281	0.4115	0.4948	0.5781	0.6615	0.7448	0.8281	0.9115	0.9948
31/32	.0807	0.1641	0.2474	0.3307	0.4141	0.4974	0.5807	0.6641	0.7474	0.8307	0.9141	0.9974

PROPERTIES OF SOME METALLIC ELEMENTS

NAME.	SYM-BOL.	ATOMIC WEIGHT.	SPECIFIC GRAVITY.	SPECIFIC HEAT.	MELTING POINT (CENTI-GRADE).	COEFFICIENT OF LINEAR EXPANSION.
					deg.	
Aluminum .	Al	27.1	2.67	.2140	657	.0000231
Antimony .	Sb	120.2	6.71–6.85	.0508	630	.0000105
Barium . .	Ba	137.4	3.8	.068	850	—
Cadmium .	Cd	112.4	8.546–8.66	.0548	322	.000027
Calcium . .	Ca	40.1	1.578	.1700	800	.0000269
Chromium .	Cr	52.0	6.8–7.3	.1200	1,700	—
Cobalt . .	Co	59.0	8.5–8.7	.1070	90	.0000123
Copper . .	Cu	63.6	8.9	.0952	1,100	.0000167
Gold . .	Au	197.2	19.265	.0324	1,065	.0000136
Iron . .	Fe	55.9	7.84	.1140	1,550	.0000116
Lead . .	Pb	207.1	11.25–11.38	.0314	328	.000027
Lithium . .	Li	7.02	.59	.9410	180	—
Magnesium .	Mg	24.30	1.75	.2500	750	.0000269
Manganese .	Mn	55.0	8.0	.1220	1,245	—
Mercury .	Hg	200.0	13.594	.0319	−40	.0000610
Molybdenum	Mo	96.0	8.6	.0722	1,600	—
Nickel . .	Ni	58.7	8.9	.1080	1,450	.0000127
Platinum .	Pt	195.2	21.5	.0324	1,780	.0000089
Potassium .	K	39.10	.875	.1660	60	.000084
Radium . .	Ra	225.0	—	—	—	—
Silver . .	Ag	107.90	10.4–10.57	.056	962	.0000192
Sodium . .	Na	23.0	.98	.293	96	.000071
Tellurium .	Te	127.5	6.25	.049	452	.0000167
Thallium .	Tl	204.0	11.8	.0335	303	.0000302
Thorium .	Th	232.4	11.2	.0276	1,690	—
Tin. . .	Sn	119.0	7.293	.0559	232	.0000203
Titanium .	Ti	48.1	3.6	.13	1,800	—
Tungsten .	W	184.0	19.129	.0334	1,700	—
Uranium .	U	238.5	18.33	.0277	1,600	—
Vanadium .	V	51.1	5.9	.125	1,680	—
Zinc . .	Zn	65.4	7.1	.0935	419	.0000274
Zirconium .	Zr	90.6	4.15	.0662	over 1,300	—

POWER AND HEAT EQUIVALENTS

1 horsepower-hour = 0.746 kilowatt-hour = 1,980,000 foot-pounds = 2550 B.T.U. (British thermal units) = 2.64 pounds of water evaporated at 212° F. = 17 pounds of water raised from 62° to 212° F.

1 kilowatt-hour = 1000 watt-hours = 1.34 horsepower-hour = 2,653,200 foot-pounds = 3,600,000 joules = 3420 B.T.U. = 3.54 pounds of water evaporated at 212° F. = 22.8 pounds of water raised from 62° to 212° F.

1 horsepower = 746 watts = 0.746 kilowatt = 33,000 foot-pounds per minute = 550 foot-pounds per second = 2550 B.T.U. per hour = 42.5 B.T.U. per minute = 0.71 B.T.U. per second = 2.64 pounds of water evaporated per hour at 212° F.

1 kilowatt = 1000 watts = 1.34 horsepower = 2,653,200 foot-pounds per hour = 44,220 foot-pounds per minute = 737 foot-pounds per second = 3420 B.T.U. per hour = 57 B.T.U. per minute = 0.95 B.T.U. per second = 3.54 pounds of water evaporated per hour at 212° F.

1 watt = 1 joule per second = 0.00134 horsepower = 0.001 kilowatt = 3.42 B.T.U. per hour = 44.22 foot-pounds per minute = 0.74 foot-pounds per second = 0.0035 pound of water evaporated per hour at 212° F.

1 B.T.U. (British thermal unit) = 1052 watt-seconds = 778 foot-pounds = 0.252 calorie = 0.000292 kilowatt-hour = 0.000391 horsepower-hour = 0.00104 pound of water evaporated at 212° F.

1 foot-pound = 1.36 joule = 0.000000377 kilowatt-hour = 0.00129 B.T.U. = 0.0000005 horsepower-hour.

1 joule = 1 watt-second = 0.000000278 kilowatt-hour = 0.00095 B.T.U. = 0.74 foot-pound.

TEMPERATURE CONVERSION FORMULA

To convert temperatures from degrees Centigrade to degrees Fahrenheit, use the following equation: $F = 9/5\ (C + 32)$
  where C represents the temperature in degrees Centigrade and F represents the temperature in degrees Fahrenheit.
To convert temperatures from degrees Fahrenheit to degrees Centigrade, use the following equation: $C = 5/9\ (F - 32)$

SINES AND TANGENTS

In a right-angled triangle, the horizontal side is called the base, the vertical side the perpendicular, and the side opposite the right angle the hypotenuse. In all right-angled triangles which have the same angle included between base and hypotenuse or perpendicular and hypotenuse (which, since the sum of the angles is always 180 deg. is really the same thing), the ratios between base and hypotenuse, perpendicular and hypotenuse, and base and perpendicular are constant.

In other words, in two triangles *ABC* and *DEF*, where the right angles are at the corners *B* and *E*, and where the angle at the corner *A* is equal to the angle at the corner *D*, then

$$\frac{AB}{BC} = \frac{DE}{EF}, \quad \frac{BC}{AC} = \frac{EF}{DF},$$

and

$$\frac{AB}{AC} = \frac{DE}{DF}.$$

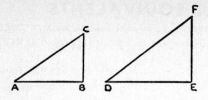

These ratios have been given names. It will be seen that each of the angles other than the right angles is adjoined by the hypotenuse and one of the other sides. The side adjoining the angle is called the "adjacent" side; that opposite it is the "opposite" side. Thus, in the triangle *ABC*, *AB* is the side adjacent to the angle *A*, and *CB* is the side opposite it.

The ratio $\dfrac{\text{opposite side}}{\text{hypotenuse}}$ (in the case of angle *A*, $\dfrac{BC}{AC}$) is called the sine of the angle.

The ratio $\dfrac{\text{adjacent side}}{\text{hypotenuse}}$ (in the case of angle *A*, $\dfrac{AB}{AC}$) is called the cosine.

The ratio $\dfrac{\text{opposite side}}{\text{adjacent side}}$ (in the case of angle *A*, $\dfrac{AB}{BC}$) is called the tangent.

For a mnemonic to help in remembering these ratios, and some illustration of their uses, see Chapter 15, "Measuring and Testing."

It will be seen that $\dfrac{BC}{AC}$, which is the sine of angle *A*, is also the cosine of angle *B*. In other words, the sine of any angle is the same as the cosine of its complement (*i.e.* the difference between it and 90 deg.).

Since these ratios are constant for the same angles irrespective of the lengths of the sides of the triangle, they can be tabulated in order to save working them out each time. On the following pages will be found the Tables of sines and of tangents. It is unnecessary to print a table of cosines, since the cosine of an angle can be discovered from the sine Table by looking up the sine of its complement.

To find the sine or tangent of an angle, the number of degrees in it is located in the left-hand column in the appropriate Table. The figure opposite this in the next column is the required ratio. If, however, the angle is not an exact number of degrees, the number of minutes must be located in the heading of the Table, and the required sine or tangent is the figure that appears at the junction of the degree line and the minute line. To find the cosine, the angle must first be subtracted from 90 deg., and the sine of the remainder looked up in the sine Table. In using these Tables, the minutes should be taken to the nearest 6 min.; this is accurate enough for normal use.

Examples: 1. Find the sine of 42 deg., 83 deg. 30 min., 27 deg. 40 min.

2. Find the cosine of 37 deg., 6 deg. 30 min., 27 deg. 40 min.

3. Find the tangent of 19 deg., 83 deg. 54 min., 27 deg. 40 min.

Answers: 1. .6691; .9936; .4648.

2. .7986; .9936; .8854.

3. .3443; 9.357; .5250.

It is of some interest, and sometimes useful if only a sine Table is available, that the tangent of an angle is equal to its sine divided by its cosine, *i.e.* $\tan A \text{ deg.} = \dfrac{\sin A \text{ deg.}}{\cos A \text{ deg.}}$.

NATURAL SINES

DEG.	0 MIN.	6 MIN.	12 MIN.	18 MIN.	24 MIN.	30 MIN.	36 MIN.	42 MIN.	48 MIN.	54 MIN.
0	—	.0017	.0035	.0052	.0070	.0087	.0105	.0122	.0140	.0157
1	.0175	.0192	.0209	.0227	.0244	.0262	.0279	.0297	.0314	.0332
2	.0349	.0366	.0384	.0401	.0419	.0436	.0454	.0471	.0488	.0506
3	.0523	.0541	.0558	.0576	.0593	.0610	.0628	.0645	.0663	.0680
4	.0698	.0715	.0732	.0750	.0767	.0785	.0802	.0819	.0837	.0854
5	.0872	.0889	.0906	.0924	.0941	.0958	.0976	.0993	.1011	.1028
6	.1045	.1063	.1080	.1097	.1115	.1132	.1149	.1167	.1184	.1201
7	.1219	.1236	.1253	.1271	.1288	.1305	.1323	.1340	.1357	.1374
8	.1392	.1409	.1426	.1444	.1461	.1478	.1495	.1513	.1530	.1547
9	.1564	.1582	.1599	.1616	.1633	.1650	.1668	.1685	.1702	.1719
10	.1736	.1754	.1771	.1788	.1805	.1822	.1840	.1857	.1874	.1891
11	.1908	.1925	.1942	.1959	.1977	.1994	.2011	.2028	.2045	.2062
12	.2079	.2096	.2113	.2130	.2147	.2164	.2181	.2198	.2215	.2233
13	.2250	.2267	.2284	.2300	.2317	.2334	.2351	.2368	.2385	.2402
14	.2419	.2436	.2453	.2470	.2487	.2504	.2521	.2538	.2554	.2571
15	.2588	.2605	.2622	.2639	.2656	.2672	.2689	.2706	.2723	.2740
16	.2756	.2773	.2790	.2807	.2823	.2840	.2857	.2874	.2890	.2907
17	.2924	.2940	.2957	.2974	.2990	.3007	.3024	.3040	.3057	.3074
18	.3090	.3107	.3123	.3140	.3156	.3173	.3190	.3206	.3223	.3239
19	.3256	.3272	.3289	.3305	.3322	.3338	.3355	.3371	.3387	.3404
20	.3420	.3437	.3453	.3469	.3486	.3502	.3518	.3535	.3551	.3567
21	.3584	.3600	.3616	.3633	.3649	.3665	.3681	.3697	.3714	.3730
22	.3746	.3762	.3778	.3795	.3811	.3827	.3843	.3859	.3875	.3891
23	.3907	.3923	.3939	.3955	.3971	.3987	.4003	.4019	.4035	.4051
24	.4067	.4083	.4099	.4115	.4131	.4147	.4163	.4179	.4195	.4210
25	.4226	.4242	.4258	.4274	.4289	.4305	.4321	.4337	.4352	.4368
26	.4384	.4399	.4415	.4431	.4446	.4462	.4478	.4493	.4509	.4524
27	.4540	.4555	.4571	.4586	.4602	.4617	.4633	.4648	.4664	.4679
28	.4695	.4710	.4726	.4741	.4756	.4772	.4787	.4802	.4818	.4833
29	.4848	.4863	.4879	.4894	.4909	.4924	.4939	.4955	.4970	.4985
30	.5000	.5015	.5030	.5045	.5060	.5075	.5090	.5105	.5120	.5135
31	.5150	.5165	.5180	.5195	.5210	.5225	.5240	.5255	.5270	.5284
32	.5299	.5314	.5329	.5344	.5358	.5373	.5388	.5402	.5417	.5432
33	.5446	.5461	.5476	.5490	.5505	.5519	.5534	.5548	.5563	.5577
34	.5592	.5606	.5621	.5635	.5650	.5664	.5678	.5693	.5707	.5721
35	.5736	.5750	.5764	.5779	.5793	.5807	.5821	.5835	.5850	.5864
36	.5878	.5892	.5906	.5920	.5934	.5948	.5962	.5976	.5990	.6004
37	.6018	.6032	.6046	.6060	.6074	.6088	.6101	.6115	.6129	.6143
38	.6157	.6170	.6184	.6198	.6211	.6225	.6239	.6252	.6266	.6280
39	.6293	.6307	.6320	.6334	.6347	.6361	.6374	.6388	.6401	.6414
40	.6428	.6441	.6455	.6468	.6481	.6494	.6508	.6521	.6534	.6547
41	.6561	.6574	.6587	.6600	.6613	.6626	.6639	.6652	.6665	.6678
42	.6691	.6704	.6717	.6730	.6743	.6756	.6769	.6782	.6794	.6807
43	.6820	.6833	.6845	.6858	.6871	.6884	.6896	.6909	.6921	.6934
44	.6947	.6959	.6972	.6984	.6997	.7009	.7022	.7034	.7046	.7059

NATURAL SINES

DEG.	0 MIN.	6 MIN.	12 MIN.	18 MIN.	24 MIN.	30 MIN.	36 MIN.	42 MIN.	48 MIN.	54 MIN.
45	.7071	.7083	.7096	.7108	.7120	.7133	.7145	.7157	.7169	.7181
46	.7193	.7206	.7218	.7230	.7242	.7254	.7266	.7278	.7290	.7302
47	.7314	.7325	.7337	.7349	.7361	.7373	.7385	.7396	.7408	.7420
48	.7431	.7443	.7455	.7466	.7478	.7490	.7501	.7513	.7524	.7536
49	.7547	.7559	.7570	.7581	.7593	.7604	.7615	.7627	.7638	.7649
50	.7660	.7672	.7683	.7694	.7705	.7716	.7727	.7738	.7749	.7760
51	.7771	.7782	.7793	.7804	.7815	.7826	.7837	.7848	.7859	.7869
52	.7880	.7891	.7902	.7912	.7923	.7934	.7944	.7955	.7965	.7976
53	.7986	.7997	.8007	.8018	.8028	.8039	.8049	.8059	.8070	.8080
54	.8090	.8100	.8111	.8121	.8131	.8141	.8151	.8161	.8171	.8181
55	.8192	.8202	.8211	.8221	.8231	.8241	.8251	.8261	.8271	.8281
56	.8290	.8300	.8310	.8320	.8329	.8339	.8348	.8358	.8368	.8377
57	.8387	.8396	.8406	.8415	.8425	.8434	.8443	.8453	.8462	.8471
58	.8480	.8490	.8499	.8508	.8517	.8526	.8536	.8545	.8554	.8563
59	.8572	.8581	.8590	.8599	.8607	.8616	.8625	.8634	.8643	.8652
60	.8660	.8669	.8678	.8686	.8695	.8704	.8712	.8721	.8729	.8738
61	.8746	.8755	.8763	.8771	.8780	.8788	.8796	.8805	.8813	.8821
62	.8829	.8838	.8846	.8854	.8862	.8870	.8878	.8886	.8894	.8902
63	.8910	.8918	.8926	.8934	.8942	.8949	.8957	.8965	.8973	.8980
64	.8988	.8996	.9003	.9011	.9018	.9026	.9033	.9041	.9048	.9056
65	.9063	.9070	.9078	.9085	.9092	.9100	.9107	.9114	.9121	.9128
66	.9135	.9143	.9150	.9157	.9164	.9171	.9178	.9184	.9191	.9198
67	.9205	.9212	.9219	.9225	.9232	.9239	.9245	.9252	.9259	.9265
68	.9272	.9278	.9285	.9291	.9298	.9304	.9311	.9317	.9323	.9330
69	.9336	.9342	.9348	.9354	.9361	.9367	.9373	.9379	.9385	.9391
70	.9397	.9403	.9409	.9415	.9421	.9426	.9432	.9438	.9444	.9449
71	.9455	.9461	.9466	.9472	.9478	.9483	.9489	.9494	.9500	.9505
72	.9511	.9516	.9521	.9527	.9532	.9537	.9542	.9548	.9553	.9558
73	.9563	.9568	.9573	.9578	.9583	.9588	.9593	.9598	.9603	.9608
74	.9613	.9617	.9622	.9627	.9632	.9636	.9641	.9646	.9650	.9655
75	.9659	.9664	.9668	.9673	.9677	.9681	.9686	.9690	.9694	.9699
76	.9703	.9707	.9711	.9715	.9720	.9724	.9728	.9732	.9736	.9740
77	.9744	.9748	.9751	.9755	.9759	.9763	.9767	.9770	.9774	.9778
78	.9781	.9785	.9789	.9792	.9796	.9799	.9803	.9806	.9810	.9813
79	.9816	.9820	.9823	.9826	.9829	.9833	.9836	.9839	.9842	.9845
80	.9848	.9851	.9854	.9857	.9860	.9863	.9866	.9869	.9871	.9874
81	.9877	.9880	.9882	.9885	.9888	.9890	.9893	.9895	.9898	.9900
82	.9903	.9905	.9907	.9910	.9912	.9914	.9917	.9919	.9921	.9923
83	.9925	.9928	.9930	.9932	.9934	.9936	.9938	.9940	.9942	.9943
84	.9945	.9947	.9949	.9951	.9952	.9954	.9956	.9957	.9959	.9960
85	.9962	.9963	.9965	.9966	.9968	.9969	.9971	.9972	.9973	.9974
86	.9976	.9977	.9978	.9979	.9980	.9981	.9982	.9983	.9984	.9985
87	.9986	.9987	.9988	.9989	.9990	.9990	.9991	.9992	.9993	.9993
88	.9994	.9995	.9995	.9996	.9996	.9997	.9997	.9997	.9998	.9998
89	.9998	.9999	.9999	.9999	.9999	1.0000	1.0000	1.0000	1.0000	1.0000

NATURAL TANGENTS

DEG.	0 MIN.	6 MIN.	12 MIN.	18 MIN.	24 MIN.	30 MIN.	36 MIN.	42 MIN.	48 MIN.	MIN. 54
0	—	.0017	.0035	.0052	.0070	.0087	.0105	.0122	.0140	.0157
1	.0175	.0192	.0209	.0227	.0244	.0262	.0279	.0297	.0314	.0332
2	.0349	.0367	.0384	.0402	.0419	.0437	.0454	.0472	.0489	.0507
3	.0524	.0542	.0559	.0577	.0594	.0612	.0629	.0647	.0664	.0682
4	.0699	.0717	.0734	.0752	.0769	.0787	.0805	.0822	.0840	.0857
5	.0875	.0892	.0910	.0928	.0945	.0963	.0981	.0998	.1016	.1033
6	.1051	.1069	.1086	.1104	.1122	.1139	.1157	.1175	.1192	.1210
7	.1228	.1246	.1263	.1281	.1299	.1317	.1334	.1352	.1370	.1388
8	.1405	.1423	.1441	.1459	.1477	.1495	.1512	.1530	.1548	.1566
9	.1584	.1602	.1620	.1638	.1655	.1673	.1691	.1709	.1727	.1745
10	.1763	.1781	.1799	.1817	.1835	.1853	.1871	.1890	.1908	.1926
11	.1944	.1962	.1980	.1998	.2016	.2035	.2053	.2071	.2089	.2107
12	.2126	.2144	.2162	.2180	.2199	.2217	.2235	.2254	.2272	.2290
13	.2309	.2327	.2345	.2364	.2382	.2401	.2419	.2438	.2456	.2475
14	.2493	.2512	.2530	.2549	.2568	.2586	.2605	.2623	.2642	.2661
15	.2679	.2698	.2717	.2736	.2754	.2773	.2792	.2811	.2830	.2849
16	.2867	.2886	.2905	.2924	.2943	.2962	.2981	.3000	.3019	.3038
17	.3057	.3076	.3096	.3115	.3134	.3153	.3172	.3191	.3211	.3230
18	.3249	.3269	.3288	.3307	.3327	.3346	.3365	.3385	.3404	.3424
19	.3443	.3463	.3482	.3502	.3522	.3541	.3561	.3581	.3600	.3620
20	.3640	.3659	.3679	.3699	.3719	.3739	.3759	.3779	.3799	.3819
21	.3839	.3859	.3879	.3899	.3919	.3939	.3959	.3979	.4000	.4020
22	.4040	.4061	.4081	.4101	.4122	.4142	.4163	.4183	.4204	.4224
23	.4245	.4265	.4286	.4307	.4327	.4348	.4369	.4390	.4411	.4431
24	.4452	.4473	.4494	.4515	.4536	.4557	.4578	.4599	.4621	.4642
25	.4663	.4684	.4706	.4727	.4748	.4770	.4791	.4813	.4834	.4856
26	.4877	.4899	.4921	.4942	.4964	.4986	.5008	.5029	.5051	.5073
27	.5095	.5117	.5139	.5161	.5184	.5206	.5228	.5250	.5272	.5295
28	.5317	.5340	.5362	.5384	.5407	.5430	.5452	.5475	.5498	.5520
29	.5543	.5566	.5589	.5612	.5635	.5658	.5681	.5704	.5727	.5750
30	.5774	.5797	.5820	.5844	.5867	.5890	.5914	.5938	.5961	.5985
31	.6009	.6032	.6056	.6080	.6104	.6128	.6152	.6176	.6200	.6224
32	.6249	.6273	.6297	.6322	.6346	.6371	.6395	.6420	.6445	.6469
33	.6494	.6519	.6544	.6569	.6594	.6619	.6644	.6669	.6694	.6720
34	.6745	.6771	.6796	.6822	.6847	.6873	.6899	.6924	.6950	.6976
35	.7002	.7028	.7054	.7080	.7107	.7133	.7159	.7186	.7212	.7239
36	.7265	.7292	.7319	.7346	.7373	.7400	.7427	.7454	.7481	.7508
37	.7536	.7563	.7590	.7618	.7646	.7673	.7701	.7729	.7757	.7785
38	.7813	.7841	.7869	.7898	.7926	.7954	.7983	.8012	.8040	.8069
39	.8098	.8127	.8156	.8185	.8214	.8243	.8273	.8302	.8332	.8361
40	.8391	.8421	.8451	.8481	.8511	.8541	.8571	.8601	.8632	.8662
41	.8693	.8724	.8754	.8785	.8816	.8847	.8878	.8910	.8941	.8972
42	.9004	.9036	.9067	.9099	.9131	.9163	.9195	.9228	.9260	.9293
43	.9325	.9358	.9391	.9424	.9457	.9490	.9523	.9556	.9590	.9623
44	.9657	.9691	.9725	.9759	.9793	.9827	.9861	.9896	.9930	.9965

NATURAL TANGENTS

DEG.	0 MIN.	6 MIN.	12 MIN.	18 MIN.	24 MIN.	30 MIN.	36 MIN.	42 MIN.	48 MIN.	54 MIN.
45	1.0000	1.0035	1.0070	1.0105	1.0141	1.0176	1.0212	1.0247	1.0283	1.0319
46	1.0355	1.0392	1.0428	1.0464	1.0501	1.0538	1.0575	1.0612	1.0649	1.0686
47	1.0724	1.0761	1.0799	1.0837	1.0875	1.0913	1.0951	1.0990	1.1028	1.1067
48	1.1106	1.1145	1.1184	1.1224	1.1263	1.1303	1.1343	1.1383	1.1423	1.1463
49	1.1504	1.1544	1.1585	1.1626	1.1667	1.1708	1.1750	1.1792	1.1833	1.1875
50	1.1918	1.1960	1.2002	1.2045	1.2088	1.2131	1.2174	1.2218	1.2261	1.2305
51	1.2349	1.2393	1.2437	1.2482	1.2527	1.2572	1.2617	1.2662	1.2708	1.2753
52	1.2799	1.2846	1.2892	1.2938	1.2985	1.3032	1.3079	1.3127	1.3175	1.3222
53	1.3270	1.3319	1.3367	1.3416	1.3465	1.3514	1.3564	1.3613	1.3663	1.3713
54	1.3764	1.3814	1.3865	1.3916	1.3968	1.4019	1.4071	1.4124	1.4176	1.4229
55	1.4281	1.4335	1.4388	1.4442	1.4496	1.4550	1.4605	1.4659	1.4715	1.4770
56	1.4826	1.4882	1.4938	1.4994	1.5051	1.5108	1.5166	1.5224	1.5282	1.5340
57	1.5399	1.5458	1.5517	1.5577	1.5637	1.5697	1.5757	1.5818	1.5880	1.5941
58	1.6003	1.6066	1.6128	1.6191	1.6255	1.6319	1.6383	1.6447	1.6512	1.6577
59	1.6643	1.6709	1.6775	1.6842	1.6909	1.6977	1.7045	1.7113	1.7182	1.7251
60	1.7321	1.7391	1.7461	1.7532	1.7603	1.7675	1.7747	1.7820	1.7893	1.7966
61	1.8040	1.8115	1.8190	1.8265	1.8341	1.8418	1.8495	1.8572	1.8650	1.8728
62	1.8807	1.8887	1.8967	1.9047	1.9128	1.9210	1.9292	1.9375	1.9458	1.9542
63	1.9626	1.9711	1.9797	1.9883	1.9970	2.0057	2.0145	2.0233	2.0323	2.0413
64	2.0503	2.0594	2.0686	2.0778	2.0872	2.0965	2.1060	2.1155	2.1251	2.1348
65	2.1445	2.1543	2.1642	2.1742	2.1842	2.1943	2.2045	2.2148	2.2251	2.2355
66	2.2460	2.2566	2.2673	2.2781	2.2889	2.2998	2.3109	2.3220	2.3332	2.3445
67	2.3559	2.3673	2.3789	2.3906	2.4023	2.4142	2.4262	2.4383	2.4504	2.4627
68	2.4751	2.4876	2.5002	2.5129	2.5257	2.5386	2.5517	2.5649	2.5782	2.5916
69	2.6051	2.6187	2.6325	2.6464	2.6605	2.6746	2.6889	2.7034	2.7179	2.7326
70	2.7475	2.7625	2.7776	2.7929	2.8083	2.8239	2.8397	2.8556	2.8716	2.8878
71	2.9042	2.9208	2.9375	2.9544	2.9714	2.9887	3.0061	3.0237	3.0415	3.0595
72	3.0777	3.0961	3.1146	3.1334	3.1524	3.1716	3.1910	3.2106	3.2305	3.2506
73	3.2709	3.2914	3.3122	3.3332	3.3544	3.3759	3.3977	3.4197	3.4420	3.4646
74	3.4874	3.5105	3.5339	3.5576	3.5816	3.6059	3.6305	3.6554	3.6806	3.7062
75	3.7321	3.7583	3.7848	3.8118	3.8391	3.8667	3.8947	3.9232	3.9520	3.9812
76	4.0108	4.0408	4.0713	4.1022	4.1335	4.1653	4.1976	4.2303	4.2635	4.2972
77	4.3315	4.3662	4.4015	4.4373	4.4737	4.5107	4.5483	4.5864	4.6252	4.6646
78	4.7046	4.7453	4.7867	4.8288	4.8716	4.9152	4.9594	5.0045	5.0504	5.0970
79	5.1446	5.1929	5.2422	5.2924	5.3435	5.3955	5.4486	5.5026	5.5578	5.6140
80	5.671	5.730	5.789	5.850	5.912	5.976	6.041	6.107	6.174	6.243
81	6.314	6.386	6.460	6.535	6.612	6.691	6.772	6.855	6.940	7.026
82	7.115	7.207	7.300	7.396	7.495	7.596	7.700	7.806	7.916	8.028
83	8.114	8.264	8.386	8.513	8.643	8.777	8.915	9.058	9.205	9.357
84	9.51	9.68	9.84	10.02	10.20	10.39	10.58	10.78	10.99	11.20
85	11.43	11.66	11.91	12.16	12.43	12.71	13.00	13.30	13.62	13.95
86	14.30	14.67	15.06	15.46	15.89	16.35	16.83	17.34	17.89	18.46
87	19.08	19.74	20.45	21.20	22.02	22.90	23.86	24.90	26.03	27.27
88	28.64	30.14	31.82	33.69	35.80	38.19	40.92	44.07	47.74	52.08
89	57.29	63.66	71.62	81.85	95.49	114.6	143.2	191.0	286.5	573.0

LOGARITHMS

	0	1	2	3	4	5	6	7	8	9	1	2	3	4	5	6	7	8	9
10	.0000	.0043	.0086	.0128	.0170	.0212	.0253	.0294	.0334	.0374	4	8	12	17	21	25	29	33	37
11	.0414	.0453	.0492	.0531	.0569	.0607	.0645	.0682	.0719	.0755	4	8	11	15	19	23	26	30	34
12	.0792	.0828	.0864	.0899	.0934	.0969	.1004	.1038	.1072	.1106	3	7	10	14	17	21	24	28	31
13	.1139	.1173	.1206	.1239	.1271	.1303	.1335	.1367	.1399	.1430	3	6	10	13	16	19	23	26	29
14	.1461	.1492	.1523	.1553	.1584	.1614	.1644	.1673	.1703	.1732	3	6	9	12	15	18	21	24	27
15	.1761	.1790	.1818	.1847	.1875	.1903	.1931	.1959	.1987	.2014	3	6	8	11	14	17	20	22	25
16	.2041	.2068	.2095	.2122	.2148	.2175	.2201	.2227	.2253	.2279	3	5	8	11	13	16	18	21	24
17	.2304	.2330	.2355	.2380	.2405	.2430	.2455	.2480	.2504	.2529	2	5	7	10	12	15	17	20	22
18	.2553	.2577	.2601	.2625	.2648	.2672	.2695	.2718	.2742	.2765	2	5	7	9	12	14	16	19	21
19	.2788	.2810	.2833	.2856	.2878	.2900	.2923	.2945	.2967	.2989	2	4	7	9	11	13	16	18	20
20	.3010	.3032	.3054	.3075	.3096	.3118	.3139	.3160	.3181	.3201	2	4	6	8	11	13	15	17	19
21	.3222	.3243	.3263	.3284	.3304	.3324	.3345	.3365	.3385	.3404	2	4	6	8	10	12	14	16	18
22	.3424	.3444	.3464	.3483	.3502	.3522	.3541	.3560	.3579	.3598	2	4	6	8	10	12	14	15	17
23	.3617	.3636	.3655	.3674	.3692	.3711	.3729	.3747	.3766	.3784	2	4	6	7	9	11	13	15	17
24	.3802	.3820	.3838	.3856	.3874	.3892	.3909	.3927	.3945	.3962	2	4	5	7	9	11	12	14	16
25	.3979	.3997	.4014	.4031	.4048	.4065	.4082	.4099	.4116	.4133	2	3	5	7	9	10	12	14	15
26	.4150	.4166	.4183	.4200	.4216	.4232	.4249	.4265	.4281	.4298	2	3	5	7	8	10	11	13	15
27	.4314	.4330	.4346	.4362	.4378	.4393	.4409	.4425	.4440	.4456	2	3	5	6	8	9	11	13	14
28	.4472	.4487	.4502	.4518	.4533	.4548	.4564	.4579	.4594	.4609	2	3	5	6	8	9	11	12	14
29	.4624	.4639	.4654	.4669	.4683	.4698	.4713	.4728	.4742	.4757	1	3	4	6	7	9	10	12	13
30	.4771	.4786	.4800	.4814	.4829	.4843	.4857	.4871	.4886	.4900	1	3	4	6	7	9	10	11	13
31	.4914	.4928	.4942	.4955	.4969	.4983	.4997	.5011	.5024	.5038	1	3	4	6	7	8	10	11	12
32	.5051	.5065	.5079	.5092	.5105	.5119	.5132	.5145	.5159	.5172	1	3	4	5	7	8	9	11	12
33	.5185	.5198	.5211	.5224	.5237	.5250	.5263	.5276	.5289	.5302	1	3	4	5	6	8	9	10	12
34	.5315	.5328	.5340	.5353	.5366	.5378	.5391	.5403	.5416	.5428	1	3	4	5	6	8	9	10	11
35	.5441	.5453	.5465	.5478	.5490	.5502	.5514	.5527	.5539	.5551	1	2	4	5	6	7	9	10	11
36	.5563	.5575	.5587	.5599	.5611	.5623	.5635	.5647	.5658	.5670	1	2	4	5	6	7	8	10	11
37	.5682	.5694	.5705	.5717	.5729	.5740	.5752	.5763	.5775	.5786	1	2	3	5	6	7	8	9	10
38	.5798	.5809	.5821	.5832	.5843	.5855	.5866	.5877	.5888	.5899	1	2	3	5	6	7	8	9	10
39	.5911	.5922	.5933	.5944	.5955	.5966	.5977	.5988	.5999	.6010	1	2	3	4	5	7	8	9	10
40	.6021	.6031	.6042	.6053	.6064	.6075	.6085	.6096	.6107	.6117	1	2	3	4	5	6	8	9	10
41	.6128	.6138	.6149	.6160	.6170	.6180	.6191	.6201	.6212	.6222	1	2	3	4	5	6	7	8	9
42	.6232	.6243	.6253	.6263	.6274	.6284	.6294	.6304	.6314	.6325	1	2	3	4	5	6	7	8	9
43	.6335	.6345	.6355	.6365	.6375	.6385	.6395	.6405	.6415	.6425	1	2	3	4	5	6	7	8	9
44	.6435	.6444	.6454	.6464	.6474	.6484	.6493	.6503	.6513	.6522	1	2	3	4	5	6	7	8	9
45	.6532	.6542	.6551	.6561	.6571	.6580	.6590	.6599	.6609	.6618	1	2	3	4	5	6	7	8	9
46	.6628	.6637	.6646	.6656	.6665	.6675	.6684	.6693	.6703	.6712	1	2	3	4	5	6	7	7	8
47	.6721	.6730	.6739	.6749	.6758	.6767	.6776	.6785	.6794	.6803	1	2	3	4	5	5	6	7	8
48	.6812	.6821	.6830	.6839	.6848	.6857	.6866	.6875	.6884	.6893	1	2	3	4	4	5	6	7	8
49	.6902	.6911	.6920	.6928	.6937	.6946	.6955	.6964	.6972	.6981	1	2	3	4	4	5	6	7	8
50	.6990	.6998	.7007	.7016	.7024	.7033	.7042	.7050	.7059	.7067	1	2	3	3	4	5	6	7	8
51	.7076	.7084	.7093	.7101	.7110	.7118	.7126	.7135	.7143	.7152	1	2	3	3	4	5	6	7	8
52	.7160	.7168	.7177	.7185	.7193	.7202	.7210	.7218	.7226	.7235	1	2	2	3	4	5	6	7	7
53	.7243	.7251	.7259	.7267	.7275	.7284	.7292	.7300	.7308	.7316	1	2	2	3	4	5	6	6	7
54	.7324	.7332	.7340	.7348	.7356	.7364	.7372	.7380	.7388	.7396	1	2	2	3	4	5	6	6	7

LOGARITHMS

	0	1	2	3	4	5	6	7	8	9	1	2	3	4	5	6	7	8	9
55	.7404	.7412	.7419	.7427	.7435	.7443	.7451	.7459	.7466	.7474	1	2	2	3	4	5	5	6	7
56	.7482	.7490	.7497	.7505	.7513	.7520	.7528	.7536	.7543	.7551	1	2	2	3	4	5	5	6	7
57	.7559	.7566	.7574	.7582	.7589	.7597	.7604	.7612	.7619	.7627	1	2	2	3	4	5	5	6	7
58	.7634	.7642	.7649	.7657	.7664	.7672	.7679	.7686	.7694	.7701	1	1	2	3	4	4	5	6	7
59	.7709	.7716	.7723	.7731	.7738	.7745	.7752	.7760	.7767	.7774	1	1	2	3	4	4	5	6	7
60	.7782	.7789	.7796	.7803	.7810	.7818	.7825	.7832	.7839	.7846	1	1	2	3	4	4	5	6	6
61	.7853	.7860	.7868	.7875	.7882	.7889	.7896	.7903	.7910	.7917	1	1	2	3	4	4	5	6	6
62	.7924	.7931	.7938	.7945	.7952	.7959	.7966	.7973	.7980	.7987	1	1	2	3	3	4	5	6	6
63	.7993	.8000	.8007	.8014	.8021	.8028	.8035	.8041	.8048	.8055	1	1	2	3	3	4	5	5	6
64	.8062	.8069	.8075	.8082	.8089	.8096	.8102	.8109	.8116	.8122	1	1	2	3	3	4	5	5	6
65	.8129	.8136	.8142	.8149	.8156	.8162	.8169	.8176	.8182	.8189	1	1	2	3	3	4	5	5	6
66	.8195	.8202	.8209	.8215	.8222	.8228	.8235	.8241	.8248	.8254	1	1	2	3	3	4	5	5	6
67	.8261	.8267	.8274	.8280	.8287	.8293	.8299	.8306	.8312	.8319	1	1	2	3	3	4	5	5	6
68	.8325	.8331	.8338	.8344	.8351	.8357	.8363	.8370	.8376	.8382	1	1	2	3	3	4	4	5	6
69	.8388	.8395	.8401	.8407	.8414	.8420	.8426	.8432	.8439	.8445	1	1	2	2	3	4	4	5	6
70	.8451	.8457	.8463	.8470	.8476	.8482	.8488	.8494	.8500	.8506	1	1	2	2	3	4	4	5	6
71	.8513	.8519	.8525	.8531	.8537	.8543	.8549	.8555	.8561	.8567	1	1	2	2	3	4	4	5	5
72	.8573	.8579	.8585	.8591	.8597	.8603	.8609	.8615	.8621	.8627	1	1	2	2	3	4	4	5	5
73	.8633	.8639	.8645	.8651	.8657	.8663	.8669	.8675	.8681	.8686	1	1	2	2	3	4	4	5	5
74	.8692	.8698	.8704	.8710	.8716	.8722	.8727	.8733	.8739	.8745	1	1	2	2	3	4	4	5	5
75	.8751	.8756	.8762	.8768	.8774	.8779	.8785	.8791	.8797	.8802	1	1	2	2	3	3	4	5	5
76	.8808	.8814	.8820	.8825	.8831	.8837	.8842	.8848	.8854	.8859	1	1	2	2	3	3	4	5	5
77	.8865	.8871	.8876	.8882	.8887	.8893	.8899	.8904	.8910	.8915	1	1	2	2	3	3	4	4	5
78	.8921	.8927	.8932	.8938	.8943	.8949	.8954	.8960	.8965	.8971	1	1	2	2	3	3	4	4	5
79	.8976	.8982	.8987	.8993	.8998	.9004	.9009	.9015	.9020	.9025	1	1	2	2	3	3	4	4	5
80	.9031	.9036	.9042	.9047	.9053	.9058	.9063	.9069	.9074	.9079	1	1	2	2	3	3	4	4	5
81	.9085	.9090	.9096	.9101	.9106	.9112	.9117	.9122	.9128	.9133	1	1	2	2	3	3	4	4	5
82	.9138	.9143	.9149	.9154	.9159	.9165	.9170	.9175	.9180	.9186	1	1	2	2	3	3	4	4	5
83	.9191	.9196	.9201	.9206	.9212	.9217	.9222	.9227	.9232	.9238	1	1	2	2	3	3	4	4	5
84	.9243	.9248	.9253	.9258	.9263	.9269	.9274	.9279	.9284	.9289	1	1	2	2	3	3	4	4	5
85	.9294	.9299	.9304	.9309	.9315	.9320	.9325	.9330	.9335	.9340	1	1	2	2	3	3	4	4	5
86	.9345	.9350	.9355	.9360	.9365	.9370	.9375	.9380	.9385	.9390	1	1	2	2	3	3	4	4	5
87	.9395	.9400	.9405	.9410	.9415	.9420	.9425	.9430	.9435	.9440	0	1	1	2	2	3	3	4	4
88	.9445	.9450	.9455	.9460	.9465	.9469	.9474	.9479	.9484	.9489	0	1	1	2	2	3	3	4	4
89	.9494	.9499	.9504	.9509	.9513	.9518	.9523	.9528	.9533	.9538	0	1	1	2	2	3	3	4	4
90	.9542	.9547	.9552	.9557	.9562	.9566	.9571	.9576	.9581	.9586	0	1	1	2	2	3	3	4	4
91	.9590	.9595	.9600	.9605	.9609	.9614	.9619	.9624	.9628	.9633	0	1	1	2	2	3	3	4	4
92	.9638	.9643	.9647	.9652	.9657	.9661	.9666	.9671	.9675	.9680	0	1	1	2	2	3	3	4	4
93	.9685	.9689	.9694	.9699	.9703	.9708	.9713	.9717	.9722	.9727	0	1	1	2	2	3	3	4	4
94	.9731	.9736	.9741	.9745	.9750	.9754	.9759	.9763	.9768	.9773	0	1	1	2	2	3	3	4	4
95	.9777	.9782	.9786	.9791	.9795	.9800	.9805	.9809	.9814	.9818	0	1	1	2	2	3	3	4	4
96	.9823	.9827	.9832	.9836	.9841	.9845	.9850	.9854	.9859	.9863	0	1	1	2	2	3	3	4	4
97	.9868	.9872	.9877	.9881	.9886	.9890	.9894	.9899	.9903	.9908	0	1	1	2	2	3	3	4	4
98	.9912	.9917	.9921	.9926	.9930	.9934	.9939	.9943	.9948	.9952	0	1	1	2	2	3	3	4	4
99	.9956	.9961	.9965	.9969	.9974	.9978	.9983	.9987	.9991	.9996	0	1	1	2	2	3	3	3	4

SQUARES, CUBES, SQUARE ROOTS, CUBE ROOTS

Numbers 1–50.

NO.	SQUARE.	CUBE.	SQUARE ROOT.	CUBE ROOT.
1	1	1	1.000	1.0000
2	4	8	1.4142	1.2599
3	9	27	1.7321	1.4422
4	16	64	2.0000	1.5874
5	25	125	2.2361	1.7100
6	36	216	2.4495	1.8171
7	49	343	2.6458	1.9129
8	64	512	2.8284	2.0000
9	81	729	3.0000	2.0801
10	100	1,000	3.1623	2.1544
11	121	1,331	3.3166	2.2240
12	144	1,728	3.4641	2.2894
13	169	2,197	3.6056	2.3513
14	196	2,744	3.7417	2.4101
15	225	3,375	3.8730	2.4662
16	256	4,096	4.0000	2.5198
17	289	4,913	4.1231	2.5713
18	324	5,832	4.2426	2.6207
19	361	6,859	4.3589	2.6684
20	400	8,000	4.4721	2.7144
21	441	9,261	4.5826	2.7589
22	484	10,648	4.6904	2.8020
23	529	12,167	4.7958	2.8439
24	576	13,824	4.8990	2.8845
25	625	15,625	5.0000	2.9240
26	676	17,576	5.0990	2.9625
27	729	19,683	5.1962	3.0000
28	784	21,952	5.2915	3.0366
29	841	24,389	5.3852	3.0723
30	900	27,000	5.4772	3.1072
31	961	29,791	5.5678	3.1414
32	1,024	32,768	5.6569	3.1748
33	1,089	35,937	5.7446	3.2075
34	1,156	39,304	5.8310	3.2396
35	1,225	42,875	5.9161	3.2711
36	1,296	46,656	6.0000	3.3019
37	1,369	50,653	6.0828	3.3322
38	1,444	54,872	6.1644	3.3620
39	1,521	5,9319	6.2450	3.3912
40	1,600	64,000	6.3246	3.4200
41	1,681	68,921	6.4031	3.4482
42	1,764	74,088	6.4807	3.4760
43	1,849	79,507	6.5574	3.5034
44	1,936	85,184	6.6332	3.5303
45	2,025	91,125	6.7082	3.5569
46	2,116	97,336	6.7823	3.5830
47	2,209	103,823	6.8557	3.6088
48	2,304	110,592	6.9282	3.6342
49	2,401	117,649	7.0000	3.6593
50	2,500	125,000	7.0711	3.6840

DIAMETERS, CIRCUMFERENCES AND AREAS OF CIRCLES

DIA.	CIRCUM-FERENCE.	AREA.	DIA.	CIRCUM-FERENCE.	AREA.
⅛	.3927	.01227	24	75.398	452.389
¼	.7854	.04909	25	78.540	490.874
⅜	1.1781	.1104	26	81.681	530.929
½	1.5708	.1963	27	84.823	572.555
⅝	1.9635	.3068	28	87.965	615.752
¾	2.3562	.4417	29	91.106	660.520
⅞	2.7489	.6013	30	94.248	706.858
1	3.142	.7854	31	97.389	754.768
2	6.283	3.1416	32	100.531	804.248
3	9.425	7.0686	33	103.673	855.299
4	12.566	12.5664	34	106.814	907.920
5	15.708	19.6350	35	109.956	962.113
6	18.850	28.2743	36	113.097	1,017.88
7	21.999	38.4845	37	116.239	1,075.21
8	25.133	50.2655	38	119.381	1,134.11
9	28.274	63.6173	39	122.522	1,194.59
10	31.416	78.5398	40	125.66	1,256.64
11	34.558	95.0332	41	128.81	1,320.25
12	37.699	113.097	42	131.95	1,385.44
13	40.841	132.732	43	135.09	1,452.20
14	43.985	153.938	44	138.23	1,520.53
15	47.124	176.715	45	141.37	1,590.43
16	50.265	201.062	46	144.51	1,661.90
17	53.407	226.980	47	147.65	1,734.94
18	56.549	254.469	48	150.80	1,809.56
19	59.690	283.529	49	153.94	1,885.74
20	62.832	314.159	50	157.08	1,963.50
21	65.973	346.361	51	160.22	2,042.82
22	69.115	380.113	52	163.36	2,123.72
23	72.257	415.476	53	166.50	2,206.18

ALLOWANCES FOR FITS

The allowances given in the table are recommended for use in the manufacture of machine parts, to produce satisfactory commercial work. For special cases, it may be necessary to increase or decrease the allowances given in the table.

Running Fits for Shafts—Speeds Under 600 R.P.M.—Ordinary Working Conditions

Diameter, Inches	Allowances, Inches
Up to ½	− 0.0005 to − 0.001
½ to 1	− 0.00075 to − 0.0015
1 to 2	− 0.0015 to − 0.0025
2 to 3½	− 0.002 to − 0.003
3½ to 6	− 0.0025 to − 0.004

Running Fits for Shafts—Speeds Over 600 R.P.M.—Heavy Pressure—Working Conditions Severe

Up to ½	− 0.0005 to − 0.001
½ to 1	− 0.001 to − 0.002
1 to 2	− 0.002 to − 0.003
2 to 3½	− 0.003 to − 0.004
8½ to 6	− 0.004 to − 0.005

Sliding Fits for Shafts with Gears, Clutches, or Similar Parts which must be Free to Slide

Up to ½	− 0.0005 to − 0.001
½ to 1	− 0.00075 to − 0.0015
1 to 2	− 0.0015 to − 0.0025
2 to 3½	− 0.002 to − 0.003
3½ to 6	− 0.0025 to − 0.004

Standard Fits for Light Service where Part is Keyed to Shaft and Clamped Endwise—No Fitting

Up to ½	Standard to − 0.00025
½ to 3½	Standard to − 0.0005
3½ to 6	Standard to − 0.00075

Standard Fits with Play Eliminated—Parts Should Assemble Readily—Some Fitting and Selecting may be Required

Up to ½	Standard to + 0.00025
½ to 3½	Standard to + 0.0005
3½ to 6	Standard to + 0.00075

Driving Fits for Permanent Assembly of Parts so Located that Driving cannot be done readily

Up to ½	Standard to + 0.00025
½ to 1	+ 0.00025 to + 0.0005
1 to 2	+ 0.0005 to + 0.00075
2 to 6	+ 0.0005 to + 0.001

Driving Fits for Permanent Assembly and Severe Duty and where there is Ample Room for Driving

Up to 2	+ 0.0005 to + 0.001
2 to 3½	+ 0.00075 to + 0.00125
3½ to 6	+ 0.001 to + 0.0015

Forced Fits for Permanent Assembly and Very Severe Service—Hydraulic Press Used for Larger Parts

Up to ½	+ 0.00075 to + 0.001
½ to 1	+ 0.001 to + 0.002
1 to 2	+ 0.002 to + 0.003
2 to 3½	+ 0.003 to + 0.004
3½ to 6	+ 0.004 to + 0.005

AMERICAN NATIONAL COARSE AND FINE THREAD DIMENSIONS AND TAP DRILL SIZES

NOMINAL SIZE.	OUTSIDE DIAMETER, INCHES.	PITCH DIAMETER, INCHES.	ROOT DIAMETER, INCHES.	TAP DRILL.	DECIMAL EQUIVALENT OF TAP DRILL.
*0–80	.0600	.0519	.0438	³⁄₆₄	.0469
*1–64	.0730	.0629	.0527	53	.0595
72	.0730	.0640	.0550	53	.0595
*2–56	.0860	.0744	.0628	50	.0700
64	.0860	.0759	.0657	50	.0700
*3–48	.0990	.0855	.0719	47	.0785
56	.0990	.0874	.0758	45	.0820
*4–40	.1120	.0958	.0795	43	.0890
48	.1120	.0985	.0849	42	.0935
*5–40	.1250	.1088	.0925	38	.1015
44	.1250	.1102	.0955	37	.1040
*6–32	.1380	.1177	.0974	36	.1065
40	.1380	.1218	.1055	33	.1130
*8–32	.1640	.1437	.1234	29	.1360
36	.1640	.1460	.1279	29	.1360
*10–24	.1900	.1629	.1359	25	.1495
32	.1900	.1697	.1494	21	.1590
*12–24	.2160	.1889	.1619	16	.1770
28	.2160	.1928	.1696	14	.1820
¼–20	.2500	.2175	.1850	7	.2010
28	.2500	.2268	.2036	3	.2130
⁵⁄₁₆–18	.3125	.2764	.2403	F	.2570
24	.3125	.2854	.2584	I	.2720
³⁄₈–16	.3750	.3344	.2938	⁵⁄₁₆	.3125
24	.3750	.3479	.3209	Q	.3320
⁷⁄₁₆–14	.4375	.3911	.3447	U	.3680
20	.4375	.4050	.3726	²⁵⁄₆₄	.3906
½–13	.5000	.4501	.4001	²⁷⁄₆₄	.4219
20	.5000	.4675	.4351	²⁹⁄₆₄	.4531
⁹⁄₁₆–12	.5625	.5084	.4542	³¹⁄₆₄	.4844
18	.5625	.5264	.4903	³³⁄₆₄	.5156
⁵⁄₈–11	.6250	.5660	.5069	¹⁷⁄₃₂	.5312
18	.6250	.5889	.5528	³⁷⁄₆₄	.5781
¾–10	.7500	.6850	.6201	²¹⁄₃₂	.6562
16	.7500	.7094	.6688	¹¹⁄₁₆	.6875

* American National Standard Wood Screws are made in same numbers and corresponding body diameters as starred sizes.

AMERICAN NATIONAL THREAD DIMENSIONS AND TAP DRILL SIZES (Cont'd)

NOMINAL SIZE.	OUTSIDE DIAMETER, INCHES.	PITCH DIAMETER, INCHES.	ROOT DIAMETER, INCHES.	TAP DR'LL.	DECIMAL EQUIVALENT OF TAP DRILL.
7/8– 9	.8750	.8029	.7307	49/64	.7656
14	.8750	.8286	.7822	13/16	.8125
1– 8	1.0000	.9188	.8376	7/8	.8750
14	1.0000	.9536	.9072	15/16	.9375
1 1/8– 7	1.1250	1.0322	.9394	63/64	.9844
12	1.1250	1.0709	1.0168	1 3/64	1.0469
1 1/4– 7	1.2500	1.1572	1.0644	1 7/64	1.1094
12	1.2500	1.1959	1.1418	1 11/64	1.1719
1 3/8– 6	1.3750	1.2667	1.1585	1 7/32	1.2187
12	1.3750	1.3209	1.2668	1 19/64	1.2969
1 1/2– 6	1.5000	1.3917	1.2835	1 11/32	1.3437
12	1.5000	1.4459	1.3918	1 27/64	1.4219
1 3/4– 5	1.7500	1.6201	1.4902	1 9/16	1.5625
2– 4 1/2	2.0000	1.8557	1.7113	1 25/32	1.7812
2 1/4– 4 1/2	2.2500	2.1057	1.9613	2 1/32	2.0312
2 1/2– 4	2.5000	2.3376	2.1752	2 1/4	2.2500
2 3/4– 4	2.7500	2.5876	2.4252	2 1/2	2.5000
3– 4	3.0000	2.8376	2.6752	2 3/4	2.7500
3 1/4– 4	3.2500	3.0876	2.9252	3	3.0000
3 1/2– 4	3.5000	3.3376	3.1752	3 1/4	3.2500
3 3/4– 4	3.7500	3.5876	3.4252	3 1/2	3.5000
4– 4	4.0000	3.8376	3.6752	3 3/4	3.7500

TAP DRILL SIZES FOR AMERICAN NATIONAL PIPE THREAD

SIZES OF PIPE, INCHES.	NUMBER OF THREADS TO INCH.	ROOT DIAMETER SMALL END OF PIPE AND GAGE, INCHES.	TAP DRILL.	
			—SIZE.	DECIMAL EQUIVALENT.
1/8	27	.3339	R	.339
1/4	18	.4329	7/16	.437
3/8	18	.5676	37/64	.578
1/2	14	.7013	23/32	.719
3/4	14	.9105	59/64	.921
1	11 1/2	1.1441	1 5/32	1.156
1 1/4	11 1/2	1.4876	1 1/2	1.500
1 1/2	11 1/2	1.7265	1 47/64	1.734
2	11 1/2	2.1995	2 7/32	2.218
2 1/2	8	2.6195	2 5/8	2.625
3	8	3.2406	3 1/4	3.250
3 1/2	8	3.7375	3 3/4	3.750
4	8	4.2344	4 1/4	4.250

SHARP V THREAD TAP DRILL SIZES

SIZE OF TAP.	NO. OF THREADS.	DRILL NO.	SIZE OF TAP.	NO. OF THREADS.	DRILL NO.	SIZE OF TAP.	NO. OF THREADS.	DRILL NO.
1/16	60	55	9/64	32	32	13/64	28	20
5/64	60	52	9/64	36	35	13/64	32	20
3/32	48	47	9/64	40	33	7/32	22	19
3/32	56	46	5/32	30	31	7/32	24	18
3/32	60	46	5/32	32	30	7/32	28	17
7/64	32	45	5/32	36	29	7/32	30	15
7/64	36	44	5/32	40	29	7/32	32	13
7/64	40	43	11/64	32	30	15/64	22	10
7/64	44	43	11/64	36	29	15/64	24	10
7/64	48	42	11/64	40	28	15/64	28	9
1/8	32	40	3/16	24	27	15/64	32	9
1/8	36	38	3/16	28	26	1/4	20	7
1/8	40	37	3/16	30	23	1/4	22	5
1/8	44	36	3/16	32	23	1/4	24	2
9/64	30	35	13/64	24	21	1/4	32	2

ACME STANDARD OR 29° THREADS

DIAMETER, INCHES.	THREADS PER INCH.	DIAMETER, INCHES.	THREADS PER INCH.
1/2″	10	1″	6
5/8″	9	1 1/4″	5
3/4″	8	1 1/2″	4
7/8″	7	2″	3

SQUARE THREADS

DIAMETER, INCHES.	THREADS PER INCH.	DIAMETER, INCHES.	THREADS PER INCH.
1/2″	10	1″	6
5/8″	9	1 1/4″	5
3/4″	8	1 1/2″	4
7/8″	7	2″	3

BRITISH STANDARD—WHITWORTH FORM THREAD DIMENSIONS AND TAP DRILL SIZES

NOMINAL SIZE.	MAJOR DIAMETER INCHES.	PITCH DIAMETER INCHES.	ROOT DIAMETER INCHES.	COMMERCIAL TAP DRILL TO PRODUCE APPROXIMATELY FULL THREAD.	DECIMAL EQUIVALENT OF DRILL.
$\frac{1}{16}$–60	.0625	.0518	.0412	57	.0430
$\frac{3}{32}$–48	.0938	.0804	.0671	50	.0700
$\frac{1}{8}$–40	.1250	.1090	.0930	40	.0980
$\frac{5}{32}$–32	.1563	.1362	.1162	31	.1200
$\frac{3}{16}$–24	.1875	.1608	.1341	28	.1405
$\frac{7}{32}$–24	.2188	.1921	.1654	17	.1730
$\frac{1}{4}$–20	.2500	.2180	.1860	9	.1960
26	.2500	.2254	.2001	4	.2090
$\frac{9}{32}$–26	.2813	.2566	.2321	C	.2420
$\frac{5}{16}$–18	.3125	.2769	.2414	$\frac{1}{4}$	.2500
22	.3125	.2834	.2543	G	.2610
$\frac{3}{8}$–16	.3750	.3350	.2950	$\frac{5}{16}$	.3125
20	.3750	.3430	.3110	P	.3230
$\frac{7}{16}$–14	.4375	.3918	.3460	T	.3580
18	.4375	.4019	.3665	$\frac{3}{8}$	.3750
$\frac{1}{2}$–12	.5000	.4466	.3933	Z	.4130
16	.5000	.4600	.4200	$\frac{7}{16}$	.4375
$\frac{9}{16}$–12	.5625	.5091	.4558	$\frac{15}{32}$	.4687
16	.5625	.5225	.4825	$\frac{1}{2}$	.5000
$\frac{5}{8}$–11	.6250	.5668	.5086	$\frac{17}{32}$	.5312
14	.6250	.5793	.5336	$\frac{35}{64}$	.5469
$\frac{11}{16}$–11	.6875	.6293	.5711	$\frac{19}{32}$	.5937
14	.6875	.6418	.5961	$\frac{39}{64}$	.6094
$\frac{3}{4}$–10	.7500	.6860	.6219	$\frac{41}{64}$	.6406
12	.7500	.6966	.6434	$\frac{21}{32}$	.6562
$\frac{13}{16}$–10	.8125	.7485	.6844	$\frac{45}{64}$	.7031
12	.8125	.7591	.7059	$\frac{23}{32}$	.7187
$\frac{7}{8}$– 9	.8750	.8039	.7327	$\frac{3}{4}$	.7500
11	.8750	.8168	.7586	$\frac{25}{32}$	.7812
$\frac{15}{16}$– 9	.9375	.8664	.7952	$\frac{13}{16}$	.8125
1 – 8	1.0000	.9200	.8399	$\frac{55}{64}$	.8593
10	1.0000	.9360	.8720	$\frac{57}{64}$	.8906
1 $\frac{1}{8}$– 7	1.1250	1.0335	.9420	$\frac{31}{32}$	.9687
9	1.1250	1.0539	.9828	1	1.0000
1 $\frac{1}{4}$– 7	1.2500	1.1585	1.0670	1 $\frac{3}{32}$	1.0937
9	1.2500	1.1789	1.1078	1 $\frac{1}{8}$	1.1250
1 $\frac{3}{8}$– 6	1.3750	1.2683	1.1616	1 $\frac{3}{16}$	1.1875
8	1.3750	1.2950	1.2150	1$\frac{15}{64}$	1.2343
1 $\frac{1}{2}$– 6	1.5000	1.3933	1.2866	1 $\frac{5}{16}$	1.3125
8	1.5000	1.4200	1.3400	1 $\frac{3}{8}$	1.3750

BRITISH STANDARD—WHITWORTH THREAD DIMENSIONS AND TAP DRILL SIZES (Cont'd)

NOMINAL SIZE.	MAJOR DIAMETER INCHES.	PITCH DIAMETER INCHES.	ROOT DIAMETER INCHES.	COMMERCIAL TAP DRILL TO PRODUCE APPROXIMATELY FULL THREAD.	DECIMAL EQUIVALENT OF DRILL.
1 5/8–5	1.6250	1.4969	1.3689	1 13/32	1.4062
1 3/4–5	1.7500	1.6219	1.4939	1 17/32	1.5312
1 7/8–4½	1.8750	1.7327	1.5904	1 5/8	1.6250
2 –4½	2.0000	1.8577	1.7154	1 3/4	1.7500
2 1/8–4½	2.1250	1.9827	1.8404	1 7/8	1.8750
2 1/4–4	2.2500	2.0899	1.9298	1 31/32	1.9687
2 3/8–4	2.3750	2.2149	2.0548	2 3/32	2.0937
2 1/2–4	2.5000	2.3399	2.1798	2 7/32	2.2187
2 3/4–3½	2.7500	2.5671	2.3841	2 7/16	2.4375
3 –3½	3.0000	2.8171	2.6341	2 43/64	2.6718
3 1/4–3½	3.2500	3.0530	2.8560	2 7/8	2.8750
3 1/2–3¼	3.5000	3.3030	3.1060	3 1/8	3.1250
3 3/4–3	3.7500	3.5366	3.3231	3 11/32	3.3437
4 –3	4.0000	3.7866	3.5731	3 19/32	3.5937

BROWN & SHARPE 29° WORM THREAD PARTS

	P	D	F	W	T	A	C	S	B
NUMBER OF THREADS PER INCH.	PITCH OF SINGLE THREAD.	DEPTH OF THREAD.	WIDTH OF TOP OF THREAD.	WIDTH OF SPACE AT BOTTOM.	THICKNESS OF THREAD AT PITCH LINE.	THREAD ABOVE PITCH LINE.	CLEARANCE AT BOTTOM OF THREAD.	WIDTH OF SPACE AT TOP.	THICKNESS AT ROOT OF THREAD.
1	1.0	.6866	.3350	.3100	.5000	.3183	.05	.665	.69
1¼	.8	.5492	.2680	.2480	.4000	.2546	.04	.532	.552
1½	.6666	.4577	.2233	.2066	.3333	.2122	.0333	.4433	.4599
2	.5	.3433	.1675	.1550	.2500	.1592	.0250	.3325	.345
2½	.4	.2746	.1340	.1240	.2000	.1273	.0200	.2660	.276
3	.3333	.2289	.1117	.1033	.1666	.1061	.0166	.2216	.2299
3½	.2857	.1962	.0957	.0886	.1429	.0909	.0143	.1901	.2011
4	.250	.1716	.0838	.0775	.1250	.0796	.0125	.1637	.1725
4½	.2222	.1526	.0744	.0689	.1111	.0707	.0111	.1478	.1533
5	.2	.1373	.0670	.0620	.1000	.0637	.0100	.1330	.138
6	.1666	.1144	.0558	.0517	.0833	.0531	.0083	.1108	.115
7	.1428	.0981	.0479	.0443	.0714	.0455	.0071	.095	.0985
8	.125	.0858	.0419	.0388	.0625	.0398	.0062	.0818	.0862
9	.1111	.0763	.0372	.0344	.0555	.0354	.0055	.0739	.0766
10	.10	.0687	.0335	.0310	.0500	.0318	.005	.0665	.069
12	.0833	.0572	.0279	.0258	.0416	.0265	.0042	.0551	.0575
16	.0625	.0429	.0209	.0194	.0312	.0199	.0031	.0409	.0431
20	.050	.0343	.0167	.0155	.0250	.0159	.0025	.0332	.0345

TAPERS FROM $\frac{1}{16}$ TO $1\frac{1}{4}$ INCH PER FOOT

Amount of Taper for Lengths up to 24 Inches

LENGTH TAPERED, INCHES.	TAPER PER FOOT.									
	$\frac{1}{16}$	$\frac{3}{32}$	$\frac{1}{8}$	$\frac{1}{4}$	$\frac{3}{8}$	$\frac{1}{2}$	$\frac{5}{8}$	$\frac{3}{4}$	1	$1\frac{1}{4}$
$\frac{1}{32}$	.0002	.0002	.0003	.0007	.0010	.0013	.0016	.0020	.0026	.0033
$\frac{1}{16}$	.0003	.0005	.0007	.0013	.0020	.0026	.0033	.0039	.0052	.0065
$\frac{1}{8}$	.0007	.0010	.0013	.0026	.0039	.0052	.0065	.0078	.0104	.0130
$\frac{3}{16}$	.0010	.0015	.0020	.0039	.0059	.0078	.0098	.0117	.0156	.0195
$\frac{1}{4}$	.0013	.0020	.0026	.0052	.0078	.0104	.0130	.0156	.0208	.0260
$\frac{5}{16}$	.0016	.0024	.0033	.0065	.0098	.0130	.0163	.0195	.0260	.0326
$\frac{3}{8}$	.0020	.0029	.0039	.0078	.0117	.0156	.0195	.0234	.0312	.0391
$\frac{7}{16}$	.0023	.0034	.0046	.0091	.0137	.0182	.0228	.0273	.0365	.0456
$\frac{1}{2}$	.0026	.0039	.0052	.0104	.0156	.0208	.0260	.0312	.0417	.0521
$\frac{9}{16}$	.0029	.0044	.0059	.0117	.0176	.0234	.0293	.0352	.0469	.0586
$\frac{5}{8}$	.0033	.0049	.0065	.0130	.0195	.0260	.0326	.0391	.0521	.0651
$\frac{11}{16}$	.0036	.0054	.0072	.0143	.0215	.0286	.0358	.0430	.0573	.0716
$\frac{3}{4}$	.0039	.0059	.0078	.0156	.0234	.0312	.0391	.0469	.0625	.0781
$\frac{13}{16}$	.0042	.0063	.0085	.0169	.0254	.0339	.0423	.0508	.0677	.0846
$\frac{7}{8}$	.0046	.0068	.0091	.0182	.0273	.0365	.0456	.0547	.0729	.0911
$\frac{15}{16}$	.0049	.0073	.0098	.0195	.0293	.0391	.0488	.0586	.0781	.0977
1	.0052	.0078	.0104	.0208	.0312	.0417	.0521	.0625	.0833	.1042
2	.0104	.0156	.0208	.0417	.0625	.0833	.1042	.125	.1667	.2083
3	.0156	.0234	.0312	.0625	.0937	.1250	.1562	.1875	.250	.3125
4	.0208	.0312	.0417	.0833	.125	.1667	.2083	.250	.3333	.4167
5	.0260	.0391	.0521	.1042	.1562	.2083	.2604	.3125	.4167	.5208
6	.0312	.0469	.0625	.125	.1875	.250	.3125	.375	.500	.625
7	.0365	.0547	.0729	.1458	.2187	.2917	.3646	.4375	.5833	.7292
8	.0417	.0625	.0833	.1667	.250	.3333	.4167	.500	.6667	.8333
9	.0469	.0703	.0937	.1375	.2812	.375	.4687	.5625	.750	.9375
10	.0521	.0781	.1042	.2083	.3125	.4167	.5208	.625	.8333	1.0417
11	.0573	.0859	.1146	.2292	.3437	.4583	.5729	.6875	.9167	1.1458
12	.0625	.0937	.125	.250	.375	.500	.625	.750	1.000	1.250
13	.0677	.1016	.1354	.2708	.4062	.5417	.6771	.8125	1.0833	1.3542
14	.0729	.1094	.1458	.2917	.4375	.5833	.7292	.875	1.1667	1.4583
15	.0781	.1172	.1562	.3125	.4687	.625	.7812	.9375	1.250	1.5625
16	.0833	.125	.1667	.3333	.500	.6667	.8333	1.000	1.3333	1.6667
17	.0885	.1328	.1771	.3542	.5312	.7083	.8854	1.0625	1.4167	1.7708
18	.0937	.1406	.1875	.3750	.5625	.750	.9375	1.125	1.500	1.875
19	.0990	.1484	.1979	.3958	.5937	.7917	.9896	1.1875	1.5833	1.9792
20	.1042	.1562	.2083	.4167	.625	.8333	1.0417	1.250	1.6667	2.0833
21	.1094	.1641	.2187	.4375	.6562	.875	1.0937	1.3125	1.750	2.1875
22	.1146	.1719	.2292	.4583	.6875	.9167	1.1458	1.375	1.8333	2.2917
23	.1198	.1797	.2396	.4792	.7187	.9583	1.1970	1.4375	1.9167	2.3958
24	.125	.1875	.250	.500	.750	1.000	1.250	1.500	2.000	2.500

SPEEDS AND FEEDS FOR DRILLING

High Speed Steel Drills

SIZE OF DRILL.	FEED PER REV.	BRONZE, BRASS, 300 FEET.	CAST IRON, AN-NEALED, 170 FEET.	CAST IRON, HARD, 80 FEET.	MILD STEEL, 120 FEET.	DROP FORG., 60 FEET.	MAL. IRON, 90 FEET.	TOOL STEEL, 60 FEET.	CAST STEEL, 40 FEET.
INS.	INS.	R.P.M.	R.P.M.	R.P.M.	R.P.M.	R.P.M.	R.P.M.	R.P.M.	R.P.M.
1/16	0.003	....	....	4880	....	3660	....	3660	2440
1/8	0.004	....	5185	2440	3660	1830	2745	1830	1220
3/16	0.005	....	3456	1626	2440	1210	1830	1220	807
1/4	0.006	4575	2593	1220	1830	915	1375	915	610
5/16	0.007	3660	2074	976	1464	732	1138	732	490
3/8	0.008	3050	1728	813	1220	610	915	610	407
7/16	0.009	2614	1482	628	1046	522	784	522	348
1/2	0.010	2287	1296	610	915	458	636	458	305
5/8	0.011	1830	1037	488	732	366	569	366	245
3/4	0.012	1525	864	407	610	305	458	305	203
7/8	0.013	1307	741	349	523	261	392	261	174
1	0.014	1143	648	305	458	229	349	229	153
1 1/4	0.016	915	519	244	366	183	275	183	122
1 1/2	0.016	762	432	204	305	153	212	153	102
1 3/4	0.016	654	371	175	262	131	196	131	87
2	0.016	571	323	153	229	115	172	115	77

Carbon Steel Drills

SIZE OF DRILL.	FEED PER REV.	BRONZE, BRASS, 150 FEET.	CAST IRON, AN-NEALED, 85 FEET.	CAST IRON, HARD, 40 FEET.	MILD STEEL, 60 FEET.	DROP FORG., 30 FEET.	MAL. IRON, 45 FEET.	TOOL STEEL, 30 FEET.	CAST STEEL, 20 FEET.
INS.	INS.	R.P.M.	R.P.M.	R.P.M.	R.P.M.	R.P.M.	R.P.M.	R.P.M.	R.P.M.
1/16	0.003	....	5185	2440	3660	1830	2745	1830	1220
1/8	0.004	4575	2593	1220	1840	915	1375	915	610
3/16	0.005	3050	1728	813	1220	610	915	610	407
1/4	0.006	2287	1296	610	915	458	636	458	305
5/16	0.007	1830	1037	488	732	366	569	366	245
3/8	0.008	1525	864	407	610	305	458	305	203
7/16	0.009	1307	741	349	523	261	392	261	174
1/2	0.010	1143	648	305	458	229	343	229	153
5/8	0.011	915	519	244	366	183	275	183	122
3/4	0.012	762	432	204	305	153	212	153	102
7/8	0.013	654	371	175	262	131	196	131	87
1	0.014	571	323	153	229	115	172	115	77
1 1/4	0.016	458	260	122	183	92	138	92	61
1 1/2	0.016	381	216	102	153	77	106	77	51
1 3/4	0.016	327	186	88	131	66	98	66	44
2	0.016	286	162	77	115	58	86	58	39

TWIST DRILLS

Decimal Equivalents of Letter Size Drills

LETTER	SIZE OF DRILL IN INCHES.	LETTER	SIZE OF DRILL IN INCHES.	LETTER	SIZE OF DRILL IN INCHES.	LETTER	SIZE OF DRILL IN INCHES.
Z	0.413	S	0.348	L	0.290	E	0.250
Y	0.404	R	0.339	K	0.281	D	0.246
X	0.397	Q	0.332	J	0.277	C	0.242
W	0.386	P	0.323	I	0.272	B	0.238
V	0.377	O	0.316	H	0.266	A	0.234
U	0.368	N	0.302	G	0.261	..	.....
T	0.358	M	0.295	F	0.257	..	.....

TWIST DRILL AND STEEL WIRE GAGE

Decimal Equivalents of Number Size Drills

NO.	SIZE OF DRILL IN INCHES.	NO.	SIZE OF DRILL IN INCHES.	NO.	SIZE OF DRILL IN INCHES.	NO.	SIZE OF DRILL IN INCHES.
1	0.2280	21	0.1590	41	0.0960	61	0.0390
2	0.2210	22	0.1570	42	0.0935	62	0.0380
3	0.2130	23	0.1540	43	0.0890	63	0.0370
4	0.2090	24	0.1520	44	0.0860	64	0.0360
5	0.2055	25	0.1495	45	0.0820	65	0.0350
6	0.2040	26	0.1470	46	0.0810	66	0.0330
7	0.2010	27	0.1440	47	0.0785	67	0.0320
8	0.1990	28	0.1405	48	0.0760	68	0.0310
9	0.1960	29	0.1360	49	0.0730	69	0.0292
10	0.1935	30	0.1285	50	0.0700	70	0.0280
11	0.1910	31	0.1200	51	0.0670	71	0.0260
12	0.1890	32	0.1160	52	0.0635	72	0.0250
13	0.1850	33	0.1130	53	0.0595	73	0.0240
14	0.1820	34	0.1110	54	0.0550	74	0.0225
15	0.1800	35	0.1100	55	0.0520	75	0.0210
16	0.1770	36	0.1065	56	0.0465	76	0.0200
17	0.1730	37	0.1040	57	0.0430	77	0.0180
18	0.1695	38	0.1015	58	0.0420	78	0.0160
19	0.1660	39	0.0995	59	0.0410	79	0.0145
20	0.1610	40	0.0980	60	0.0400	80	0.0135

DIFFERENT STANDARDS FOR WIRE GAGES

In use in the United States

Dimensions of Sizes in Decimal Parts of an Inch

NUMBER OF WIRE GAGE.	AMERICAN OR BROWN & SHARPE.	BIRMINGHAM, OR STUBS' IRON WIRE.	WASHBURN & MOEN, OR STEEL WIRE GAGE.	AMERICAN S. & W. CO.'S MUSIC WIRE.	IMPERIAL WIRE.	STUBS' STEEL WIRE.	U. S. STANDARD GAGE FOR SHEET AND PLATE IRON AND STEEL.	NUMBER OF WIRE GAGE.
00000000	....	....	....	....	....	....	....	00000000
0000000	....	....	.4900	....	....	....	....	0000000
000000	....	....	.4615	.004	.464	....	.46875	000000
00000	....	....	.4305	.005	.432	....	.4375	00000
0000	.460	.454	.3938	.006	.400	....	.40625	0000
000	.40964	.425	.3625	.007	.372	....	.375	000
00	.3648	.380	.3310	.008	.348	....	.34375	00
0	.32486	.340	.3065	.009	.324	....	.3125	0
1	.2893	.300	.2830	.010	.300	.227	.28125	1
2	.25763	.284	.2625	.011	.276	.219	.265625	2
3	.22942	.259	.2437	.012	.252	.212	.250	3
4	.20431	.238	.2253	.013	.232	.207	.234375	4
5	.18194	.220	.2070	.014	.212	.204	.21875	5
6	.16202	.203	.1920	.016	.192	.201	.203125	6
7	.14428	.180	.1770	.018	.176	.199	.1875	7
8	.12849	.165	.1620	.020	.160	.197	.171875	8
9	.11443	.148	.1483	.022	.144	.194	.15625	9
10	.10189	.134	.1350	.024	.128	.191	.140625	10
11	.090742	.120	.1205	.026	.116	.188	.125	11
12	.080808	.109	.1055	.029	.104	.185	.109375	12
13	.071961	.095	.0915	.031	.092	.182	.09375	13
14	.064084	.083	.0800	.033	.080	.180	.078125	14
15	.057068	.072	.0720	.035	.072	.178	.0703125	15
16	.05082	.065	.0625	.037	.064	.175	.0625	16
17	.045257	.058	.0540	.039	.056	.172	.05625	17
18	.040303	.049	.0475	.041	.048	.168	.050	18
19	.03589	.042	.0410	.043	.040	.164	.04375	19
20	.031961	.035	.0348	.045	.036	.161	.0375	20
21	.028462	.032	.0317	.047	.032	.157	.034375	21
22	.025347	.028	.0286	.049	.028	.155	.03125	22
23	.022571	.025	.0258	.051	.024	.153	.028125	23
24	.0201	.022	.0230	.055	.022	.151	.025	24
25	.0179	.020	.0204	.059	.020	.148	.021875	25
26	.01594	.018	.0181	.063	.018	.146	.01875	26
27	.014195	.016	.0173	.067	.0164	.143	.0171875	27
28	.012641	.014	.0162	.071	.0149	.139	.015625	28
29	.011257	.013	.0150	.075	.0136	.134	.0140625	29
30	.010025	.012	.0140	.080	.0124	.127	.0125	30
31	.008928	.010	.0132	.085	.0116	.120	.0109375	31
32	.00795	.009	.0128	.090	.0108	.115	.01015625	32
33	.00708	.008	.0118	.095	.0100	.112	.009375	33
34	.006304	.007	.0104	....	.0092	.110	.00859375	34
35	.005614	.005	.0095	....	.0084	.108	.0078125	35
36	.005	.004	.0090	....	.0076	.106	.00703125	36
37	.004453	....	.0085	....	.0068	.103	.006640625	37
38	.003965	....	.0080	....	.0060	.101	.00625	38
39	.003531	....	.0075	....	.0052	.099	....	39
40	.003144	....	.0070	....	.0048	.097	....	40

CUTTING SPEEDS

FEET PER MINUTE.	15	17.5	20	22.5	25	27.5	30	35	40	45	50	55
DIAM., INCHES.	REVOLUTIONS PER MINUTE.											
$\frac{1}{16}$	917	1070	1222	1375	1528	1681	1833	2139	2445	2750	3056	3361
$\frac{1}{8}$	458	535	611	688	764	840	917	1070	1222	1375	1528	1681
$\frac{3}{16}$	306	357	407	458	509	560	611	713	815	917	1019	1120
$\frac{1}{4}$	229	267	306	344	382	420	458	535	611	688	764	840
$\frac{5}{16}$	183	214	244	275	306	336	367	428	489	550	611	672
$\frac{3}{8}$	153	178	204	229	255	280	306	357	407	458	509	560
$\frac{7}{16}$	131	153	175	196	218	240	262	306	349	393	437	480
$\frac{1}{2}$	115	134	153	172	191	210	229	267	306	344	382	420
$\frac{5}{8}$	91.7	107	122	138	153	168	183	214	244	275	306	336
$\frac{3}{4}$	76.4	89.1	102	115	127	140	153	178	204	229	255	280
$\frac{7}{8}$	65.5	76.4	87.3	98.2	109	120	131	153	175	196	218	240
1	57.3	66.8	76.4	85.9	95.5	105	115	134	153	172	191	210
$1\frac{1}{8}$	50.9	59.4	67.9	76.4	84.9	93.4	102	119	136	153	170	187
$1\frac{1}{4}$	45.8	53.5	61.1	68.8	76.4	84.0	91.7	107	122	138	153	168
$1\frac{3}{8}$	41.7	48.6	55.6	62.5	69.5	76.4	83.3	97.2	111	125	139	153
$1\frac{1}{2}$	38.2	44.6	50.9	57.3	63.7	70.0	76.4	89.1	102	115	127	140
$1\frac{5}{8}$	35.3	41.1	47.0	52.9	58.8	64.6	70.5	82.3	94.0	106	118	129
$1\frac{3}{4}$	32.7	38.2	43.7	49.1	54.6	60.0	65.5	76.4	87.3	98.2	109	120
$1\frac{7}{8}$	30.6	35.7	40.7	45.8	50.9	56.0	61.1	71.3	81.5	91.7	102	112
2	28.7	33.4	38.2	43.0	47.7	52.5	57.3	66.8	76.4	85.9	95.5	105
$2\frac{1}{4}$	25.5	29.7	34.0	38.2	42.4	46.7	50.9	59.4	67.9	76.4	84.9	93.4
$2\frac{1}{2}$	22.9	26.7	30.6	34.4	38.2	42.0	45.8	53.5	61.1	68.8	76.4	84.0
$2\frac{3}{4}$	20.8	24.3	27.8	31.3	34.7	38.2	41.7	48.6	55.6	62.5	69.5	76.4
3	19.1	22.3	25.5	28.6	31.8	35.0	38.2	44.6	50.9	57.3	63.7	70.0
$3\frac{1}{4}$	17.6	20.6	23.5	26.4	29.4	32.3	35.3	41.1	47.0	52.9	58.8	64.6
$3\frac{1}{2}$	16.4	19.1	21.8	24.5	27.3	30.0	32.7	38.2	43.7	49.1	54.6	60.0
$3\frac{3}{4}$	15.3	17.8	20.4	22.9	25.5	28.0	30.6	35.7	40.7	45.8	50.9	56.0
4	14.3	16.7	19.1	21.5	23.9	26.3	28.7	33.4	38.2	43.0	47.7	52.5
$4\frac{1}{2}$	12.7	14.9	17.0	19.1	21.2	23.3	25.5	29.7	34.0	38.2	42.4	46.7
5	11.5	13.4	15.3	17.2	19.1	21.0	22.9	26.7	30.6	34.4	38.2	42.0
$5\frac{1}{2}$	10.4	12.2	13.9	15.6	17.4	19.1	20.8	24.3	27.8	31.3	34.7	38.2
6	9.5	11.1	12.7	14.3	15.9	17.5	19.1	22.3	25.5	28.6	31.8	35.0
$6\frac{1}{2}$	8.8	10.3	11.8	13.2	14.7	16.2	17.6	20.6	23.5	26.4	29.4	32.3
7	8.2	9.5	10.9	12.3	13.6	15.0	16.4	19.1	21.8	24.5	27.3	30.0
$7\frac{1}{2}$	7.6	8.9	10.2	11.5	12.7	14.0	15.3	17.8	20.4	22.9	25.5	28.0
8	7.2	8.4	9.5	10.7	11.9	13.1	14.3	16.7	19.1	21.5	23.9	26.3
$8\frac{1}{2}$	6.7	7.9	9.0	10.1	11.2	12.4	13.5	15.7	18.0	20.2	22.5	24.7
9	6.4	7.4	8.5	9.5	10.6	11.7	12.7	14.9	17.0	19.1	21.2	23.3
$9\frac{1}{2}$	6.0	7.0	8.0	9.1	10.1	11.1	12.1	14.1	16.1	18.1	20.1	22.1
10	5.7	6.7	7.6	8.6	9.5	10.5	11.5	13.4	15.3	17.2	19.1	21.0
11	5.2	6.1	6.9	7.8	8.7	9.5	10.4	12.2	13.9	15.6	17.4	19.1
12	4.8	5.6	6.4	7.2	8.0	8.8	9.5	11.1	12.7	14.3	15.9	17.5
13	4.4	5.1	5.9	6.6	7.3	8.1	8.8	10.3	11.8	13.2	14.7	16.2
14	4.1	4.8	5.5	6.1	6.8	7.5	8.2	9.5	10.9	12.3	13.6	15.0
15	3.8	4.5	5.1	5.7	6.4	7.0	7.6	8.9	10.2	11.5	12.7	14.0
16	3.6	4.2	4.8	5.4	6.0	6.6	7.2	8.4	9.5	10.7	11.9	13.1
17	3.4	3.9	4.5	5.1	5.6	6.2	6.7	7.9	9.0	10.1	11.2	12.4
18	3.2	3.7	4.2	4.8	5.3	5.8	6.4	7.4	8.5	9.5	10.6	11.7
FEET PER MINUTE.	15	17.5	20	22.5	25	27.5	30	35	40	45	50	55

CUTTING SPEEDS (Continued)

FEET PER MINUTE.	60	65	70	75	80	90	100	110	120	130	140	150
DIAM., INCHES.	REVOLUTIONS PER MINUTE.											
1/16	3667	3973	4278	4584	4889	...	...	...	...	...	...	...
1/8	1833	1986	2139	2292	2445	2750	3056	3361	3667	3973	4278	4584
3/16	1222	1324	1426	1528	1630	1833	2037	2241	2445	2648	2852	3056
1/4	917	993	1070	1146	1222	1375	1528	1681	1833	1986	2139	2292
5/16	733	794	856	917	978	1100	1222	1345	1467	1589	1711	1833
3/8	611	662	713	764	815	917	1019	1120	1222	1324	1426	1528
7/16	524	568	611	655	698	786	873	960	1048	1135	1222	1310
1/2	458	497	535	573	611	688	764	840	917	993	1070	1146
5/8	367	397	428	458	489	550	611	672	733	794	856	917
3/4	306	331	357	382	407	458	509	560	611	662	713	764
7/8	262	284	306	327	349	393	437	480	524	568	611	655
1	229	248	267	287	306	344	382	420	458	497	535	573
1 1/8	204	221	238	255	272	306	340	373	407	441	475	509
1 1/4	183	199	214	229	244	275	306	336	367	397	428	458
1 3/8	167	181	194	208	222	250	278	306	333	361	389	417
1 1/2	153	166	178	191	204	229	255	280	306	331	357	382
1 5/8	141	153	165	176	188	212	235	259	282	306	329	353
1 3/4	131	142	153	164	175	196	218	240	262	234	306	327
1 7/8	122	132	143	153	163	183	204	224	244	265	285	306
2	115	124	134	143	153	172	191	210	229	248	267	287
2 1/4	102	110	119	127	136	153	170	187	204	221	238	255
2 1/2	91.7	99.3	107	115	122	138	153	168	183	199	214	229
2 3/4	83.3	90.3	97.2	104	111	125	139	153	167	181	194	208
3	76.4	82.8	89.1	95.5	102	115	127	140	153	166	178	191
3 1/4	70.5	76.4	82.3	88.2	94.0	106	118	129	141	153	165	176
3 1/2	65.5	70.9	76.4	81.9	87.3	98.2	109	120	131	142	153	164
3 3/4	61.1	66.2	71.3	76.4	81.5	91.7	102	112	122	132	143	153
4	57.3	62.1	66.8	71.6	76.4	85.9	95.5	105	115	124	134	143
4 1/2	50.9	55.2	59.4	63.6	67.9	76.4	84.9	93.4	102	110	119	127
5	45.8	49.7	53.5	57.3	61.1	68.8	76.4	84.0	91.7	99.3	107	115
5 1/2	41.7	45.1	48.6	52.1	55.6	62.5	69.5	76.4	83.3	90.3	97.2	104
6	38.2	41.4	44.6	47.8	50.9	57.3	63.7	70.0	76.4	82.8	89.1	95.5
6 1/2	35.3	38.2	41.1	41.1	47.0	52.9	58.8	64.6	70.5	76.4	82.3	88.2
7	32.7	35.5	38.2	40.9	43.7	49.1	54.6	60.0	65.5	70.9	76.4	81.9
7 1/2	30.6	33.1	35.7	38.2	40.7	45.8	50.9	56.0	61.1	66.2	71.3	76.4
8	28.7	31.0	33.4	35.8	38.2	43.0	47.7	52.5	57.3	62.1	66.8	71.6
8 1/2	27.0	29.2	31.5	33.7	36.0	40.4	44.9	49.4	53.9	58.4	62.9	67.4
9	25.5	27.6	29.7	31.8	34.0	38.2	42.4	46.7	50.9	55.2	59.4	63.6
9 1/2	24.1	26.1	28.2	30.2	32.2	36.2	40.2	44.2	48.3	52.3	56.3	60.3
10	22.9	24.8	26.7	28.7	30.6	34.4	38.2	42.0	45.8	49.7	53.5	57.3
11	20.8	22.6	24.3	26.0	27.8	31.3	34.7	38.2	41.7	45.1	48.6	52.1
12	19.1	20.7	22.3	23.9	25.5	28.6	31.8	35.0	38.2	41.4	44.6	47.8
13	17.6	19.1	20.6	22.0	23.5	26.4	29.4	32.3	35.3	38.2	41.1	44.1
14	16.4	17.7	19.1	20.5	21.8	24.5	27.3	30.0	32.7	35.5	38.2	40.9
15	15.3	16.6	17.8	19.1	20.4	22.9	25.5	28.0	30.6	33.1	35.7	38.2
16	14.3	15.5	16.7	17.9	19.1	21.5	23.9	26.3	28.7	31.0	33.4	35.8
17	13.5	14.6	15.7	16.9	18.0	20.2	22.5	24.7	27.0	29.2	31.5	33.7
18	12.7	13.8	14.9	15.9	17.0	19.1	21.2	23.3	25.5	27.6	29.7	31.8
FEET PER MINUTE.	60	65	70	75	80	90	100	110	120	130	140	150

WEIGHT OF SQUARE AND ROUND BARS OF STEEL

In Pounds per Linear Foot

Based on 489.6 lbs. per cubic foot. For Wrought Iron deduct 2 per cent.
For High Speed Steel add 10 per cent.

THICKNESS OR DIAMETER, INCHES.	WEIGHT OF SQUARE BAR 1 FOOT LONG.	WEIGHT OF ROUND BAR 1 FOOT LONG.	THICKNESS OR DIAMETER, INCHES.	WEIGHT OF SQUARE BAR 1 FOOT LONG.	WEIGHT OF ROUND BAR 1 FOOT LONG.
1/32	.0033	.0026	2½	21.25	16.69
1/16	.0133	.0104	9/16	22.33	17.53
1/8	.0531	.0417	5/8	23.43	18.40
3/16	.1195	.0938	11/16	24.56	19.29
1/4	.2123	.1669	3/4	25.00	20.20
5/16	.3333	.2608	13/16	26.90	21.12
3/8	.4782	.3756	7/8	28.10	22.07
7/16	.6508	.5111	15/16	29.34	23.04
1/2	.8500	.6676	3	30.60	24.03
9/16	1.076	.8449	1/16	31.89	25.04
5/8	1.328	1.043	1/8	33.20	26.08
11/16	1.608	1.262	3/16	34.55	27.13
3/4	1.913	1.502	1/4	35.92	28.20
13/16	2.245	1.763	5/16	37.31	29.30
7/8	2.603	2.044	3/8	38.73	30.42
15/16	2.989	2.347	7/16	40.18	31.56
1	3.400	2.670	1/2	41.65	32.71
1/16	3.838	3.014	9/16	43.14	33.90
1/8	4.303	3.379	5/8	44.68	35.09
3/16	4.795	3.766	11/16	46.24	36.31
1/4	5.312	4.173	3/4	47.82	37.56
5/16	5.857	4.600	13/16	49.42	38.81
3/8	6.428	5.019	7/8	51.05	40.10
7/16	7.026	5.518	15/16	52.71	41.40
1/2	7.650	6.008	4	54.40	42.73
9/16	8.301	6.520	1/16	56.11	44.07
5/8	8.978	7.051	1/8	57.85	45.44
11/16	9.682	7.604	3/16	59.62	46.83
3/4	10.41	8.178	1/4	61.41	48.24
13/16	11.17	8.773	5/16	63.23	49.66
7/8	11.95	9.388	3/8	65.08	51.11
15/16	12.76	10.02	7/16	66.95	52.58
2	13.60	10.68	1/2	68.85	54.07
1/16	14.46	11.36	9/16	70.78	55.59
1/8	15.35	12.06	5/8	73.73	57.12
3/16	16.27	12.78	11/16	74.70	58.67
1/4	17.22	13.52	3/4	76.71	60.25
5/16	18.19	14.28	13/16	78.74	61.84
3/8	19.18	15.07	7/8	80.81	63.46
7/16	20.20	15.86	15/16	82.89	65.10

INDEX

(An asterisk indicates an illustration.)